SOIL MECHANICS
AND FOUNDATIONS

SOIL MECHANICS AND FOUNDATIONS

James V. Parcher

Raymond E. Means

Oklahoma State University

CHARLES E. MERRILL PUBLISHING COMPANY
A Bell & Howell Company

Preface

This book is intended as an introduction to the study of soil mechanics and may be used as the beginning text. For those wishing to incorporate an extensive coverage of soil properties, this text would be a logical sequel to *Physical Properties of Soils*, published by Charles E. Merrill Books, Inc. in 1963. In the interests of continuity and completeness in the treatment of soil mechanics, some portions of soil mechanics which were included in *Physical Properties of Soils* are repeated in this book on soil mechanics and foundations. This is especially true of some material on flow of water through soils and settlement analysis.

Part of the information contained in this book comes as a result of our own research and experience. A great deal of this experience has been with the overconsolidated desiccated clays of the south central United States and with foundations for compressor stations and other structures on wind-deposited loess and river-deposited sands and silts of the Arkansas River and its tributaries.

The contents of the book are based for the most part upon research and experience of others who have shared their information and knowledge in papers presented in the technical literature. We are especially indebted to the Soil Mechanics and Foundations Division of the American Society of Civil Engineers, *Geotechnique*, Quarterly of the Colorado

School of Mines, and the Building Research Advisory Board Report to the Federal Housing Authority.

Stillwater, Oklahoma
September, 1967

James V. Parcher
Raymond E. Means

Notation and Symbols

Symbol	Property	Typical dimensions
Å	Angstrom	1×10^{-7} mm
A	Area	cm²
a_v	Coefficient of compressibility, $\dfrac{de}{dp}$	cm² g⁻¹
b	Breadth or width	cm
C	(a) Resultant or total cohesion (b) Constant	g
C_c	Compression index	Dimensionless
C_s	Swelling index	Dimensionless
C_u	Uniformity coefficient	Dimensionless
c	Unit cohesion	g cm⁻²
c_v	Coefficient of consolidation	cm² sec⁻¹
D	Diameter	cm
D_d (D_R)	Degree of density (Relative density)	Dimensionless
d	(a) Differential (b) Distance	cm
E	(a) Modulus of elasticity (b) Resultant earth pressure	g cm⁻² g

Symbol	Property	Typical dimensions
E_a	Active earth pressure	g
E_o	Earth pressure at rest	g
E_p	Passive earth pressure	g
E_l	Energy loss	g cm
e	(a) Void ratio (b) Base of natural logarithm	Dimensionless
F	Total force	g
f	Force per unit of area	g cm^{-2}
G	Specific gravity	Dimensionless
g	Acceleration of gravity	cm sec^{-2}
H	(a) Height, depth, or thickness (b) Horizontal force	cm g
h	Head or height	cm
h_c	Capillary rise	cm
I	(a) Index (Subscript indicates particular) (b) Moment of inertia	cm^4
i	(a) Hydraulic gradient (b) Slope angle or angle of incidence	Dimensionless
J	Resultant seepage force	g
j	Unit seepage force, $i\gamma_w$	g
K	Stiffness factor for straight Prismatic member, $\dfrac{I}{L}$	cm^3
K_a	Coefficient of active earth pressure $\tan^2\left(45-\dfrac{\phi}{2}\right)$	Dimensionless
K_o	Coefficient of earth pressure at rest	Dimensionless
K_p	Coefficient of passive earth pressure $\tan^2\left(45+\dfrac{\phi}{2}\right)$	Dimensionless
k	Coefficient of permeability	cm sec^{-1}
L	Distance, length, or span	cm
M	Moment	cm g
N	Total normal force	g
n	Porosity	Dimensionless
P	Total force or load	g
p	(a) Unit pressure (b) Load per unit of length	g cm^{-2} g cm^{-1}

Symbol	Property	Typical dimensions
p_o	Overburden pressure	$\mathrm{g\,cm^{-2}}$
p_p	Preconsolidation pressure	$\mathrm{g\,cm^{-2}}$
Q	Total quantity	$\mathrm{cm^3}$
q	(a) Quantity per unit of time	$\mathrm{cm^3\,sec^{-1}}$
	(b) Load per unit of area	$\mathrm{g\,cm^{-2}}$
q_u	Unconfined compression strength	$\mathrm{g\,cm^{-2}}$
q_Q	Unconsolidated undrained triaxial strength	$\mathrm{g\,cm^{-2}}$
q_R	Consolidated undrained triaxial strength	$\mathrm{g\,cm^{-2}}$
q_S	Consolidated drained triaxial strength	$\mathrm{g\,cm^{-2}}$
R	(a) Reading	
	(b) Resultant	
	(c) Radius	cm
r	Radius	cm
S	(a) Degree of saturation	Dimensionless
	(b) Settlement	cm
	(c) Section modulus, $\dfrac{I}{A}$	$\mathrm{cm^2}$
s	Unit shear stress or strength	$\mathrm{g\,cm^{-2}}$
T	(a) Temperature	Degree
	(b) Time factor	Dimensionless
	(c) Total force or load, tension	g
T_s	Surface tension	$\mathrm{g\,cm^{-1}}$
t	Time	sec
U	(a) Average degree of consolidation	Dimensionless
	(b) Total water pressure	g
u	Unit excess hydrostatic pressure	$\mathrm{g\,cm^{-2}}$
V	(a) Volume	$\mathrm{cm^3}$
	(b) Vertical force	g
v	Velocity	$\mathrm{cm\,sec^{-1}}$
W	Weight	g
w	(a) Water content	Dimensionless
	(b) Load per unit of area	$\mathrm{g\,cm^{-2}}$
X, Y, Z	Coordinate axes	
x, y, z	Coordinate distance	cm
z	Depth or distance from surface	cm
$\alpha, \beta, \theta, \lambda$	Angle	
γ	Unit weight	$\mathrm{g\,cm^{-3}}$
γ_e	Unit weight of earth	$\mathrm{g\,cm^{-3}}$

Symbol	Property	Typical dimensions
γ_w	Unit weight of water	g cm^{-3}
γ_0	Unit weight of water at 4° C	g cm^{-3}
Δ	(a) Increment	
	(b) Deflection	cm
δ	Angle of friction between soil and surface of other material	
∂	Partial differential	
ϵ	Unit strain	Dimensionless
ξ	Base of natural logarithm	
η	(a) Coefficient of absolute viscosity	g sec cm^{-2}
	(b) Coefficient used in Brom's horizontal resistance of piles	
μ	Poisson's ratio	Dimensionless
ν	Coefficient of kinematic viscosity	cm sec
ρ	(a) Mass density, $\dfrac{\gamma}{g}$	$\text{g sec}^2 \text{ cm}^{-4}$
	(b) Flexibility number (Anchored bulkheads)	g cm^{-1}
σ	Normal unit stress	g cm^{-2}
$\overline{\sigma}$	Effective normal unit stress	g cm^{-2}
σ_1	Major principal stress	g cm^{-2}
σ_2	Intermediate principal stress	g cm^{-2}
σ_3	Minor principal stress	g cm^{-2}
τ	Shearing unit stress	g cm^{-2}
ϕ	Angle of internal friction	
ψ	(a) Angle of rotation of member, $\dfrac{\Delta}{L}$	Radian
	(b) Slope angle of Resultant Earth Pressure	

Note: Unless a symbol designates a specific unit, given dimensions are to designate their character and are not necessarily in the most convenient or common units. For example, g indicates weight, cm indicates distance, and sec indicates time.

Table of Contents

Chapter 2
Types of Foundations and their Suitability   79

Chapter 3
Seepage or Flow of Water Through Soils   101

Chapter 4

Settlement of Foundations   **181**

Chapter 7

Earth Pressures   **381**

Chapter 8

Slope Stability   **466**

SOIL MECHANICS
AND FOUNDATIONS

1   Field Exploration, Measurements, and Controls

1.01   General

In order for the engineer to design a beam to carry known loads without failure or excessive deflection, he must know the material of which the beam is to be made and the properties of that material. Given this information, he can determine the required dimensions of the beam. In some materials, such as concrete and steel, these properties can be controlled to some extent. Other materials, such as wood, must be used with the properties that nature has provided.

Soil materials used for foundations are most often used in their natural state. The natural properties, the quantities, and the extent of the soils must be used as they exist. Since the engineer usually cannot control the extent or the properties of these materials, he must control the loading conditions. In order to provide loading conditions that will not exceed

1

the carrying capacity or allowable deformation, the extent and certain properties of the soil must be determined during the field exploration.

At the beginning of an investigation to determine the extent and properties of soils underlying a site, the engineer must decide how to gain access to the different layers and how deeply and extensively to explore the area to be covered by the investigation. He must decide upon the spacing and location of test holes, the manner and frequency of taking samples, and the type of tests to be made on the soil in place. Some of these decisions, such as the manner and frequency of taking samples and the type of tests to be made on the soil in place, may have to be made during the progress of the exploration after the nature of the materials has been determined. Following, or sometime during the exploration, it must be decided whether additional investigation is needed, such as taking undisturbed samples for laboratory testing, making penetration tests, or following other procedures designed to determine needed properties either directly or indirectly.

The methods used for the exploration should be chosen carefully so that at the end the exploration has provided more than just a hole in the ground. It is, therefore, necessary that the exploration be planned and supervised by the engineer who designs the structure.

1.02   Purpose and Extent of Exploration

The exploration should determine the nature and the dimensions of the underlying materials. It should tell whether the soil is gravel, sand, silt, clay, or a mixture of clay and sand or silt. The water table should always be located if practicable. The depth and thickness of all layers should be determined. If rock is encountered, the extent of its surface should be defined and its thickness and nature determined.

If cohesionless material (gravel, sand, or silt) is found, it should be examined to determine if it is clean and cohesionless or if it contains a clay binder or other material. It should also be determined whether the cohesionless material is coarse, medium, or fine gravel, sand, or silt and whether the grains are of uniform size or graded from fine to coarse. The shape of the grains should also be noted. An attempt should be made to determine whether the material is dense or loose and, as nearly as possible, to determine the degree of density.

If the material is clay, it should be examined for plasticity. Texture as indicated by the approximate amount of gravel, sand, or silt, should be noted. The natural water content should be determined, especially for cohesive soils. Some attempt should be made to determine whether the clay is a recent deposit or an old one that has been compressed by previous overburden which has been removed by erosion, and whether the clay has been subjected to cycles of wetting and drying. Consistency, odor, and color are indications of properties which are significant in guiding the judgment in the choice of a foundation, and these properties should be noted.

Methods of describing soils are taken up in *Physical Properties of Soils*. Some simple tests that can be made in the field are described later in this chapter.

1.03   Bore Holes

Usually the cheapest and most common method of examining the soil below the surface is by means of bore holes. Test pits are too expensive for general exploration, but they may be used for further and more careful examination if found to be needed after a preliminary examination.

The method adopted or allowed for drilling the holes should be one that will allow the taking of samples in as nearly their natural state as possible, and one that will facilitate obtaining as much data as possible as outlined in Section 1.02. Holes above the water table should usually be drilled dry. Obviously, any method that uses drilling water above the water table will not supply the greatest amount of information.

1.04   Extent and Location of Bore Holes

Bore holes should be located so as to determine the extent, thickness, and depth of the soil layers underlying the entire site. First, the holes could be drilled near the extremities and in the middle of the area to be covered by the structure. If the underlying layers appear to be nearly uniform in type of soil and thickness, and are level or have uniform slopes, it is usually safe to assume that soil conditions are uniform over the site, especially if the holes are not more than 50 ft apart.

If non-uniformities occur, intermediate holes should be drilled to define the conditions. If rock is encountered in one of the bore holes and not in others, adjacent holes should be drilled to determine the extent of the rock; i.e., whether the rock is only a boulder, the upper surface of a fault, the top of a buried rock cliff, or an escarpment.

1.05   Depth of Bore Holes

The depth to which the exploration should be carried depends upon the type of soil encountered and the loading conditions. If rock is encountered, the auger drilling must stop and other methods which will be described later must be used for determining the quality and thickness of the rock layers.

If the material is very hard clay that has been subjected to repeated cycles of drying out and wetting, an effort should be made to determine the water table, even though the loading conditions should indicate that for this material this knowledge is unimportant. Such materials are capable of supporting very heavy loads without failure and with very little settlement. Clays are subject to shrinking and swelling with change in water content. The depth to which drying out will occur in a given climate depends partly upon the depth to the water table.

When soft clay or other weak material is encountered, the investigation should determine the thickness of the layers and bore holes should be extended to a depth of about 1½ times the least dimension of the loaded area. The loaded area in this case is the area of the entire structure and not just the area of a single footing.

The thickness of sand layers and the nature of the underlying materials should be determined. The depth to which a sand layer should be investigated depends upon the amount of overburden above the sand and the load to be applied to the sand. A layer of dense sand with several feet of overburden will distribute the load of a light one, two, or three story building over the building area similarly to a mat in a raft type foundation. An effort should be made to determine the density of all clean sand layers. Methods of estimating the density of sand in place are described later in this chapter.

Except under unusual conditions, it is not necessary to investigate deeper than about 1½ times the least dimension of the loaded area.

1.06   Wash Borings

Wash borings are made by pumping water down the inside of a drill stem through a cutting bit and washing the cuttings to the surface up through the space between the outside of the drill stem and the sides of the hole.

The apparatus consists of a hollow drill stem or pipe with a cutting bit on the lower end, and a swivel for a hose connection at the upper end. At the surface a means is provided for loading and turning the drill stem.

A pump forces water through the swivel down the inside of the drill stem, out the side or bottom of the bit, and up the outside of the drill stem bringing the cuttings to the surface. A short piece of casing with a tee spout emptying into a tub or slush pit is usually placed at the top of the hole. Samples of the soil cuttings are collected at the top of the hole as they flow into the slush pit or tub.

Wash borings can be made by hand. Usually three men operate the equipment; one man pumps water from the slush pit or tub through the swivel at the top of the drill pipe; another churns the drill pipe and bit in the hole with a rope threaded through a pulley or block at the top of a tripod set over the hole, and a third turns the top of the drill pipe with a pipe wrench or cross handle to cut the soil loose at the bottom of the hole.

Wash boring equipment often consists of separate portable parts assembled for use as illustrated in Figure 1.06a. The pump is a small centrifugal

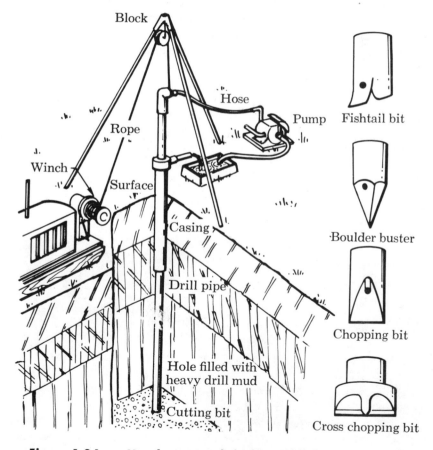

Figure 1.06a   Hand operated rig for making wash borings

one coupled to a small air cooled gasoline engine mounted on a light frame to rest on the ground. The winch is a smooth concave pulley mounted on a small gasoline engine. The drill stem may be a 1 in. I.D. steel pipe in 5 or 6 ft sections. The casing is usually a short section (the length depending on the thickness of the top soil) of $2\frac{1}{2}$ or 3 in. I.D. steel pipe, with a tee and a short length of pipe to act as a spout.

Rotary drill rigs operate in the same way as the equipment just described, except that the cutting bit is rotated continuously by means of a power connection. This equipment is usually mounted on a truck. Such a truck mounted drill rig can be used to make wash borings as described, to drill holes dry with an auger, and to core rock. The weight of the truck can be used to apply pressure to the cutting bit and to force sampling tubes into the soil at the bottom of the hole.

A hole that will not stand open may be cased its entire length by driving the casing as the hole is advanced. The hole can sometimes be held open without casing by using a heavy drill mud instead of water as the drilling liquid. The heavy mud is usually made by mixing bentonite and water. The pressure of this heavy liquid against the sides of the hole prevents collapse of the hole and enables the hole to be drilled without the use of a casing. Some soils require heavier drill mud than others.

An advantage of wash borings is that for holes more than 15 or 20 ft in depth, they are economical and fast. A disadvantage of wash borings

Figure 1.06b   Truck mounted rotary drill rig

is that they give comparatively little information about the soils which they penetrate. As the soil particles are brought to the surface by the velocity of the rising drill fluid, the finer particles do not settle against the current as rapidly as the coarse particles, and so reach the surface before the coarser particles. This segregation of soil particles makes it almost impossible to determine the true composition and structure of a deposit from wash boring samples. This is especially true when the deposits are varied, and in thin layers. Some information regarding the hardness of the layers can be obtained from the resistance to drilling and the "feel" of the cutting bit as it is turned by the operator. Wash boring samples are of very little value in the investigation of soils for foundations.

This disadvantage can be overcome to some extent by taking split spoon or Shelby tube samples of each soil layer. Each time a sample is taken, the drill stem and bit must be removed. A tube sample taken from a wash boring above the water table will show the structure of the deposit, but may not reflect its natural water content.

1.07   Fishtail Boring with Compressed Air Lift

Above the water table, cuttings from a fishtail bit operated by a rotary drill rig as described and illustrated in Section 1.06 are sometimes lifted to the surface by compressed air instead of water. The operation of the equipment is the same as for wash borings except that compressed air is introduced into the drill pipe instead of water. A pipe tee at the top of the hole directs the cuttings, which are blown to the surface to the side of the hole. A weighted rubber cover around the drill stem at the top of the tee prevents cuttings from flying out of the hole vertically. This compressed air lift has the advantage that cuttings are brought to the surface with their natural water content and in pieces that are not disintegrated and segregated by water.

1.08   Auger Holes

Holes can be drilled in soils above the water table with augers that do not require water, which bring up cuttings of the soil with its natural water content in small, undisturbed pieces.

Several types of augers are used. Most of these augers are relatively short, varying in length from a few in. to 2 or more ft. They are turned in the bottom of the hole through a drill pipe or stem. The soil cuttings are held in the auger and are drawn to the surface by pulling the auger out of the hole each time the auger is filled. Augers may be turned and lifted by hand or by power. Two general types of earth augers are used for soil exploration.

One is a spiral type auger, some with the helical blade secured to a solid center shaft like a wood auger, and others without a center shaft, like a corkscrew. These augers are screwed into the soil and pulled straight out, retaining the soil cuttings in the space between the helical blades. The soil cuttings are usually remolded and broken up. The amount of soil

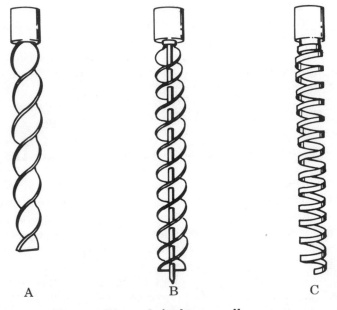

A   B   C

Figure 1.08a   Spiral type soil augers

removed each time the auger is taken out is quite small, making the drilling slow. This type of auger tends to anchor itself in the soil or wedge the soil sample against the side of the hole and to resist withdrawal. Crumbly or cohesionless soils, such as sand, will not stay in the auger. An advantage that spiral type augers have over the bucket type is that they are relatively easy to clean of their load of soil.

A second type of earth auger consists essentially of a pipe with two cutters on the bottom secured to the edge of the pipe and extending downward and inward. As the auger is turned, the cutters slice the soil from the bottom of the hole and force the cuttings up into the pipe. Slots in the sides of the pipe allow the soil cuttings to be shaken or forced out of the auger. The larger the slots and the less metal in the sides of the auger, the easier

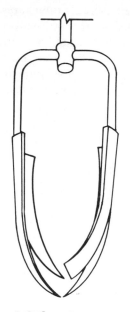

Figure 1.08b   Iwan type auger

it is to remove the soil, but the auger is more likely to expand against the sides of the hole when filled with soil. Some of the larger sizes have one side hinged at the top to facilitate emptying. Some of the very large bucket type augers are not provided with slots in the sides and are emptied by dumping the cuttings out at the top. In most soils this type of auger retains better samples than the spiral type.

In relatively soft soils above the water table holes up to about 20 ft in depth can be drilled quickly and economically with simple apparatus consisting of a small auger, sectional steel pipe drill stem, a cross handle, two small pipe wrenches, and tools to clean the soil out of the auger. Larger holes, usually at least 4 or 5 in. in diameter, can be drilled with the same rotary rig used for making wash borings. Usually, the auger used with the truck mounted rotary rig is similar to that shown in Figure 1.08a at C. Holes to a depth equal to one drill stem section can be drilled rapidly with an auger on a rotary rig. After approximately each foot of drilling, depending upon the length of the auger, the auger is lifted to the surface and cleaned of its load of earth by spinning rapidly. In drilling holes deeper than the length of one drill stem, the stem must be broken into sections each time the auger is lifted. This taking apart and reassembling of the drill stem for each augerful of earth makes this method of advancing the hole slow and expensive. This disadvantage can be eliminated by lifting the cuttings from a fishtail bit with compressed air.

Other power driven augers are continuous spiral types made up of sections about 6 ft in length similar to *B* of Figure 1.08*a*. This type of auger screws the soil cuttings to the top of the hole without removing the auger. By the time the soil samples reach the top of the hole, they are broken up, mixed, and remolded until they are not of much value as soil samples. It is practically impossible to determine the horizon from which the soil came

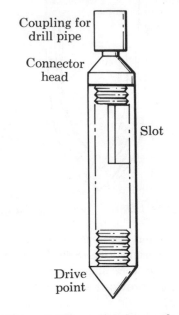

Coupling for
drill pipe

Connector
head

Slot

Drive
point

Figure 1.08c   Sand sampler

after it reaches the surface. None of the augers so far described will retain a sample of clean sand. A closed end bucket type auger with a slot and a cutter blade in the top half, as shown in Figure 1.08*c,* can be used to scrape sand from the sides of the hole after the sampler has been pushed or driven into the layer of sand. Such a sidewall sampler can furnish only the general characteristics of the sampled formation.

1.09   Recovering Samples from Bore Holes

Wash boring samples are of comparatively little value and are hardly worth saving. Continous auger boring samples are somewhat better, but must be supplemented with less disturbed samples of the different soil strata. Cuttings from spiral or bucket type augers are very useful. The percentages of sand, silt, and clay as they exist together can be observed. Usually, some of the cuttings will be large enough to disclose the structure of the soil. These samples can be used for determining the natural water content and Atterberg limits of the soil for use in comparing properties of this soil with the properties found for undisturbed samples.

In nearly all cases, these auger samples should be supplemented by less disturbed samples. Such samples can be recovered from bore holes with some sort of sampling spoon which is forced into the tube that receives and retains the sample.

The simplest of sampling spoons consists of a seamless thin walled steel tube secured to a head, as shown in Figure 1.09a. These tubes vary in size from 2 to 4 in. O.D. and are often called Shelby tubes. The tube is fastened to the head with set screws arranged so that the tube with the sample can be removed from the head. Holes through the head allow water to drain from the drive pipe or push stem to prevent a column of water from forcing the sample from the tube as it is withdrawn from the hole. Also, when water or fluid is in the hole, the ports allow the water to be forced from the tube as the soil enters. Otherwise, very high fluid pressures may be created inside the tube. In some cases a ball check in the head helps to create a partial vacuum at the top of the sample to compensate for the vacuum formed at the bottom as the sample is withdrawn from the soil. Samples are preserved in the tubes by covering the ends with melted wax, or in the field, temporarily, with sheet plastic. In order to keep disturbance to a minimum, the sharpened edges of the tubes should be rolled slightly inward to reduce friction along the sides of the

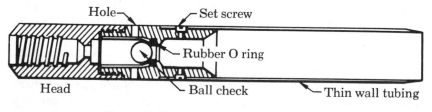

Figure 1.09a   Shelby tube sampler

tubes. Friction along the sides of the tubes having the same diameter as the cutting edges often causes distortion and makes pushing the samples out of the tubes difficult. Sometimes side friction causes so much distortion that the length of the sample entering the tube is less than the penetration of the sampler into the soil. Remolding of the soil next to the tube walls may cause the soil to stick to the tubes so tightly that a snugly fitting piston used to push the sample from the tube penetrates through the sample, leaving a thin layer of clay adhering to the walls of the tube.

A number of variations of the thin wall sampler have been devised for special purposes. One called a piston sampler is provided with a piston which fits snugly inside the thin wall tube and is operated by a rod extending up through the drive pipe. The piston is positioned at the bottom of the hole initially; it is then held stationary by clamping the piston rod in a fixed position while the tube is pushed into the soil at the bottom of the

Spring ⌐Piston lock ⌐Set screw

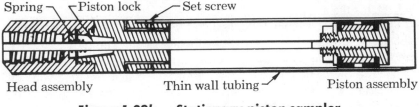

Head assembly   Thin wall tubing ⌐   Piston assembly

Figure 1.09b   Stationary piston sampler

hole. During the taking of the sample, the piston is pulled up with the sampler and it carries the weight of the column of water above the sample and creates a vacuum between the piston and the sample, which helps to hold the sample in the tube. A disadvantage of the piston sampler is the difficulty in holding the piston stationary as the sampler is pushed into the soil. If the piston is held stationary, excellent control of the length of push is possible. When this is compared with the length of the recovered sample, a sound basis is provided for estimating the per cent recovery and, possibly, the severity of disturbance. Another disadvantage of the piston sampler is that the samples either must be removed from the tube in the field where the possibility of disturbance is great, or a new tube must be provided for each sample. Sampling tubes should be sharpened, the cutting edges rolled slightly inward and reamed to size, the upper end drilled for attachment to the sampler head, and the inner surface coated to prevent corrosion. Obviously such tubes are expensive. Dr. Jorj Osterberg has improved the piston sampler, simplifying the holding of the piston stationary during the taking of the sample and providing thin liners so that samples may be removed from the sampler inside the liner and protected and stored in the liner. This device is known as the Osterberg sampler. The piston sampler is particularly useful in sandy soils and in soft to firm clays.

Another sampling device is known as a split spoon sampler. It consists of a split barrel held together at the bottom with a shoe having a cutting edge tapered on the outside, and at the top with a head for fastening to the push pipe or stem, and is pushed or driven into the soil to obtain a sample. The sample is removed by taking off the head and shoe and pulling the two halves of the barrel apart. The split spoon sampler may be of any size. A thin tube liner is often provided in which the sample is preserved after being removed from the sampler.

The split spoon sampler used in the so-called standard penetration test and sometimes called a Gow spoon has an inside diameter of 1⅜ in. and an outside diameter of 2 in. The core barrel is 22 in. long. It has ⅝ in. round water ports at the top. Because of the thickness of the walls of the split spoon sampler, samples taken with it are more disturbed than those taken with a Shelby tube or other thin walled samplers.

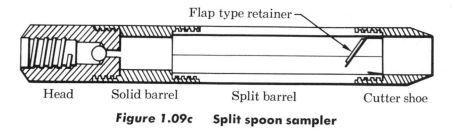

Flap type retainer

Head   Solid barrel   Split barrel   Cutter shoe

Figure 1.09c   Split spoon sampler

The Swedish foil sampler is a recent development which allows continuous sampling up to 50 ft or more. The sampler consists of a sampler head which is pushed or jacked into the soil through a sampling tube. As the sample enters the sampler head, thin metal foils unwind from 16 reels in the sampler head and follow the sample into the sampling tube, completely encasing the continuous sample in the foil. As the sampler advances into the soil, sections of sampling tube are added at the top. At the end of the sampling operation, as the sampler is withdrawn, the continuous sample is broken into sections in the sampling tube sections. The samples are extruded from the sampling tube sections by pulling out the foil covered section of the sample. A strip of foil can then be removed for visual inspection of the continuous soil sample and for removing sections for testing. An advantage of the foil sampler is that a continuous core of the underlying soil is obtained which allows inspection of the strata as they exist and the taking of test specimens which are more representative of the underlying soil than those taken with short sampling spoons. The foil sampler can be used in most soils into which it can be pushed.

One of the more successful samplers, especially for hard clays, is the Denison barrel sampler. It was originally devised and used for exploration of the site of the Denison Dam on Red River between Oklahoma and Texas. It is now used extensively by the U.S. Army Engineer Corps, the U.S. Bureau of Reclamation, and the U.S. Soil Conservation Service. This sampler consists of an inner split spoon sampler with a thin liner and core catcher, and an outer rotating barrel with teeth on the cutting edge. As the outer barrel is rotated, water is forced through the drill stem down between the outer barrel and the sampler, out under the cutting edge and up between the outer barrel and the sides of the holes, bringing the soil cuttings to the top of the hole. As the outer barrel advances, the sampler is pushed into the soil. The liner is 24 in. long and 6 in. in diameter. With this device, almost continuous samples can be taken and preserved in the liners in 24 in. sections. Such sampling is expensive and is commonly used only on large projects for which the expense is justified. The sampler is described by H. L. Johnson in *Civil Engineering*, Vol. 10, 1940 and in *Earth Manual* of the Bureau of Reclamation.

The Denver sampler is a double barrel sampler similar to the Denison barrel sampler and is described in *Earth Manual*.

Other more complicated samplers have been devised. Some have a loop of fine wire in a groove in the cutting shoe for cutting off the sample after penetration and before extraction of the sampler. Some are provided with a compressed air outlet in the cutting shoe for applying air pressure to the bottom of the sample to help hold it in the sampler. These complicated samplers are made in large sizes for obtaining undisturbed samples of soft clays for consolidation tests.

The amount of disturbance of samples taken with samplers from bore holes is dependent upon the ratio of the area of the sampler walls to the total cross sectional area of the sampler and the method of forcing the sampler into the soil. Driving the sampler with successive blows of a hammer produces the most disturbance. Pushing the sampler into the soil continuously and rapidly produces the least disturbance. Samples for accurate laboratory testing of compressibility and strength should be at least 4 in. in diameter. Such a large sampler requires a large bore hole, which adds materially to the cost of exploration. Shelby tube samples of 2 in. cannot be considered as undisturbed, but if nothing better is available, they can be used for consolidation and shear tests. In cased holes in soft clay, samples should be taken just below the bottom of the casing. If the hole is drilled ahead of the casing before the sample is taken, the soft clay may partially fill the drilled hole below the casing and result in a highly disturbed sample.

Samples kept for extensive periods should be stored in a humid room to prevent loss of natural water.

An exhaustive study of soil sampling has been made by Dr. Juul Hvorslev. The Swedish Geotechnical Institute has for some years been continuously engaged in the design and testing of improved sampling devices. References to some of these studies are given at the end of this chapter.

1.10   Test Pits

Shallow test pits up to about 12 ft deep above the water table and in soil that will stand without lateral support can be dug quickly and economically with a back hoe. Deeper pits are usually dug by hand and are expensive. Where lateral support is required, the pits should be shored in such a way that the shoring can be placed with spaces between the sheathing boards to facilitate examination of the soil in the sides of the pit. One

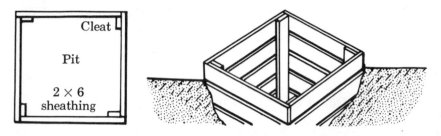

Figure 1.10a   Shoring for test pit

method of shoring a small test pit is the use of 2 by 6 in. or 2 by 8 in. wood horizontal sheathing with a cleat near one end of each piece, so that a shoring bent can be placed below the bents already in place as the pit is dug, as shown in Figure 1.10a. These horizontal bents can be placed vertically a short distance apart. The vertical spacing of bents will depend upon the nature of the soil. The bents can be supported vertically with vertical supports inside the pit and with blocks between the sheathing bents.

1.11   Undisturbed Samples from Test Pits

In general, it is much easier to take a soil sample with little disturbance from a test pit than from a bore hole. A test pit has the advantage of affording visual inspection of the soil as it actually exists. Its only disadvantages are its high cost and the limitation of depth. Test pits are limited practically to soil above the water table or a short distance below where the water can be lowered by pumping.

One of the simplest and best methods of taking a sample from a test pit is to expose a block of soil of any size and shape desired, or one that will stand without damage, leaving the block to stand on its bottom as shown in Figure 1.11a. The block should be trimmed to the desired size and shape and wrapped with one or two layers of cheese cloth. Melted wax should be applied to the cheese cloth covered surface with a paint brush, building to a thickness of about ⅛ in. If greater reinforcement is needed, the waxed covering may be wrapped with another layer of cheese cloth and another coating of melted wax applied. The sample can be loosened from its bed by inserting the blade of a spade below the block and prying

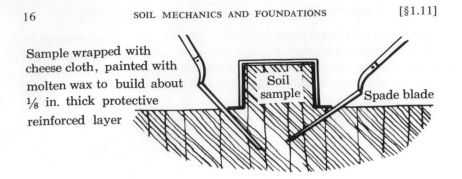

Sample wrapped with cheese cloth, painted with molten wax to build about ⅛ in. thick protective reinforced layer

Soil sample

Spade blade

Figure 1.11a   Hand sample in test pit

it loose. The sample can then be turned over, the excess soil cut off, and the bottom reinforced with cheese cloth and melted wax to form a completely protected sample.

Samples of soil having little cohesion can be taken from a test pit or excavation with a thin walled sharpened cylinder about 6 in. in diameter and 4 to 6 in. long. The sample is cut out for as deep as it will stand without damage and slightly larger than the tube. The sharpened cylinder is then pushed over the trimmed portion of the sample, and the excess soil cut off as the cylinder is pushed down over the sample. Then more of the sample is exposed and trimmed below the cylinder, after which the cylinder is pushed down again. This procedure is continued until a sample of the desired length is obtained. Great care must be exercised to see that the sample is not broken as the cylinder is pushed over it. The sample is preserved in the cylinder by covering the ends with melted wax.

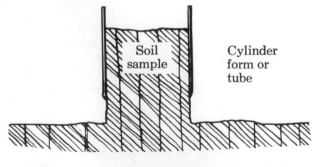

Soil sample

Cylinder form or tube

Figure 1.11b   Soil sample from test pit in sharpened cylinder

When a sample of fissured clay is to be taken from below the water table in a test pit in which water has been lowered by pumping, it may be necessary to drive or push a short 6 in. diameter sharpened cylinder the full length into the bottom of the pit. The water in the clay coming to the surface at the sides of an excavated block after the external pressure has been relieved causes the clay to crumble. This may occur in very hard clay having a high shear strength when supported by surrounding clay and its overburden.

1.12   Rock Drilling and Coring

When rock is encountered by any of the boring methods described heretofore, only the surface position of the rock can be determined. The thickness, kind, and nature of the rock can be determined only by drilling through or into the rock and possibly by taking cores. How deeply the rock should be investigated depends upon the type of rock encountered and the type of structure to be supported. For buildings not more than 15 stories in height, it is usually not necessary to drill more than 10 ft into the rock if it is found to be solid and hard.

Rock drilling and coring can be done with the same truck mounted rig used for making wash borings. Several types of bits are available for drilling and coring rock. Each of the different types of rock bits is fitted for drilling soft, medium, or hard rock.

Three cone or roller rock bits are commonly used for drilling ordinary overburden and rock. Cores cannot be taken with a cone or roller bit. The roller bit consists of a steel body with a threaded connection for attachment to the rotary drill stem and is fitted with 3 hardened toothed rollers arranged on bearings, so that as the bit is turned in the hole, the rock is powdered over the entire area of the hole. The powdered rock is

Figure 1.12a   Cone or roller rock bit

washed to the surface by water pumped down the drill stem and through a jet in the center of the bit. Compressed air is sometimes used to blow the powdered rock to the surface.

Carbide tipped cross bits are also used for general drilling of overburden and soft rock. These bits are operated with an ordinary rotary drill rig in the same manner as for roller bits. Soil cuttings and rock powder are lifted to the surface with water or compressed air.

For drilling through hard rock, non-coring diamond bits are often used. These bits consist essentially of a plug threaded at the end for connection to the rotary drill stem, with the cutting end consisting of a matrix with inset small commercial diamonds. A small opening extends through the bit for the introduction of water or compressed air for lifting the cuttings to the surface. Diamond rock coring bits consist of a thick walled hollow cylinder with provision for connection to a core barrel, and with commercial diamonds set in the bottom end of the thick wall. A core barrel is provided between the coring bit and the drill stem to receive the core after it has been formed by the bit. Rock cuttings are brought to the surface with water or compressed air. These diamond bits will cut a hole through hard rock or concrete with little drift, even when used in a horizontal position. Carbide bits are considerably cheaper than diamond bits and can be used for taking cores of soft rock formations.

  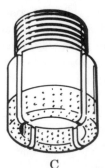

| A | B | C |
| Diamond pilot non-coring bit | Carbide insert coring bit | Diamond coring bit |

Figure 1.12b   Non-coring and coring diamond carbide rock bits

The shot or calyx drill is sometimes used for taking large cores. The shot drill consists of a hollow thick wall with openings in the bottom through which hardened steel shot are introduced to the cutting edge in the wash water. As the shot are worn away more shot are introduced.

An accurate record of the drilling should be kept showing the location and thickness of cavities and the per cent recovery of the core. The cores should be preserved in boxes in the order in which they are removed, so that they can be laid out to show the section of the cored stratum.

1.13   Evaluation of Samples

The soil samples recovered from a bore hole are always disturbed to some extent. Split spoon and Shelby tube samples cannot be considered as undisturbed. From these disturbed samples, the engineer must gain as much information as possible about the stress-deformation-strength characteristics of the soil as it exists under the site.

Several simple field tests of disturbed samples may be used as rough aids in estimating the stress-deformation-strength characteristics of the soil. Some of these simple field tests are described below.

a.   Texture

As mentioned in *Physical Properties of Soils*, the composition of the soil as to percentages of sand, silt, and clay is known as texture. The composition of the soil can be roughly estimated by the following method.

Mix a small sample of the soil with water in a dish or bowl, using a knife or spatula to form a smooth, creamy paste. Pour or rinse all this paste into a glass jar or bottle of relatively small diameter and add water to make a dilute suspension. Shake the bottle vigorously to disperse the soil grains uniformly throughout the suspension. Set the bottle on a table and allow the soil to settle out of suspension. The soil grains will be segregated into layers of sand, silt, and clay. The thickness of the layers can be measured and the percentages of each estimated.

Often the colloidal clay particles will not settle out of suspension. A few drops of hydrochloric acid added to the suspension will cause the clay to flocculate and settle out. These flocks of clay will be very loose, so that the height of the layer of clay will not indicate the true volume of clay in the sample in comparison with the sand and silt. The clear water above the soil can be syphoned off and the water in the clay allowed to evaporate, after which the amount of clay can be estimated fairly accurately. In a qualitative way, this information is useful because of the characteristics described in the next paragraph.

Soils with considerable amounts of cohesionless materials (sand, gravel, and silt) are, in general, more stable than pure clay. Pure clay shrinks as it dries out and swells when it becomes wet. When soft and saturated, pure clay allows settlements when subjected to static loads. Clean sands and silts in a loose condition decrease in volume when subjected to vibration. A small amount of clay in the sand or silt acts as a stabilizing agent, preventing the collapse of the structure of the soil when subjected to vibration. Dense sands and silts, when confined under several feet of overburden, are stable soils which resist volume change from both static load and change in water content. Clean sands can be compacted by vibration but not by static load. Moist clays containing some sand or silt can be readily compacted by tamping or with a sheepsfoot roller.

b.   Color

Dark drab colors are usually indicative of the presence of organic matter in the soil. Bright and soft pastel hues indicate inorganic soils. Soils are nearly always lighter in color when dry than when wet.

In general, organic soils are less stable than inorganic soils. If the soil contains much organic matter, it is likely to be quite compressible under load and may decrease in volume due to decomposition of the organic matter.

c.   Odor

Odor is indicative of the presence and type of organic matter in a soil. Clean sands and silts have no odor. Clean clays possess the peculiar odor associated with kaolin. Sulphur (rotten egg) and ammonia (barnyard) smells are almost sure signs that organic matter is present in the soil. The intensity of the odor is indicative of the amount of organic matter.

d.   Moisture Content

Sometimes the moisture content of the soil as it exists in its natural environment is significant. Dry sands and silts have no shear strength and will flow into uncased holes and excavations. When moist, these soils possess some shear strength developed by the capillary pore water. Holes of considerable diameter can be drilled in moist fine sands and silts. If the fine sands and silts are saturated and loose, they will liquefy when subjected to sudden shock. Loose fine sands and silts below the water table will flow up into the bore hole when the confining overburden is punctured.

The shear strength of clays is dependent upon the water content. Dry clays swell when they become wet and wet clays shrink when they are dried out.

If a sample of clay crumbles when remolded in the fingers, and if small pieces will not stick together, it should be described as dry. The soil should be described as moist if the crumbs will stick together and can be rolled into a thread about $\frac{1}{16}$ in. in diameter without sticking to the fingers. If the soil is soft and sticks to the fingers during remolding, it should be described as wet.

The water content of saturated clay below the water table is indicative of the compressibility of the clay.

e.   Consistency

Descriptions of consistency and simple tests for determining the consistency of soils are given in *Physical Properties of Soils*.

f.   Macroscopic Structure

Macroscopic structure is the arrangement of the larger constituents of the soil that can be observed with the naked eye.

Macroscopic examination may give important clues to the history of the formation. Alternate thin layers ($\frac{1}{8}$ to $\frac{1}{4}$ in.) of dark colored clay and light colored silt are indicative of a soil formed in glacial lakes. A homogeneous mixture of large rounded boulders, gravel, sand, and silt was probably formed by moving ice in a glacier. Lenses of sand or silt in clay indicate that the soil was probably formed in a flood plain of a flowing stream. Peat pockets indicate that the soil was formed in a shallow swamp or bog supporting a luxuriant growth of vegetation. Rock fragments are often found in soils that have migrated to the foot of steep slopes protected by a cap rock, or with rock layers in the soil.

Some soils in the undisturbed state show a granular structure like granite. These soils can be remolded into clay with sharp gravel intrusions. These are residual soils formed by the weathering of quartz bearing igneous rock strata into clay, with the quartz minerals remaining as sharp gravel.

A light gray homogeneous soil in thick deposits which is lightly cemented with montmorillonite and usually with a small amount of calcium carbonate, but which can be easily crumbled between the fingers into fine dust, is probably a wind blown deposit called loess. Loess stands in vertical banks even when exposed to the weather for long periods of time.

Fissures and joints in clay that allow the clay in the undisturbed state to be broken into small blocks along planes of weakness are probably indications of clay that has been dried out at some time, even though it may at present be under the water table. Such a soil will probably shrink and swell with change in water content. These clays may possess a high shear strength when confined by their overburden, but break into small pieces when removed.

g.   *Plasticity*

Of the properties that can be determined from disturbed soils, plasticity is probably the one best suited to inferring the stress-deformation-strength characteristics of the undisturbed soil. In general, plasticity is indicative of compressibility. Highly plastic soils are highly compressible. However, a soft loose soil is more compressible than the same soil in a hard dense state, regardless of plasticity.

Several simple field tests are available for estimating the plasticity of soil samples.

(1)   *Shaking Test*

This test is sometimes called the dilatency test. A small sample of soil about ¾ in. in diameter is remolded with enough water to make the soil soft but not sticky. Gravel or coarse sand particles should be removed from the sample. The pat of soil is placed in the palm of one hand and the back of the hand containing the pat of soil is tapped rapidly with the other hand. If the soil reacts to this test, the surface of the sample will become shiny with the water which comes to the surface as the loose material becomes denser as a result of the vibration. The pat of soil is then deformed by folding the palm of the hand containing it. In a positive reaction to the test, the surface water will be drawn into the sample when deformed and the surface of the pat will become dull.

Fine clean sands react quickly and distinctly to the shaking test. Very fine grained cohesionless soils, like silt and rock flour, react to the shaking test but more slowly than do fine sands. Plastic clays do not react to the shaking test. Cohesionless soils when moist do not stain the hands.

(2)   *Surface Test*

Cohesive soils can be identified by rubbing a small ball of remolded moist soil with a knife blade or fingernail. A small sample of the soil at about the plastic limit is kneaded into a ball about 1 in. in diameter and rubbed with a clean knife blade or fingernail. If the blade leaves a shiny slick surface, the soil is highly plastic. The plastic limit is the water content at which the soil starts to crumble when rolled into a thread about $\frac{1}{8}$ in. in diameter.

(3)   Dry Strength Test

The dry strength test requires two pieces of undisturbed soil about 1 in. in each dimension. One of the pieces of soil is remolded thoroughly and rolled into a ball. The undisturbed and the remolded samples are allowed to stand at room temperature for two or three days until they are thoroughly air dried. An attempt should then be made to crush these two specimens of dry soil between the fingers, noting whether they crush easily or with difficulty. If they cannot be crushed with the fingers, at attempt should be made to crush them under the ball of the hand with the aid of body weight. If they cannot be crushed in this manner, perhaps they can be crushed under foot. The hardness should be tested by crushing a small piece between the fingers or the fingernails.

The dry strength increases with increasing plasticity. A high dry strength indicates a high plasticity. A large difference in the dry strengths of the undisturbed and the remolded specimens may indicate that the soil in the undisturbed state has a well defined open structure. Silty fine sands and silts have about the same very slight dry strength. Fine sand feels gritty, whereas typical silt has the smooth feel of flour.

(4)   Toughness Test

The toughness test furnishes a rough means of determining the amount and type of colloidal materials in the soil. Toughness refers to a high strength coupled with a large deformation before rupture.

A specimen of soil about $\frac{1}{2}$ in. in diameter is remolded with enough water to make it slightly above the plastic limit, but not sticky. The remolded specimen is rolled on a smooth surface under the palm of the hand into a thread about $\frac{1}{8}$ in. in diameter. After rolling the thread, which probably does not break after the first rolling, it is again rerolled into a thread. This procedure is repeated until the water content has been reduced to such an extent that the thread breaks when rolled to a diameter of about $\frac{1}{8}$ in. When the thread breaks at $\frac{1}{8}$ in. diameter, the soil is at the plastic limit. Toughness is indicated by the amount of pressure required to roll the soil into a thread at the plastic limit.

High toughness and stiffness at the plastic limit indicates a high percentage of colloidal clay particles in the soil. It also indicates that the clay probably contains a high percentage of montmorillonite or other highly active clay particles. Weakness and lack of cohesion in the thread at the plastic limit indicates an inorganic clay of low plasticity, probably containing a considerable amount of kaolin. Organic clays are weak and have a spongy feel at the plastic limit.

The *Guide for Identification and Classification of Soils* given in *Physical Properties of Soils* can be of considerable assistance in the interpretation of these simple field tests.

1.14   *Penetration Tests*

It is somewhat difficult to obtain undisturbed samples for laboratory tests to determine the shear strength of soils. This is especially true for bore holes. Any method that allows the shear strength of the soil in place to be determined has a decided advantage. So far no method that is completely reliable for even a single set of conditions has been devised for that purpose. Some methods are more useful for some conditions, and other methods are more useful for other conditions.

Dynamic penetration tests are those in which a standard point or other penetration device is driven with a hammer of standard weight and height of fall. The resistance to penetration is measured by counting the number of blows of the hammer required to drive the device 1 ft or some other standard distance into the undisturbed soil at the bottom of a bore hole.

Static penetration tests are those in which the penetration device is pushed into the soil a standard distance by a steadily applied force. The load test consisting of a small area (usually 1 sq ft) loaded to failure in the bottom of a test pit might be considered as one form of penetration test.

In general, dynamic penetration tests give more reliable results in cohesionless soils (especially coarse grained) and static penetration tests are more reliable for cohesive soils. In either case, the results of penetration tests must be interpreted intelligently to be of any practical value, and should be used with caution. In practically no case should the resistance to penetration be interpreted as a safe contact pressure for loading a soil with a footing.

In the planning of a test program and in the interpretation of the results of penetration tests, a knowledge of the nature of the resistance to penetration is useful.

When a solid device of given volume is pushed into the soil, the penetrating device displaces an equal volume of soil. This volume displacement can be divided into two parts; one, volume change of the soil caused by the penetration; and two, displacement or movement of a portion of the soil to make room for the penetrating device. If the soil penetrated is saturated or if it is cohesionless and dense, the volume change will be negligible, except as consolidation is allowed to occur. In coarse grained soils, like sand, this consolidation will take place immediately. In the case of clay, the permeability is so low that a considerable amount of time is required for the excess pore water to be squeezed out.

For those cases where there is no volume change, the resistive forces can be illustrated as shown in Figure 1.14a.

As the penetrating rod is forced into the soil, wedges of soil are pushed up as shown in Figure 1.14a. The displacing of this volume of soil is resisted by the weight of the soil in the displaced wedges and the shear

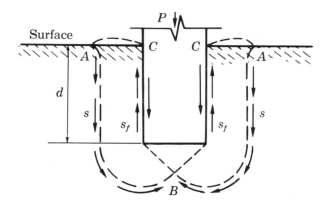

Figure 1.14a   **General shear failure**

resistance of the soil along surfaces A-B and the frictional resistance along surfaces C-B. For soft clays, $s = c$ and is approximately constant over the entire surface of failure. For sensitive clays (those in which the shear strength of the undisturbed clay is much greater than the shear strength after remolding), the resistance is greater over that portion of the failure surface where the deformation has not progressed enough to produce complete failure. For cohesionless materials, $s = \sigma \tan \phi$. σ is the normal earth pressure against the surface of failure, and, since σ varies with depth, the shear resistance varies with depth also.

If there is a rapid volume change as the penetrating device enters the soil (which cannot occur in saturated clay or dense sand), a rational analysis of the resistance is more complicated. Very loose non-saturated cohesive soil is compacted below the bottom of the penetrating device. In loose cohesionless soils, static penetration will possibly resemble that in dense

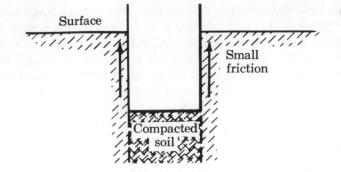

Figure 1.14b   Local shear failure

sand, except for greater deformation and lower shear resistance because of a lower value of ϕ. A dynamic test in loose cohesionless material breaks down the loose structure to a denser one because of the vibration produced. The looser the sand, the greater will be the volume change produced before appreciable displacement and the development of appreciable shear resistance.

1.15   Equipment for Penetration Tests

A number of penetration devices and methods have been devised for estimating the shear strength of soils in place. Some of them are listed and described below.

a.   Pocket Penetrometer

A hand operated pocket penetrometer resembling the sketch in Figure 1.15a is available commercially. This penetrometer consists of a small stem of constant cross section with a flat end which fits into a handle enclosing a compression coil spring. The stem is pushed into the handle against the resistance of the spring. A pointer is secured to the stem to

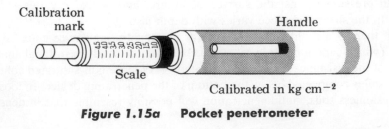

Figure 1.15a   Pocket penetrometer

register on a scale on the handle. The scale is calibrated to register shear strength of the soil in kg cm^{-2} or tons per sq ft when the stem is pushed into the soil until the calibration mark about $\frac{1}{4}$ in. from the end is even with the surface of the soil.

b.   *Dutch Penetrometer*

Another larger type of static penetration device for use in the bottom of a bore hole or at depth below the surface was devised in Holland and is often referred to as the Dutch Penetrometer. This device consists of

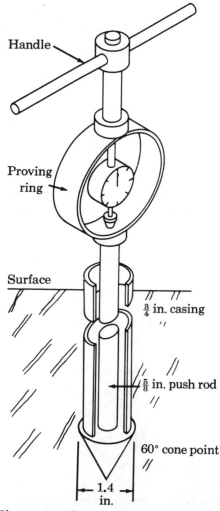

Handle

Proving ring

Surface

$\frac{3}{4}$ in. casing

$\frac{5}{8}$ in. push rod

60° cone point

1.4 in.

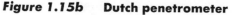

Figure 1.15b   **Dutch penetrometer**

a 1.4 in. diameter 60° steel cone at the end of a ⅝ in. diameter rod. The push rod is threaded through lengths of ¾ in. diameter steel pipe casing used to drive the point and eliminate friction, except at the point. With this device, the casing is driven, using the cone as a point. At the elevation where a test is desired, the point is slowly pushed into the soil by pressing on the handle. The pressure required to push the point into the soil is read on the calibrated dial in the proving ring. In Holland this device has been calibrated for use in soft clays. The shear vane or some other method of investigation is probably more reliable for determining the shear strength of soft clays. It might have a useful application for determining the density of sands and silts when properly used. Pulling the casing and point after use would probably be difficult without power equipment. The use of this type of penetration test for estimating the carrying capacity of sands and silts is discussed in a paper, *Penetration Tests and Bearing Capacity of Cohesionless Soils*, by G. G. Meyerhof.

c.   Wash Point for Sand

By referring to Figure 1.14a, one can readily see that the resistance to penetration is affected by the depth of penetration.

Attempts have been made to eliminate the effect of overburden by loosening the sand above the point with a stream of water and then immediately jacking the point a standard distance into the undisturbed sand. The point is used at the bottom of a cased bore hole and the water is pumped down the drive pipe and out the top of the point as shown in Figure 1.15c. A jacking arrangement is provided at the top of the hole with provision for reading the force applied to the point. For a descrip-

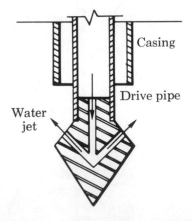

Figure 1.15c   Wash point penetrometer

tion of the procedure for the use of the wash point penetration test and results of calibration tests, see Article 44, *Soil Mechanics in Engineering Practice* by Terzaghi and Peck.

d.   Penetration Cone for Dynamic Test

A simple and fairly reliable method of estimating the density of sand deposits consists of driving a cone into the deposit and measuring the resistance to penetration. Two sizes of cones are commonly used for investigating the density of sand deposits. For this purpose, the cone is driven at the end of a drive pipe for a distance of 1 ft into the sand layer with a standard hammer falling a standard distance. The density of the sand is estimated from the resistance to penetration; i.e., the number of blows required to produce the 1 ft penetration.

A simple cone and hammer that can be used in a bore hole and operated manually is illustrated in Figure 1.15*d*. The cone is a 1.5 in. diameter, 60° steel point threaded for attachment to a 1 in. I.D. steel drive pipe. The drive stem is 1 in. I.D. steel pipe in 4 to 6 ft sections, the same as is

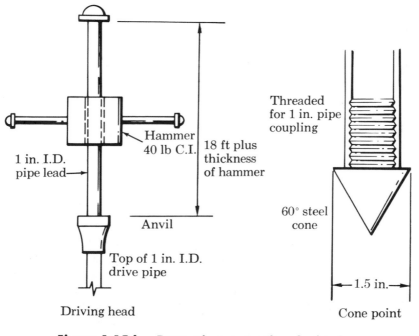

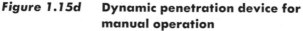

Figure 1.15d   Dynamic penetration device for manual operation

used for turning hand augers and applying torque to shear vanes. The hammer is a 40 lb cast iron weight with a hole to slide over a 1 in. pipe lead. The height of fall is regulated with a pipe lead with a cap at the top and threaded anvil or striking head at the bottom which screws to the top of the drive pipe. The lead is of such length that the hammer falls 18 in. when dropped from the cap to the anvil. The cone can be extracted by driving upward against the cap at the top of the lead.

A larger cone and a heavier hammer have been used for exploring gravel, sand, and glacial deposits where power is available. The drive point is usually a 2.5 in. diameter 60° steel cone fitted loosely into the bottom of a flush joint 2 in. O.D. drive pipe. The point is driven into the soil without a previously drilled hole with a 140 lb hammer falling 30 in. The number of blows required to drive the point 1 ft is used as an indication of the relative density of the deposit at the depth of penetration. At the end of the test, the drive pipe is pulled out, leaving the point in the soil.

In using this continuous driving method, it should be kept in mind that the friction along the sides of the drive pipe becomes greater with depth, so that the resistance to penetration in material of the same density appears to be greater at depth than near the surface.

e.   Standard Penetration Test

The standard penetration test was developed and adopted by the Raymond Concrete Pile Company in its exploration work. In 1958 the test was adopted by ASTM. The penetrating device is a split spoon sampler of standard dimensions, sometimes called a Gow spoon. It is driven into the soil at the bottom of a bore hole through a drive pipe with a 140 lb hammer falling 30 in. The sampler is 32 in. long and has an outside diameter of 2 in. and an inside diameter of 1.375 in.

The hammer used in the standard penetration test is a cube of cast iron or steel mounted at one end of a steel rod about 4 ft long with an eye on the other side of the hammer as shown in Figure 1.15e. The sampler is usually used in a wash boring or a drilled hole, with the sampler replacing the cutting bit or the auger at the bottom of the drill stem in the drill rigs described in Section 1.06. The swivel at the top of the drive stem is replaced with a driving head. The hammer is tied to the lifting rope in place of the swivel and placed on top of the driving head with the rod projecting down into the drive pipe to act as a guide. The driving is done by lifting the hammer with a winch to a mark on the rod 30 in. below the bottom of the hammer and dropping the hammer onto the driving head.

The standard penetration test determines the number of blows, N, required to drive the sampler into the soil a distance of 1 ft.

Figure 1.15e   140 lb hammer for standard penetration test

f.   Self Recording Penetrometer

A penetrometer which drills the test hole and performs static penetration tests as the hole is advanced has been developed and tested by the Shell Development Company, Exploration and Research Laboratory, Houston, Texas, and has been described by Broms and Broussard.

The penetrometer is enclosed in a 3½ in. diameter casing about 8 ft long with a rotary drill bit at the lower end. The penetrating device is a solid cone probe on the end of a stem which projects through and 10 in. beyond the outer case and the drill bit. As the cutting bit drills the hole, the cone probe is forced into the soil ahead of the bored hole by pressure applied by the drill rig through the drill stem. Hydraulic pressure which is built up by pressure on the probe is registered on a pressure recording device included in the case as a part of the penetrometer. With this penetrometer, a continuous record is made of the resistance to penetration of the cone from a depth of about 10 ft to the depth of the hole.

The penetrometer is operated with a rotary rig the same as that used for making wash borings. Soil cuttings are brought to the surface around the drill stem in the same manner as in a wash boring.

1.16   Interpretation of Penetration Tests in Sand

Dense cohesionless materials are very stable under both static and vibrating loads. The shearing resistance and carrying capacity of these materials are dependent upon the confining pressure. Loose cohesionless materials are reduced in volume by vibrating. Vibrating loads, earthquakes, or other vibrations cause large and sudden settlements of structures on loose cohesionless materials. Where clean cohesionless materials are found, the only concern of the investigator is to determine whether the materials are dense or loose and, if possible, the approximate degree of density.

If the cohesionless material is loose and saturated, the grain size may be important, because loose, saturated, fine grained, cohesionless materials become liquid when subjected to sudden deformation. Unless heavy drill mud is used, fine grained, loose, cohesionless materials (fine sands) below the water table will flow up into a drill hole from the bottom. The resistance to penetration in such loose, fine sand below the water table is practically zero. On the other hand, dense sand offers a very high resistance to penetration.

The resistance is affected by several factors other than density. A sand composed of angular grains offers somewhat greater resistance than one at the same density composed of round grains. Grain size and the condition of the pore water, whether in tension or compression, have some effect upon the penetration resistance. The resistance to penetration in coarse sands and gravels is probably little affected by the amount of pore water. In these coarse, cohesionless materials, the capillary rise is too small to cause much additional pressure between the grains in the capillary zone, and the permeability is great enough to make the pore water migrate readily and produce little resistance to volume change. Fine grained sands and silts, on the other hand, offer considerable resistance to the flow of water through the pores. Below the water table, sudden increase in volume such as occurs in dense sands produces momentary tension in the pore water with a resultant increase in pressure between the grains. This increase in pressure between the grains increases the shear strength of cohesionless materials, thus increasing the penetration resistance of a probe. Below the water table, dense, fine grained, cohesionless materials offer increased resistance to penetration, and loose, fine grained, cohesionless materials offer less resistance than above the water table.

The penetration test should be used mainly for comparison purposes. Where possible, the test should be calibrated for the particular site by direct measurement of the density in a test pit adjacent to a penetration test. Load tests in a pit may also be used for comparison of penetration resistance with density, but since a load test is required at each depth at which a penetration test is made, this method is expensive. Undisturbed samples can be taken from an adjacent bore hole by freezing the sand or by cementing with asphalt to maintain the granular structure while a core is removed. After the volume of the sample has been determined, the sample can be thawed or the asphalt dissolved and the unit dry weight determined. This method is also expensive. The static penetration test is actually a miniature load test.

a.   *Manual Dynamic Test*

This test determines the number of blows, N, of a 40 lb hammer falling 18 in. required to drive a 1.5 in. diameter $60°$ cone 1 ft into cohesionless materials not containing boulders in the bottom of a 3 in. bore hole.

The following results of attempts to calibrate the number of blows with density are given in Table 1.16*a*. A better picture of the data is given in Figure 1.16*a*.

Table 1.16a

Calibrating Data Relating Penetration to Density
1½ in. Diameter Cone
40 lb Hammer Falling 18 in.

Location	e_n	No. blows per ft	Description	Depth feet	Distance from W.T.
Blackwell, Oklahoma	0.72	72	Clean coarse sand	16.6	2.0
Greensburg, Kansas	0.51	118	Fine sand	9.8	9.0
	0.61	90	Fine sand	11.8	7.0
	0.66	72	Silty sand	13.3	5.5
	0.59	40	Fine sand	15.1	3.7
	0.58	15	Silt	17.1	1.7
Oklahoma City Fair Ground	0.63	33	Fine silty sand	5.5	1.5
	0.74	24	Fine silty sand	5.5	1.5
North Platte, Nebraska	N.D.	20	Medium sand*	5.0	−2.5
	N.D.	18	Medium sand*	10.0	−7.5
	N.D.	80	Dense gravel	20.0	−17.5
Stafford, Kansas	0.68	24	Fine silty sand	10.6	5.0
	0.58	40	Fine silty sand	13.6	2.0
	0.53	103	Fine silty sand	8.5	5.0

* A compressor station on a mat foundation laid on the sand at the water table 2.5 ft below the original surface with 4 ft of added overburden settled 3.5 in. after 6 years of operation under a vibrating load.

The reader is warned not to take the data too seriously. Most of these comparative calibrations were made from samples taken from test pits and from penetration measurements made in bore holes adjacent to the test

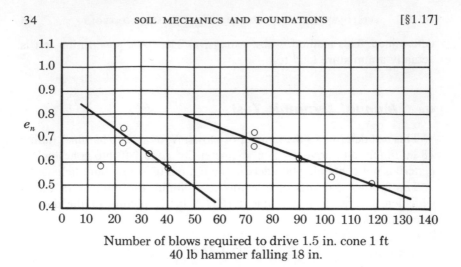

Number of blows required to drive 1.5 in. cone 1 ft
40 lb hammer falling 18 in.

Figure 1.16a   Relationship between number of blows and void ratio of cohesionless material

pits. They do indicate that there is a relationship between number of blows and natural void ratio. But for these comparisons, there appear to be two relationships. In general, the relationships shown for the larger number of blows is for coarser materials in a comparatively dry state a considerable distance above the water table. The relationship for the smaller number of blows is for fine grained materials near the water table.

At best, the resistance to penetration of a small probe driven into a deposit of cohesionless material is only indicative of the density, which may be used as an aid to the judgment. Consideration should be given to the condition of the cohesionless material.

b.   Standard Penetration Test in Sand

The so-called Standard Penetration Test was adopted by ASTM in 1958. Accepted relationships for number of blows and relative density of cohesionless materials, together with a comparison of the standard test with the manual test, are described and given in Table 1.16b.

1.17   Penetration Test in Clay

The pocket penetrometer is designed for use on the surface of clay. It is calibrated for that purpose and shear strength can be read directly. It is not practical for use in clays containing gravel.

Table 1.16b

Relationship Between Number of Blows and Density for Cohesionless Soils

ASTM standard Gow spoon 140 lb 30 in.	Manual 1½ in. cone 40 lb 18 in.	Relative density	Stability
No. of blows	No. of blows		
0–4	---	Very loose	Subject to liquefaction if fine grained and saturated
4–10	Below 25	Loose	Subject to volume decrease from vibration
10–30	25–50	Medium	Questionable
30–50	50–80	Dense	Little decrease in volume from vibration
over 50	over 80	Very dense	No volume decrease

The static cone test has been used in Europe, especially in Holland, where it has been calibrated for soft clays. Dynamic penetration tests are not easily related to shear strength of clays, although the number of blows required to drive a sampling spoon is indicative of the shear strength. Fortunately, the vane test is a reliable one for estimating the shear strength of clays, so there is not much need for a reliable dynamic test.

The standard penetration test described above has been calibrated as accurately as could be done after thousands of tests and checks. The correlation is not very accurate and results of the test in clay should be used with caution. The relationship between strength in unconfined compression, q_u, and number of blows, N, required to produce 1 ft penetration of the Gow split spoon which has come into quite common use in the U.S.A., is $q_u = \dfrac{N}{6}$ tons per square ft. As reported by Peck and Reed, extensive investigations in Chicago clays show that the relationship $q_u = \dfrac{N}{6}$ when compared with unconfined compression tests on split spoon and Shelby tube samples is quite close for very soft clays in that area and becomes increasingly conservative for stiffer and harder clays. However, some tests in the 1½ to 6 ton per sq ft range show strengths considerably less than indicated by this relationship.

The standard classification in common use in the U.S.A. is as follows:

Table 1.17a

Relationship Between Number of Blows and Unconfined Compression for Standard Penetration Test in Clay

No. of blows N	Uncon. comp. q_u ton ft^{-2}	Consistency	
0–2	Less than 0.25	*Very sort*	Core (height twice dia.) sags under own weight
2–4	0.25–0.5	*Soft*	Can be pinched in two between thumb and forefinger
4–8	0.5–1.0	*Medium*	Can be imprinted easily with fingers
8–15	1.0–2.0	*Stiff*	Can be imprinted with considerable pressure with finger
15–30	2.0–4.0	*Very stiff*	Can barely be imprinted with fingers
Over 30	Over 4.0	*Hard*	Cannot be imprinted with fingers

One should remember that these comparisons are for unconfined compression strengths, which may not be a very good indication of the shear strength under all conditions. In any event, the carrying capacity or safe contact pressure under a footing should not be taken as the unconfined compression strength without question. The safe contact pressure under a footing is dependent upon the size, shape, and depth below the surface as well as upon the shear strength of the soil. In soft clays, where the unconfined compression strength might be a fairly good criterion for carrying capacity, the controlling factor is probably settlement instead of carrying capacity. For soft clays the shear strength may be considered for practical purposes as one-half the unconfined compression strength.

1.18   Shear Vane Test

The shear vane has been found to be a relatively reliable tool for determining the shearing strength of soft clays in place. The vane consists of crossed thin blades on the end of a stem. The vane is pushed into the soil at the bottom of a bore hole to a depth somewhat greater than the length of the vane. The torque is applied to the stem at the top of the hole and the angle of rotation and the resistance measured. From this data a stress-strain curve can be plotted for the undisturbed soil. If the vane is rotated two or three full turns, the clay along the failure surface will be remolded, and a stress-strain curve for the remolded soil can be plotted from data found by measuring the torque and angle of rotation.

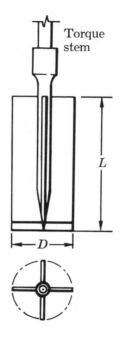

Figure 1.18a   Shear vane

Several sizes of vanes have been used. Studies were made in Sweden during the late 1940's by Cadling and Odenstad to determine the reliability of the results obtained by the rotating vane, the number of wings for least disturbance, and the size of vanes for most accurate results. The conclusions reported by Cadling and Odenstad in 1950 were that the best results were obtained with a vane of four wings, with a length equal to two diameters. Common sizes of vanes in the U.S.A. are 2 in. by 4 in., 3 in. by 6 in., and 4 in. by 8 in.

The relationship between torque and shear may be stated by assuming that the shear is uniformly distributed over the surface of the cylinder, and that it varies uniformly from zero at the center to a maximum at the periphery over the end surfaces of the soil cylinder. If this assumption is used, and if s is the maximum shear stress, the resisting moment of the shear along the side surface of the soil cylinder is $M_s = s\pi LD\left(\dfrac{D}{2}\right).$

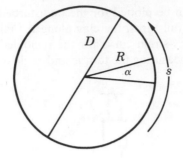

Figure 1.18b   Shearing surface of vane

If the resistance offered by shear at the ends of the soil cylinder is assumed to vary uniformly from the center to the periphery, its moment
arm is $\frac{2R}{3}$ or $\frac{D}{3}$. When the vane is inserted far enough below the surface so
that the soil fails at the top of the vane, the resisting moment of the shear
at the two ends of the soil cylinder is $M_e = 2\left(\frac{s}{2} \frac{\pi D^2}{4}\right)\frac{D}{3}$. The total resisting moment is $M = M_s + M_e$, and, if L is equal to $2D$, $M = T = \frac{13}{12} s\pi D^3$
or $s = \frac{12T}{13\pi D^3}$. If the vane is pushed only part way into the soil and L
is the depth of penetration, the resistance $M = s\pi D^2\left(\frac{L}{2} + \frac{D}{24}\right)$.

Shearing strain is measured as the angle of distortion in radians. As
seen in Figure 1.18c, if a block is distorted in shear through an angle α,
the total deformation is αL and the unit deformation is $\frac{\alpha L}{L} = \alpha$ radians.
The rotation of the shear vane does not measure the true shearing strain,
but, if the movement per unit of length along the shearing surface at the

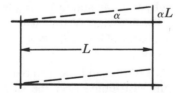

Figure 1.18c   Shearing strain

edge of the vane be called strain, the total strain between adjacent blades
is αR, and the unit strain is $\dfrac{\alpha R}{\dfrac{2\pi R}{4}} = \dfrac{2\alpha}{\pi}$ when α is in radians. If α is

measured in degrees, the unit strain is $\frac{2\pi\alpha^\circ}{\pi 180} = \frac{\alpha^\circ}{90}$. Plotting this strain against shear stress probably has no more meaning than plotting the angle of rotation against stress, but some may like the units better.

The angle of rotation measured at the top of the torque stem is not the angle of rotation of the vane, but includes the angle of twist in the torque stem. Therefore, the vane apparatus must be calibrated for twist of the torque stem. This calibration can be accomplished by attaching one section of the stem to the vane in a tight connection so that part of the rotation is not spent in tightening joints, the vane clamped to prevent rotation, and torque applied to the free end of the stem. Torque is applied in increments, with the angle of twist measured for each increment. A second section of the stem should be added and checked for twist. This procedure should be repeated for each increased length of stem and the angle of twist plotted against torque for each length of stem. The angle of rotation of the vane is equal to the measured angle less the angle of twist for the applied torque on the length of stem.

Some engineers prefer a vane in which the top and bottom of the wings are sloped so that they come to a point at the center. For a pointed vane, the relationship between torque and shearing resistance is slightly different from the relationship given above.

1.19   Equipment for Shear Vane Test

Although shear vanes are commercially available, a shear vane could consist of four wings about $\frac{1}{8}$ in. thick welded at right angles to a center shaft or stem about $\frac{5}{8}$ in. in diameter and 1 ft long. The center welds should be ground smooth and the end edges of the wings sharpened, so that the vane produces as little disturbance as possible when pushed into the soil. The torque can be applied with a torque wrench, attached at any height on the torque stem. A 1 in. steel pipe can be used as the torque stem.

The angle of rotation can be measured on a circular disk fastened to a short piece of 4 in. steel pipe pushed into the top of the bore hole or fastened to the top of the casing in a cased hole. The protractor disk may lie against the ground and be pinned in place to prevent rotation if necessary. A collar with a pointer is clamped to the torque stem with the pointer set at 0 on the protractor disk.

Torque assemblies are also available which apply moment to the torque stem through reduction gears by turning a crank handle. Torque is measured by a micrometer dial in some form of proving ring. The angle of

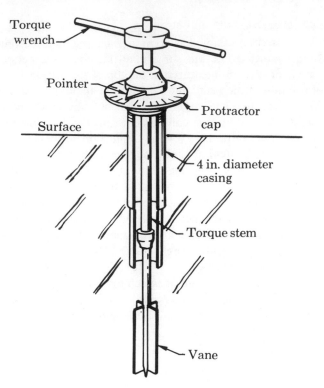

Figure 1.19a   Shear vane apparatus

rotation is measured by counting the turns of the handle and multiplying by the gear ratio, which is usually about 1800 to 1.

In the investigation for a bridge across Lake Pend Oreille, Bennet and Mecham used a vane borer which was used to advance the hole as well as to make the shear tests. The vane was secured to a solid stem which extended through a bullet-nose, grease-packed bearing or packing gland at the bottom of a 3 in. pipe. The vane was turned by a $1\frac{1}{2}$ in. pipe torque tube inside the 3 in. pipe. At the top of the torque tube, a solid extension rod extended above the 3 in. pipe through a packed bearing at the top of the casing. Torque was applied by means of a drum keyed to the extension rod above the torque tube. The drum was turned by a small cable through a pulley on one side of a proving ring, and wound around a small cylinder or capstan. The capstan was turned by a handle through a worm gear.

The hole was advanced by removing the torque frame and applying a driving head in its place at the top of the casing. Water was pumped into the space between the 3 in. pipe casing and the torque tube and out through

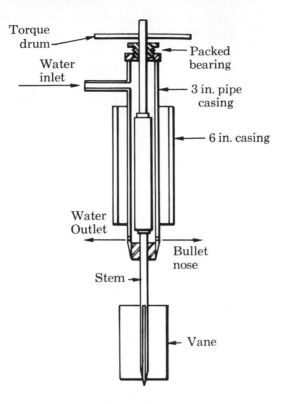

Figure 1.19b   Idaho vane borer

holes in the bullet nose at the bottom of the casing. The 3 in. casing was then driven down with the bullet nose against the vane. When a test was desired, the vane was pushed 30 in. farther into the soil below the bullet nose, the driving head was replaced by the torque frame, and the test was performed.

1.20   Reliability of Shear Vane Tests

The resistance of cohesive soils to shear deformation is dependent to a considerable degree upon the rate of deformation. Two methods of loading unconfined compression and triaxial tests are in common use. One method of testing applies the load in increments of sufficient intensity to produce failure after the addition of 5 to 10 increments. For a quick test, the increments are usually applied at 1 minute intervals, with deformation readings taken after each increment has been on for $\frac{1}{2}$ minute. Another method of loading applies the strain at a uniform rate with the load readings taken at regular intervals.

One method of making a shear vane test is to apply a small torque, holding it constant for 1 minute, after which the torque is increased another increment and held constant for 1 minute. This should be continued to a maximum and backed off. Readings of angular rotation should be taken midway between applications of increments of torque. This method of loading produces a good stress-strain curve up to the maximum stress, but since it is difficult to back the load off at a proper rate, it is not likely to produce a good stress-strain relationship beyond the maximum.

Another method of applying the torque is to increase the rotation or deformation at a uniform rate and to read the angle change and torque at regular intervals. After reaching a maximum, the torque drops off to a value corresponding to the deformation produced, making it easier to continue the curve beyond the maximum.

The measured shear strength of clay is influenced by the rate of deformation. Cadling and Odenstad recommend that the vane be rotated at the rate of 0.1° per sec or 6° per min which should cause failure in about 10 min.

The clay tested by Bennet and Mecham in Lake Pend Oreille is soft, having a shear strength varying with depth of from about 500 to 1800 lb per sq ft. A large number of undisturbed samples were taken at the same depth from bore holes adjacent to the vane tests for correlation of laboratory compression and field vane tests. Unconfined compression, undrained, and consolidated undrained triaxial tests were made in the laboratory on the undisturbed samples. In most cases, the unconfined compression and undrained tests gave nearly the same shear strength, which was about equal to one-half that given by the consolidated undrained and the vane tests. The vane tests and the consolidated undrained tests gave essentially the same shear values.

On the other hand, Anderson reports good correlation between shear strengths as determined by the vane and by unconfined compression tests on undisturbed samples of the soft clays of Great Salt Lake. The correlation was not so good between shear vane and penetration tests in the Great Salt Lake clays. Hall reports in ASTM Symposium the results of comparative tests made by the Corps of Engineers, U. S. Army, in the soft clays of the San Francisco Bay area. This investigation shows fairly close agreement between shear strengths found by the shear vane, unconfined compression, and undrained tests; with the shear vane indicating shear values consistently slightly higher than those determined on samples taken with a Swedish foil sampler and a 6 in. diameter push tube sampler. This finding was attributed to the disturbance produced in recovering the so-called undisturbed samples with the sampling devices.

If the clay is soft enough for the vane to be pushed into the soil at the bottom of the bore hole, the shear strength can often be measured more accurately with a shear vane than by laboratory tests on undisturbed samples. This is especially true of very soft clays and fissured clays lying below the water table. Fissured clays, which can be sampled fairly easily above the water table, are difficult to sample when they lie below the water table, except by pushing a sharpened cylinder into the clay without lowering the water table. Unconfined compression tests tell practically nothing about the shear strength of these fissured clays. Triaxial tests are difficult, time-consuming, and expensive. Testing of these clays with a shear vane for determining shear strength is likely to be more reliable than laboratory tests.

Overconsolidated desiccated clays are hard and bricklike when dry and cannot be tested with a shear vane. The vane cannot be forced into the brittle clay without some shattering and breaking up. There is not much point in trying to determine the shear strength of the dry clay because under foundations it will at some time become wet. Even when saturated, the shear strength of these overconsolidated clays is usually very high and is not often a factor in foundation design. Volume change due to change in water content is a more important factor than shear strength of overconsolidated desiccated clays, especially under light structures.

1.21   Load Tests

When properly made and interpreted, a load test is a reliable method of determining the shear strength of a thin layer of soil at the surface or at the elevation at which the load test is applied. The thickness of the soil affected by the test is approximately equal to the width of the loaded area. The load test can also be of some help in estimating the settlement to be expected from static compaction of loose soil under footings. But the test is usually expensive and gives relatively little information for the money expended. The test should be used intelligently and with caution.

The load test is usually applied to an area 1 ft square on the surface of the soil to be tested in the bottom of a test pit at least as large as five times the size of the footing. Sometimes the load is applied to a 1 ft square concrete footing cast in an excavation in the soil. The load is applied to the footing through a post or column with a loading platform or jacking system at the top. The post must be guyed or braced in an upright position without restraining vertical movement. The load may consist of weighed bags of sand or other material, bricks or other masonry units, steel beams, or a tank into which water can be pumped. The platform can be built in such a way that the back wheels of a loaded truck can be placed as a load. The load can be applied to the top of the post by means of a calibrated hydraulic jack. An advantage of applying the load by means of a jack is that the load can be applied more accurately, and the time of loading is much more easily controlled than by piling bricks on a platform. A dis-advantage of jack loading lies in the difficulty of providing a reaction for the jack. A reaction can be provided by supporting a heavily loaded truck or some other machine over the pit, or by driving piles or burying dead-men some distance on each side of the pit and anchoring a steel beam between them over the pit.

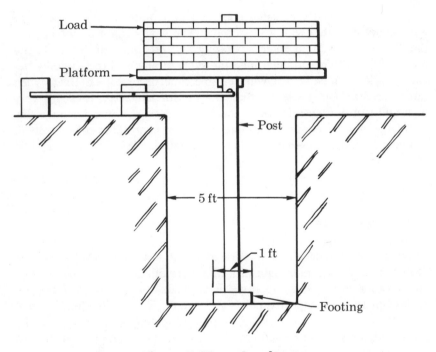

Figure 1.21a   Load test

An accurate method of measuring settlement must be provided. This can be done with a magnifying lever arm or by reference to a bench mark with a precision level.

On soil whose shear strength can be stated approximately by the Coulomb equation, $s = c + \sigma \tan \phi$, a single load test is not sufficient to determine both c and ϕ.

On clean cohesionless materials having a single grained structure in which for practical purposes c is equal to zero, a load test consisting of a 1 ft square footing resting on the surface can be used to estimate the angle of internal friction ϕ or the relative density. For this condition a diagram can be prepared showing the relationship between load at failure, P, and ϕ. For a footing 1 ft square $P = w$. Using an average unit dry weight of clean sand as $\gamma_e = 105$ lb ft^{-3}, the estimated approximate test loads at failure as computed by the sliding wedge and the principal stress methods are given in Table 1.21a.

Table 1.21a

ϕ	P Dry sand, $\gamma_e = 105$		P Submerged sand, $\gamma_e = 66$	
	Sliding wedge	Principal stress	Sliding wedge	Principal stress
0	0	0	0	0
10	62	60	39	38
15	138	116	87	81
25	417	356	266	223
35	1259	1118	790	702
45	4223	4368	2660	2737
50	8106	9708	5100	6117

This relationship applies only to fairly coarse, clean, cohesionless materials having a single grained structure or to fine single grained structure at or below the water table or at a considerable distance above. The ϕ value is the same for submerged as for dry cohesive materials, but the unit weight of submerged materials is less, making the carrying capacity less. In the capillary zone, which may extend several feet above the water table in fine cohesionless material, tension in the capillary water produces pressure between the grains. The relationship given in Table 1.21a is reproduced in Figure 1.12b.

The principal stress method of analysis for estimating the carrying capacity of footings on sand is conservative; based on this analysis the load test is likely to yield values of the internal friction that are higher than the actual values, which could lead to unsafe design of footings for carrying capacity. Also, it is difficult to define failure in this case because it indicates the beginning of movement of the sand grains to new positions or the load at which settlement is very small. As settlement occurs after failure as measured by the above analysis, the resistance of the sand is increased because of the increase in overburden as the footing sinks into the sand, and because of increase in density as the grains slip to positions of greater stability. In the interpretation of the above analysis for deter-

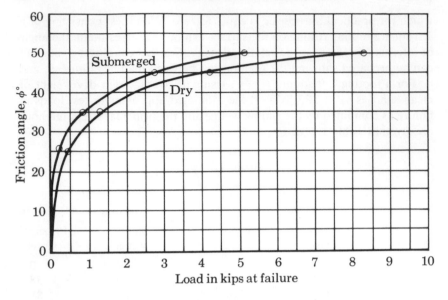

Figure 1.21b   1 ft sq footing on surface of clean sand

mining ϕ from the results of a standard load test, failure should be considered as occurring at a settlement of 0.1 in. or less.

Perhaps a better interpretation of the settlement record of a load test can be made from the results of standard load tests made in the calibration of wash point explorations, as reported in *Soil Mechanics in Engineering Practice* by Terzaghi and Peck. In this calibration, standard load tests on a 1 foot square area were applied to the surface of sand in test pits at the same depth and adjacent to drill holes in which wash point tests were made. Records were kept of the load-settlement relationship on sands of different densities. From these relationships the curves of Figure 1.21c were drawn. This chart is taken from Art. 45, *Soil Mechanics in Engineering Practice*. The relative density of sand can be estimated from the position of the load settlement curve with reference to the division lines on the diagram.

Great care must be exercised in the interpretation of load tests on sand. It should be kept in mind that the soil affected by the test extends only to a depth below the footing equal approximately to the width of the footing. A load test applied to dense sand overlying loose sand indicates a dense sand. A larger loaded area would affect the loose sand below, causing a much larger settlement than indicated by the load test. If the footing is placed some distance below the surface, the surcharge must be considered in computing carrying capacity. This can be done conservatively

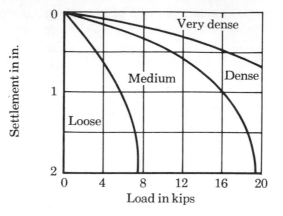

**Figure 1.21c   Relationship between settlement and load on
footing 1 ft square on surface of sand**

by applying the principal stress method of analysis, which is discussed in
Chapter 5.

Theoretically, a single load test on plastic clay in which the angle of
internal friction ϕ can be assumed as zero will determine the cohesion c.
If the surface of failure for a load test on plastic clay is assumed approx-

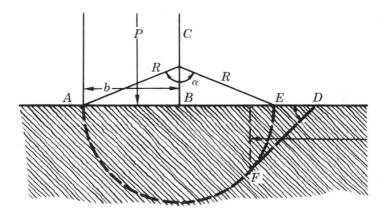

Figure 1.21d   Shear failure for footing on surface of clay

imately as shown in Figure 1.21d along AFD, little error is introduced
by assuming the failure surface to be cylindrical following the arc AFE.
Using this assumption with the added simplifying assumption that the
center of rotation is located on the edge of the loaded area, the value of

c along the surface of failure can be found by taking moments about the center of rotation C.

$\dfrac{Pb}{2} = cR^2\alpha$, and if α be made $x\pi$, $R = \dfrac{b}{\sin x \dfrac{\pi}{2}}$

Then,

$$\frac{P}{2\pi b} = c \frac{x}{\sin^2 x \dfrac{\pi}{2}}$$

For the standard load test on a footing 1 ft wide, $b = 1$ and

$$c = \frac{P}{6.28 \dfrac{x}{\sin^2 x \dfrac{\pi}{2}}}$$

Failure will occur along that surface where the c produced by the load is a maximum. When x is allowed to vary from 1 to 0.5, the maximum value of c is found to be $c = \dfrac{P}{5.55}$.

If the center of rotation is assumed to occur at the edge of the footing at B, the value of c is found to be $c = \dfrac{P}{6.28}$, which is a conservative method of estimating the cohesion of plastic clay from a load test but which should not be used for estimating carrying capacity of footings. The principal stress method of analysis yields a value of c equal to $c = \dfrac{P}{4.5}$, which is too high and should not be used in estimating the value of c from a load test.

If the clay in the test pit is flooded before application of the load test long enough to completely saturate the clay and to allow swelling to occur, and kept flooded during the test in order to prevent drying out, the compressibility of the clay can be estimated from time settlement curves made for the load increments. Each load increment should be left without change until settlement under the applied load has practically stopped. After cessation of settlement, the next increment of load should be added, and this procedure kept up until failure.

1.22   California Bearing Ratio

The California Bearing Ratio, or, as it is familiarly called the CBR test, is a load test applied to the surface and is used extensively for soil investigation as an aid to the design of surfaces for highways and airfield runways.

The test consists of applying a load to a circular area by means of a stiff plate to which the load is applied with a calibrated hydraulic jack. The loading plates vary in size from a diameter of 6 in. to 30 in. in steps of 6 in. Each plate is 1 in. thick. In order to provide stiffness, the plates are stacked pyramid fashion with the load applied to the topmost 6 in. plate. Reaction for the calibrated hydraulic jack is provided by a loaded truck whose supporting wheels are not less than 8 ft from the loaded area. Settlement under load and recovery upon release of load are measured with dial gages (usually 3 at 120°) supported on a beam that is supported on the ground at points not closer than 8 ft from the loaded area.

In preparing for the test, the ground is cleaned of grass, weeds, and other organic matter and smoothed for the reception of the loading plate. A thin layer of fine sand or sand and plaster of paris is laid on the smooth surface and the loading plate is placed on the sand and worked until it is level and makes contact over its entire area. All of the smaller plates are piled concentrically on the bottommost plate, the jack fixed in place, and the dial gages adjusted in place and set at zero reading. Enough load is applied to produce a settlement of from 0.01 to 0.02 in. The load is then released to one-half that required to seat the plate, and the dials again set to read zero.

The test is made by applying the load in uniform increments with settlement readings taken after the rate of settlement has decreased to 0.01 in. per minute. After the desired load has been applied, the load is released in increments and the recovery recorded. From the data obtained from the test, a load settlement curve is plotted.

This test has been standardized by ASTM Designation 1195-64 and 1196-64.

1.23   Coefficient of Subgrade Reaction

Because the load in the CBR test is applied to the existing soil, which is the subgrade for pavements, the applied load is often referred to as the subgrade reaction. The ratio of the subgrade reaction to the settlement produced by the applied load is called the coefficient of subgrade reaction, and is usually designated $k_s = \dfrac{w}{\delta}$ in which w is tons per sq ft or kg per sq cm and δ is the settlement in in. or cm. The dimensions of the coefficient of subgrade reaction are usually $\dfrac{\text{tons}}{\text{ft}^2 \text{ in.}}$ or $\dfrac{\text{kg}}{\text{cm}^3}$.

Use of the coefficient of subgrade reaction is based upon the erroneous assumption that the footing is supported on soil which has no shear strength and behaves similarly to elastic springs, as shown in Figure 1.23a.

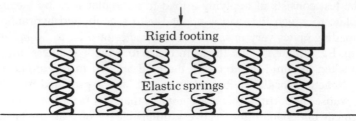

Figure 1.23a   Rigid footing on elastic springs

Actually, load from a footing is distributed over an area which becomes increasingly larger with depth, causing settlement for the same unit contact pressure to vary with size and shape of the footing. Also, the settlement is not proportional to the load on the same loaded area. Therefore, the coefficient of subgrade reaction is not a constant for a given soil and should not be used for estimating settlements of footings. It is commonly used in the design of pavements for highways and airport runways. H. M. Westergaard devised a method of analysis for the design of structural

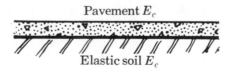

Pavement E_c

Elastic soil E_c

Figure 1.23b   Slab supported on elastic layer

slabs with loads applied over small areas, using the assumption that the slabs are supported continuously on an elastic material. The coefficient of subgrade reaction fulfills the assumption for the theoretical design of slabs of an elastic material supported on an elastic layer and is, therefore, used for that purpose.

1.24   Symbols

The log of each bore hole or test pit and a profile through the soil should show the thickness of the different materials encountered. These can best be shown and identified with the description by indicating the material in the log with characteristic symbols. The symbols should be simple so that they can be drawn freehand in the field and few enough so that they can be kept in mind by the person keeping the log.

The symbols suggested by the Texas Committee on Soil Mechanics and Foundation Engineering seem to be adequate and sensible for this purpose and are illustrated below.

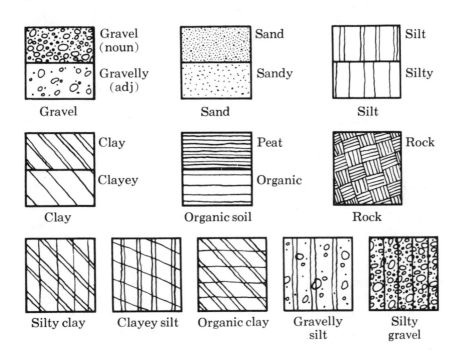

1.25   Observation of Existing Structures

A fruitful source of information concerning the action of the soil in an area under building loads is the physical condition of structures in the immediate neighborhood.

A building supported on continuous footings on hard clay 4 or 5 ft below the surface and some distance above the water table, and having diagonal cracks in the exterior walls, with floors on earth humped up in the middle of rooms, floor cracks radiating outward from the high points, and partitions broken and door openings out of square, speaks eloquently of a soil that has changed volume near the surface due to change in moisture content. A building on clay with diagonal cracks indicating that the interior columns are lower than the corners, indicates settlement due to consolidation of the clay. If a building with footings on sand several feet below the surface has experienced large rapid deformation, one suspects that the sand is loose and that vibration will cause large sudden settlements.

Nearly every structure tells something of the strength deformation properties of the soil that supports it. However, not all cracks in structures are caused by faulty foundations. Partitions or walls are often damaged by the deflection of supporting members which are sufficiently strong to carry their loads without distress and which are themselves not damaged structurally by the deflection. Damage caused by excessive deflection of a supporting member often occurs as a horizontal crack starting at the top of a door or some other opening. Such damage can often be prevented by preloading the flexible member to produce the deflection before the application of the permament load. The preload should be removed as the permanent load is applied. Cracks may be caused by unequal expansion of different materials tied together, especially on the exterior of structures where they are subjected to wide temperature variations. A steel or concrete member 100 ft long changes in length about ¾ in. for a temperature change of 100F°. The change in length of brickwork is only slightly over one half that of steel or concrete. Cracks are often produced in exterior walls by the expansion of roof slabs. One should, therefore, be careful during the observation of existing buildings to lay the blame for failures where it properly belongs.

A complete record of the condition of the buildings in the vicinity of the building site under investigation should be made as a part of the investigation and submitted with the report of findings. Photographs showing the condition of existing buildings are useful, and in some cases almost necessary for the protection of the new building owner against claims for damages during construction.

1.26 Recording and Preserving Data

An accurate and complete record of the investigation should be made. This record should be made in the field with the data being recorded immediately upon being determined. One should not rely upon memory to supply information to be recorded at some convenient future time. In order that the information may be gathered and presented in an orderly and complete manner, forms should be provided the investigator for recording data as it is gathered in the field.

A plot plan of the site should be given to the drilling foreman. If the site has been previously surveyed and reference points established, the location of the bore holes should be indicated on the plot plan by the person who is planning the investigation. If the holes have not been accurately located before drilling, the driller should determine the location of the bore holes and locate them accurately on the plot plan.

An accurate log of the bore holes should be made as the drilling progresses. If possible, the elevation of the top of the holes should be given. Depths and thicknesses of the different strata should be recorded and the materials described. The type of drill rig and method of taking samples should be indicated. The exact depth from which a sample is taken, as well as the penetration and the number of blows required in the standard penetration test, should be accurately measured and recorded. A form for recording this data should be given to the driller or drilling foreman.

Existing buildings or other structures in the vicinity of the site should be carefully examined and their condition recorded as a part of the investigation. In order that this part of the investigation may not be neglected, or done in a haphazard manner, forms for recording information gained in this part of the investigation are useful. Such information is needed not only to protect the owner against damage claims but also as an aid to the engineer in choosing a suitable type of foundation. Photographs of already damaged portions of existing structures are excellent aids when properly identified.

1.27   Compaction of Soils

a.   Compacting Equipment

A variety of equipment is available for compacting soils. Some are devised for compacting the soil in its original position and others for compacting the soil in artificially placed fills. These devices range from simple hand operated equipment such as the end of a 2 by 4, a 6 or 8 in. block with attached handles, gasoline powered "jumping jack" compactors, and gasoline engine vibratory compactors mounted on two wheels and moved about like a wheelbarrow, to self propelled rubber tired and drum type vibratory compactors. Dynamite and foam type explosives have been used to compact soils in place.

Before the development and use of mechanically powered equipment, soils for forming earth dams and other fills were compacted in thin layers by driving flocks of sheep or cattle over the freshly spread layers. The hooves of sheep are so small that the unit contact pressure of the hoof with the soil is high, and so provide an excellent compacting instrument.

One of the most common and versatile modern powered devices is the sheepsfoot roller which consists of a weighted cylinder with blunt toothed projections extending from the surface of the cylinder. The projections or feet are staggered over the face of the cylinder so that the entire area

Figure 1.27a   Sheepsfoot type compactor

covered by the width of the roller is subjected to heavy pressure as it is moved over the surface. Some rollers are smooth steel cylinders. Both of these types are available with a gasoline engine mounted on the frame which drives an eccentric flywheel that vibrates the whole device as it is pulled over the soil being compacted. Some of these compactors are made to be pulled behind a caterpillar type tractor, and others are self propelled with a roller on each end, so that compaction can be achieved by a back and forth movement without turning. Some compactors consist of a heavily weighted small truck mounted on multiple rubber tired wheels placed side by side a short distance apart across the width of the truck. These large powered compactors are used for building fills for dams, highway fills, and other fills covering a large area.

The hand operated jumping jack and vibratory type compactors are used next to retaining walls and in areas where large powered equipment cannot be used. The jumping jack compactor consists of a gasoline powered cylinder on a frame with the piston connected directly to a tamper or foot about 8 to 10 in. in diameter, having somewhat the appearance of an elephant's foot. A handle is attached to the frame by which the operator can hold the compactor upright and move it about over the area being compacted. As the tamper makes contact with the ground, the gas in the cylinder is compressed and fired, causing the device to jump off the ground and deliver a blow of about 1000 lbs each time it jumps. The vibratory type of hand operated compactor is mounted on two wheels for maneuverability and delivers 2000 to 4000 lb blows at 1500 to 3000 blows per minute.

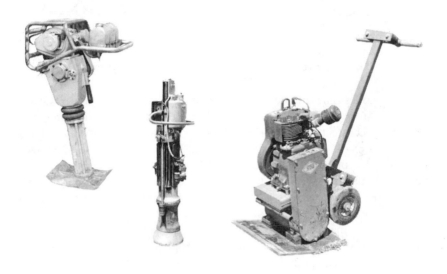

Figure 1.27b
"Jumping jack" compactor

Figure 1.27c
Hand operated vibratory compactor

b.   *Compaction of Cohesionless Soils*

Cohesionless soils consist of bulky grains and possess no inherent shear strength. Shear strength in such soils is produced by pressure between the grains. As illustrated in Figure 1.27d, simple static pressure applied to a layer of loose cohesionless material is transferred to the soil grains, thus increasing the shearing resistance with comparatively little deformation and volume change. However, if the material is vibrated so that pressure between the grains is momentarily relieved, the shear strength is reduced to such an extent that the grains roll down hill under the force of gravity to a denser state as shown in Figure 1.27e.

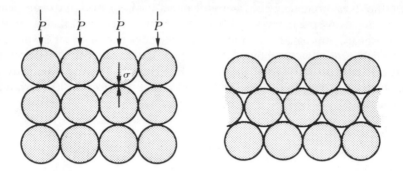

Figure 1.27d
Loose spheres

Figure 1.27e
Dense spheres

Clean cohesionless materials cannot be compacted by static pressure. The sheepsfoot roller without vibration is not effective in compacting these materials. The feet on the roller keep the surface sand stirred and loose and do not walk out to the surface of the layer with repeated passages.

When dry or submerged, clean cohesionless materials can be compacted readily by vibration. Capillary forces in moist medium and fine sands and silts produce pressure between the grains and resist relieving of the pressure during compaction. Clean sands and silts are, therefore, more difficult to compact when moist than when submerged or dry. Submerged sand can be compacted with a properly applied concrete vibrator. Dry clean cohensionless soils in fills can be compacted in thin layers with a vibratory type roller or compactor.

Medium sand in place below the water table in the bottom of an excavation has been successfully compacted to a depth of about 4 ft with a steel blade fastened to a capsule type concrete vibrator. The blade was 4 in. wide by ¼ in. thick and 4 ft long, fastened to a large pneumatic capsule type concrete vibrator with U bolts. Two men held the blade upright allowing it to sink into the sand below the bottom of the excavation. After the blade had sunk its full length, it was pulled out and moved about 6 in. along a 2 in. by 6 in. guide, where it was allowed to penetrate the sand again. In this case, all of the sand below the bottom of the excavation was submerged. This method would not be effective in compacting moist sand.

Loose sand can sometimes be compacted in place by the patented "Vibroflotation" method. This method employs a large self-contained motor driven capsule type vibrator 15 in. in diameter and 6 ft long called a "Vibroflot" on the end of a hollow pipe stem. Ports are provided in the bottom of the Vibroflot and in the stem at the top so that water can be forced into the sand at the bottom or top of the vibrator at will. In use, the vibrator is started, water is forced through the bottom jets, and the apparatus is allowed to sink to the required depth in the sand. At the extreme depth of penetration the water is cut off at the bottom ports and forced through the top ports. The vibrator is allowed to operate at the bottom until the desired compaction is attained. The apparatus is then raised to the surface in 1 ft steps, allowing the vibrator to operate at each level to compact the sand. Each penetration of the apparatus compacts a cylinder of sand about 8 to 10 ft in diameter.

Another method of compacting loose sand in place is by driving displacement piles into the sand. A disadvantage of this method is that piles are difficult to drive into sand and gravel and are usually jetted down, which keeps the sand loose. Piles driven into loose sand for the purpose of compacting it should be only large enough to effect the reduction in voids from the loose to the dense state.

When a loose saturated soil is deformed causing a decrease in volume, the relatively incompressible pore water is subjected to a compressive stress in excess of the hydrostatic pressure. This excess pore water pressure carries all or part of the gravity load until the excess pressure is relieved by flow of water from the voids. In a cohesionless soil, the excess pore pressure and resultant relief of pressure between the grains reduces the shear resistance of the soil. The pores in a coarse sand or gravel are so large that the water can flow readily through the soil and thus relieve the excess pore pressure immediately. In a fine grained cohesionless soil, however, the permeability is so low that the excess pore pressure cannot be immediately relieved. Therefore, a sudden deformation of a saturated, loose, fine grained, cohesionless soil may cause the pore water to carry the entire weight of the soil, causing the mass of soil to become liquid. On the other hand, if the soil is dense, deformation is accompanied by an increase in volume which produces tension in the pore water, thus increasing the shearing resistance. Between these extreme loose and dense states is a state for which the void ratio does not change with deformation. Below this critical void ratio, saturated fine grained cohesionless soils cannot liquefy. Above this critical void ratio, sudden deformation may cause liquefaction and failure of a slope made of this material. It is, therefore, important that fine grained cohesionless soils be compacted to void ratios below this critical void ratio. The critical void ratio is not a constant for a given soil but is dependent to some extent upon the confining pressure. Furthermore, the critical void ratio found in the laboratory may not be reliable for field work.

c. *Compaction of Cohesive Soils*

Clays, and sands which contain some clay, can be compacted by pressure or by a combination of kneading and pressure. They compact readily under a sheepsfoot roller without vibration. The clay is spread in thin layers, usually about 8 in. thick, the thickness depending to some extent upon the nature of the soil and the type of compacting equipment. The compacting equipment is passed over the layer until the desired degree of compaction is attained. When the clay contains the proper water content, the feet of the sheepsfoot roller or compactor penetrate less deeply into the layer with each passage until eventually they roll near the top of the hard compacted layer.

The water content for maximum compaction for a given amount of compactive effort is for most clays quite critical, but the optimum moisture content is not constant for a given soil but is dependent upon the amount of compactive effort expended.

The thin scale-like clay particles attract to their surfaces relatively thick layers of water. This adsorbed water is for practical purposes immobile at the particle surface but becomes gradually disoriented with distance from the surface, until at some distance its full freedom is regained. When there is only a small amount of water present, it behaves as if it were highly viscous, somewhat like asphalt. When pressure is applied to the soil, the asphalt-like water between the grains resists movement of the grains to positions of greater density. So, if the water content of the clay is low, a large amount of effort is required to produce compaction. If the water content is high, the grains are separated by water of low viscosity and are easily moved past each other and the soil is easy to compact. However, because the voids contain more water, a soil with a high water content cannot be compacted to as dense a state as the same soil with a lesser water content.

Figure 1.27f   Loose clay with low water content

When the clay is near saturation it cannot be compacted to a greater density than could be attained by simple flooding. In clay with a low water content the voids are not filled with incompressible water, so that under pressure the particles can move to positions of greater density as

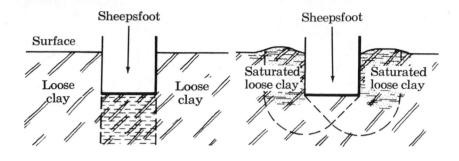

Figure 1.27g
Compaction of clay at near optimum w

Figure 1.27h
Failure of clay at high water content

shown in Figure 1.27*g*. In the nearly saturated state the voids are filled or nearly filled with incompressible water so that the volume cannot be reduced until some of the water has moved out of the voids. The permeability of clay is so low that considerable time is required for the water to flow out of the voids and the foot of the compactor forces the soil aside without reducing its volume.

d. Control of Compaction

(1) Optimum Moisture Content

The optimum moisture content of the soil used for making a fill is determined as already described by the Standard AASHO (Proctor) or the modified AASHO test. These tests can be varied to suit the equipment and materials used for making the fill by using a different number of blows per layer, or by using fewer or more layers than used in the standard tests. As shown by a typical water content-unit dry weight (dry density) curve for clay, the optimum moisture content for most clays is somewhat critical. For a lesser amount of compactive effort (fewer blows of the hammer or fewer passes of the compactor), the optimum moisture content increases. Therefore, if a unit dry weight or void ratio less than obtained by a standard test is desired, a moisture content slightly greater than the optimum as determined by the test will result in a more economical compaction. If the clay is wetter than the optimum for the desired density, it usually must be allowed to dry to near the optimum before compacting. However, some soils with a fairly high permeability will allow the excess

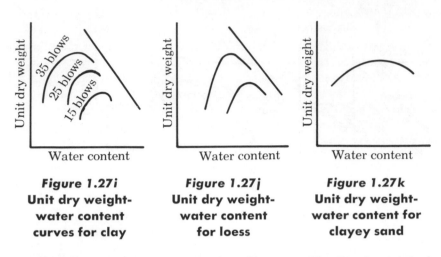

Figure 1.27i
Unit dry weight-
water content
curves for clay

Figure 1.27j
Unit dry weight-
water content
for loess

Figure 1.27k
Unit dry weight-
water content for
clayey sand

water to be driven out as compaction progresses. Usually, the required density of clays cannot be attained by additional passes over the too wet layer or by the use of heavier equipment. If the water content is slightly less than optimum, the required density of the clayey soil can be attained by additional compactive effort. The water content for silt with a small amount of montmorillonite (loess) for maximum compaction is critical. The water content for sand with only a small amount of clay in order to obtain maximum density is not critical. Clean sands can be compacted by vibration when either dry or submerged.

In the field, if the water content of the soil in the borrow pit is below optimum, the soil is usually spread in its final position in the fill after removal from the borrow pit and water added by sprinkling before compaction. If the soil in the borrow pit is wetter than the optimum water content, it must usually be removed to higher ground and allowed to dry to optimum before placing in the fill. Sometimes, when the water content for optimum compaction is quite critical, the soil is spread on high ground, sprinkled, and turned with a blade until the optimum water content is obtained. Sometimes moistening or aeration is accomplished in the borrow pit.

(2) Density of Soil In Place

Specifications for construction of compacted fills usually call for compaction to a certain percentage of dry density at optimum obtained by one of the standard tests. Contractors know about how many passes of their equipment are required to produce the same amount of compactive effort that is used in the standard tests and can, therefore, make a better estimate of the work required than under a specification requiring a certain unit dry weight or void ratio. However, the engineer is interested in the density or void ratio and, except as it influences cost of construction, is not interested in the amount of work required to produce the required density. Checking the density of the soil in place after compaction as construction progresses is a part of the engineer-inspector's duty.

The unit dry weight or so-called dry density of a soil in place can be determined by taking a sample of known volume V, driving off the water in a drying oven, and determining the dry weight W_s. The unit dry weight is $\gamma_{\text{dry}} = \frac{W_s}{V}$. The void ratio of a soil in place can be determined from the total dry weight W_s of the known original volume V and the specific gravity of the solids G_s. The volume of solids, $V_s = \frac{W_s}{G_s \gamma_o}$. The volume of the voids, $V_v = V - V_s$. The void ratio, $e = \frac{V_v}{V_s}$.

The most difficult part of this problem is to determine the original volume of the soil removed as the sample. There are three methods in general use for this purpose.

(a)   *Undisturbed Sample*

In this case, the sample is taken as nearly as possible in its original undisturbed or compacted state in a sharpened cylinder of known volume.

The cylinder is carefully pressed a short distance into the soil and the soil excavated around the outside to the bottom of the cylinder. The cylinder is pressed a further short distance into the soil and the soil again excavated to the bottom of the cylinder on the outside. This is repeated until the soil protrudes above the top of the cylinder. The excess soil

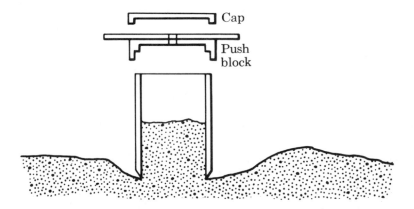

Figure 1.271   Taking undisturbed sample

is struck off with a steel straight edge and the top of the cylinder covered with a smooth plate, preferably in the form of a cap which remains in place when the cylinder is turned upside down. The cylinder can then be lifted out by inserting a trowel or shovel beneath it. The covered cylinder is turned upside down and struck off to a smooth plane surface. In taking samples of clean cohesionless materials, extreme care must be exercised that the soil in the cylinder is not disturbed by vibration or erratic movements of the cylinder.

The soil in the cylinder can then be emptied into a clean container and sealed with an air tight cover to prevent evaporation of moisture. The soil is then weighed as taken from its position to determine the weight wet W_{wet}, dried in a drying oven and weighed to determine its dry weight W_s. From these two weights and the volume, the unit dry weight, water content, and void ratio can be determined.

(b)   Sand Cone

Another commonly used method for finding the volume of the sample removed for determining the void ratio of soils in place is by means of the so-called sand cone.

The apparatus consists of a steel plate with a hole approximately 4 in. in diameter in the center, a hollow cone which fits over this hole with a fruit jar connection above, and a 1 gallon fruit jar. Between the cone and the fruit jar connection there is a valve which allows sand to run from the fruit jar into the cone below.

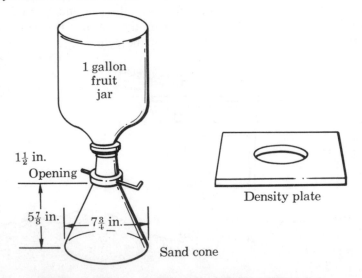

1 gallon
fruit
jar

$1\frac{1}{2}$ in.
Opening

Density plate

$5\frac{7}{8}$ in. $7\frac{3}{4}$ in.

Sand cone

Figure 1.27m   Sand cone density apparatus

Before using the sand cone apparatus, it must be calibrated to determine the unit weight of the sand and the weight of the sand which runs out of the fruit jar in excess of that required to fill the cavity from which the earth sample was removed. The sand cone apparatus can be calibrated by carrying out the following procedure:

1. Fill fruit jar with clean dry sand and weigh.
2. Assemble sand cone apparatus with valve closed.
3. Place density plate over container of known volume, such as compaction mold.
4. Place cone with jar of sand over hole in density plate, open valve and allow sand to fill container and cone.
5. Close valve, lift cone off plate, turn upside down, and remove cone from jar.
6. Weigh jar and remaining sand. Difference in two weighings is weight of sand required to fill container, cone, and plate.
7. Strike off sand in container, being careful not to vibrate to a denser state, weigh sand and compute its unit weight.
8. Determine weight of sand required to fill cone and plate from difference in weight of sand emptied from fruit jar and weight of sand used to fill container. This could also be accomplished by laying the density plate on a flat surface and allowing the sand to fill the cone and hole in the density plate.

In using the sand cone apparatus, the following procedure may be followed.

1. Smooth off surface of soil and lay plate on the smooth surface.
2. Excavate from inside the opening in the plate a pit about 6 in. deep, removing all loose particles and saving all soil removed in an airtight container for future drying to determine W_s.
3. Place cone and weighed jar of calibrated sand over the opening.
4. Open valve and allow sand to fill cone and pit.
5. Close valve, turn jar and cone upside down, remove cone, and weigh jar and remaining sand.
6. Determine weight of sand required to fill pit from difference in weighings of jar and sand minus weight of sand required to fill cone and hole in plate as determined by calibration.
7. Divide weight of sand required to fill pit by unit weight of sand to determine volume of pit, which is total in place volume of the sample removed.

In using the sand cone method, the density of the sand as used must be the same as that used in the calibration. If the sand in the cone and pit is vibrated more or less than in the calibration, the density will not be the same and the volume of the excavated soil will not be determined accurately.

(c)   *Rubber Balloon*

Still another method of determining the volume of the sample removed is by the use of a rubber balloon which is expanded to fill the pit.

The apparatus consists of a density plate and a graduated glass or lucite cylinder enclosed in an airtight aluminum case with an opening in the bottom sealed by a latex balloon which may extend up into the cylinder or out through the bottom. The cylinder is partially filled with water. A double acting rubber bulb is attached to the bottom of the cylinder with which either pressure or a vacuum can be applied to the inside of the cylinder for forcing the balloon out of the bottom of the case through the hole in the density plate and into the excavated pit, or for pulling the balloon up into the cylinder.

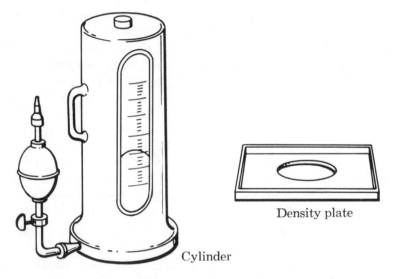

Density plate

Cylinder

Figure 1.27n   Rubber balloon density apparatus

The volume of a pit from which a sample of soil has been removed can be determined with the rubber balloon apparatus by following these instructions:

1. Smooth off surface of soil and lay plate on this surface.
2. Place cylinder over plate, open air valve, and pump air into the cylinder until balloon is completely deflated against the surface of the soil in the opening, and read volume of water in cylinder.
3. Remove cylinder from plate.
4. Excavate pit through hole in plate, removing all loose particles and

saving all soil in an airtight container for future drying out to determine W_s.

5. Place cylinder over opening in plate, open air valve and pump air into cylinder, forcing balloon into excavation until cylinder is raised off plate.
6. Push cylinder down on plate and read volume of water in cylinder.
7. Determine volume of in place soil sample removed from the excavated pit by taking the difference of the readings taken in Steps 6 and 2.

In using this method, care should be exercised to have the inside of the pit smooth with rounded corners so that the balloon will completely fill the excavated pit and not bridge over small pits and corners in the surface.

1.28   Measurement of Settlements

No point in space remains fixed or moves except with reference to some other point in space. Every point on the surface of the earth has changed and is constantly changing with reference to the center of the earth. Movements of structures built on the earth's surface occur with reference to other natural or artificial structures on the surface of the earth. Settlements of buildings and other structures can be measured only with reference to some other point. For the measurement of settlements it is necessary to establish a bench mark (B.M.) which is attached to the natural or artificial structure with reference to which the settlement is to be measured. Settlements due to loads caused by consolidation of a compressible layer with reference to an underlying incompressible layer cannot be measured from a bench mark on the surface too near the structure

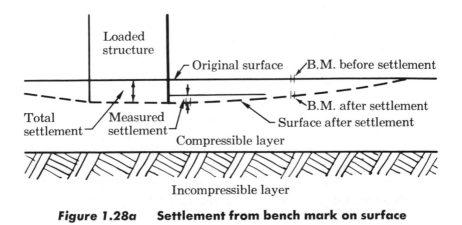

Figure 1.28a   Settlement from bench mark on surface

which applies the load. In order to measure properly the settlement contributed by the compressible layer, the bench mark must be anchored into the incompressible layer and be protected against interference from the volume change of the compressible layer. Figure 1.28a illustrates a possible result when settlements are referred to a surface B.M. Furthermore, the elevation of the ground surface varies erratically due to changing moisture and temperature regimes.

a.   Bench Marks

A bench mark for measuring vertical movements with reference to a rock layer below the surface can be constructed by drilling through the compressible layer and extending a pipe casing to the rock. A hole about 2 in. in diameter is drilled into the rock. A smooth rod with the end split several inches and bent slightly outward is lowered into the cased hole and driven into the hole in the surface of the rock to cause the split end to wedge itself into the rock. The vertical central rod should be provided with 3 guide pins fastened at 120° around the rod at about 20 ft intervals in order to prevent buckling. The casing is cut off a short distance below the surface and a short length of pipe large enough to slip over the casing with little friction is fitted over the top of the casing and anchored to a

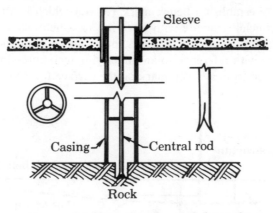

Figure 1.28b   Bench mark in rock

concrete slab or pedestal. The casing is filled with light grease similar to 600w. Measurements can be taken from a punch mark in the top of the central rod or a dial gage support can be placed on top of the sleeve that extends above the casing and a dial gage arranged to register relative movement of the surface to which the sleeve is attached and the under-lying rock layer.

A bench mark can be anchored to a layer of sand or other soil at a depth below the surface by the use of a Boros point. The Boros point consists of a bullet shaped metal head through which 3 flexible steel prongs can be forced outward into the soil. The flexible prongs are fastened to

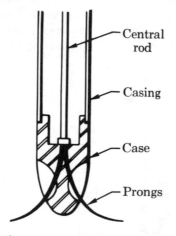

Central rod

Casing

Case

Prongs

Figure 1.28c   **Boros point**

the central rod which is withdrawn so that the prongs do not project beyond the point case. The point is driven by the casing which rests on a shoulder on the point case. After the point has reached the desired depth, the central rod is pushed or driven down, forcing the prongs out through openings in the side of the case and into the surrounding soil. The casing is then pulled a few inches off the point.

It is sometimes desirable to measure the settlement of earth fills with reference to the surface on which the fill rests or to an incompressible layer which may exist below the base of the fill. Bench marks similar to those just described may be installed and extended as the fill is made, but they interfere seriously with the work of compaction and usually are not tolerated by either the contractor or the inspecting engineer.

A device for measuring the settlement of intermediate depths in an earth dam or fill has been made and used by the U.S. Bureau of Reclamation. A complete description of the device and its use is given in *Earth Manual*. The device consists of cross arm anchors which are buried at the reference elevation at the bottom of the embankment and at intermediate elevations where settlement observations are to be made. Each cross arm anchor is attached midway between the two ends of a short length of $1\frac{1}{2}$ in. std. steel pipe. Between the cross arm assemblies lengths of 2 in. std. steel pipe 18 in. shorter than the distance between cross arms act as a casing into which the $1\frac{1}{2}$ in. pipes can slide. The cross arms, which are anchored into the compacted fill, follow the settlement of the fill and slide the $1\frac{1}{2}$ in. pipes inside the 2 in. casing. The bottom section is a 2 in. casing section 7 ft 9 in. long, with a latching plate above the bottom. The latching plate serves the purpose of locking the pawls in the measuring probe in a retracted position so that the probe can be withdrawn from the hole. The top section is an extension of the pipe above the topmost cross arm anchor to a point above the surface of the fill.

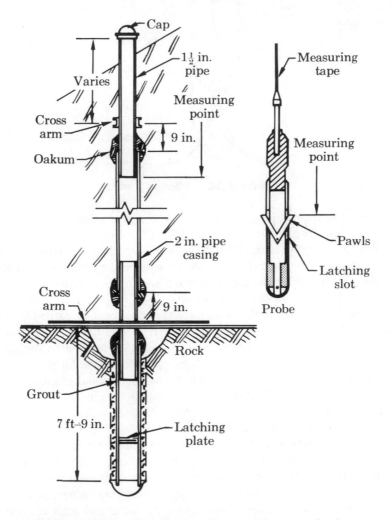

Figure 1.28d   Internal vertical settlement device

Measurements of elevations of the bottom ends of the $1\frac{1}{2}$ in. pipes extending below the cross arms, with reference to the bottom end of the $1\frac{1}{2}$ in. pipe which extends below the bottommost cross arm, are made with a probe which is moved inside the pipe with a steel measuring tape. Pawls extend at an angle upward through slots in the probe and are held with a spring in an extended position. As the probe is lowered in the pipe the pawls are held retracted against the sides of the pipe. At the bottom end of the smaller pipe, the pawls expand so that the probe can be withdrawn only until the pawls are in contact with the bottom end of the pipe attached to the cross arm. With the pawls against the bottom end of the pipe section, a reading on the steel tape can be made at the top of the pipe, at the surface. Readings are taken consecutively at all the measuring points from top to bottom. After a reading has been made for the bottommost point, the probe is lowered to below the latching plate which locks the pawls in a retracted position, after which the probe can be withdrawn from the hole.

Bench marks for measuring the heave of excavated areas can be installed without serious interference with the work of excavation. For this purpose, a metal plate can be anchored in the bottom of an uncased bore hole before excavation is started. Wings can be welded to the bottom of the plate, which can be driven into the ground below the bottom of the hole to anchor the plate and hold it level. The uncased hole is filled with soft drill mud to which a dye has been added so that the hole can be

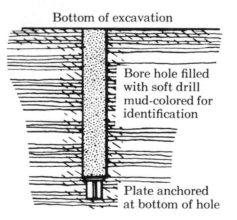

Bottom of excavation

Bore hole filled with soft drill mud-colored for identification

Plate anchored at bottom of hole

Figure 1.28e   Bench mark for measurement of heave

found on the excavated surface. At any time, during or after excavation, a rod can be pushed or driven into the colored spot marking the bore hole to the plate at the bottom of the hole and elevations taken. The rod can then be pulled out and the excavation proceed without interference.

b.   Measuring Settlement

If the settlement of only the point at which the bench mark is located is desired, a dial gage can be arranged at the top of the bench mark as described above. If the bench mark and the point of measurement are located so that they can both be seen from a common point, the measurement can be made with an ordinary precision surveyor's level. In buildings, and sometimes in other structures, the stations for which settlement readings are desired are located in different rooms or in other locations, where they cannot be seen from the bench mark or from another station.

The water level, consisting of a rubber hose with a glass tube on each end, has been used by lathers and others for transferring the same elevation from one location to another for a long time. Some years ago Terzaghi adapted this water level to the accurate measurement of settlements or small differences in elevation by applying micrometer adjusted pointed rods to the top of the glass tubes. When the point on the end of the rod comes in contact with the water surface, it picks up a meniscus which can easily be seen and which permits readings to be made with a high degree of accuracy.

(1)   The Micrometer Water Level

The water level must provide a means of supporting the cylinders at the ends of the level at exactly the same elevation on a leveling station. The level used by the Soil Mechanics Laboratory of the School of Civil Engineering at Oklahoma State University was designed and built in the Research Development Laboratory at Oklahoma State University.

The glass cylinders in this level are encased in brass cylinders with sliding windows for protection of the glass cylinders. At the bottom of each cylinder, a pet cock is provided so that the connecting tube can be closed to prevent loss of water when one end is raised higher than the other. The adjustable pointed rods are of stainless steel threaded with a pitch of 1 millimeter. The front of the rod is flattened so that it can be held against turning when the adjusting nut is turned, and is calibrated and marked on the flat side. Movement of the pointed rod is produced by turning the adjusting nut which screws the rod up and down at the rate of 1 mm for each revolution. The adjusting nut is calibrated in 0.001 cm with each 0.01 cm marked.

The supports for the cylinders are cantilever brackets with chisel supports to fit into notches in the leveling stations. Two adjusting screws are provided near the bottom of each cylinder for plumbing the cylinder

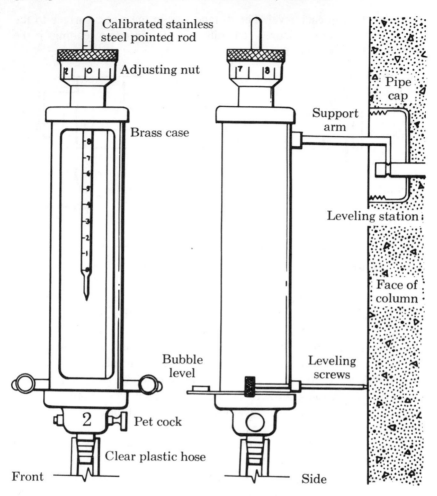

Figure 1.28f   Micrometer water level

after it is supported on the leveling station. A spot level is attached to each cylinder for use in plumbing the cylinder.

(2)   *Application of Water Level to Differential Leveling*

In applying the water level to differential leveling, stations to support the cylinders must be established which differ not more than a few inches in elevation. In using the level, one cylinder is supported on one station and the other cylinder on another station. The water will stand at the same elevation in each level. The distances from the water surface to the leveling stations are measured. The difference in these two readings is the difference in elevation of the two stations.

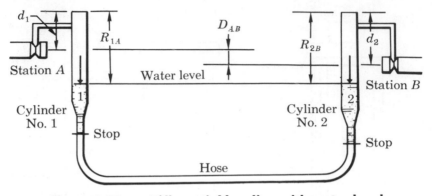

Figure 1.28g   Differential leveling with water level

In practice, the cylinders at the ends of the level are supported on two leveling stations as shown in Figure 1.28g. Measurements from the water surface to a leveling station are made by means of the calibrated rods read at the surface of each cylinder. The points are lowered simultaneously by the micrometer adjustments until they just pick up menisci. The readings R_{1A} and R_{2B} are taken and recorded. If the distance from the point of support to the reading surfaces d_1 and d_2 are equal, the difference in R_{1A} and R_{2B} is the difference in elevation of the two stations. However, these two distances are usually not equal, due to manufacturing inaccuracies or to bending or other damage to the supporting arms, so it is necessary to cancel out these inaccuracies by reversing the position of the cylinders for a second set of readings. When cylinder No. 1 is on station A the distance from the water surface to station A is $R_{1A} - d_1$ and the distance from the water surface to station B is $R_{2B} - d_2$.

The difference in elevation between stations A and B is

$$D_{AB} = (R_{1A} - d_1) - (R_{2B} - d_2) \qquad \text{(Eq. 1.28a)}$$

If d_1 and d_2 are not known, the difference in elevation cannot be determined from this one set of readings. But if the cylinders are reversed, the difference in elevation of the two stations is

$$D_{BA} = (R_{2A} - d_2) - (R_{1B} - d_1) \qquad \text{(Eq. 1.28b)}$$

When Equations 1.28a and 1.28b are added, d_1 and d_2 cancel and

$$2D_{AB} = (R_{1A} + R_{2A}) - (R_{2B} + R_{1B}) \qquad \text{(Eq. 1.28c).}$$

The symbols used in this discussion of the use of water levels are

R_{1A} = Reading of level No. 1 on station A

R_{2A} = Reading of level No. 2 on station A

d_1 = Distance between leveling station and reference elevation of level No. 1

d_2 = Distance between leveling station and reference elevation of level No. 2

S_A = Sum of R_{1A} and R_{2A}

S_B = Sum of R_{1B} and R_{2B}

If Equation 1.28b is subtracted from Equation 1.28a,

$$(R_{1A} + R_{1B}) - (R_{2A} + R_{2B}) = 2(d_1 - d_2) \quad \text{(Eq. 1.28d)}$$

Since d_1 and d_2 are constants unless changed by bending of the supporting arms or other damage, the difference between the two reading sums may be checked as the leveling operation is carried on.

(3)   Data and Computations

The data and computations may be recorded on a form such as shown below.

Check = $S_1 - S_2 = 2(d_1 - d_2)$ = Constant = _____ ___

Station	Reading		Sum	D	Elevation
	No. 1 Cyl. R_1	No. Cyl. R_2	$R_1 + R_2 = S$	$\dfrac{S_A - S_B}{2}$	
A	R_{1A}	R_{2A}	$R_{1A} + R_{2A} = S_A$	XX	XX
B	R_{1B}	R_{2B}	$R_{1B} + R_{2B} = S_B$		XX
Check	$R_{1A} + R_{1B} = S_1$	$R_{2A} + R_{2B} = S_2$	$S_1 - S_2$		
B				XX	
C					
Check					

In recording the simultaneous readings for a given setup on this form, care should be taken that the values are set down in the proper place; i.e., diagonally from each other, and not in the same line. In determining the difference in elevation of any two stations A and B, if the lower written sum S_B is subtracted from the sum S_A above, the sign of the difference indicates whether A is above or below B. When the sign is positive, the station listed above is higher than the station listed below and when negative the reverse is true.

(4)   Precautions in the Use of the Water Level

In order to obtain accurate measurements, the elevation of the water surface in each cylinder must be exactly equal. An air bubble in the water line will produce a difference in elevation of the two water surfaces and cause inaccurate and erratic readings. It is, therefore, imperative that the water in the level be free of air bubbles. Once air has been entrapped in the tube, it is difficult to remove. Possibly the best method of filling the tube is to fill slowly from an air free source under pressure applied to the lower end when the tube is inclined. This procedure allows the air to move ahead of the water and out of the upper end of the tube.

Another precaution is to see that the connecting tube is not moved, stepped on, or otherwise compressed between adjustments of the points of the two cylinders for any one setup. In order to make accurate readings, the points in the two cylinders should be adjusted to pick up the menisci as nearly simultaneously as possible so that the water elevation does not change between the two adjustments.

Although it is not necessary, it is convenient to have the level calibrated before starting to take differential levels. This is especially true after a new filling of the tube with water, or after the level has been shipped or handled a great deal after its last use. The calibration may consist simply of making several differential determinations on the same two fixed stations. Between setups for taking readings the hose should be moved and manipulated to move any air bubbles that may be in it. If the same difference in elevation and the same check constant, $S_1 - S_2$, is obtained for each of 3 or 4 determinations, one may assume that there is no air in the tube and proceed to use the level with confidence. The check constant may then be used as a check for each subsequent differential determination.

1.29   Field Measurement of Pore Water Pressure

Because the strength of soils in place is affected by the stress in the pore water and because the pressure in excess of the hydrostatic pressure is indicative of the progress of consolidation, it is often desirable to be able to measure the pore water pressure in the interior of a mass of soil. Pressure in the pore water is commonly measured by means of a piezometer, which is a device for measuring the head of water at a point. The simplest piezometer is a tube or pipe with its top end open to the atmosphere and the bottom end located at the point where the pressure or head is desired. Pressure in the water forces water up the tube to a height $h = \dfrac{p}{\gamma_w}$ when p is the unit pressure in the water at the point of measurement and γ_w is the unit weight of water. The ordinary well point used for wells driven into sand can be used as a piezometer.

The porous tube piezometer is probably the simplest and most commonly used piezometer. It consists of a length of porous alundum or other porous material about 2 ft long and 1½ in. in diameter, with a stopper in the bottom end and a small plastic standpipe attached to the upper end with a watertight connection. The piezometer is installed in a drilled hole backfilled with saturated clean sand around the porous tube and sealed above with portland cement grout or some other impervious material.

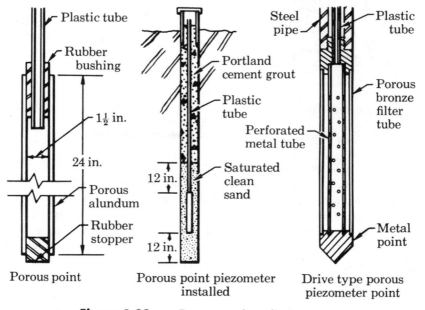

Porous point   Porous point piezometer installed   Drive type porous piezometer point

Figure 1.29a   Porous point piezometers

If the pore water pressure is great enough to force the water in the standpipe as high as, or higher than, the observation point, the head of water can be read directly by observing the surface of the water in a clear plastic standpipe or with a Bourdon gage attached to the top of the standpipe at some point below the head of water. If the water surface in the standpipe is below the observation point, the water level can be read with an electric probe.

The electric probe consists of two waterproofed insulated wires and

a steel measuring tape enclosed in a small clear plastic tube. The two conductors terminate at the bottom of the probe in separated electrodes.
The probe is small enough to be dropped down the standpipe. At the observation point, the two conductors are connected to an ohmmeter. The
ohmmeter reads infinity until the probe reaches the surface of the water,
when a dip in the ohmmeter reading occurs.

Another type of piezometer developed and used by the U.S. Bureau
of Reclamation consists of a plastic body hollowed out for the reception
of a porous disk on the bottom and leaving a conical void above the porous
disk. Two plastic tubes enter the top of the plastic body and connect to
the conical void space above the porous disk. A Bourdon tube type

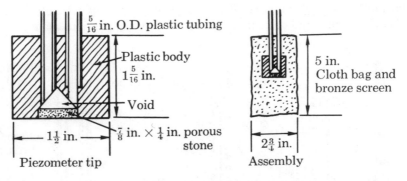

Figure 1.29b   Two tube piezometer

gage graduated to read feet head of water is connected to each of the
piezometer tubes. Through a system of valves connection is made to an
air trap containing a valved bleeder connection at the top, an inlet near
the top from a flushing valve which allows return water from the piezometer to enter the trap, an inlet in the bottom connected to a water supply, and an outlet for a pump connection for pumping water into one of
the piezometer tubes to circulate water through the system so that it
will be filled with water free of air. In order to take accurate pore pressure
readings, the system must be airtight and completely filled with water.
Before taking readings it is necessary to purge the system of air. This is
done by pumping water from the bottom of the air trap into one of the
piezometer tubes, through the piezometer tip, up the other tube and into
the air trap. This circulation is continued until no air bubbles appear in
the air trap. Circulation is reversed until the system is completely purged
of air. After the system has been purged of air, all the inlet and outlet
valves to the tip should be closed and two separate gages which are connected to the system read. The true gage reading is taken as the average
of the two gage readings. This reading must be added to the difference in

elevation of the piezometer tip and the gages, positive if the tip is below the gages and negative if the tip is above the gages, in order to obtain the head of water at the piezometer tip.

REFERENCES

Anderson, H. V., "New Sampler Speeds Design of 31,000,000 cu.yd Fill," *Civil Engineering*, Vol. 27 (December, 1957).

ASTM *Symposium on Nuclear Methods for Measuring Soil Density and Moisture*, Special Tech. Publ. No. 293 (March, 1961).

ASTM *Symposium on Vane Shear Testing of Soils*, Special Tech. Publ. No. 193, 1957.

ASTM *Symposium on Soil Exploration*, Special Tech. Publ. No. 351, 1963.

Bennett, G. B., and J. G. Mecham, "Use of the Vane Borer on Foundation Investigation of Fill," *Proc. 32nd Annual Meeting Highway Research Board* (1953).

Broms, Bengt B., "Self Recording Soil Penetrometer," *Journal Soil Mechanics and Foundations Division*, Proc. Am. Soc. C.E., Vol. 91, No. SM1 (January, 1965).

Casagrande, A., "Role of Calculated Risk in Earthwork and Foundation Engineering," *Journal Soil Mechanics and Foundations Division*, Proc. Am. Soc. C.E., Vol. 91, No. SM4 (July, 1965).

Cadling, L., and S. Odenstad, "Vane Borer," *Royal Swedish Geotechnical Inst.*, Proc. No. 2 (1950).

Fletcher, Gordon F. A., "Standard Penetration Test: Its Uses and Abuses," *Journal Soil Mechanics and Foundations Division*, Proc. Am. Soc. C.E., Vol. 91, SM4 (July, 1965).

Goodman, L. J., A. R. Aidun, and C. S. Grove, Jr., "Soil Surface Compaction with a Foam Type Explosive," *Journal Soil Mechanics and Foundations Division*, Proc. Am. Soc. C.E., Vol. 91, No. SM1 (January, 1965).

Hvorslev, M. J., "Subsurface Exploration and Sampling of Soils for Civil Engineering Purposes," Publication of Waterways Experiment Station, Vicksburg, Mississippi (1949).

Johnson, H. L., "Improved Sampler and Sampling Technique for Cohesionless Materials," *Civil Engineering* (June, 1940).

Kallstenius, T., "Studies on Clay Samples Taken with Standard Piston Samplers," *Royal Swedish Geotechnical Inst.*, Proc. No. 21, Stockholm (1963).

Kjellman, W., T. Kallstenius, and O. Wagner, "Soil Sampler with Metal Foils," *Royal Swedish Geotechnical Inst.*, Proc. No. 1 (1950).

Means, R. E., and J. V. Parcher, *Physical Properties of Soils*, Columbus: Charles E. Merrill Books, Inc. (1963).

Parsons, P. J., "Multiple Soil Sampler," *Journal Soil Mechanics and Foundations Division*, Proc. Am. Soc. C.E., Vol. 87, No. SM6 (December, 1961).

Peck, R. B., and W. C. Reed, "Engineering Properties of Chicago Subsoils," *Engr. Exper. Sta. Bulletin No. 423*, University of Illinois, Urbana, Illinois (1945).

Prugh, B. J., "Densification of Soils by Explosive Vibrations," *Journal Construction Division*, Proc. Am. Soc. C.E., Vol. 89, No. CO1 (March, 1963).

Sikso, H. A., and C. V. Johnson, "Pressure Cell Observation-Garrison Project," *Journal Soil Mechanics and Foundations Division*, Proc. Am. Soc. C.E., Vol. 90, No. SM4 (September, 1964).

Standard Tests,
   "Density of Soil in Place by Rubber Balloon Method," *ASTM*, D2167-64.

   "Density of Soil in Place by Sand Cone Method," *ASTM*, D1556-64.

   "Bearing Capacity of Soil for Static Load on Spread Footings," *ASTM*, D1194-57.

   "Diamond Core Drilling for Site Investigation," *ASTM*, D113-62T.

   "Penetration Test and Split Barrel Sampling of Soils," *ASTM*, D1586-64T.

   "Soil Investigation and Sampling by Auger Borings," *ASTM*, D1452-63T.

   "Thin Walled Tube Sampling of Soils," *ASTM*, D1587-63T.

   "Repetitive Static Plate Load Test of Soils and Flexible Pavement Components, for Use in Evaluation and Design of Airport and Highway Pavements," *ASTM*, D1195-64.

Terzaghi, Karl, and R. B. Peck, *Soil Mechanics in Engineering Practice*, New York: John Wiley and Sons (1948).

U. S. Bureau of Reclamation, *Earth Manual*, Denver, 1963.

Westergaard, H. M., "Stresses in Concrete Pavements Computed by Theoretical Analysis," *Public Roads*, Vol. 7 (1926).

2   Types of Foundations and their Suitability

2.01   *General*

A foundation is usually considered to be that portion of a structure that transmits the loads from the superstructure to the earth. But the foundation is part of the structure, and should be designed as an integral part of the structure. The purpose of the foundation is to transmit loads from the superstructure to earth in such a manner as to limit deformation of the structure to values that the materials of the structure can experience without impairing its function. In general, the foundation and the super-structure perform as a unit.

No one type of foundation, regardless of cost, is the best foundation for all conditions. In some cases, the cheapest foundation may fulfill requirements better than any other. Sometimes, as a simple matter of economy, it is necessary to use a type of foundation which limits deformation to what is permissible rather than to what is desirable. For the same soil conditions, one might use a different type of foundation under a structure that can undergo a large deformation without damage to its materials or impairment of its function, than under a structure that can withstand only a small deformation without damage.

In the design of a foundation, two factors must be considered: deformation, and failure. Any load, however small, placed on a beam, however strong, causes some deflection. To fulfill its function, the beam must be designed sufficiently stiff to limit deflection to that which the materials supported by the beam can withstand without failure, and at the same time strong enough that it can carry its superimposed load without failure of the material of the beam and resultant collapse of the structure. Any load on a foundation causes settlement, even though the soil supporting the foundation is capable of supporting a much heavier load without failure. The function of the foundation is not to prevent settlements but to limit and control them. The stresses in the soil produced by the foundation loads must be low enough so that they do not cause failure of the soil under the foundation.

Sometimes a foundation is selected for its greater feasibility from the standpoint of economics and construction procedures, even though, from a functional viewpoint, another type of foundation would be a better choice. Occasionally, a highly desirable type of foundation has to be eliminated from consideration because it is impractical to construct.

2.02 Continuous Foundations

A continuous foundation consists of a continuous footing slab on which rests a foundation wall that extends to the desired height above the surface and carries the building loads to the footing. The load is transferred

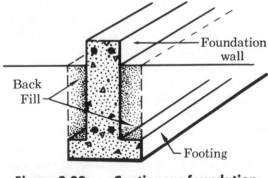

Figure 2.02a   **Continuous foundation**

by the footing to the earth as two cantilevers. If reinforcement is needed in the footing, it should be placed near the bottom perpendicular to the wall. No reinforcement is needed lengthwise in the footing. The strength lengthwise is provided by the foundation wall, which should be reinforced top and bottom to transfer nonuniform loads to the footing and to bridge over soft spots in the soil.

Although continuous foundations are commonly used for light buildings, they are one of the least suitable for general use. Probably, more foundation trouble is caused by the use of continuous foundations in soil unsuited to their use than from any other cause. In dense sands and gravels, where the footing is placed deep enough to prevent exposure by erosion and to develop sufficient shear strength to support the superimposed loads, continuous foundations are suitable and economical for many buildings.

2.03   Independent Footings and Columns

This type of foundation consists of independent footings of the proper size to transmit the building loads to ground with a constant contact pressure or to hold differential settlements within certain limits. The load is transmitted to the footings by means of columns that carry the reactions from grade beams, which take the place of the foundation wall in the continuous type.

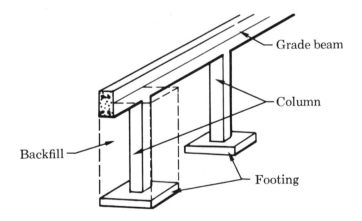

Figure 2.03a   Independent column footing foundation

An advantage of the independent column footing type of foundation is that the sizes of footings can be adjusted for the same or different contact pressures, and footings can be located so as to distribute the load advantageously over the site. For depths greater than 4 or 5 ft, the independent column footing foundation becomes more economical than the continuous type. All that is needed to increase the depth of this type of foundation is the deeper excavation of the footing area and the extension of the length of the small column.

A disadvantage of the independent column footing type as described above is the cost of the necessary hand excavation for footings.

2.04   Pier and Flared Footing

Another type of foundation intermediate between the independent column footing type and the pier type consists of small piers with flared footings cast in drilled and underreamed holes. This type of foundation is commonly used in the southwestern United States above the water table, where the soil has sufficient shear strength so that the underreamed hole will stand open until after the concrete has been placed. The advantage of this type of foundation over the independent column footing type is that under proper conditions it is much more economical. For that reason, where it can be used, it has practically replaced the independent column footing type in some areas.

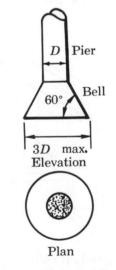

Figure 2.04a   Pier and flared footing

Holes for the pier and flared footings are drilled by a truck mounted rig which turns an auger of the spiral type. The auger is rotated in the hole to pick up a load of earth, after which it is raised to just above the surface and spun rapidly to throw its load of earth onto the surface around the hole. These augers are available in steps of 2 in. from a minimum diameter of 12 in. to a maximum of 30 in. Special bucket type augers are available in larger sizes.

After the hole has been advanced to the required depth, the auger is removed and a conical reamer put in its place. This reamer consists of a steel cylinder barrel of the same diameter as the auger that drilled the hole, with a large slot cut out of two opposite sides. At the top of each

Figure 2.04b   Earth auger

of the two slots a triangular shaped cutter is hinged. These two cutters are connected with a linkage so that when pressure is applied with the barrel on the bottom of the hole, the cutters are forced outward at the bottom against the walls of the hole. As the reamer is turned, the cutters shave off the soil and force it into the barrel. When the barrel is full, the reamer is lifted and the linkage pulls the cutters in to close the slots and leave a round barrel that can be lifted out of the hole. The barrel is cleaned of its load of earth by setting it on a small wooden platform laid over the top of the hole under the reamer, and forcing the cutters out of the barrel by pressure on the linkage at the top. The cutters when fully extended slope to form a conical cavity at the bottom of the hole at 60° from the

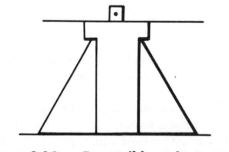

Figure 2.04c   Expansible under reamer

bottom to an intersection with the sides of the drilled hole. The diameter of the bottom of the cone may be made any dimension between the diameter of the hole and three times that diameter.

In suitable soil, the diameter of the bell can be increased by hand to a diameter greater than three times the diameter of the shaft.

The action of this type of foundation unit in transmitting loads to ground is somewhat different from the independent column footing described earlier. The independent column footing transmits its load to ground through contact pressure on the bottom of the footing and the earth. The cast in place pier and flared footing transmits its load to ground through contact pressure on the bottom of the footing and by friction along the surface of the pier. How much of the load is transferred by contact pressure and how much through friction depends upon the type of soil, its condition at the time of placing concrete in the hole, and subsequent loading and moisture conditions.

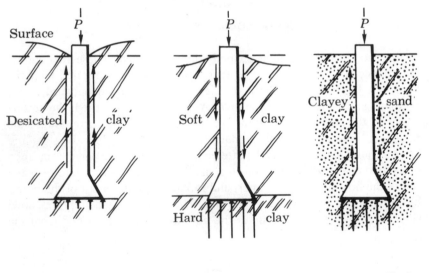

| Cast in dry stiff | Cast in soft | Cast in soil of |
| overconsolidated clay | unconsolidated clay | low cohesion |

Figure 2.04d   Transfer of load to ground pier and flared footing

If the unit is cast in loose unconsolidated fill just able to maintain an open hole, and the bottom is firm material, the frictional resistance may be negative and the contact pressure will be greater that that produced by the superimposed load. As the material around the pier consolidates and settles more than the pier, friction between the earth and the pier imposes an additional load on the pier.

A unit cast in firm soil of low plasticity will carry its superimposed load partly by friction along the sides of the pier and partly by contact pressure on the bottom of the footing.

If, on the other hand, the unit is cast in dry clay, when the moisture content of the clay increases the clay will swell. The resulting friction on the sides of the pier may carry the entire load and lift the footing off its bottom, or pull the pier in two. Further discussion of the action of this type of foundation will be given in Chapter 6.

Regardless of whether or not it is needed to add compressive strength to the pier, steel reinforcement should always be placed in the pier and extended to within a few inches of the bottom of the bell in order to tie the pier and bell together. In casting these small cast-in-place piers, care should be exercised to see that the concrete does not arch over in the hole and leave a void.

2.05   Pier Foundations

A pier foundation is a cast-in-place large diameter pier of considerable length with the bottom of the pier acting as the footing, or with an enlarged bottom little greater in diameter than the pier.

Piers may be cast in open wells with the sides braced by various means, such as the poling board or the Chicago method. Open caissons may be constructed on the surface and sunk by excavating the earth from the inside. These caissons are usually made of concrete with a steel cutting edge, although they are sometimes made of timber. As the soil is excavated from the inside, the caisson is weighted to overcome the friction around the outside. As the sinking progresses, the caisson is lengthened by casting another section on top. The bottoms of concrete caissons are seldom made larger than the caisson. Steel tubes 4 ft or more in diameter are also used for supporting the earth around the well. The steel tubes are placed in short sections which may be welded together as sinking progresses. Frictional resistance to sinking a long tube of uniform diameter increases with depth, making it difficult to force the tubes through the overburden to a deep firm layer. The so-called Gow caisson eliminates this difficulty by using telescoping steel tubes in sections about 4 ft long. The largest and topmost section is forced into the surface and excavated. Next, a section 2 in. smaller in diameter is forced into the soil inside the already placed section and excavated. This procedure is repeated to the desired depth, producing an open well of decreasing diameter. The joint

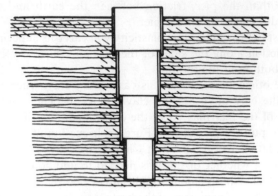

Figure 2.05a   Gow caisson

between two sections can be caulked in an attempt to prevent leakage of ground water, but such procedure may not be successful under all conditions. Under some conditions, the bottom of the open well can be belled out by hand to form a slightly larger bearing area than the pier.

Excavation in open wells is usually done by hand or with a small clam shell or orange peel bucket. In soil that will stand without lateral support, open wells are sometimes dug with a power driven rig similar to that used for drilling and underreaming holes for pier and flared footings. The auger used may consist of a steel disk of the same diameter as the hole and 4 to 6 in. thick. Offset slots in the disk are arranged from the periphery to the center, so that as the disk is rotated the entire area under the disk is exposed to one or more slots. Each slot is fitted with a blade like the bit of a woodworking plane. The bits are set to plough the earth from the bottom of the hole up through the slots to the top of the disk as the disk is turned in the hole. When about 12 in. of soil has been collected on top of the disk, the disk is raised to the top of the hole and spun rapidly enough to throw its load of soil to the surface around the hole. Large bucket type augers consisting of large diameter tubes or buckets with slots fitted with cutting knives in their bottoms, are sometimes used to drill open wells above the water table in soil containing no boulders and possessing sufficient shear strength so that the hole will stand open without lateral support.

Open wells can be sunk below the water table through soft materials to a hard underlying layer to depths of about 25 ft by means of steel tubes up to about 4 ft in diameter with a truck mounted rig similar to that used for drilling and underreaming holes. The steel tubes are notched with cutting teeth on the bottom and with notches on opposite sides at the top. A steel bar is fitted into the slots in the top and used to twist the tube as pressure is applied with the truck. After the tube has been forced into the ground some distance, the inside of the tube is cleaned out with an auger slightly smaller in diameter than the tube. When the underlying material is suitable, such as stiff clay, the tube can be forced into the underlying material to seal out the water so that the inside of the tube can be pumped dry for the reception of the concrete. As concrete is placed, the tube is withdrawn from the hole.

Where water is encountered in soil that cannot be dewatered, pneumatic caissons may be required. The pneumatic caisson consists of a caisson or box working chamber, a pier with access shafts for men and materials, and decompression chambers at the top of the pier. Air pressure sufficient to counterbalance water or soil pressure to prevent their entrance into the working chamber is applied. The decompression chamber is provided with two doors for access of men and materials into and out of the pressurized zone. Under working conditions for men entering the pressurized zone, trap door A is closed and door B is open. After a man enters the decompression chamber, door B is closed, the chamber subjected to an equalizing pressure, and door A is opened. In coming out of the pressurized zone, the opposite procedure is followed. In addition to the high cost of excavating the materials for sinking the caisson, a health hazard exists because men are working under heavy pressure. During ex-

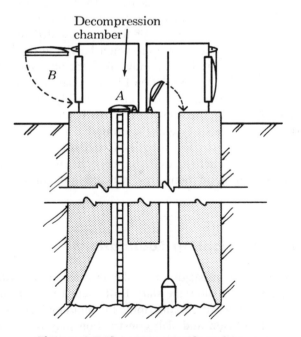

Figure 2.05b   Pneumatic caisson

posure to the high pressure, air is absorbed and compressed in the tissues and blood. Upon sudden release of pressure, the air in the tissues expands, causing intense pain and sometimes death. This condition is called caisson disease, or the bends. Therefore, after men have been exposed to high pressure for some time, they must be depressurized slowly by staying in a decompression chamber in which the pressure is gradually lowered. Laws in most states limit the intensity of pressure under which men can work and the time of exposure to high pressure. Pneumatic caissons are, therefore, used as a last resort.

The carrying capacity of piers is provided by friction along the sides and by contact pressure on the bottom. Usually piers are extended through soft material to a hard stratum so that the load is carried primarily by contact pressure on the bottom.

2.06   Mat Foundations

A mat foundation consists of a single thick slab upon which the structure rests. Such slabs are commonly used under compressor stations. The slab, usually about 30 in. thick, is cast on the surface of the excavated area and the compressor blocks are cast where needed on top of the mat. Sometimes a basement is used in which case the basement walls are cast above and at the outer edges of the mat, bonded to the mat with dowels and possibly with a groove and water barrier at the joint. In other cases, the area around the blocks above the mat and under the floor is backfilled and the building foundation placed separate from the mat.

Closely related to the mat foundation, or possibly a form of mat foundation, is the stiffened slab consisting of cross beams cast integrally with a thin slab placed on the surface of the ground, sometimes called a waffle slab. These stiffened slabs are used as foundations for residences and small light buildings on active desiccated clays in areas having erratic climates. Stiffened slab foundations are discussed in detail in Chapter 6.

2.07   Raft or Floating Foundations

A raft foundation consists of a thin slab cast integrally with reinforced beams either above or below the slab. Raft foundations are usually used on compressible soil in order to distribute the building load over the entire building area. The beam and slab construction may be the same as an inverted roof slab, with the concentrated loads applied at the top and the uniform loads applied at the bottom. The basement walls are made integral with the raft construction. Sometimes stiffening walls are used, making a large cellular construction.

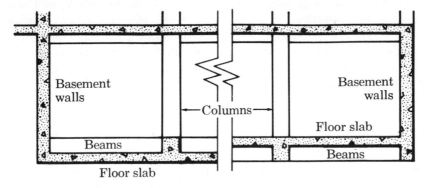

Figure 2.07a   Raft foundations

The raft with the beams formed above the slab has an advantage in design because the load from the slab is transferred to the beams in a conventional manner, producing compression and diagonal tension due to shear. It has the disadvantage that the beams are difficult to form and the basement floor is obstructed by them. The raft with the beams below the slab has the advantage of ease of construction and a smooth basement floor, but has a disadvantage in design because the loads from the slabs are transferred to the beams by tension. Sometimes the beams are omitted and a flat plate is used to transmit the contact pressure to the columns.

What has been described as a raft foundation is sometimes used to support a building on very soft soil with the weight of the excavated material from the basement approximately equal to the superimposed weight of the building. Such a compensated foundation is often called a floating foundation. The use of a floating foundation is probably the most effective and practical method of controlling total settlement. Stiffening walls are usually used in floating foundations in order to control differential settlements.

2.08   Pile Foundations

Piles may be classified as to their method of penetration as displacement and non-displacement, and as to their method of transferring their load to ground as floating, point friction, and point bearing.

Displacement piles are those constructed in such a way that when driven, a volume of earth equal to the volume of the pile is displaced. Examples of displacement piles are wood piles, precast concrete piles, closed end steel pipe piles, and closed end thin shells driven with a mandrel inside. Non-displacement piles are those in which only a small volume of soil compared to the volume of the pile is displaced during driving. Open end pipe piles and steel H section piles are classed as nondisplacement piles. When open end pipes or tubes are driven into the ground, the earth fills the interior of the pipe. After driving, the soil is blown out of the pipe with compressed air and the pipe filled with concrete.

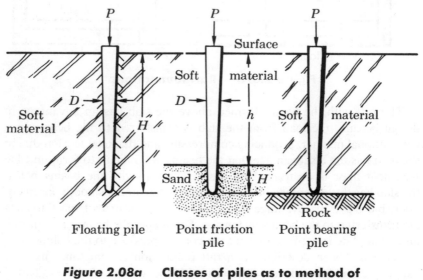

Figure 2.08a   Classes of piles as to method of transferring load

Piles transfer their load to ground by means of skin friction and by end bearing. The three classes of piles illustrating methods of transferring their loads to ground are shown in Figure 2.08a.

A floating pile, sometimes called friction pile, is one that is driven into soft material with no harder stratum immediately below. The load is transferred from the pile to the ground by skin friction alone. The carrying capacity of the floating pile depends entirely upon the shear strength of the soil into which the pile is driven.

A point friction pile is one that is driven through a soft material and into a layer of sand below. The pile cannot be driven very far into the sand unless the sand is very loose. The carrying capacity of a point friction pile is due almost entirely to the friction on the contact surface in the sand and a small amount of end bearing.

Point bearing piles are driven through soft material to rock or a layer of hard, relatively incompressible materal, and they transfer their load to earth entirely by end bearing.

2.09   Foundations on Sand

The shear strength of sand is dependent upon the angle of internal friction. Therefore, the carrying capacity of a foundation on sand increases with the depth from the surface to the bottom of the footing. Methods of estimating the carrying capacity of foundations on sand are discussed in Chapter 5.

A little experimentation will show that dense sand confined under several feet of overburden can be considered about the same as rock for foundation purposes. Failure of foundations on sand can be produced by an adjacent excavation which decreases the confining pressure. A very high carrying capacity may be reduced practically to zero by such excavation. Almost any type of foundation can be used successfully in dense sand if it is placed far enough below the surface.

Settlements in sand are caused by vibration of loose sand to a denser state. These settlements may be quite large and can occur relatively suddenly as compared to settlements in clay. Static loads produce comparatively little settlement in sand.

Coarse sands and gravels are usually deposited in a fairly dense state. Medium and fine sands are often quite loose. As described in the previous chapter, loose sands lying on or near the surface can sometimes be compacted in place. Sands, unless they are very coarse and of uniform grain size, cannot be solidified by pumping portland cement grout into them. The sand is a filter which prevents passage of the cement grains into the pores of the sand. When pumped into fine sand under pressure, grout does not enter the sand but forms fingers and lenses of grout.

A thick layer of sand underlying soft compressible material at not more than 100 to 150 ft below the surface can be made to carry heavy loads with little settlement by driving point friction piles through the soft material into the sand layer. However, point bearing piles driven through sand to rock do not always produce a successful foundation. If the sand is dense (in which case piles are probably unnecessary), piles cannot be driven through the sand but must be jetted down by applying a stream of water at the point of the pile in order to loosen the sand ahead of the pile as it is being driven. This procedure may eventually loosen the entire mass of sand in the construction area.

A gas compressor station consisting of several 1000 hp horizontal gas engine driven gas compressors was supported on piles through the Arkansas River sand to hardpan about 50 ft below the surface. The compressors were mounted on concrete blocks extending through a basement and resting on a 30 in. thick reinforced concrete mat. Piles were jetted through the sand layer and driven into the hardpan layer below. The con-

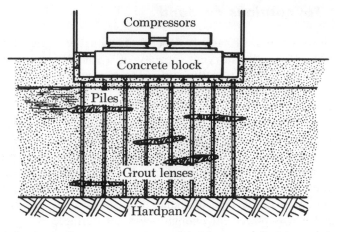

Figure 2.09a   Compressor station on piles in sand

crete mat was cast on the sand with the pile caps extending a few inches into the slab. These engines as they operate get in step to produce in- and out-of-phase cycles. While operating in step they produce large horizontal forces on the slab at the pile caps. Almost immediately after the station was placed in operation large earthquake like deformations were produced during the in-step portion of the operating cycle. Horizontal acceleration of the building caused rivets to break and to fall out of the joints in the steel building frame. Investigation revealed that the sand had settled away from the bottom of the mat, leaving a void of several inches. Pressure grouting into the sand at depth closed the void and applied pressure to the sand at the bottom of the mat. This treatment reduced the horizontal motion to a value comparable to that produced by similar stations on stiff clay. At the time the grouting was done, a desynchronizing device was installed to prevent the units from getting in step. The station was operated normally for about 8 years when the desynchronizing device was removed. Gradually the amplitude of the horizontal deformations increased until they became the same as before the grout treatment. Exploration revealed that a small void, not more than $\frac{1}{32}$ to $\frac{1}{16}$ in., existed between the slab and the sand between the piles. In all this time no appreciable vertical settlement had occurred. Undoubtedly, when the pressure was relieved at the bottom of the mat, the sand lost its shear strength and offered little resistance to lateral deformation of the pile caps. Several feet below the pile tops the weight of the sand above created considerable resistance. When the sand was grouted, the cement paste did not enter the pores of the sand of this grain size, but formed fingers and lenses which lifted the sand and exerted pressure against the bottom of the mat. The sand between the lenses of grout was subjected to static pressure which had little effect upon the density of the sand. The original shaking had compacted the sand to such an extent that the vibration caused without synchronization was not sufficient to produce additional compaction, but the sand was not dense enough to prevent a small amount of volume decrease under the greater force exerted when the units were allowed to get in step. This small decrease in volume removed the pressure from the sand under the mat, causing the sand to lose its strength and to allow lateral deformation similar to that experienced originally. In such cases where piles are driven through sand to a hard layer below, the pile heads should probably be cut off a few inches below the bottom of the mat and the mat cast on a thin layer of sand above the piles.

2.10   Foundations on Silt

Clean silt is usually deposited out of suspension in water in a loose honeycomb structure with a high void ratio. This arched structure is capable of carrying light loads without failure and with comparatively little settlement. When such a saturated silt, which in the undisturbed state may possess considerable shear strength, is remolded, it becomes practically liquid with very little shear strength.

Heavy loads break down the arches of the honeycomb structure and remold the soil to a nearly liquid state. There is, therefore, a critical load which these soils will bear with little settlement. Loads greater than this critical value produce large settlements and foundation failures. This critical load might be estimated from a load test or by observation of existing structures.

For heavy loads, piles driven to an unyielding layer of rock, dense sand,

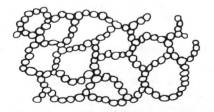

Figure 2.10a   Honeycomb structure of silt

or hardpan will possibly provide a good foundation. The piles should be of the non-displacement type, such as open end pipe piles, or steel H sections, in order not to break down the structure of the soil more than necessary. Driving displacement piles into such a saturated material destroys the structure, producing a liquid state in the vicinity of the piles. Because the soil is too fine for rapid drainage, consolidation cannot occur for a considerable time after driving the piles. Negative frictional loads may then unexpectedly increase the settlement of the piles. Such a soil, which can carry light loads satisfactorily, can be ruined by driving floating displacement piles into it.

Buildings of only a few stories can be supported satisfactorily on these soils by using a basement of such depth that the weight of excavated earth substantially compensates for the weight of the building. In this case, the building should be supported on a raft type foundation which distributes the building load uniformly over the building area. Obviously, independent column footings which carry concentrated loads to the soil should not be used.

The effect of dynamic loading on silt is difficult to predict, but there is certainly an increased likelihood of liquefaction and consequent flow in the case of poorly confined materials. A breakdown of the loose structure may, itself, lead to large settlements. Saturated silts should probably not be used to support structures subjected to significant (especially repeated) dynamic forces unless extreme precautions are taken to reduce the porosity in advance of construction.

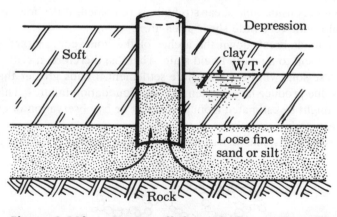

Figure 2.10b   Open well through fine sand or silt

Pier foundations cast in open wells formed with steel tubes might be used to penetrate silt or fine sand to reach a hard layer below. If, however, the silt or fine sand lies below the water table and is subjected to the weight of considerable overburden, as shown in Figure 2.10*b*, it will flow up into the well. Continued removal of the soil that has flowed up into the well removes the silt or fine sand for some distance from the well and can result in a subsidence of the surrounding area and serious damage to other structures in the neighborhood.

2.11   Foundations on Loess

Loess is a deposit of wind blown dust, mostly silt with small amounts of montmorillonite or other clay mineral, deposited in a loose state in an arid or semiarid climate. In some areas the dust was deposited above limestone or caliche. Capillary water often has brought up calcium carbonate which coats the grains of silt upon evaporation of the water. This very loose, lightly cemented soil can be pulverized between the fingers. The material stands for years in vertical banks when exposed to the weather. Fairly large caves can be dug in embankments of loess.

Samples of loess taken from a few feet below the surface seem always to be dry or only moist even after long wet periods. Shallow ponds stand on level surfaces and seem to remain until the water is removed by evaporation. It is believed that the montmorillonite swells and forms a gel which fills the pores on the surface of the loess and seals the surface against the penetration of water for more than a few feet below the surface. Silt in such a loose state without the binder would allow water to penetrate at a relatively rapid rate.

Dry loess will support fairly heavy loads with only a small amount of settlement. The strength of the loess is materially reduced by the presence of water. Loss of strength of the loess caused by water probably depends upon the water content of the soil. If there is only a small amount of water present, the montmorillonite binds the loose silt grains with a highly viscous water in the double layer attached to the montmorillonite particles. More water increases the thickness of the double layer, but with water of lesser viscosity. The cohesive action of this lower viscosity water is less than that of the smaller amount of more viscous water.

Contrary to the argument that water does not reach the loess more than a few feet below the surface in a natural deposit, experience has shown that under some conditions water does get to the loess under foundations. Fireplace chimneys built against frame houses have settled badly when placed on loess. Water fed to the loess under the chimneys through the porous backfill from rain and watering of plants has been sufficient to cause collapse of the soil structure under the weight of the chimneys. Small compressor stations with provision for trapping water draining down through backfill at the bottom of the fill and draining it into a catch basin inside the building have operated for several years with no appreciable settlement.

Loess is quite easy to excavate and compacts readily into a hard dense state. Successful foundations over large areas have been constructed economically on loess that has been removed from its original position and compacted back into the same area from which it was removed.

2.12   Foundations on Soft Clay

If clay is too weak to support a structure on independent column footings or some other type of shallow foundation without excessive settlement, piles can be driven through the soft clay to a layer of sand or rock. Floating piles are sometimes driven into thick layers of soft clay. Often, these piles in soft clay do more harm than good, especially if the clay possesses some sensitivity. The pile remolds the clay adjacent to the pile. After considerable time, the remolded clay consolidates and offers greater shear strength than it originally possessed. However, in the consolidation process, the volume of the clay decreases, which may result in the pile supporting a part of the clay between piles in addition to its superimposed load.

The effect of a group of floating piles is to apply the load to the soil at a greater depth than would be the case for the load applied on the surface. If the clay has been normally consolidated under its present overburden, the same stress applied at the greater depth produces less volume change than when applied higher where the preconsolidation (over-

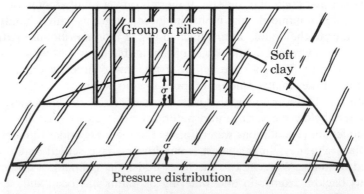

Figure 2.12a   **Pressure distribution of a group of piles in soft clay**

burden) pressure is less. However, the added load because of remolding may cause greater settlement than the same load applied to the undisturbed clay on the surface.

Point friction or point bearing piles driven through the soft clay to a layer of sand or rock may provide a successful foundation. The volume of saturated clay does not change except as water escapes from the pores in the clay. Piles driven into the saturated clay displace an amount of clay equal to the volume of the piles. Therefore, driving piles into the soft clay causes heave of the surface which lifts the piles that have previously been driven to a bearing layer. The piles must then be redriven to the bearing layer.

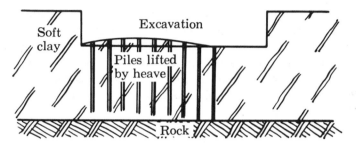

Figure 2.12b   Piles lifted by heave

In extremely loose clays below the water table, in which large settlements are produced by small superimposed loads, the settlement of the surrounding surface around the building supported on point friction or point bearing piles may present almost as great a problem as does the settlement of the building.

The volcanic clay on which much of Mexico City is built has a void ratio of approximately 5 and a water content of about 250 per cent. Settlements of 10 ft with reference to the surface are not uncommon. At the same time that buildings are settling, the surrounding ground surface is settling due to added loads and lowering of ground water. A layer of sand exists at about 150 ft below the surface. Buildings supported on piles driven through the loose clay into the sand remain high while the surrounding surface settles, making it necessary to build ramps in the sidewalks in order to gain entrance into the buildings. The Tacubaya Pumping Station was built with a basement below the first floor that was only a short step above the surface. The building is supported on point friction piles in sand. Accelerated by the pumping of water from the soil in the surrounding area, the surface of the ground has settled about 11 ft, exposing the basement walls. Some buildings on piles have been provided with adjustable first floors so that they can follow the sidewalks down.

Gonzales Flores has devised a compensated pile foundation consisting of independent column footings, which apply loads to the clay near the surface, and piles on each side of the footings with beams and hydraulic jacks so arranged that the column loads can be transferred from footings to piles. When the sidewalk settles more than the building, some load is transferred from the piles to the footings and vice versa.

The use of a floating foundation, sometimes called a compensated foundation, in which enough overburden is removed to compensate for the weight of the building, may provide a satisfactory foundation in soft clay. Heave in the bottom of an excavation in soft clay usually necessitates the use of stiffening walls in the basement area. Reloading the heaved area, even if no greater load than that provided by the removed overburden is applied, recompresses the soil and produces the same effect on the building as any other type of differential settlement. In extreme cases, the clay may be excavated as the building load is applied, thus attempting to maintain the stress produced by the overburden at all times. Such a procedure is difficult and expensive and is seldom attempted. The magnitude of heaving and recompression is difficult to predict accurately.

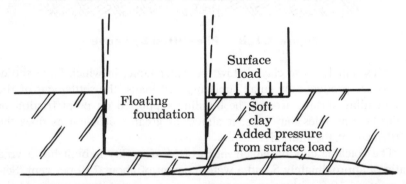

Figure 2.12c   Settlement and tilting of building on floating foundation caused by adjacent surface load

Tilting of the building may result if the load is not uniformly distributed over the area of a floating foundation on soft clay. If another structure is erected on the surface adjacent to the building on the floating foundation, consolidation of the underlying clay causes more settlement of the floating foundation adjacent to the surface load than on the side away from the surface load, thus causing a tilting toward the surface load.

A light building on a shallow foundation which is adequate for the light building, may be damaged by the erection of a heavier building adjacent to it. The heavier building produces more settlement than the light

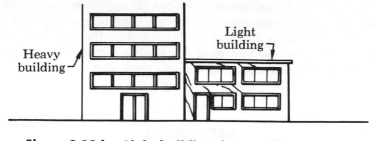

Figure 2.12d   Light building damaged by adjacent heavy building

one and causes additional settlement of that part of the light building adjacent to it.

Sometimes a group of light structures is to be erected on a fill applied over a layer of very soft unconsolidated clay. Damage to the light structures can often be avoided by constructing the fill long enough before construction of the light structures for consolidation of the clay to occur under the weight of the fill. Consolidation of the clay can often be accelerated by the use of sand drains. For structures for which differential settlements are not critical, such as storage tanks and highway embankments, preloading to produce pressures greater than the stresses to be produced by the structures can produce consolidation sufficient to support the structures with little settlement. The preload should be left on the soft clay long enough to produce about the same void ratio as would be produced after consolidation under the load of the structures, and removed before construction of the structures.

Sometimes fairly heavy loads on soft clay cause excessive settlement due to creep of the clay as shown in Figure 2.12e. In one case, an asphalt tank on very soft clay caused upheaval of the surface around the tank,

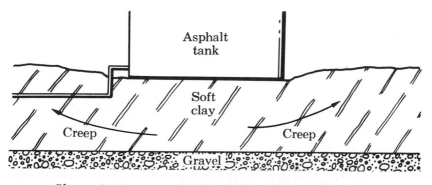

Figure 2.12e   Creep of soft clay from under load

causing breaks in the connecting pipe lines. The problem was solved by loading the surface around the tank with a layer of gravel several feet thick and extending for considerable distance from the tank. The gravel berm did not reduce the settlement due to consolidation, but it stopped the creep and forced the pipe connections down with the tank.

REFERENCES

Golden, Hugh Q., "State of the Art of Floating Foundations," *Journal Soil Mechanics and Foundations Division*, Proc. Am. Soc. C.E., Vol. 91, No. SM2 (March, 1965).

Jacoby, H. S., and R. P. Davis, *Foundations of Bridges and Buildings*, New York: McGraw Hill Book Company, Inc., 1941.

Meyerhof, George C., "Shallow Foundations," *Journal Soil Mechanics and Foundations Division*, Proc. Am. Soc. C.E., Vol. 91, No. SM2 (March, 1965).

Parsons, James D., "Piling Deficiencies in New York Area," *Journal Soil Mechanics and Foundations Division*, Proc. Am. Soc. C.E., Vol. 92, No. SM1 (January, 1966).

Peck, Ralph B., "Pile and Pier Foundations," *Journal Soil Mechanics and Foundations Division*, Proc. Am. Soc. C.E., Vol. 91, No. SM2 (March, 1965).

3   Seepage or Flow of Water through Soils

3.01   General

The stability of earth structures and of natural deposits is dependent not only upon the static properties of the soil but also upon the forces produced by water as it seeps or flows through the pores of the soil. As an aid to his judgment in the design of earth structures or the stabilization of earth deposits, the engineer should be able to estimate through analyses the magnitude of seepage forces and pressures, and the quantities of water flowing through the soil.

Because the loss of head as water flows through soils is a reaction against the soil grains, and because the strength of cohesionless soils is produced by pressure between the grains, water flowing downward through fine grained soils increases the strength of such soils. Slopes of fine sand may be excavated below the natural water table by lowering the water table as shown in Figure 3.01a. Such soils stabilized by the downward flowing water and the capillary water hanging in tension from the soil grains will stand in steeper slopes than in the dry state. When water flows upward through the soil, gravity pressure between the grains is reduced by the seepage forces and the strength of the soil is reduced. If the pumps

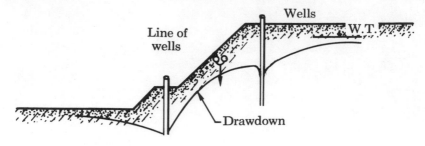

Figure 3.01a   **Stabilization of slope by lowering
ground water**

should fail during stabilization of a slope by ground water lowering in
fine sand, as shown in Figure 3.01a, water would flow upward into the
excavation and the slope would collapse. The carrying capacity of footings on cohesionless material is decreased by upward flowing water and
increased by downward flowing water.

Soil grains on the surface may be lifted by the seepage forces of upward
flowing water, causing the soil grains to be carried away. This phenomenon
is known as piping. Loss of soil by piping can be prevented by the use of
properly designed filters.

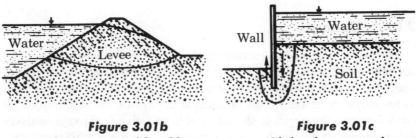

Figure 3.01b
Piping on outside of levee

Figure 3.01c
Piping in excavation

Lowering the ground water under existing foundations on compressible
soils causes an increase in the settlement of such foundations. The yield of
single wells and of a group of wells, and the resulting lowering of the
ground water, is of importance in the design of a water supply from wells
and the lowering of ground water for construction purposes.

Methods of drawing flow nets, estimating loss of water through and
under levees and dams, uplift pressures under dams, drawdown from
pumping operations, yield of wells, magnitude of seepage forces, and
design of filters to prevent piping are the subject of this chapter. The
effect of lowering the ground water table is treated in Chapter 4.

3.02   Basic Conditions of Flow

Darcy's Law for smooth, one directional flow through a length of soil of uniform cross section has been discussed in *Physical Properties of Soils*. In general, the flow of water through a natural deposit of soil is not uniform over the entire area perpendicular to the flow, and the flow does not occur in one direction only.

If piezometer tubes which measure the head of water at different points were placed in the ground through which water is flowing, the top of the water in the tubes would lie on a smooth, curved surface. A plane tangent to this phreatic surface at any point indicates the gradient in any direction at that point. The maximum slope of the plane indicates the steepest gradient and the direction of maximum flow.

The hydraulic gradients causing flow in all directions are illustrated in Figure 3.02*a*.

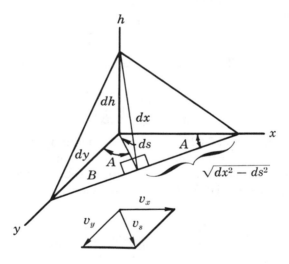

Figure 3.02a   **Element of tangent plane and velocity vectors on phreatic surface**

From the geometry of the upper portion of Figure 3.02*a*,

$$\frac{ds}{dy} = \frac{\sqrt{dx^2 - ds^2}}{dx}$$

and

$$\frac{ds^2}{dy^2} = \frac{dx^2 - ds^2}{dx^2} = 1 - \frac{ds^2}{dx^2}$$

from which,

$$\frac{1}{ds^2} = \frac{1}{dy^2} + \frac{1}{dx^2}$$

After multiplying the above equation by dh^2, it becomes

$$\frac{dh^2}{ds^2} = \frac{dh^2}{dy^2} + \frac{dh^2}{dx^2} \qquad \text{(Eq. 3.02}a\text{)}$$

Darcy's Law applied to flow in s, x, and y directions gives the relationships as follows:

$$v_s = k_s i_s = k_s \frac{dh}{ds}, v_x = k_x i_x = k_x \frac{dh}{dx}, \text{ and } v_y = k_y \frac{dh}{dy}$$

The maximum velocity v_s and its components v_x and v_y must conform to the relationship shown by the vector diagram, which is

$$v_s^2 = v_x^2 + v_y^2$$

Applying Darcy's Law to the vector relationship,

$$k_s^2 \frac{dh^2}{ds^2} = k_y^2 \frac{dh^2}{dy^2} + k_x^2 \frac{dh^2}{dx^2}$$

If the k values are all the same, they cancel out of the equation, which makes the equation become

$$\frac{dh^2}{ds^2} = \frac{dh^2}{dy^2} + \frac{dh^2}{dx^2} \qquad \text{(Eq. 3.02}b\text{)}$$

Equations 3.02a and 3.02b are identical, indicating that Darcy's Law satisfies both the geometric and vectorial relationships if the coefficients of permeability are the same in all directions (isotropic material). Therefore, Darcy's Law is valid for flow in all directions in isotropic materials and

$$v_s = k \frac{dh}{ds}, v_y = k \frac{dh}{dy}, \text{ and } v_x = k \frac{dh}{dx}$$

It is also of interest to know if the velocity of flow in all directions is proportional to any but the first power of the hydraulic gradient.

The general case for any power of the hydraulic gradient is

$$v_s = k \left(\frac{dh}{ds}\right)^m, v_y = k \left(\frac{dh}{dy}\right)^m, \text{ and } v_x = k \left(\frac{dh}{dx}\right)^m$$

Substituting these general values in the relationship which must be true for velocities, $v_s^2 = v_y^2 + v_x^2$, the relationship becomes

$$k^2 \left(\frac{dh}{ds}\right)^{2m} = k^2 \left(\frac{dh}{dy}\right)^{2m} + k^2 \left(\frac{dh}{dx}\right)^{2m} \qquad \text{(Eq. 3.02}c\text{)}$$

But, to satisfy the requirements of geometry, the relationship must be

$\dfrac{dh^2}{ds^2} = \dfrac{dh^2}{dy^2} + \dfrac{dh^2}{dx^2}$. This condition can be met by Equation 3.02c only

when m is equal to unity. Therefore, the velocity of flow in different directions is proportional to the first power of the hydraulic gradient only; i.e., for laminar flow.

It is also desirable to know if the developed relationships are true for flow in different directions in soils having different coefficients of permeabilities in different directions (anisotropic materials).

Consider an elemental block of the soil through which water is flowing as shown in Figure 3.02b. If there is steady flow through the block so that there is no volume change produced in the block during the flow, the quantity of water flowing into the block in an interval of time is equal

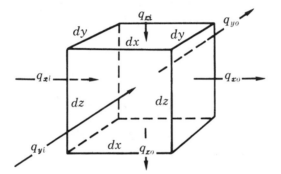

Figure 3.02b   Elemental block through which water is flowing

to the amount flowing out. For steady flow the velocity is a function of the head h and the coordinates, x, y, and z; i.e., $v = f(h)(x,y,z)$.

If the hydraulic gradient at a face of the block in a given direction z is $i_z = \partial h/\partial z$, the hydraulic gradient at the opposite face dx away is $i_z + (\partial i/\partial z)\,dz = (\partial h/\partial z) + (\partial^2 h/\partial z^2)\,dz$. The quantity of water flowing in a z direction into face $dx\,dy$ in a unit of time is

$$q_{zi} = k_z \frac{\partial h}{\partial z} dx\,dy$$

and the quantity of water flowing out the opposite face is

$$q_{zo} = k_z \left(\frac{\partial h}{\partial z} + \frac{\partial^2 h}{\partial z^2}\,dz \right) dx\,dy = k_z \frac{\partial h}{\partial z} dx\,dy + k_z \frac{\partial^2 h}{\partial z^2} dx\,dy\,dz$$

The difference in the quantities of water flowing in and out of the $dx\ dy$ faces is

$$q_{zo} - q_{zi} = k_z \frac{\partial^2 h}{\partial z^2}\ dz\ dy\ dx$$

Similarly, the difference in the quantities flowing in and out of the block in an x direction is

$$q_{xo} - q_{xi} = k_x \frac{\partial^2 h}{\partial x^2}\ dx\ dy\ dz$$

and the difference in quantities flowing in and out of the block in a y direction is

$$q_{yo} - q_{yi} = k_y \frac{\partial^2 h}{\partial y^2}\ dy\ dx\ dz$$

Because the volume of the block does not change during steady flow, the quantity of water flowing into the block must be equal to the quantity flowing out, or

$$k_z \frac{\partial^2 h}{\partial z^2}\ dz\ dx\ dy + k_x \frac{\partial^2 h}{\partial x^2}\ dx\ dy\ dz + k_y \frac{\partial^2 h}{\partial y^2}\ dy\ dx\ dz = 0$$

or,
$$k_z \frac{\partial^2 h}{\partial z^2} + k_x \frac{\partial^2 h}{\partial x^2} + k_y \frac{\partial^2 h}{\partial y^2} = 0$$

If the material through which the water flows is isotropic, the k values are all equal and the equation becomes

$$\frac{\partial^2 h}{\partial z^2} + \frac{\partial^2 h}{\partial x^2} + \frac{\partial^2 h}{\partial y^2} = 0 \qquad\qquad \text{(Eq.3.02}d\text{)}$$

This equation represents three families of curves meeting at 90°.

If the water is assumed to be flowing in two directions only, as might be the case for water flowing through and under earth dams, under impervious cutoff walls, etc., the relationship becomes

$$\frac{\partial^2 h}{\partial x^2} + \frac{\partial^2 h}{\partial y^2} = 0$$

This equation represents two families of curves meeting at 90°. One family of these curves might represent the flow lines in a flow net and the other family the equipotential lines in the flow net. In the simple case shown in Figure 3.02c, which is a sheet pile wall driven half way into a previous layer of soil, one-half of a family of ellipses and of hyperbolas meeting at 90°, except immediately adjacent to the cut off wall, form the true flow net for the flow of water under the cut off wall due to a head of water on one side.

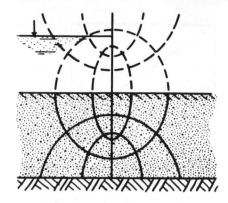

Figure 3.02c   Two families of curves meeting at 90°

For anisotropic soils in which k_x and k_y are not equal, the relationship for two directional flow is

$$k_x \frac{\partial^2 h}{\partial x^2} + k_y \frac{\partial^2 h}{\partial y^2} = 0$$

This relationship represents two families of curves which do not meet at 90°.

3.03   Flow Lines

A droplet of water, in flowing from position A to position B under a hydraulic gradient, follows a certain path through the soil. The path of the droplet through the soil is referred to as the flow line. Except for sim-

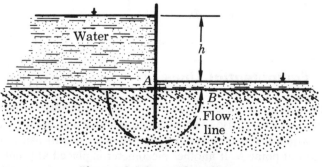

Figure 3.03a   Flow line

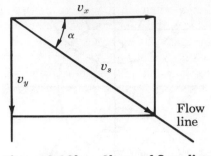

Figure 3.03b   Slope of flow line

ple symmetrical cases, the shape of the flow lines cannot be readily determined mathematically. But, enough is known about the flow lines in isotropic materials and, under certain conditions, in anisotropic materials, so that a flow net of flow lines and equipotential lines can be drawn experimentally.

Water is forced to flow through soil against frictional resistance by a difference in head. The head is a function of the coordinates x and y. The hydraulic gradients in the x and y directions are $i_x = \partial h/\partial x$ and $i_y = \partial h/\partial y$.

At a point along the flow line the water flows with a velocity v_s. The components of v_s are $v_x = k_x(\partial h/\partial x)$ and $v_y = k_y(\partial h/\partial y)$. The slope of the flow line at this point is

$$\frac{v_y}{v_x} = \frac{k_y \dfrac{\partial h}{\partial y}}{k_x \dfrac{\partial h}{\partial x}}$$

For isotropic soils, the slope of the flow line is

$$\tan \alpha = \frac{\dfrac{\partial h}{\partial y}}{\dfrac{\partial h}{\partial x}} = \text{slope of flow line}$$

3.04   Equipotential Lines

If a piezometer is placed at point A in the soil through which water is flowing, the water will rise to some height h above a reference plane. This height to which the water rises in the piezometer is a measure of the potential head at point A. If another piezometer is placed at point B, where the water rises to the same elevation as in the piezometer at point A, the two points are of equal potential. A line drawn through all the points in the soil having the same potential is an equipotential line.

It should be observed that equipotential lines do not join points of equal pressure. The pore water pressure at any point is equal to the head of water in the tube times the unit weight of water, which is not equal to the pressure at another point on the equipotential line.

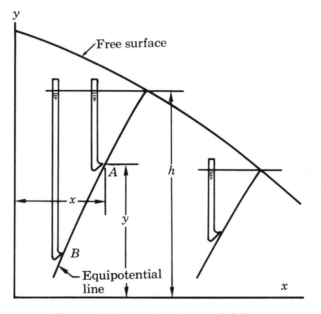

Figure 3.04a   Equipotential line

The potential head h is a function of x and y; i.e., $h = f(x,y)$. For equipotential lines, h is constant. Therefore, $dh = 0$ along the line, and the total differential is

$$dh = \frac{\partial h}{\partial x}\, dx + \frac{\partial h}{\partial y}\, dy = 0$$

The slope of the equipotential line at x, y is

$$\frac{dy}{dx} = -\frac{\dfrac{\partial h}{\partial x}}{\dfrac{\partial h}{\partial y}}$$

which is the negative reciprocal of the slope of the flow line at point x, y in

an isotropic material. Therefore, flow lines and equipotential lines in isotropic materials meet at 90°.

3.05   Flow Nets

A family of flow lines and equipotential lines is called a flow net.
Forchheimer devised a method of choosing flow lines and equipotential
lines in such a way that the quantity of water q_1 flowing between any two
adjacent flow lines (flow channel) is equal to the quantity flowing between any other two flow lines. In such a flow net the total quantity of

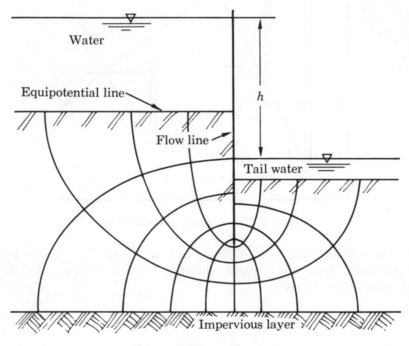

Figure 3.05a   Flow net

water flowing per unit of time through the soil q_T is equal to the quantity
flowing through one flow channel q_1 times the number of flow channels in
the net N_f, or $q_T = N_f q_1$. Forchheimer also chose equipotential lines such
that the drop in head between any two adjacent equipotential lines is
equal to the drop between any other two adjacent equipotential lines. In
such a flow net, the total drop in head h is equal to the number of equipotential intervals N_e times Δh, in which case $\Delta h = h/N_e$.

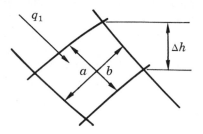

Figure 3.05b   One rectangle of flow net

Consider one rectangle of a flow net for isotropic material having an area between flow lines equal to a for a unit thickness, and a distance between equipotential lines equal to b, as shown in Figure 3.05b.

Applying Darcy's Law to the flow through this channel,

$$q_1 = \kappa i a = \kappa \frac{\Delta h}{b} a$$

Therefore, if a flow net is drawn consisting of rectangles in which the ratio of breadth to length is the same ($a/b = $ constant), the drop in head, Δh, between any two adjacent equipotential lines is h/N_e, and the flow through each flow channel is q_T/N_f.

Obviously, the simplest ratio of sides for use in constructing a flow net is unity. If, then, a flow net made up of "squares" is drawn to scale on a section through the structure or deposit through which the water is flowing, the net will be a true one. With such a flow net, pore pressures, uplift pressures, quantity of water flowing, and seepage forces at any point in the flow net can be determined.

When the flow net consists of squares, the total quantity of water flowing in a unit of time is

$$q_T = q_1 N_f$$

in which

$$q_1 = k\,\Delta h \cdot 1 = k\frac{h}{N_e} \cdot 1$$

so that

$$q_T = kh\frac{N_f}{N_e} \tag{Eq. 3.05a}$$

Equation 3.05a is a statement of Darcy's Law in another form for the special case in which the flow net consists of squares. The ratio N_f/N_e is often called the shape factor.

Flow nets drawn by eye, fulfilling the conditions listed above, are quite accurate for isotropic soils and can be drawn rather quickly in a series of successive trial sketches.

In a flow net an impervious surface is a flow line, and a surface of permeable material into which the water enters or from which it flows is an equipotential line, except for the special case of the free surface. The free surface, or phreatic surface, is a flow line having the special property that vertical distances between intersections with equipotential lines are constant and equal to Δh.

3.06   Free Surface—Seepage Line

As water flows through soil, except where it is confined by an impervious surface, there exists a surface on which the pressure in the pore water is zero. This surface of zero pressure is called the free surface or the phreatic surface. The soil above the free surface may be saturated with capillary water in tension. Below the free surface the water is in compression.

Along the free surface the change in potential head, Δh, is the actual vertical distance from one point on the free surface to another. Free surfaces exist either above or below the surface of the soil. In this text the line of intersection between a vertical plane and the free surface below the surface of the soil is called the seepage line. The seepage line is a flow line and marks the boundary of the flow net. Equipotential lines must meet the seepage line at 90° and they must be spaced so that all the vertical distances between intersections are the same.

Before a flow net for water flowing through soil can be drawn, the seepage line must be defined. In simple cases where water stands on each side of an impervous barrier, the free surface is a level plane.

The shape of the seepage line can be determined approximately by means of the assumptions suggested by Dupuit that the hydraulic gradient is equal to $dy/dx = \tan \theta$, and that the hydraulic gradient is constant in a vertical plane from the free surface to an impervious layer or a surface in which there is no transverse flow. Neither of these assumptions is accurate in a general sense. The true hydraulic gradient is $i_s = dy/ds = \sin \theta$. But for values of θ less than 30°, the error in using $\tan \theta$ instead of $\sin \theta$ is small.

Using the Dupuit assumptions, the shape of the seepage line can be determined as follows:

Assume that one point on the free surface and seepage line is known at

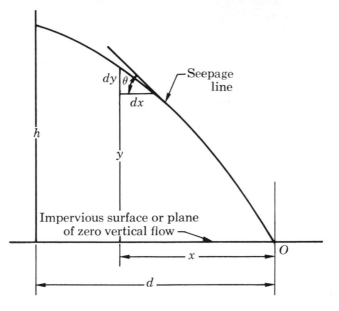

Figure 3.06a   Seepage line

$x = d$, $y = h$, and that the free surface meets the impervious layer or tail water at point 0.

The same quantity of water in a thickness of unity and in a unit of time flows through any one vertical plane between the free surface and the impervious layer as through any other. The quantity of water flowing through a vertical plane at x distance from 0, having an area equal to y, is

$$q = kiy = ky\frac{dy}{dx}$$

$$q\,dx = ky\,dy$$

$$\int q\,dx = \int ky\,dy, \text{ from which } qx = k\frac{y^2}{2} + C$$

At $x = d$, $y = h$ the equation above becomes

$$qd = k\frac{h^2}{2} + C$$

from which it is found that

$$C = qd - k\frac{h^2}{2}$$

Placing this value of C in the equation above, the equation for the seepage line becomes

$$q(x - d) = \frac{k}{2}(y^2 - h^2) \qquad \text{(Eq. 3.06}a\text{)}$$

The above equation for the seepage line represents a parabola.

a.   *Downstream Slope without Filter*

The free surface for flow in the soil must come to the surface of the slope at some distance above an impermeable layer or a tail water surface. The seepage line meets the slope surface in such a manner that the water

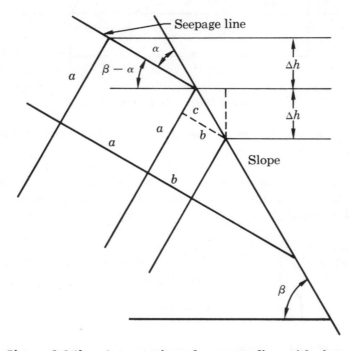

Figure 3.06b   Intersection of seepage line with slope

leaves the soil either tangent to the surface or at some angle α. Since the surface represented by the seepage line, and the surface of the slope from which water is emerging, is a free surface, the equipotential lines must meet the seepage line and the slope at a constant Δh. If the flow net consists of squares above the exit of the seepage line, it must consist of squares below. From Figure 3.06b

$$\frac{\Delta h}{a} = \sin(\beta - \alpha)$$

$$\frac{\Delta h}{c} = \sin\beta$$

$$\frac{b}{c} = \cos\alpha$$

Then

$$\frac{\Delta h}{b} = \frac{\sin\beta}{\cos\alpha}$$

When $a = b$ (squares), since Δh is constant,

$$\frac{\Delta h}{a} = \frac{\Delta h}{b} = \sin(\beta - \alpha) = \frac{\sin\beta}{\cos\alpha}$$

from which, $\sin\beta = \cos\alpha \sin(\beta - \alpha)$.

The only possible solution for this relationship is for $\alpha = 0$ and $\cos\alpha = 1$. Therefore, the seepage line is tangent to the discharge face of the slope when β is less than 90°.

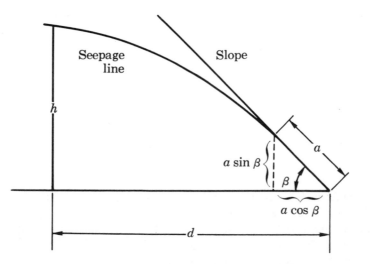

Figure 3.06c   Tangent point seepage line and slope

Before the seepage line can be drawn as the boundary of the flow net, it is necessary to determine the point of tangency of the seepage line and the slope. This can be determined approximately by the following reasoning, based on the Dupuit assumptions:

At the discharge point, the vertical area through which the water flows is $a \sin \beta$ and the hydraulic gradient is the slope of the discharge face,

$$\frac{dy}{dx} = \tan \beta.$$

The quantity of water flowing through this area per unit of time is

$$q = k \frac{dy}{dx} A = k \tan \beta \, a \sin \beta$$

Putting this value of q in the equation for the seepage line (Eq. 3.06a),

$$ka \tan \beta \sin \beta (x - d) = \frac{k}{2}(y^2 - h^2)$$

or,

$$a \tan \beta \sin \beta (x - d) = \tfrac{1}{2}(y^2 - h^2)$$

To determine a, put its coordinates $x = a \cos \beta$, $y = a \sin \beta$ in the equation, and solve for a.

$$a \tan \beta \sin \beta (d - a \cos \beta) = \tfrac{1}{2}(h^2 - a^2 \sin^2 \beta)$$

$$a \frac{\sin^2 \beta}{\cos \beta}(d + a \cos \beta) = \tfrac{1}{2}(h^2 - a^2 \sin^2 \beta)$$

$$ad - a^2 \cos \beta = \frac{h^2 \cos \beta}{2 \sin^2 \beta} - \frac{a^2 \cos \beta}{2}$$

$$a^2 \cos \beta - 2ad + \frac{h^2 \cos \beta}{\sin^2 \beta} = 0$$

$$a = \frac{2d \pm \sqrt{4d^2 - 4\dfrac{h^2 \cos^2 \beta}{\sin^2 \beta}}}{2 \cos \beta}$$

$$a = \frac{d}{\cos \beta} - \sqrt{\frac{d^2}{\cos^2 \beta} - \frac{h^2}{\sin^2 \beta}} \qquad \text{(Eq. 3.06b)}$$

Schaffernach devised a simple graphical solution for Equation 3.06b as follows: (See Figure 3.06d)

a. Extend vertically from $x = d$ at 2 to the slope surface at 1. Distance along slope 0–1 $= d/\cos \beta$
b. With 0–1 as a diameter, draw the semicircle 0–1.
c. Extend horizontally from point 3(d,h) to intersection with slope at 4.
d. With 0 as a center, strike arc 4–5.
e. With point 1 as a center, strike arc 5–6.
f. Point 6 is where seepage line joins the discharge slope and distance 0–6 $= a$.

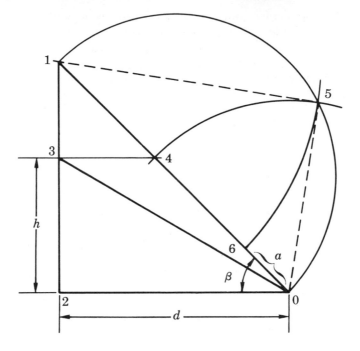

**Figure 3.06d   Schaffernach solution for exit
of seepage line**

Proof of Schaffernach solution:

Distance
$$0\text{–}1 = \frac{d}{\cos \beta}$$

$$0\text{–}4 = \frac{h}{\sin \beta} = 0\text{–}5$$

$$1\text{–}5 = \overline{0\text{–}1}^2 - \overline{0\text{–}5}^2 = \sqrt{\frac{d^2}{\cos^2 \beta} - \frac{h^2}{\sin^2 \beta}} = 1\text{–}6$$

$$0\text{–}6 = (0\text{–}1) - (1\text{–}6) = a = \frac{d}{\cos \beta} - \sqrt{\frac{d^2}{\cos^2 \beta} - \frac{h^2}{\sin^2 \beta}}$$

Except at the seepage line, the water is emerging from the slope under a positive head. The slope surface covered with the flow is a free surface but not an equipotential line. Flow lines may intersect this portion of the slope at any angle between 0° and 90°. If the toe of the slope is under tail water, that portion of the slope covered with tail water is an equipotential line and the flow lines are perpendicular to the slope.

On the upstream face of an earth dam, which is an equipotential line, the water enters the embankment at 90° to the face. But the flow lines turn immediately to form the squares of the flow net, and the free surface follows the parabolic seepage line.

A. Casagrande determined experimentally that a parabola drawn from the upstream surface of water above the dam at a point $m/3$ from the intersection of the water surface with the upstream face to the exit point

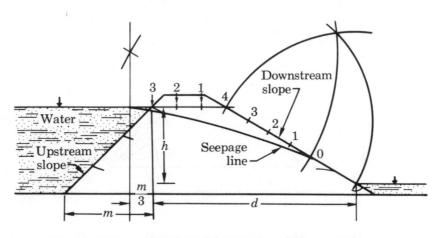

Figure 3.06e   **Section through dam of homogeneous, isotropic material**

at a distance a up from the toe, closely followed the seepage line, except for a small portion at the upstream slope. A short curve perpendicular to the slope at the entrance to the parabola corrects the seepage line in that portion.

A graphical method of laying out the seepage line for a dam of homogeneous, isotropic material without a downstream filter is shown in Figure 3.06e. Such a dam, which allows the seepage line to come to the downstream surface, is hydraulically unstable. In order for the dam to be stable, the seepage line must remain well below the downstream surface. This can be accomplished by means of properly designed filters at or near the toe of the dam.

b.   *Downstream Slope with Blanket Filter*

The requirement that the seepage line must leave the downstream face tangent to the slope is valid for slopes up to 90°. For downstream slopes greater than 90° and from which the seepage water leaves the surface into free space or into a material of much greater permeability than the embankment, so that there is no seepage or hydrostatic pressure produced at the boundary, the seepage line and flow lines into the free space must leave the downstream surface vertically. A very porous blanket filter extending under the toe of the dam, as shown in Figure 3.06*f*, provides a horizontal discharge surface.

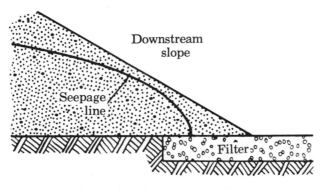

Figure 3.06f   Blanket filter

A solution for the exit point of the seepage line and its shape for a horizontal discharge surface was devised by Vreendenburgh in 1928 and independently a little later by Kozeny. About the same time, and independently, A. Casagrande solved the problem graphically.

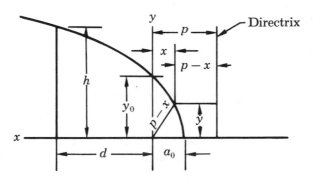

Figure 3.06g   Basic parabola

For the special case of a horizontal discharge surface, the flow lines are common focus parabolas. By definition, a parabola is a line every point of which is equidistant from a point focus and a line directrix. If *p* is the distance along the *X*-axis from a point focus to the directrix, the equation for a parabola with its focus at the origin of the coordinate system is

$$y^2 = (p - x)^2 - x^2 = p^2 - 2px$$

When $y = 0$, $x = \dfrac{p}{2}$, and if the distance along the X axis is a_0, then $a_0 = \dfrac{p}{2}$ or $p = 2 a_0$. Therefore, $y^2 = 4 a_0^2 - 4 a_0 x$. When $x = 0$, $y_0^2 = 4 a_0^2$, or $y_0 = 2 a_0$. When $y = h$, $x = -d$, and $h^2 = 4 a_0^2 + 4 a_0 d$

or

$$4 a_0^2 + 4 ad - h^2 = 0$$

from which

$$a_0 = \tfrac{1}{2}\sqrt{d^2 + h^2} - \frac{d}{2}$$

and

$$y_0 = 2 a_0 = \sqrt{d^2 + h^2} - d$$

When h and d and the focus are known, a graphical solution for the point of exit of the seepage line into the filter is available as shown in Figure 3.06h.

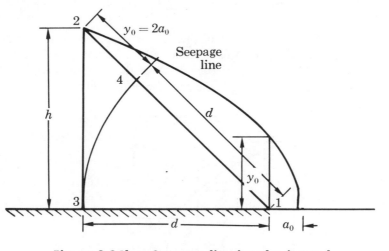

Figure 3.06h   Seepage line into horizontal discharge surface

Locate the intersection of the impermeable base and the top of the filter (focus), point 1, and locate the start of the parabolic seepage line at $m/3$ on the water surface from the upstream slope, point 2. Draw line 1-2. With point 1 as a center, strike arc 3-4 so that 1-4 $= d$. Then 2-4 $= y_0 = 2 a_0$. The vertical distance y_0 to the parabola from the focus can now be laid off vertically from the focus, and a_0 laid off horizontally to the point where the seepage line enters the filter. The seepage line can then be constructed through these points.

Proof of graphical construction of Figure 3.06h:

$$1\text{-}2 = \sqrt{h^2 + d^2}$$
$$1\text{-}4 = d$$

Therefore,

$$2\text{-}4 = \sqrt{h^2 + d^2} - d = y_0 = 2\,a_0$$

The quantity of water flowing between the seepage line and the impervious boundary into the filter can be estimated in accordance with the following reasoning.

For the parabolic seepage line

$$y^2 = 4\,a_0^2 - 4\,a_0 x$$

and

$$2y\,dy = -4\,a_0\,dx$$

The slope of the tangent at any point x,y is

$$\frac{dy}{dx} = -\frac{4\,a_0}{2y}$$

At $x = 0$, $y = y_0$

$$\frac{dy}{dx} = -\frac{4\,a_0}{2y_0} = -\frac{4\,a_0}{4\,a_0} = -1$$

Therefore, the slope of the tangent to the seepage line at $x = 0$, $y = y_0$ is 45°, and, since $y_0 = h_0$ at $x = 0$, $dh_0/dx = 1$ at $x = 0$.

Using Dupuit's assumption that dh/dx is the hydraulic gradient instead of its true value dh/ds, and that the hydraulic gradient is constant from the seepage line to the impermeable surface,

$$\frac{dh_0}{dx} = 1 = i$$

and for a unit thickness the area at $x = 0$ is y_0, so that

$$q = k\,i\,A = k\,y_0 = 2\,k\,a_0$$

c. *Downstream Slope with Rock Toe Filter*

No rigorous algebraic solution has been made for slopes of the discharge surface between 90° and 180°. In the early 1930's, Leo Casagrande conducted a series of tests using sand as an embankment and tracing the seepage line and flow lines by means of dye inserted at the entrance of the flow into the embankment. Following this series of tests, Arthur Casagrande painstakingly prepared a series of flow nets following the Forchheimer graphical method. These carefully prepared flow nets gave quite good agreement with the model tests.

As a result of this investigation, A. Casagrande devised a method for estimating the seepage line for an overhanging discharge surface in accordance with the following reasoning.

The seepage line must leave the overhanging discharge face vertically and it must, therefore, be somewhat lower than the basic parabola for

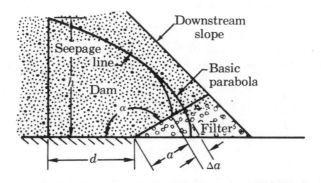

Figure 3.06i   Altered parabola at overhanging discharge surface

a horizontal discharge face. The parabola will be little affected except in the vicinity of the discharge face. If the lower extremity of the discharge surface be designated as a, and the distance between the intersections of the basic parabola and the seepage line with the discharge surface as Δa, as shown in Figure 3.06i, then the ratio $\Delta a/a + \Delta a$ is a constant c of a single value of α. Values of c increase from 0 for 180° (horizontal) to 0.26 for 90°. These values as determined by graphical plotting of the flow nets were plotted on a diagram which is included in Casagrande's paper, "Seepage Through Dams," and is reproduced in Figure 3.06j.

Once the value of $\Delta a/a + \Delta a$ is known for a given slope of the discharge face, estimating the intersection of the seepage line with the discharge face becomes a simple problem and can be solved algebraically or graphically. The point of intersection of the basic parabola with the discharge face can be found from the equation of the basic parabola $y^2 = p^2 - 2px$, and the slope of the discharge face α. In the basic parabola $p = y_0$. For convenience, let $a + \Delta a = L$. Then the coordinates of the intersection are

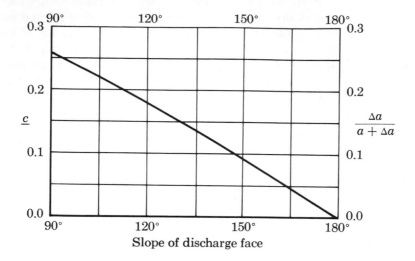

Figure 3.06j   Correction for seepage line for overhanging discharge face from basic parabola as determined by flow nets—After A. Casagrande

$x = L \cos \alpha$, and $y = L \sin \alpha$. The equation of the parabola in terms of L, and the slope of the discharge face α, becomes

$$L^2 \sin^2 \alpha = y_0^2 - 2 y_0 L \cos \alpha$$

from which comes

$$L = \frac{y_0}{\sin^2 \alpha} - y_0 \frac{\cos \alpha}{\sin^2 \alpha} = a + \Delta a$$

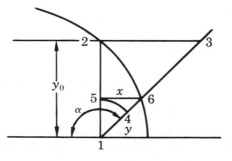

Figure 3.06k   Graphical solution for intersection of basic parabola with sloping discharge face

The point of intersection of the basic parabola and the discharge face can be found graphically as shown in Figure 3.06k. From the origin draw a line parallel to the discharge slope. Lay off vertically from the origin 1-2 $= y_0$. From point 2 draw a horizontal line to an intersection with the discharge slope 2-3. With 3 as a center, strike arc 3-4. With 1 as a center, strike arc 4-5. From point 5 draw a horizontal line to discharge face at point 6, which is the point of intersection of the basic parabola with the discharge face.

Proof of Graphical Solution:

$$2\text{--}3 = 3\text{--}4 = y_0 \cot \alpha$$

$$1\text{--}3 = \frac{y_0}{\sin \alpha} - y_0 \cot \alpha$$

$$1\text{--}6 = \frac{1\text{--}5}{\sin \alpha} = \frac{y_0}{\sin^2 \alpha} - y_0 \frac{\cos \alpha}{\sin^2 \alpha}$$

Therefore, 1-6 $= a + \Delta a$.

With $a + \Delta a$ known, and the value of $c = \Delta a / a + \Delta a$ found from the chart of Figure 3.06j, the value of Δa is readily determined, and the point of discharge of the seepage line located. A smooth curve from the vertical discharge point to the basic parabola as shown in Figure 3.06i will provide a good approximation of the seepage line for the overhanging discharge face.

3.07　Relation between Flow Lines at Joint between Materials of Different Permeabilities

In the design and construction of dams, it is necessary to construct the embankment of materials of different permeabilities. For stability, the outside or shell of the dam is usually made of more permeable material than the core which is of very low permeability. At the junction of the two materials, there is an abrupt change in the slope of the flow lines in the two materials. In this case, it is assumed that each of the materials is homogeneous and isotropic within itself, but the two materials have unlike properties. In all the following stated relationships, it is assumed that the water is flowing from material of k_1 to that of k_2.

On a flow line the change in head Δh between each adjacent equipotential lines must be the same, and the quantity of flow between flow lines must be the same on both sides of the junction between the two materials.

The quantity of water flowing between any adjacent pair of flow lines in the two materials is by reference to Figure 3.07a,

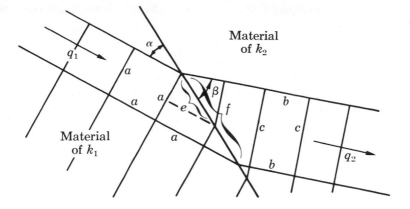

Figure 3.07a   Flow net at junction between materials of different permeabilities

$$\Delta q_1 = k_1 \frac{\Delta h}{a} a = \Delta q_2 = k_2 \frac{\Delta h}{b} c$$

Since Δh is the same on both sides,

$$\frac{k_1}{k_2} = \frac{c}{b}$$

This relationship indicates that when the flow net on the k_1 side is made up of squares, the net on the k_2 side is made up of rectangles with a ratio of sides equal to $\frac{k_1}{k_2}$. At the junction, this relationship can be expressed in terms of the angles α and β as follows:

and

$$\frac{a}{\cos \alpha} = e = \frac{b}{\cos \beta} \qquad \text{from which } a = b \frac{\cos \alpha}{\cos \beta}$$

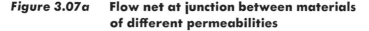

$$\frac{c}{\sin \beta} = f = \frac{a}{\sin \alpha} \qquad \text{from which } a = c \frac{\sin \alpha}{\sin \beta}$$

Therefore,

$$b \frac{\cos \alpha}{\cos \beta} = c \frac{\sin \alpha}{\sin \beta} \qquad \text{or } \frac{c}{b} = \frac{\tan \beta}{\tan \alpha} = \frac{k_1}{k_2}$$

Flow lines, therefore, must meet at the junction of materials of different coefficients of permeability at such angles that their tangents are inversely proportional to their coefficients of permeability.

It is not practical to construct a flow net with the angles at the junction between the two materials inversely proportional to their tangents, but it is practical to construct a flow net consisting of squares on one side and rectangles with their sides proportional to the k values of materials on the other; i.e.,

$$\frac{c}{b} = \frac{k_1}{k_2}$$

It should be borne in mind that on the seepage line which is a boundary of a free surface, the actual physical distance between equipotential lines Δh is a constant, and that the drop in head anywhere in the flow net between adjacent equipotential lines is constant, although the actual physical vertical distance on the flow lines between adjacent equipotential lines is usually not constant.

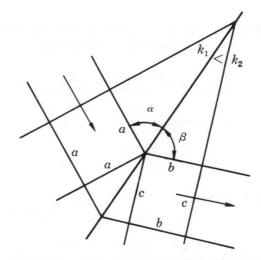

Figure 3.07b   Flow net at junction of materials of different permeabilities

For example, in the flow net shown in Figure 3.07b, if $k_1 = 0.5k_2$ and the flow net on the k_1 side is made up of squares, the flow net on the k_2 side will be made up of rectangles with a ratio of sides $c/b = 1/2$.

3.08   Angle of Seepage Line with Boundary between Materials of Different Permeabilities

Because the seepage line marks the boundary of a free surface, the actual vertical distance between adjacent equipotential lines where they join the seepage line is the same.

In a study of the seepage line at the junction of two materials of different permeabilities, there are two possible cases to consider: Case I in which the slope of the boundary is less than 90°, and Case II in which the slope is greater than 90°. Within each case there are two possible conditions; a, when k_1 is less than k_2; and b, when k_1 is greater than k_2.

Case I. $\theta < 90°$

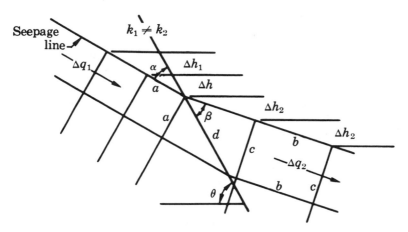

Figure 3.08a   Seepage line at junction of materials of different permeabilities

From the geometry of Figure 3.08a it can be seen that the following relationships exist:

$$\Delta h_1 = a \sin (\theta - \alpha)$$
$$\Delta h_2 = b \sin (\theta - \beta)$$

and

$$\Delta q_1 = k_1 \frac{\Delta h_1}{a} a$$

$$\Delta q_2 = k_2 \frac{\Delta h_2}{b} c$$

Equating Δq_1 and Δq_2, and substituting the equivalent values of Δh_1 and Δh_2, the following relationship is obtained:

$$k_1 a \sin (\theta - \alpha) = k_2 c \sin (\theta - \beta)$$

from which is obtained

$$\frac{k_1}{k_2} = \frac{c \sin (\theta - \beta)}{a \sin (\theta - \alpha)} = \frac{\tan \beta}{\tan \alpha}$$

But
$$\frac{a}{\sin \alpha} = d = \frac{c}{\sin \beta}$$

from which
$$\frac{c}{a} = \frac{\sin \beta}{\sin \alpha}$$

is obtained. Substituting this value of c/a in the above equation, it becomes

$$\frac{k_1}{k_2} = \frac{\tan \beta}{\tan \alpha} = \frac{\sin \beta \sin (\theta - \beta)}{\sin \alpha \sin (\theta - \alpha)} = \frac{\sin \beta \cos \alpha}{\cos \beta \sin \alpha} \qquad \text{(Eq. 3.08a)}$$

or

$$\frac{\sin (\theta - \beta)}{\sin (\theta - \alpha)} = \frac{\cos \alpha}{\cos \beta} = \frac{\sin (90 - \alpha)}{\sin (90 - \beta)} \qquad \text{(Eq. 3.08b)}$$

It is obvious from inspection that $\alpha = \beta$ satisfies equation 3.08b and is, therefore, a solution. Also it can be seen that no other solution than $\alpha = \beta$ is possible, because if α is different from β, one side of equation 3.08b will decrease as the other increases. But it has already been shown that $\dfrac{k_1}{k_2} = \dfrac{\tan \beta}{\tan \alpha}$. If $k_1 \neq k_2$, then $\dfrac{\tan \beta}{\tan \alpha} \neq 1$. The only condition in which α can equal β and $\dfrac{\tan \beta}{\tan \alpha} \neq 1$, is for $\dfrac{\tan \beta}{\tan \alpha} = \dfrac{0}{0} =$ any value.

$\alpha = \beta = 0$ is a possible solution because in equation 3.08a,

$$\frac{\sin 0 \sin (\theta - 0)}{\sin 0 \sin (\theta - 0)} = \frac{\tan \beta}{\tan \alpha} = \frac{0}{0}$$

$\alpha = \beta = \theta$ is also a possible solution because in equation 3.08a

$$\frac{\sin \theta \sin (\theta - \theta)}{\sin \theta \sin (\theta - \theta)} = \frac{\tan \beta}{\tan \alpha} = \frac{0}{0}$$

$\alpha = \beta = 90°$ appears to be a possible solution because in equation 3.08a

$$\frac{\sin 90° \cos 90°}{\cos 90° \sin 90°} = \frac{\tan \beta}{\tan \alpha} = \frac{0}{0}$$

However, for this case, where the slope of the plane between the two materials is less than 90°, the seepage line could not pass through the junction at 90° because of conditions imposed by gravity. Therefore, the only two possible values of α and β are $\alpha = \beta = 0$ and $\alpha = \beta = \theta$.

Case Ia:
$$\theta < 90° \text{ and } k_1 < k_2$$

If k_2 is not so much greater than k_1 that there is discontinuity at the junction of the two materials, there will be a gradient of flow at the seepage line from less permeable material into more permeable material, in which case $\alpha = \beta = 0$.

If k_2 is much larger than k_1, so that there is produced an equivalent free discharge, nature imposes the condition that $\alpha = 0$.

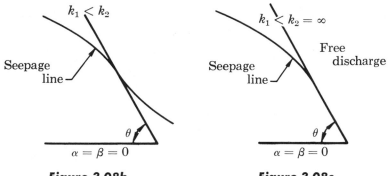

Figure 3.08b   **Figure 3.08c**

Seepage line at junction of materials of different permeabilities having slope less than 90° and for water flowing from less to more permeable material

Case Ib:

$$\theta < 90° \text{ and } k_1 > k_2$$

When k_1 is ∞ as with standing water on the k_1 side, $\alpha = \theta$ is imposed by nature, so that β must be equal to θ and the tangent to the seepage line must be horizontal, with no hydraulic gradient and no flow at the junction of the free water surface with the slope.

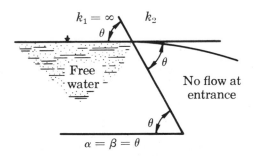

Figure 3.08d   **Seepage line at junction of materials of different permeabilities having slope less than 90° and for water flowing from more to less permeable material**

Case II:

$$\theta > 90° \text{ and } k_1 \neq k_2$$

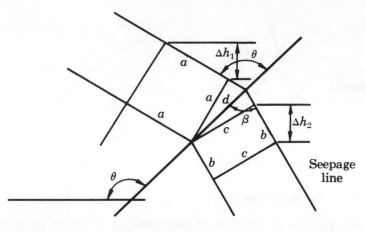

Figure 3.08e   Seepage line at junction of materials of different permeabilities

In this case, in which $\theta > 90°$ and k_1 is not equal to k_2,

$$\frac{c}{b} = \frac{k_1}{k_2} = \frac{\tan \beta}{\tan \alpha} \neq 1$$

From the geometry of Figure 3.08f, $\Delta h_1 = a \sin (\theta - \alpha)$ and $\Delta h_2 = a \sin (\theta - \beta)$. Also from the geometry of the figure,

$$\frac{c}{\cos \beta} = d = \frac{a}{\cos (180 - \alpha)}$$

and

$$\frac{c}{a} = \frac{\cos \beta}{\cos (180 - \alpha)} = \frac{\cos \beta}{- \cos \alpha}$$

Since the quantity of water flowing in a flow channel is the same on both sides of the junction,

$$\Delta q_1 = \Delta q_2 = k_1 \frac{\Delta h_1}{a} a = k_2 \frac{\Delta h_2}{b} c$$

Substituting the equivalent values of Δh_1 and Δh_2 in the equation above, it becomes

$$k_1 \frac{a \sin (\theta - \alpha)}{a} a = k_2 \frac{b \sin (\theta - \beta)}{b} c$$

Therefore,

$$\frac{k_1}{k_2} = \frac{c}{a}\frac{\sin(\theta - \beta)}{\sin(\theta - \alpha)} = \frac{\cos\beta}{-\cos\alpha}\frac{\sin(\theta - \beta)}{\sin(\theta - \alpha)} = \frac{\tan\beta}{\tan\alpha} \neq 1$$

It is obvious that α cannot be equal to β for that would make $\tan\beta/\tan\alpha = 1$, which is not true if k_1 is not equal to k_2.

$\alpha = \theta$ and $\beta = 90°$ would produce $\tan\beta/\tan\alpha = 0$, which makes this combination a possibility. $\alpha = 90°$ and $\beta = \theta$ would produce $\tan\beta/\tan\alpha = 0$, which makes this combination a possibility also.

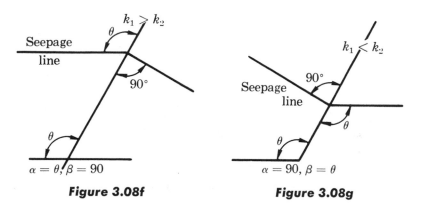

Figure 3.08f   Figure 3.08g

Seepage line at junction of materials of different permeabilities

Figure 3.08f represents the condition that exists at the upstream face of a dam. The condition shown in Figure 3.08g represents a special case of high tail water as illustrated in Figure 3.08h. If there is no tail water

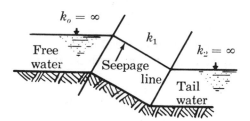

Figure 3.08h   Seepage line through tilted layer between highly permeable layers

for the special case as shown in Figure 3.08i, and the lower boundary is a discharge face, the flow net including the seepage line is discontinuous at the discharge face. In this case, the entire flow net is above the discharge face and consists of squares.

The discontinuity that exists at the discharge face imposes a different set of conditions than was considered in the above discussion. This condition of discontinuity is illustrated in Figure 3.08i.

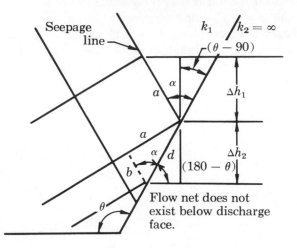

Figure 3.08i   Flow net at discharge face

From the geometry of Figure 3.08i, the following relationship exists:

$$\Delta h_1 = a \cos [\alpha - (\theta - 90)]$$

and

$$\frac{b}{\cos \alpha} = d = \frac{\Delta h_2}{\sin (180 - \theta)} = \frac{\Delta h_2}{\sin \theta}$$

Therefore,

$$\Delta h_2 = \frac{b \sin \theta}{\cos \alpha}$$

But $\Delta h_1 = \Delta h_2$ and, because all of the flow net is in the same material, $a = b$. Therefore, equating Δh_1 to Δh_2 produces the relationship

$$\cos [\alpha - (\theta - 90)] = \frac{\sin \theta}{\cos \alpha}$$

This relationship can be expanded into

$$\cos \alpha \cos (\theta - 90) + \sin \alpha \sin (\theta - 90) = \frac{\sin \theta}{\sin (90 - \alpha)}$$

This relationship is satisfied when $\alpha = (\theta - 90)$, which indicates that the seepage line at the discharge face is vertical.

The preceding relationships are summarized in Figure 3.08j.

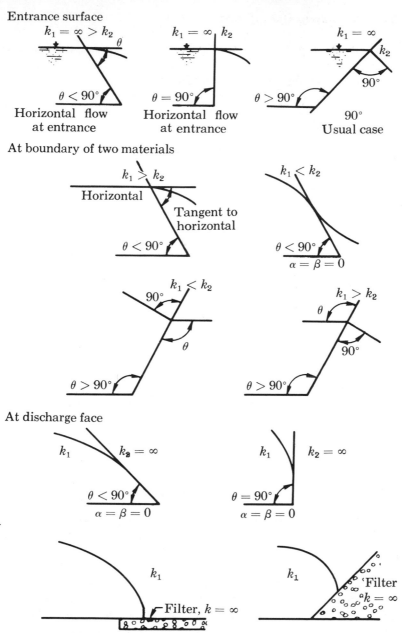

Figure 3.08j   Seepage line at boundary of materials of different permeabilities

3.09   *Equipressure Lines*

Figure 3.09*a* shows a portion of a flow net. In the figure the following symbols are used:

$p =$ pore pressure at point in flow net.

$h =$ potential head from reference plane to free surface.

$z =$ head from reference plane to point.

Subscripts 1 and 2 make symbols apply to points 1 and 2.

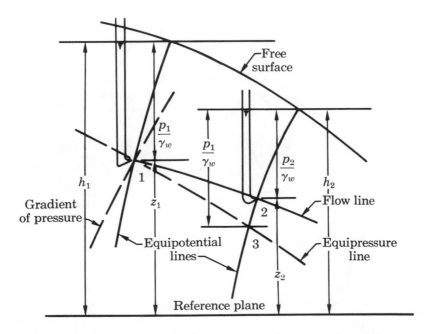

Figure 3.09a   Partial flow net showing equipressure line

If a tube were inserted to any point on the equipotential line through point 1, the water would rise to the height of the intersection of the equipotential line with the free surface. This height of water in the tube represents the pressure head at point 1; i.e., $p_1 = (h_1 - z_1)\gamma_w$. The head of water in the tube at point 1 is p_1/γ_w. The head of water at point 2 on the next equipotential line on the same flow line is p_2/γ_w, which is not the same as at point 1. If the head at point 1, p_1/γ_w, is laid off vertically from the intersection of the equipotential line through 2 with the free surface to the equipotential line through 2, point 3, having the same pressure as point 1, will be determined. Then, an equipressure line for p_1 can be drawn by laying off the distance p_1/γ_w from the intersection of each equipotential line with the free surface to the same equipotential line inside the flow net.

Lines drawn perpendicular to these equipressure lines are called pressure gradient lines. Nets of these equipressure and pressure gradient lines are sometimes drawn instead of the more common flow nets of flow lines and equipotential lines.

3.10 Seepage Forces

A drop of water as it flows through the soil is acted upon by the weight of the drop and by a force parallel to the pressure gradient line. The re-

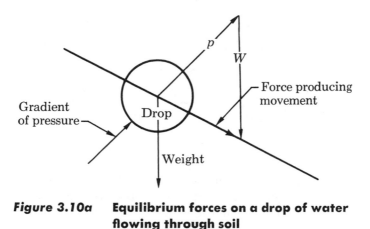

Figure 3.10a   **Equilibrium forces on a drop of water flowing through soil**

sultant of these forces produces movement resisted by friction in the direction of the flow line along which the drop moves.

A volume of water q_1 moving in a flow channel through a drop in potential head from one equipotential line to the next, Δh, does an amount of work J equal to the weight of the water times the change in potential head Δh,

$$J = q_1 \gamma_w \, \Delta h$$

This quantity of water, in dropping through the change in potential head from one equipotential line to the next, Δh, travels a distance b equal to the distance between equipotential lines along the flow line. A unit volume of water in traveling a unit distance along the flow line does work equal to

$$j = \frac{q_1 \gamma_w \, \Delta h}{q_1 b} = \frac{\gamma_w \, \Delta h}{b}$$

But $\Delta h/b = i_s$ = hydraulic gradient along the flow line.

Then

$$j = \frac{\gamma_w \Delta h}{b} = i_s \gamma_w$$

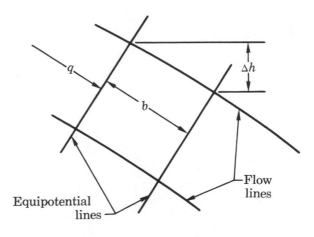

Figure 3.10b   Square of flow net

This value of j is equal to the force exerted by a unit volume of water dropping through the head lost per unit of distance traveled. This force equal to j is the force exerted by the moving water and has no relation to the pore water pressure or to the direction of flow.

The engineer is interested in the seepage force that would cause piping in sand at the bottom of an excavation or at the toe of a dam or levee.

The submerged weight in water of the solids in a unit volume of soil is

$$\gamma_{\text{sub}} = \frac{G_s - 1}{1 + e} \gamma_w$$

Equating this submerged weight of soil solids in a unit cube of soil, to the force exerted by a unit volume of water flowing the unit distance through the cube with its head loss between entrance and exit,

$$\frac{G_s - 1}{1 + e} \gamma_w = i\gamma_w$$

The hydraulic gradient required to hold grains of sand in suspension and cause piping to start is computed for sand having a specific gravity of

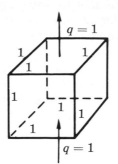

Figure 3.10c   Unit cube of soil with unit volume of water flowing through

solids equal to 2.65 and of different densities, and is shown in the following table:

Density	Void ratio	Relationship	Hydraulic gradient to start piping
Loose	1.0	$\dfrac{1.65}{2}$	0.825
Medium	0.65	$\dfrac{1.65}{1.65}$	1.00
Dense	0.40	$\dfrac{1.65}{1.4}$	1.18

This analysis indicates that the critical hydraulic gradient that will cause piping of sand by water moving vertically throught the sand is approximately unity.

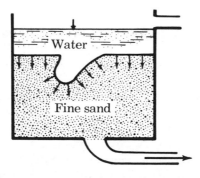

Figure 3.10d   Quicksand box

The effect of the force of moving water can be illustrated with a device consisting of a container for the sand through which water can be allowed to flow downward or forced upward at will. When the water flows downward through the sand, slopes in the submerged sand are stable even when undercut. When the water moves upward through the sand, the slopes collapse. If the hydraulic gradient is made greater than 1, the sand grains are lifted in suspension and may be washed out the top of the vessel.

This knowledge of seepage forces forms the basis for the design of filters.

3.11   Design of Filters

The purpose of a filter is two-fold; *a*, to retain the soil so that it cannot be removed by the seepage forces; and *b*, to reduce the seepage forces to such an extent that they do not produce piping of the filter material. To fulfill the first of these requirements, the pore channels of the filter material must be small enough that the grains of soil cannot pass through the filter. The filter material must also be graded so that the finer particles of the filter cannot pass through the pore spaces between the larger grains. The second requirement is met by a coarse pervious material that will pass the seepage water at a velocity low enough to reduce the seepage forces to a safe value. The filter must also have enough weight to prevent seepage pressure at or near the bottom of the filter from lifting the filter.

Terzaghi worked out a method of design based on studies he made in the design and construction of filters for some large dams in South Africa. From these studies Terzaghi formulated the following rules for the design of filters.

a.   First Condition—Retaining Soil Grains

The filter material must be fine enough that the soil grains cannot be washed through the pore spaces.

After considering the structure of the soil, it can be assumed that if one size of the soil grains can be held, all can be held. From tests, Terzaghi found that if the 85 per cent size of ordinary sand is held all will be held. The question then is what size grains in the filter will hold the 85 per cent size of the soil. If the grains in the filter are spheres of uniform size arranged in the loosest possible state, the largest sphere that can pass through the pore pace is, as shown in Figure 3.11*a*, equal to $0.41D$. If the grains of sand are spheres of uniform size and arranged in the densest state, the largest sphere that can penetrate between the grains, as shown in Figure 3.11b, is 0.15D.

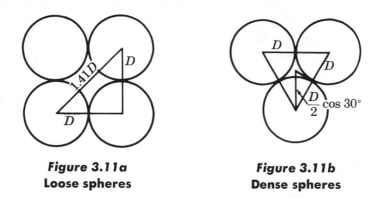

Figure 3.11a
Loose spheres

Figure 3.11b
Dense spheres

The material of the filter will not consist of uniform spheres and will be graded from fine to coarse. Also, the filter of cohesionless material will be neither in the loosest nor in the densest state, but at some intermediate density. The mean of these two pore sizes for the loosest and densest states is 0.28D. If the smaller sizes of the filter will retain the 85 per cent size of the soil, all of the soil will be retained. Terzaghi adopted the rule that if the 15 per cent size of the filter is not more than 4 times the 85 per cent size of the soil, the filter will retain the soil. G. E. Bertram found in tests that the maximum size of filter grains which will prevent soil grains from passing is 8 to 10 times the size of the grains being retained. Bertram's investigation indicates that the Terzaghi rule is conservative.

b. Second Condition—Reducing Seepage Forces

The filter should be as porous as possible in order to reduce the seepage pressures, and still be fine enough to prevent the protected soil grains from passing through the pore channels of the filter. To be effective in reducing the seepage forces, the permeability should be increased to 16 or more times the permeability of the soil.

If k_F is made 16 times k_S, and Hazen's formula for permeability, $k = CD_e^2$, is valid for the soil under consideration,

$$\frac{k_F}{k_S} = \frac{C\,D^2{}_F}{C\,D_e^2{}_S} = \frac{16}{1}$$

Thus, to maintain the 16 to 1 ratio of permeabilities, $D_{eF} = 4D_{eS}$.

Terzaghi established a rule which makes the 15 per cent size of the filter 4 times as large or larger than the 15 per cent size of the protected soil.

The use of these rules for choosing a suitable filter sand for soil having a certain grain size distribution is illustrated in Figure 3.11c. According to these rules, the 15 per cent size of the filter can be any size between 4 times the 15 per cent size of the soil and 4 times the 85 per cent size of the soil. If the filter material is homogeneous and well graded from fine to coarse, the larger grains of the filter will prevent passage of the smaller sizes. Therefore, a filter material whose grain size distribution curve lies within the shaded area of Figure 3.11c will satisfy the rules as stated above and should provide a satisfactory filter.

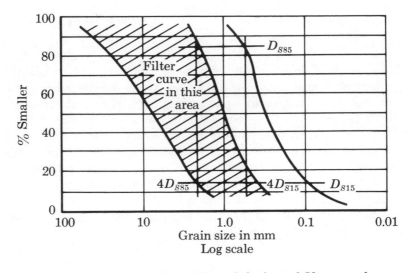

Figure 3.11c   Illustration of design of filter sand

The most efficient filter is one which reduces the hydraulic gradient most rapidly. In the equal areas of the soil and the filter between adjacent flow lines, the quantity of water flowing is the same,

$$\Delta q_S = \Delta q_F$$

and

$$\Delta q_S = v_S A \text{ and } \Delta q_F = v_F A, \text{ so } v_S = v_F$$

But,

$$v_S = k_S i_S \text{ and } v_F = k_F i_F, \text{ so } k_S i_S = k_F i_F$$

Therefore, as k increases, i decreases. The greatest reduction in i occurs when k is the largest possible. A soil of uniform grain size has a larger void ratio than a graded material, so the most efficient filter material is one of nearly uniform grain size, but small enough to retain the 85 per cent size of the soil. The most efficient filter, then, is one composed of layers of fairly uniform grain size whose grain size distribution lies between 4 times the 85 per cent size of the material which it is to retain, and 4 times the 15 per cent size of that material. Such a grain size distribution curve for the

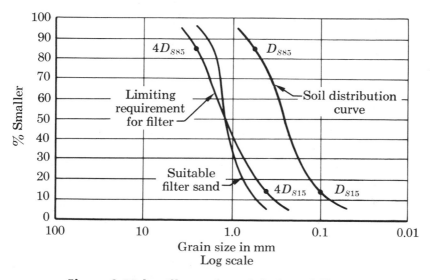

Figure 3.11d   Illustration of design of filter sand

first layer above the soil is shown in Figure 3.11d. The layer immediately above the first layer of filter should bear the same relationship to the layer below as the first layer bears to the soil retained.

c.   Thickness of Filter

If the seepage pressure at the outlet of the flow from the soil is just sufficient to cause imminent piping, a hydraulic gradient of unity, the filter would require no weight to prevent uplift from pressure beneath. If, however, the seepage pressure in the soil is more than sufficient to lift the submerged weight of the soil grains, the filter must provide sufficient weight, in addition to the seepage force within the filter itself, to resist the excess lifting force of the seepage through the soil which is acting on the bottom of the filter.

The seepage force acting on the bottom of the filter and the thickness of the filter can be estimated as follows.

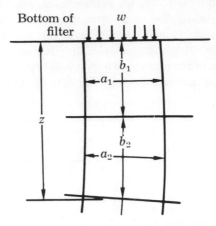

Figure 3.11e   **Flow channel at bottom of filter**

The change in pressure between equipotential lines is $\Delta h \gamma_w$. The change in pressure per unit of length is $\dfrac{\Delta h}{b} \gamma_w$. This change in seepage pressure per unit of vertical height and per unit of area is resisted by the submerged unit weight of the soil through which the water is flowing, γ_{sub}.

In any given rectangle of the flow net, the unit seepage pressure in excess of the submerged unit weight of the soil is $i_a \gamma_w - \gamma_{\text{sub}}$. The total seepage force exerted per unit of area on the bottom of the filter is

$$w = (i\gamma_w - \gamma_{\text{sub}})\, z_s = (i_{av}\gamma_w - \gamma_{\text{sub}})\, z_s$$

wherein

w = weight per unit of area of filter required

i_{av} = average i between point in flow channel where $i\gamma_w = \gamma_{\text{sub}}$ or where $i = 1$, and bottom of filter

z_s = thickness of soil between bottom of filter and point where the submerged weight of soil is able to resist the seepage pressure

Likewise, the weight provided by the filter is

$$w = (i_F \gamma_w - \gamma_{\text{sub}})\, z_F$$

wherein

i_F = hydraulic gradient in filter

z_F = thickness of filter

The thickness of the filter required for a factor safety of 1 can be stated as

$$z_F = \frac{(i_{av}\gamma_w - \gamma_{\text{sub}})\, z_s}{i_F \gamma_w - \gamma_{\text{sub}}}$$

The thickness of the filter can be stated also in terms of the effective grain sizes as follows:

From Hazen's formula, $k_S = CD_{eS}^2$ and $k_F = CD_{eF}^2$.
q through 1 flow channel $= k_S i_S a_1 = CD_{eS}^2 i_S a_1$.
q through the same area of filter $= k_F i_F a_1 = CD_{eF}^2 a_1$.

Equating these two equal values produces

$$i_F = \frac{D_{eS}^2}{D_{eF}^2} i_S$$

which can be substituted in relationships for thickness of filter.

3.12   Example of Seepage Problem in Isotropic Soil

Assume a low concrete dam as shown in Figure 3.12a on cohesionless soil having a coefficient of permeability of 20×10^{-4} cm sec^{-1}.
1. Draw flow net.
2. Determine the quantity of water flowing under the dam per foot of width per day.
3. Determine the uplift pressure on the bottom of the dam 5 ft upstream from the toe.
4. Determine the seepage force of the flowing water at the toe of the dam. Is there danger of piping at this point?

Solution:

1. See flow net in Figure 3.12a.
2. $N_f = 4$, $N_e = 17$

$$Q = \frac{20 \times 10^{-4} \times 60^2 \times 24}{2.54 \times 12} \times 10 \times \frac{4}{17}$$

$$= 13.4 \text{ cu ft per day per ft}$$

3. $[62.4] \left[13 - \left(\frac{12}{17}\right)(10) \right] = (13 - 7.06)(62.4) = 371 \text{ lb ft}^{-2}$

4. $\Delta h = \dfrac{10}{17} = 0.59$. L of square at toe $= 2$ ft

$$i \text{ at toe} = \frac{0.59}{2} = 0.29$$

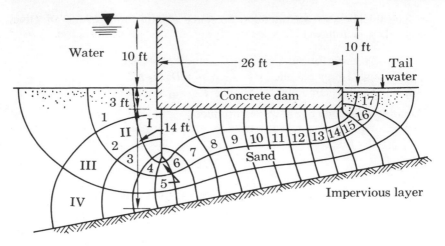

Figure 3.12a   Flow net for low dam on cohesionless soil
Scale ⅛″ = 1′ − 0″

The average hydraulic gradient in the large square next to the toe indicates that there would not be piping at the toe, but the large square should be subdivided to investigate the possibility of piping immediately adjacent to the toe.

3.13   Flow of Water into Wells

In the following discussion of drawdown and yield from wells, it is assumed that there is available to the aquifer a supply of water greater than the demand. This may or may not be an erroneous assumption. If a drought persists over the area which the area drains, the available yield of springs and wells is reduced because the water available to the aquifer is reduced. In any area, the amount of fresh water available from wells is limited either by the ability of the aquifer to allow water to flow, or by the availability of the supply to the aquifer.

The symbols used in this discussion of wells are as follows:

q = quantity of water pumped in a unit of time.

r = radius from center of well to point on drawdown curve.

r_0 = radius of well.

H = vertical distance from reference plane to point on original surface or point of 0 drawdown curve.

z = vertical distance from reference plane to point on drawdown curve.

$R =$ distance from center of well to point where water table is not influenced by pumping from well. Radius of influence.

a. Artesian Wells

An artesian well is one which taps an aquifer below an impervious layer in which hydrostatic pressure exists against the confining impervious layer.

Consider first an artesian well with a thin aquifer, as illustrated in Figure 3.13a. A relationship between the quantity of water taken out and the loss in head can be obtained as follows:

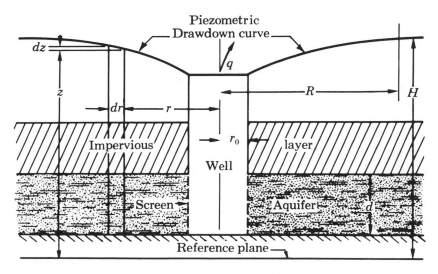

Figure 3.13a   Artesian well with thin aquifer

From Darcy's Law, $q = k i A$.

In this case,

$$i = \frac{dz}{dr} \text{ and } A = 2 \pi r d, \ q = 2 \pi d r k \frac{dz}{dr}$$

Separating variables,

$$q \frac{dr}{r} = 2 \pi d k \, dz$$

Integrating,

$$\int q \frac{dr}{r} = \int 2 \pi d k \, dz \text{ yields } q \ln r = 2 \pi d k z + C$$

When $r = r_0$, $z = z_0$ and when $r = R$, $z = H$.

Introducing these values in the general equation, the value of C is found to be

$$C = q \ln r_0 - 2 \pi d k z_0$$

Putting this value of C in the general equation, is becomes

$$q \ln \frac{r}{r_0} = 2 \pi d k(z - z_0), \text{ or } q \ln \frac{R}{r_0} = 2 \pi d k (H - z_0)$$

The relationship can be written in a more general form which does not require that H and z_0 be known, as

$$q \ln \frac{r_1}{r_2} = 2 \pi d k(z_1 - z_2) \qquad \text{(Eq. 313a)}$$

z_1 and z_2 can be measured by placing piezometers at the top of the aquifer at r_1 and r_2 distances from the center of the well, and reading the heads after steady flow has been established. From these values any factor can be determined, when the other two constants are known.

Next, consider an artesian well with a semispherical bottom in a very thick aquifer. In this case, the flow net in the aquifer consists of flow lines lying on the surface of cones radiating from the center of the well at the top of the aquifer and equipotential lines lying on the surface of equipotential semispheres with their centers at the center of the well at the top of the aquifer, as shown in Figure 3.13b.

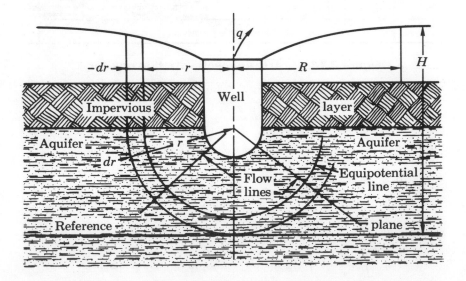

Figure 3.13b   Artesian well with thick aquifer

From Darcy's Law,

$$q = k i A$$

In this case, the water flowing in the aquifer through a semisphere of radius r passes through an area equal to $A = 2 \pi r^2$ under a hydraulic gradient of dz/dr, so that

$$q = k 2 \pi r^2 \frac{dz}{dr}$$

Integrating,

$$\int q \, r^{-2} \, dr = \int 2 \pi k \, dz, \text{ or } -\frac{q}{r} = 2 \pi k z + C$$

When $r = r_0$, $z = z_0$, and when $r = R$, $z = H$.

Introducing either of these pairs of values into the general equation, the value of C is found to be

$$C = -\frac{q}{r_0} - 2 \pi k z_0$$

Introducing the value of C into the general equation, the relationship becomes

$$-\frac{q}{r} + \frac{q}{r_0} = 2 \pi k z - 2 \pi k z_0 = q\left(\frac{r - r_0}{r \, r_0}\right) = 2 \pi k(z - z_0)$$

A more general statement of the relationship can be written as

$$q\left(\frac{r_1 - r_2}{r_1 \, r_2}\right) = 2 \pi k(z_1 - z_2) \tag{Eq. 3.13b}$$

These equations have been derived for a steady state of flow. In the early period of removal of water from the well, steady flow does not exist and these equations do not hold. After steady flow has been established, there is a distance away from the well where the head is not affected by the drawdown. This distance R from the center of the well, where the piezometric surface during pumping is tangent to the original piezometric surface, is called the radius of influence.

b.   Ordinary Wells

An ordinary well in this discussion is one from which the water is drawn from below the natural ground water table. Unlike the artesian well, there is no excess hydrostatic pressure available to help lift the water to the surface through a break in a confining impervious layer.

(1)   *Condition of Steady Flow*

In the analysis for determining the relationship of yield and draw-down, the assumption is made that it is possible to reach a state of steady flow. This assumption is not true during the drawdown period and, in general, is not true unless there is a generous supply in relation to the amount drawn from the well, so that the flow approximates that given in the artesian well solution. About the only case in which a state of steady flow would be attained during pumping is for a well in the center of an island in a body of water whose surface does not fluctuate. In this case, after the initial drawdown, a steady rate of pumping will produce an unfluctuating drawdown curve.

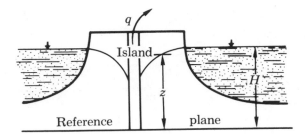

Figure 3.13c   Well in center of an island

This condition of steady flow and unfluctuating drawdown might be approached in the case of a small area around a well being fed by ground water from rains on the surrounding country.

If it be assumed that the ground water supply is great enough compared to the quantity pumped, so that steady flow without fluctuation of draw-down may be attained and that a permeable layer is underlain by an impermeable layer, and that the material of the permeable layer is isotropic, a relationship between quantity pumped and drawdown can be stated.

If it be assumed that the hydraulic gradient is dz/dr and that it is constant for the full depth of z (**Dupuit's** assumptions), the relationship can be written

$$q = k\,i\,A = k\frac{dz}{dr}\,2\,\pi\,r\,z$$

This statement of Darcy's Law is in error because the gradient is not $dz/dr = \tan\alpha$, but is

$$\frac{dz}{\sqrt{dz^2 + dr^2}} = \sin\alpha$$

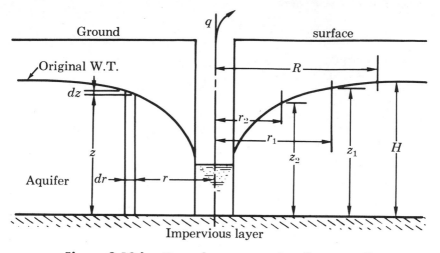

Figure 3.13d   Drawdown around ordinary well

However, this assumption is approximately true for values of α less than 30°. In the vicinity of the well, the slope is greater than 30°, so the solution is inaccurate in that area adjacent to the well. Attempts have been made to solve the problem using $\sin \alpha$ instead of $\tan \alpha$ but none has been successful.

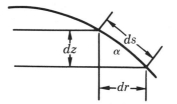

The relationship between quantity pumped and drawdown, after steady flow is established as determined by using the Dupuit assumptions, can be established as follows:

$$q = 2 \pi r z k \frac{dz}{dr}$$

$$\int \frac{q}{2 \pi k} \frac{dr}{r} = \int z \, dz = \frac{z^2}{2} = \frac{q}{2 \pi k} \ln r + C$$

or

$$z^2 = \frac{q}{\pi k} \ln r + C$$

When $z = H$, $r = R$, so

$$C = H^2 - \frac{q}{\pi k} \ln R.$$

The general equation then becomes

$$z^2 - H^2 = \frac{q}{\pi k} (\ln r - \ln R)$$

or, since H is larger than z,

$$H^2 - z^2 = \frac{q}{\pi k} \ln \frac{R}{r}, \text{ or } z = \sqrt{H^2 - \frac{q}{\pi k} \ln \frac{R}{r}} \qquad \text{(Eq. 3.13c)}$$

A more general relationship can be written for any two points on the drawdown curve as follows:

$$z_1^2 - z_2^2 = \frac{q}{\pi k} \ln \frac{r_1}{r_2}$$

Because this relationship is not true near the well, the radius of the well r_0 and the drawdown in the well z_0 cannot be used. The surface of the water in the well and the drawdown curve at the well do not coincide. Although the drawdown at the well cannot be estimated with any degree

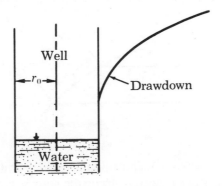

Figure 3.13e   Drawdown and surface of water in well

of accuracy, or the relationship between diameter of the well and drawdown determined, it can be seen that pumping a small quantity of water from a small well will lower the ground water over a small area adjacent to the well, and that pumping a large quantity of water from a large well will lower the ground water for a considerable distance from the well. Therefore, if the purpose of the well is to lower the ground water over a small area with a small amount of pumping, small wells should be used. If, on the other hand, the purpose is for a large yield from the well, a large well should be used.

(2)   *Influence of Time on Drawdown*

Except where there is an unlimited source of supply, such as on an island in a lake, all other factors being constant the drawdown curve is further depressed by continuous pumping, and a state of steady flow does not exist, in general, for ordinary wells.

In 1928 Hermann Weber derived a relation between the drawdown and time by assuming that the water taken out dq in time dt is equal to the water removed from the pores of the soil above the drawdown curve during time dt plus the water which flows from the source through the cylinder of area $2\pi r z$ in time dt.

In this discussion the following symbols are used.

V' = volume under drawdown curve at time t.
V_n = volume between original water table and drawdown surface after time t.
n = porosity.
n' = proportionate part of total pore space drained.
q_r = quantity of water supplied from outside source through cylinder of radius r.
q_n = quantity taken from soil in time $t = n'V_n$.
q = quantity taken from well in time $t = q_r + q_n$.

The relationship for z, h, r, and R has already been established as

$$z = \sqrt{H^2 - \frac{q}{\pi k} \ln \frac{R}{r}} \qquad \text{(Eq. 3.13c)}$$

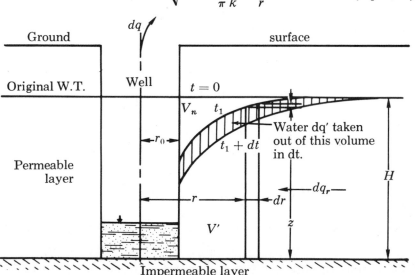

Figure 3.13f   Influence of time on drawdown

As pumping is continued and drawdown progresses, the radius of influence R increases. Under a given set of pumping conditions, therefore, if at a given time t the value of R is known, the drawdown curve for that given time could be drawn. The relationship between t and R can be estimated according to the following reasoning:

The quantity of water from the source passing through the cylinder of radius r is

$$q_r = q - q_n = 2\pi k r z \frac{dz}{dr}$$

If the quantity of water drained from the pores q_n is a proportionate part of the total quantity of water pumped q, and the proportionate factor is the ratio $\dfrac{r}{R}$ raised to some power α (not a constant), then

$$q_r = q - q\left(\frac{r}{R}\right)^\alpha = q\left(1 - \frac{r^\alpha}{R^\alpha}\right) = 2\pi r k z \frac{dz}{dr}$$

or

$$q\left[\int \frac{dr}{r} - \int \frac{r^{\alpha-1}}{R^\alpha}\,dr\right] = \int 2\pi k z\,dz =$$

$$q\left[\ln r - \frac{r^\alpha}{R^\alpha}\cdot\frac{1}{\alpha}\right] = \pi k z^2 + C$$

When $r = R$, $z = H$, so

$$C = q\left[\ln R - \frac{1}{\alpha}\right] - \pi k H^2$$

When this value of C is inserted in the above equation it becomes

$$z^2 - H^2 = \frac{q}{\pi k}\left[\ln \frac{r}{R} - \frac{r^\alpha}{\alpha R^\alpha} + \frac{1}{\alpha}\right]$$

$$z^2 = H^2\left[1 + \frac{q}{\pi k H^2}\left(\ln \frac{r}{R} - \frac{r^\alpha}{\alpha R^\alpha} + \frac{1}{\alpha}\right)\right]$$

$$z = H\sqrt{1 + \frac{q}{\pi k H^2}\left(\ln \frac{r}{R} - \frac{r^\alpha}{\alpha R^\alpha} + \frac{1}{\alpha}\right)}$$

Since z is less than H, the expression under the radical must be between 0 and 1. In the equation $\sqrt{1 + a + \dfrac{a^2}{4}} = 1 + \dfrac{a}{2}$, if a is less than 1, the value of $\dfrac{a^2}{4}$ is small compared to a. Therefore, if $\sqrt{1 + a}$ is approximately

$1 + \dfrac{a}{2}$, it follows that an approximate value of z is

$$z = H \left\{ 1 + \frac{q}{2 \pi k H^2} \left[\ln \frac{r}{R} - \frac{r^\alpha}{\alpha R^\alpha} + \frac{1}{\alpha} \right] \right\}$$

At time t the volume below the drawdown curve between the radius of influence and the radius of the well r_0 is

$$V' = \int_{r_0}^{R} 2 \pi z r \, dr$$

Inserting the equivalent value of z the value of V' becomes

$$V' = 2 \pi H \int_{r_0}^{R} \left[1 + \frac{q}{2 \pi k H^2} \left(\ln \frac{r}{R} - \frac{r^\alpha}{\alpha R^\alpha} + \frac{1}{\alpha} \right) \right] r \, dr$$

$$V' = 2 \pi H \int_{r_0}^{R} \left[\int r \, dr + \frac{q}{2 \pi k H^2} \left(\int r \ln \frac{r}{R} \, dr - \frac{1}{\alpha} \int \frac{r^\alpha}{R^\alpha} r \, dr + \frac{1}{\alpha} \int r \, dr \right) \right]$$

$$V' = 2 \pi H \int_{r_0}^{R} \left[\frac{r^2}{2} + \frac{q}{2 \pi k H^2} \left(\frac{r^2}{2} \ln \frac{r}{R} - \frac{r^2}{4} - \frac{r^{(\alpha+2)}}{\alpha R^\alpha (\alpha + 2)} + \frac{r^2}{2\alpha} \right) \right]$$

$$V' = 2 \pi H \left\{ \left[\frac{R^2}{2} + \frac{q}{2 \pi k H^2} \left(\frac{R^2}{2} \ln \frac{R}{R} - \frac{R^2}{4} - \frac{R^2}{\alpha (\alpha + 2)} + \frac{R^2}{2\alpha} \right) \right] \right.$$

$$\left. - \left[\frac{r_0}{2} + \frac{q}{2 \pi k H^2} \left(\frac{r_0}{2} \ln \frac{r_0}{R} - \frac{r_0^2}{4} - \frac{r_0^{(\alpha+2)}}{\alpha R^\alpha (\alpha + 2)} + \frac{r_0^2}{2\alpha} \right) \right] \right\}$$

If an amount of water equal to the volume of the water in the well itself (within r_0) be neglected, then

$$V' = \pi R^2 H \left[1 + \frac{q}{\pi k H^2} \left(-\frac{1}{4} - \frac{1}{\alpha (\alpha + 2)} + \frac{1}{2\alpha} \right) \right]$$

The volume of the drained portion of the cylinder above the drawdown curve at time t is equal to the volume of the entire cylinder of radius R minus V'.

$$V_n = \pi R^2 H - V' =$$

$$\pi R^2 H - \pi R^2 H \left[1 + \frac{q}{\pi k H^2} \left(-\frac{1}{4} - \frac{1}{\alpha (\alpha + 2)} + \frac{1}{2\alpha} \right) \right]$$

$$V_n = \frac{R^2 q}{k H} \left[\frac{1}{4} + \frac{1}{\alpha (\alpha + 2)} - \frac{1}{2\alpha} \right] = \frac{R^2 q}{k H} \cdot \frac{\alpha}{4 (\alpha + 2)}$$

If the water is pumped at a constant rate so the q is constant, and if it be assumed that all of the water is drained from the soil above the drawdown curve, it can be stated that the water pumped in time t is

$$n'V_n = \int_0^t q \, dt = q \, t$$

This assumption is obviously in error because it neglects the water that flows through the soil from the source. At the beginning of the pumping period, because of lack of hydraulic gradient, practically all of the water is drained from the soil above the drawdown curve, and the assumption is approximately correct. As the water table is lowered and the hydraulic gradient increases away from the well, a larger amount of the water pumped comes from the source through the soil, and a lesser amount by draining of the soil above the drawdown curve. But the acceptance of this assumption provides a means for estimating the approximate drawdown curve for any time t after start of pumping.

$$n'V_n = q \, t = n' \frac{q \, R^2}{k \, H} \cdot \frac{\alpha}{4 \, (\alpha + 2)}$$

From this relationship the value of R can be determined as

$$R = \sqrt{\frac{k \, H \, t}{n'} \cdot \frac{4 \, (\alpha + 2)}{\alpha}} = \sqrt{\frac{k \, H \, t}{n'}} \cdot \sqrt{\frac{4 \, (\alpha + 2)}{\alpha}} \qquad \text{(Eq. 3.13d)}$$

For a very short time after start of pumping there is no hydraulic gradient to produce flow of water through the soil from the source, except at the water table immediately adjacent to the well. In the beginning, practically all of the water comes from draining the soil above the drawdown curve of very small R. At this stage, r and R are approximately equal, and since q_r is nearly 0,

$$q_r = q - q_n = q - q \left(\frac{r}{R}\right)^\alpha = 0$$

or

$$q = q \left(\frac{r}{R}\right)^\alpha = q(1) = q(1)^1$$

Thus, at the beginning of pumping, the value of α is unity, but as pumping progresses, more water is supplied by percolation through the soil below the drawdown curve and less by drainage from the soil above the drawdown curve. Therefore, as pumping progresses, because $\left(\dfrac{r}{R}\right)$ is less than unity, α must increase. In equation 13.13d, it can be seen that change in the value of α produces little change in $\sqrt{\dfrac{4(\alpha + 2)}{\alpha}}$. During most of the pumping period, the value of α will be between 1 and 2. A mean of the corresponding two values is 3.15 or approximately 3. Using this approximate value of α, equation 3.13*d* becomes

For mean of $\sqrt{\dfrac{4(\alpha+2)}{\alpha}}$

$$R = 3 \sqrt{\frac{k\,H\,t}{n'}}$$

Thus, when H, k, and n' are known, the value of R can be estimated for any time t after start of pumping. With R known, the drawdown curve for time t can be drawn by application of equation 3.13*c*.

α	$\sqrt{\dfrac{4(\alpha + 2)}{\alpha}}$
1	3.46
2	2.84
10	2.19
∞	2.00

1.6 ... *3.00*

$$z = \sqrt{H^2 - \frac{q}{\pi\,k} \ln \frac{R}{r}} \qquad\qquad \text{(Eq. 3.13}c\text{)}$$

c.   *Group of Wells—Steady Flow*

The engineer is usually not concerned with only one well. In ground water lowering for construction purposes, a group of wells is required. The furnishing of water for towns and cities usually requires more than one well.

Forchheimer devised a theoretical method of estimating the drawdown as a result of pumping from more than one well when the radii of influence overlap by the use of Dupuit's assumptions and by employing the following reasoning:

In any element through which there is steady flow with no accompanying volume change of the element, the quantity of water entering the element must equal the quantity leaving the element. In the case of two-dimensional flow in which $q_i - q_o = 0$, the conditions of the LaPlace equation must be met.

At face z by dy, the quantity flowing out of the element is $dq_o = k\,i_o\,A_o$

$= k \dfrac{\partial z}{\partial x} z\,dy$. When similar relationships are stated for dq in or out of the other three faces in this same form, they cannot be put into the LaPlace form. But, since $z\,\partial\,z = \dfrac{\partial}{2}(z)^2$, the statement for dq can be put in the equivalent form $dq_o = \dfrac{k}{2}\dfrac{\partial z^2}{\partial x}\,dy$. Statements in this form can be put in the LaPlace form

$$\frac{\partial^2 z^2}{\partial x^2} + \frac{\partial^2 z^2}{\partial y^2} = 0$$

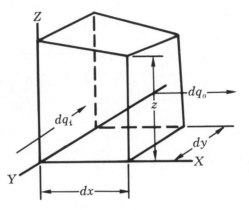

Figure 3.13g   Element through which there is steady flow

This means that the rule of superposition cannot be applied to the first power of z but can be applied to z^2. Thus, in determining the drawdown for more than one well, the z^2 for one well can be added to the z^2 for an adjacent well to obtain the z^2 at a given point for both wells; i.e., the z^2 at any point for a group of wells is

$$n\,z^2 = z_1^2 + z_2^2 + z_3^2 \ldots + z_n^2$$

The drawdown relationship for one well is

$$z^2 = H^2 - \frac{q}{\pi k}\ln\frac{R}{r} \qquad\qquad \text{(Eq. 3.13}c\text{)}$$

The z^2 for a group of wells is, therefore,

$$n\,z^2 = n\,H^2 - \sum \frac{q}{\pi k}\ln\frac{R}{r}$$

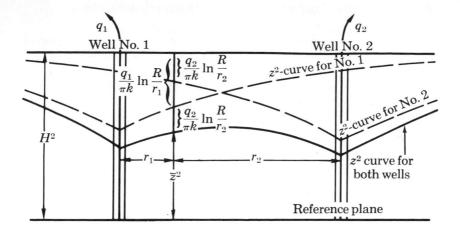

Figure 3.13h   The z^2 curve for two wells pumping simultaneously

In drawing a z^2 curve from which to plot a drawdown curve, it is convenient to reference the curves to H^2 as a boundary. The equation for a group of wells can be written

$$n(z^2 - H^2) = - \sum \frac{q}{\pi k} \ln \frac{R}{r}$$

or

$$z^2 = H^2 - \frac{1}{n} \sum \frac{q}{\pi k} \ln \frac{R}{r} \qquad \text{(Eq. 3.13e)}$$

The factor $\frac{1}{n}$ in equation 3.13e merely establishes the scale of $\sum \frac{q}{\pi k} \ln \frac{R}{r}$

to fit correctly within the boundary conditions set by H^2. If Dupuit's assumptions are valid, any convenient plane may be chosen as the reference plane from which to measure H^2 and z^2. Therefore, plotted to the

same scale as H^2, z^2 is $H^2 - \sum \frac{q}{\pi k} \ln \frac{R}{r}$. This is saying that if the z^2 curve

for drawdown from well No. 1 without pumping from well No. 2 is plotted to the same scale as H^2, and the z^2 curve for well No. 2 without pumping from well No. 1 is plotted to the same scale as shown in Figure 3.13h, the points on the z^2 curve are located at

$$\frac{q_1}{\pi k} \ln \frac{R_1}{r_1} + \frac{q_2}{\pi k} \ln \frac{R_2}{r_2} \text{ below } H^2$$

d. *Phreatic Surface in Two Dimensional Flow*

In case the ground water is flowing through the soil below a sloping seepage line toward an outlet, such as a river, the water taken out of a cylinder surrounding the well is not 100 per cent of the water entering the cylinder.   If the well is in soil in which the ground water is flowing, the drawdown around the well will not have a circular contour around the well.

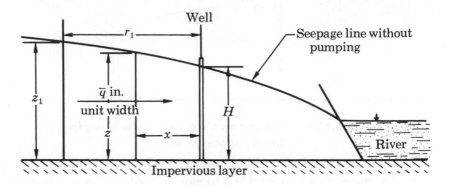

Figure 3.13i   Seepage line for flow into river

In this case, $H = z$ on the seepage line or phreatic surface at the line of wells before pumping is started.

The equation for the seepage line without the wells for two dimensional flow may be derived by reference to Figure 3.13*i* as follows:

The quantity of water flowing through a vertical plane of z height and unit width is

$$q = k \frac{dz}{dx} z$$

and

$$q \, dx = k z \, dz = q x = \frac{k z^2}{2} + C$$

When $x = 0$, $z = H$, making $C = -\dfrac{k H^2}{2}$, so that

$$z^2 = H^2 + \frac{2 q}{k} x \qquad (\text{Eq. } 3.13f)$$

or

$$H^2 - z^2 = -\frac{2 q}{k} x$$

If there are no wells, it may be more convenient to reference H and x to the water surface at the river's edge. The relationship also applies for flow away from canals.

e.　*Drawdown for More Than One Well*

As has already been shown in Section c, the $H^2 - z^2$ or $\dfrac{q}{\pi\,k} \ln \dfrac{R}{r}$ values

for individual wells can be added in order to obtain the combined $H^2 - z^2$ drawdown for more than one well; i.e.,

$$H^2 - z^2 = \Sigma \frac{q}{\pi\,k} \ln \frac{R}{r}$$

If q_1 is pumped from well No. 1 and q_2 from well No. 2, and if the water is pumped from below a seepage line,

$$H^2 - z^2 = \frac{q_1}{\pi\,k} \ln \frac{R}{r_1} + \frac{q_2}{\pi\,k} \ln \frac{R}{r_2} \pm \frac{2\,q}{k}\,x$$

In the case of lateral flow, the value of $\dfrac{2\,q}{k}\,x$ is subtracted from the

$\Sigma \dfrac{q}{\pi\,k} \ln \dfrac{R}{r}$ values upstream from the line of wells and added to the

values downstream from the wells.

If the original ground water surface were level (no lateral flow), water would flow into a single well equally from all directions and the $H^2 - z^2$ contours would be concentric circles with the well as their center. The intersection of an $H^2 - z^2$ contour for a single well being pumped independently with an $H^2 - z^2$ contour for another well, are points on the $H^2 - z^2$ contour for both wells being pumped simultaneously.

In Figure 3.13*j*, points marked 1 are on the $H^2 - z^2 = a^2 + b^2$ contour, and points marked 2 are on the $H^2 - z^2 = b^2 + c^2$ contour. Points 1 are also on the $z^2 = H^2 - (a^2 + b^2)$ contour and also on the

$z = \sqrt{H^2 - (a^2 + b^2)}$ contour.

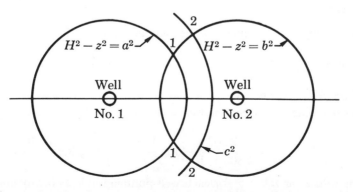

Figure 3.13j　Points on drawdown contour for two wells

If there is lateral flow through the soil perpendicular to a plane through both wells, the contours for this flow without pumping are straight lines perpendicular to the direction of seepage. These contours for the phreatic surface without pumping can be combined with those for both wells being pumped without lateral flow, to find the contours for the wells being pumped with lateral flow. Points marked 3 on Figure 3.13k which are the intersections of the $H^2 - z^2 = a^2 + b^2$ contour for both wells being pumped without lateral flow, and the $H^2 - z^2 = d^2$ contour for the seepage line without pumping. Points marked 3 are upstream from the wells, so they are on the contour for $H^2 - z^2 = a^2 + b^2 - d^2$. Points 4 are downstream from the wells, so they are on the $H^2 - z^2 = a^2 + b^2 + d^2$ contour.

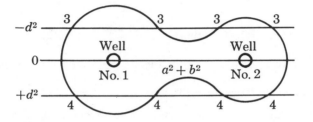

**Figure 3.13k   Points on drawdown contour for two wells
with lateral seepage across line of wells**

As an example, assume two wells 100 ft apart in a soil whose $k = 400 \times 10^{-4}$ cm sec^{-1} = 800×10^{-4} ft min^{-1}. Well No. 1 pumps 300 gpm and well No. 2 pumps 200 gpm. $R = 1500$ ft, H at line of wells before pumping = 40 ft, and 1000 ft upstream from the line of the wells, z of the seepage line = 45 ft. Plot contour lines for the phreatic surface for pumping from both wells after steady flow has been established.

Solution:

In drawing contour lines for the phreatic surface, it is usually more convenient to plot the distance $H^2 - z^2 = \dfrac{q}{\pi k} \ln \dfrac{R}{r}$ down from H^2 than to plot z^2 from the reference plane.

For pumping from only one well with level phreatic surface, $H = 40$ ft and

$$H^2 - z^2 = \frac{2.303\, q}{\pi\, 800 \times 10^{-4}} \log \frac{1500}{r} = 9.17\, q \log \frac{1500}{r}$$

The values for $H^2 - z^2$ for each well pumping independently are computed and tabulated in Table 3.13a.

Table 3.13a

R	r	$\dfrac{R}{r}$	$\log \dfrac{R}{r}$	Well No. 1 $q_1 = \dfrac{300}{7.5} = 40\,\text{cfm}$ $9.17 \times 40\log\dfrac{R}{r}$	Well No. 2 $q_2 = \dfrac{200}{7.5} = 26.7\,\text{cfm}$ $9.17 \times 26.7\log\dfrac{R}{r}$
	1500	1.0	0.0	0	0
	1000	1.5	0.176	64	43
	500	3.0	0.477	175	117
	400	3.7	0.574	210	140
	300	5.0	0.699	256	171
1500	200	7.5	0.875	321	214
	100	15.0	1.176	430	288
	50	30.0	1.477	540	362
	25	60.0	1.778	655	435
	10	150.0	2.176	796	532
	5	300.0	2.477	906	605
	2	750.0	2.875	1050	675
	1	1500.0	3.176	1162	775

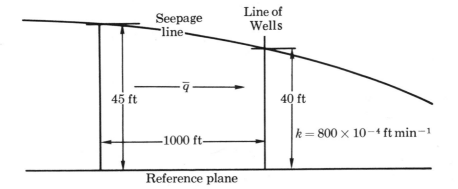

Figure 3.13l   Section perpendicular to flow

The equation for the seepage line is $H^2 - z^2 = -\dfrac{2q}{k}\,x$. For this par-

ticular case, at $x = 0$, $z_s = 40$ and at $x = 1000$, $z_s = 45$. Then

$$2025 - 1600 = \frac{2q}{k}\,1000 \quad\text{and}\quad \frac{2q}{k} = 0.425$$

Therefore, $H^2 - z_s^2 = 0.425\ x$ from which $x = 235$ ft for a contour interval of 100 ft for $H^2 - z^2$ contours.

Values of $\dfrac{H^2 - z^2}{100}$ taken from table 3.13a are plotted to scale for each well in the section through the line of wells as shown in Figure 3.13m. These values are added graphically to determine the curve for both wells being pumped simultaneously without lateral flow. Circular contours for each 100 ft radius are drawn for each well on the plan below. Radii of the circular contours for the individual wells are found by projecting down from the intersection of the single well curves with the $\dfrac{H^2 - z^2}{100}$ lines in the section, or they may be taken directly from the section. Each circle should be marked for identification with $\dfrac{H^2 - z^2}{100}$ value. Contours for the two wells pass through the intersections of these circles. The value of the contour for both wells is the sum of the values for the intersecting circles. Points on the line of wells can be taken directly from the curve for both wells on the section. Contours for the phreatic surface without pumping are then laid off as straight lines perpendicular to the seepage flow at 100 ft intervals for $\dfrac{H^2 - z^2}{100}$ which in this case is 235 ft to the same scale as the dimensions in the direction of the line of wells. The intersections of these contours with those for both wells are points on the contours whose value is the sum of the intersecting contours. The value of z for these contours is easily found from the value of $H^2 - z^2$ which is now known. The values of $H^2 - z^2$ are divided by 100 in this case simply for convenience.

f.   Ground Water Lowering within a Group of Wells

For construction below the water table, it is often necessary to lower the ground water for an excavation. If the wells are arranged in a circle around the pit, the drawdown in the center of the circular area surrounded by the wells, and the quantity of water that must be pumped from the wells in order to achieve the drawdown in a given time, can be determined approximately by application of the relationships developed by Forchheimer and Weber.

Assume wells in a circle for lowering the ground water in the center of the area shown in Figure 3.13n.

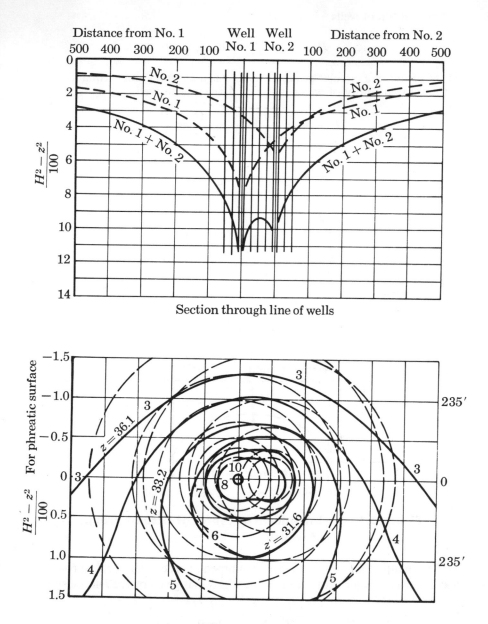

Section through line of wells

Plan of contours

Figure 3.13m   Contours for drawdown from two wells with flow across line of wells

For a group of wells

$$H^2 - z^2 = \sum \frac{q}{\pi k} \ln \frac{R}{r}$$

At the center of a circular group of wells, r is a constant and is equal to r_0. If the same quantity of water is pumped from each well,

$$H^2 - z^2 = \frac{n q}{\pi k} \ln \frac{R}{r_0} = \frac{Q}{\pi k} \ln \frac{R}{r_0}$$

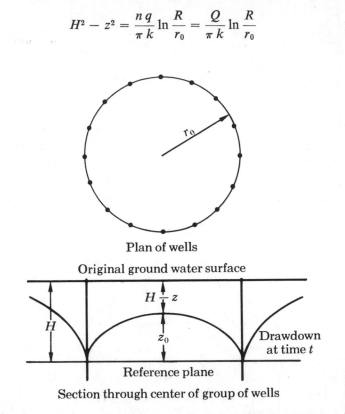

Plan of wells

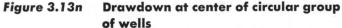

Section through center of group of wells

Figure 3.13n   Drawdown at center of circular group of wells

The quantity of water that must be pumped in order to lower the ground water a given distance at the center of the group is given by the relationship

$$Q = \frac{\pi k (H^2 - z^2)}{\ln (R/r_0)} = \frac{\pi k (H^2 - z^2)}{\ln R - \ln r_0}$$

It may also be desirable to be able to estimate the time required to lower the ground water to the required elevation. For several wells arranged in a circle, Weber has worked out the relationship

$$R = \sqrt{\left[\frac{4\,H\,k\,t}{n'} \cdot \frac{R_1^\alpha - r_0^\alpha}{R_1^\alpha} + r_0^2\right]\frac{\alpha + 2}{\alpha}}$$ (Eq. 3.13g)

in which R_1 = radius of influence for one well.

For pumping from one well only,

$$R_1 = \sqrt{\frac{4\,H\,k\,t}{n'} \cdot \frac{\alpha + 2}{\alpha}}$$ (Eq. 3.13d)

When R_1 is substituted for its equivalent in equation 3.13g, it becomes

$$R = \sqrt{R_1^2 \frac{R_1^\alpha - r_0^\alpha}{R_1^\alpha} + r_0^2 \frac{\alpha + 2}{\alpha}}$$

When R_1 is some constant times r_0 so that $R_1 = c\,r_0$, equation 3.13g becomes

$$R = \sqrt{R_1^2\left(1 - \frac{1}{c^\alpha}\right) + \frac{R_1^2}{c^2}\frac{\alpha + 2}{\alpha}} = R_1\sqrt{1 - \frac{1}{c^\alpha} + \frac{1}{c^2}\frac{\alpha + 2}{\alpha}}$$

If $\alpha = 2$ and $R_1 = 2\,r_0$, the equation above becomes

$$R = R_1\sqrt{1 - \frac{1}{2^2} + \frac{1}{2^2}\frac{2 + 2}{2}} = R_1\sqrt{\frac{5}{4}} = 1.12\,R_1$$

and if $R_1 = 10\,r_0$,

$$R = R_1\sqrt{1 - \frac{1}{10^2} + \frac{1}{10^2}\frac{2 + 2}{2}} = R_1\sqrt{\frac{100 - 1 + 2}{100}} = 1.005\,R_1$$

Therefore, there is not a great deal of variation between R for the group and R_1 for a single well from which an equal quantity of water is being pumped.

As an example of estimating ground water lowering, assume that it is desired to know the rate of pumping from wells surrounding an excavation pit 30 ft by 40 ft required to lower the ground water to a depth of 15 ft below the present ground water surface in 10 days of pumping. Assume constants for the area as $H = 50$ ft, $k = 150 \times 10^{-4}$ cm sec^{-1} = 0.03 ft min^{-1}, $n' = 0.2$, $\alpha = 2$, and in the relationship $R = C\left[\frac{H\,k\,t}{n'}\right]^{1/2}$, $C = 3.0$.

See p.155

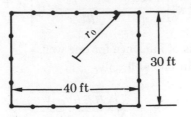

Figure 3.13o   Ground water lowering in excavation pit

An estimate of the rate of pumping required in order to lower the ground water 15 ft in 10 days can be made as follows:

$$\text{Equivalent } r_0 = \sqrt{\frac{30 \times 40}{\pi}} = 19.6 \text{ ft}$$

The value of R after 10 days of pumping, according to Weber, is

$$R_t = 3 \sqrt{\frac{40 \times 0.03 \times 10 \times 1440}{0.2}} = 882 \text{ ft}$$

From Weber's solution, the relation between rate of pumping to produce drawdown in a given time is

$$H^2 - z^2 = \frac{q}{\pi k} \ln \frac{R_t}{r} - \frac{1}{\alpha} \frac{R_t^\alpha - r_0^\alpha}{R_t^\alpha}$$

The quantity of water required to be pumped from all wells is

$$Q = \frac{\pi k (H^2 - z^2)}{\ln \dfrac{R_t}{r_0} - \dfrac{1}{\alpha}\left(1 - \dfrac{r_0^\alpha}{R_t^\alpha}\right)} = \frac{3.14 \times 0.03 (2500 - 1225)}{2.303 \log \dfrac{882}{19.6} - \dfrac{1}{2}\left(1 - \dfrac{19.6^2}{882^2}\right)}$$

$$= 38.5 \text{ cfm} = 289 \text{ gpm}$$

in order to produce a drawdown of 15 ft at the center of the excavation pit.

After steady flow has been attained, the quantity of water pumped from all wells in order to hold the water table at 15 ft below the center of the excavation is

$$Q = \frac{\pi k (H^2 - z^2)}{\ln \dfrac{R_t}{r_0}} = \frac{3.14 \times 0.03 (2500 - 1225)}{2.303 \log \dfrac{882}{19.6}} = 35.5 \text{ cfm} = 266 \text{ gpm}$$

g.   Drawdown at Distance outside a Group of Wells

Because the lowering of ground water in compressible soil can cause additional settlement of foundations resting on the compressible soil, the influence of a group of wells on the water table at a distance from the group may be of importance. As can be seen by reference to the contour map in Figure 3.13m, the contour for the two wells is approximately a circle at a distance of two times the distance between wells from the center of the group. This means that the drawdown at a distance of two or more times the distance between wells is essentially the same as it would be if the water were taken from one well at the center of the group.

The drawdown at a point a from the group of wells is

$$H^2 - z^2 = \sum \frac{q}{\pi k} \ln \frac{R}{r} \qquad \text{(Eq. 3.13c)}$$

wherein r is the distance from each well to point a. If point a is far enough away from the group so that the distance from each well to the point is approximately equal, by using the average value of r the equation may be written

$$H^2 - z^2 = \frac{\sum q}{\pi k} \ln \frac{R}{r_{av}}$$

and if q is the same from each well, and there are n wells,

$$H^2 - z_a^2 = \frac{n q}{\pi k} \ln \frac{R}{r_{av}} = \frac{Q}{\pi k} \ln \frac{R}{r_{av}}$$

As stated earlier this relationship holds approximately for points two or more times the distance between wells away from the center of the group.

3.14   Flow of Water through Anisotropic Materials

The grains of naturally deposited soils are usually oriented more or less parallel to each other, making a somewhat homogeneous but anisotropic structure. Artificially compacted fills are made by compacting thin layers with trucks, haulers, tractors, rollers, and vibrators, to some extent orienting the particles and causing some stratification. Such compacted material is seldom entirely isotropic. Nature also deposits materials in stratified layers, such as varved clays of glaciated regions, in which the different layers may have very different coefficients of permeability. All of these materials are likely to have a larger coefficient of permeability in one direction than in another.

Problems involving flow of water through these anisotropic materials can be solved in the same manner as for isotropic materials by altering the structure and soil into an equivalent isotropic body, making the body large in the direction of the minimum k and small in the direction of the maximum k. A description of the method of application and proof of its applicability follow.

a. Determination of Coefficient of Permeability of Stratified Deposit

(1) Coefficient of Permeability Parallel to Layers

If the laminations are very thin, such as varved clay, a direct permeability test can be made in each direction on samples of the soil. If thicker layers exist, each layer having a different coefficient of permeability as k_1, k_2, k_3, etc., tests can be made on small samples of each layer independently. Then, when the thickness of each layer d is known as d_1, d_2, d_3, etc., the average k_{max} parallel to the layers, and the average k_{min} normal to the layers can be estimated as follows:

Parallel to the laminations the flow through each layer is

$$q_1 = k_1 \frac{\Delta h}{1} d_1$$

$$q_2 = k_2 \frac{\Delta h}{1} d_2$$

$$q_3 = k_3 \frac{\Delta h}{1} d_3$$

and, because Δh is constant between equipotential lines,

$$q = q_1 + q_2 + q_3 = k_{max} \, \Delta h \, \Sigma d$$

Then,

$$k_{max} \, \Delta h \, \Sigma d = k_1 \, \Delta h \, d_1 + k_2 \, \Delta h \, d_3$$

or,

$$k_{max} \, \Sigma d = k_1 d_1 + k_2 \, d_2 + k_3 d_3 = \Sigma k \, d$$

Then,

$$k_{max} = \frac{k_1 d_1 + k_2 d_2 + k_3 d_3}{d} = \frac{\Sigma k \, d}{D} \qquad \text{(Eq. 3.14a)}$$

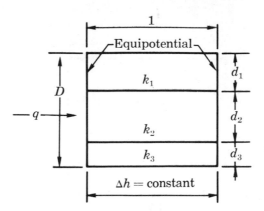

Figure 3.14a   Flow parallel to laminations

(2)   Coefficient of Permeability Normal to Laminations

Perpendicular to the laminations the flow is the same through all of the layers in a unit area,

$$q = q_1 = q_2 = q_3$$

From Darcy's Law for flow through the soil

$$q = k_{min} \frac{\Delta h}{D} A = k_1 \frac{\Delta h_1}{d_1} A_1$$

$$= k_2 \frac{\Delta h_2}{d_2} A_2 = k_3 \frac{\Delta h_3}{d_3} A_3 \cdots$$

and, because the area through which the water flows is the same in all layers

$$\Delta h = \frac{q D}{A k_{min}}, \quad \Delta h_1 = \frac{q d_1}{A k_1}, \quad \Delta h_2 = \frac{q d_2}{A k_2}, \quad \Delta h_3 = \frac{q d_3}{A k_3}$$

The total head loss through all of the laminations in a thickness D is equal to the sum of the losses through the individual layers.

$$\Delta h = \Delta h_1 + \Delta h_2 + \Delta h_3 \cdots$$

Therefore,

$$q \frac{D}{k_{min} A} = q \frac{d_1}{k_1} A + q \frac{d_2}{k_2} A + q \frac{d_3}{k_3} \cdots$$

Since q and A are the same on both sides of the equation,

$$\frac{D}{k_{min}} = \frac{d_1}{k_1} + \frac{d_2}{k_2} + \frac{d_3}{k_3} \cdots$$

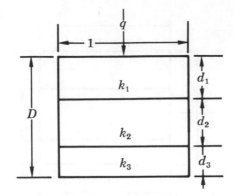

Figure 3.14b   Flow perpendicular to laminations

Therefore,

$$k_{min} = \frac{D}{\dfrac{d_1}{k_1} + \dfrac{d_2}{k_2} + \dfrac{d_3}{k_3}} = \frac{D}{\sum \dfrac{d}{k}} \qquad \text{(Eq. 3.14b)}$$

(3)   Coefficient of Permeability Oblique to Laminations

Under some circumstances, it may be desirable to know the coefficient of permeability of a stratified deposit of soil at an angle oblique to the direction of the layers. The relationship between the oblique coefficient of permeability k_θ and k_{max} and k_{min} was developed by A. F. Samsioe and published in 1931.

If there are many layers of materials of different permeabilities, the flow lines will zigzag through the deposit. If the layers are very thin, the zigzag line will approach a straight line. For convenience in the development of the relationship, assume the thin layers with the same k values to be grouped into one layer, and the layers of another k value to be grouped in a second layer. Assume the two layers to be of such a thickness that Δh in the direction of the resultant flow through both layers is unity, as shown in Figure 3.14c.

First, pertinent relationships are established. It has already been established that at the junction of two dissimilar materials, the flow lines must meet at such angles that

$$k_1 \tan \alpha = k_2 \tan \beta$$

Lay off, as shown in Figure 3.14c, the velocities v_1 through the k_1 material, and v_2 through the k_2 material, making angles at the junction of the two materials such that $k_1 \tan \alpha = k_2 \tan \beta$. These two velocities are

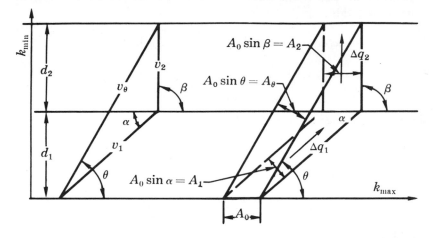

Figure 3.14c   Flow through laminations at oblique angle

the components of the velocity in the direction θ measured from the direction of maximum flow. If $\Delta h = 1$, and if the distance in the direction of k_θ is made equal to 1, then $i_\theta = \Delta h / \Delta s = 1$. The relationship between areas in the different directions of flow is

$$A_\theta = A_0 \sin \theta, \quad A_1 = A_0 \sin \alpha, \quad \text{and} \quad A_2 = A_0 \sin \beta$$

or,

$$A_1 = A_\theta \frac{\sin \alpha}{\sin \theta}, \text{ and } A_2 = A_\theta \frac{\sin \beta}{\sin \theta}$$

Also, from geometry,

$$\frac{v_1 \sin \alpha}{k_\theta \sin \theta} = \frac{d_1}{d_1 + d_2} = c_1$$

from which comes

$$v_1 = \frac{c_1 k_\theta \sin \theta}{\sin \alpha}$$

Also,

$$\frac{v_2 \sin \beta}{k_\theta \sin \theta} = \frac{d_2}{d_1 + d_2} = c_2$$

from which is obtained

$$v_2 = \frac{c_2 k_\theta \sin \theta}{\sin \beta}$$

The horizontal projection of flow in the direction of k_{max} is

$$v_\theta \cos \theta = k_\theta \cos \theta = v_1 \cos \alpha + v_2 \cos \beta$$

The vertical projection of flow in the direction of k_{min} is

$$v_\theta \sin \theta = k_\theta \sin \theta = v_1 \sin \alpha + v_2 \sin \beta$$

Inserting the equivalent values of v_1 and v_2 in the statement for horizontal flow yields

$$k_\theta \cos \theta = c_1 k_\theta \sin \theta \frac{\cos \alpha}{\sin \alpha} + c_2 k_\theta \sin \theta \frac{\cos \beta}{\sin \beta}$$

or,

$$\frac{1}{\tan \theta} = \frac{c_1}{\tan \alpha} + \frac{c_2}{\tan \beta}$$

Since $k_1 \tan \alpha$ must equal $k_2 \tan \beta$,

$$\frac{1}{\tan \theta} = \frac{c_1 k_1}{k_2 \tan \beta} + \frac{c_2}{\tan \beta}$$

from which is obtained

$$\tan \beta = \frac{c_1 k_1 + c_2 k_2}{k_2} \tan \theta = \frac{a}{k_2} \tan \theta$$

and likewise,

$$\tan \alpha = \frac{c_1 k_1 + c_2 k_2}{k_1} \tan \theta = \frac{a}{k_1} \tan \theta$$

The quantity of flow in the direction of v_θ is

$$\Delta q_\theta = k_\theta \frac{\Delta h_\theta}{\Delta s_\theta} t \, A_\theta = k_\theta \frac{\Delta h_\theta}{\dfrac{\Delta s_\theta}{t}} A_\theta = k_\theta \frac{\Delta h_\theta}{v_\theta} A_\theta = k_\theta \frac{1}{k_\theta} A_\theta = A_\theta$$

Likewise, the quantity of flow in the v_1 and v_2 directions are

$$\Delta q_1 = k_1 \frac{\Delta h_1}{\Delta s_1} t \, A_1 = k_1 \frac{\Delta h_1}{v_1} A_1 = k_1 \frac{\Delta h_1}{v_2} \frac{\sin \alpha}{\sin \theta} A_\theta$$

and

$$\Delta q_2 = k_2 \frac{\Delta h_2}{v_2} A_2 = k_2 \frac{\Delta h_2}{v_2} \frac{\sin \beta}{\sin \theta} A_\theta$$

But

$$\Delta q_\theta = \Delta q_1 = \Delta q_2$$

therefore,

$$A_\theta = k_1 \frac{\Delta h_1 \sin \alpha}{v_1 \sin \theta} A_\theta = k_2 \frac{\Delta h_2 \sin \beta}{v_2 \sin \theta} A_\theta$$

from which is obtained

$$\Delta h_1 = \frac{v_1 \sin \theta}{k_1 \sin \alpha} \text{ and } \Delta h_2 = \frac{v_2 \sin \theta}{k_2 \sin \beta}$$

But,

$$\Delta h_\theta = \Delta h_1 + \Delta h_2 = 1$$

therefore,

$$\frac{v_1 \sin \theta}{k_1 \sin \alpha} + \frac{v_2 \sin \theta}{k_2 \sin \beta} = 1 \qquad \text{(Eq. 3.14}c\text{)}$$

The remainder of the development is concerned with mathematical manipulation in order to state these relationships in terms of k_θ, k_{max}, k_{min}, and θ.

After inserting the equivalent values of v_1 and v_2 in equation 3.14c, the following relationship is found:

$$\frac{c_1 k_\theta \sin^2 \theta}{k_1 \sin^2 \alpha} + \frac{c_2 k_\theta \sin^2 \theta}{k_2 \sin^2 \beta} = 1$$

or

$$k_\theta \sin^2 \theta = \frac{1}{\dfrac{c_1}{k_1 \sin^2 \alpha} + \dfrac{c_2}{k_2 \sin^2 \beta}}$$

Change the sine functions of angles α and β into equivalent tangent functions by use of the identities

$$\sin^2 \alpha = \frac{\tan^2 \alpha}{1 + \tan^2 \alpha} \text{ and } \sin^2 \beta = \frac{\tan^2 \beta}{1 + \tan^2 \beta}$$

and the equation above becomes

$$k_\theta \sin^2 \theta = \frac{1}{\dfrac{c_1(1 + \tan^2 \alpha)}{k_1 \tan^2 \alpha} + \dfrac{c_2(1 + \tan^2 \beta)}{k_2 \tan^2 \beta}}$$

or

$$k_\theta \sin^2 \theta = \frac{k_1 k_2 \tan^2 \alpha \tan^2 \beta}{c_1(1 + \tan^2 \alpha) k_2 \tan^2 \beta + c_2(1 + \tan^2 \beta) k_1 \tan^2 \alpha}$$

Replace $\tan^2 \alpha$ with its equivalent $\dfrac{a^2}{k_1^2} \tan^2 \theta$ and $\tan^2 \beta$ with $\dfrac{a^2}{k_2^2} \tan^2 \theta$.

$$k_\theta \sin^2 \theta = \frac{k_1 k_2 \dfrac{a^2}{k_1^2} \tan^2 \theta \dfrac{a^2}{k_2^2} \tan^2 \theta}{k_2 c_1 \dfrac{k_1^2 + a^2 \tan^2 \theta}{k_1^2} \dfrac{a^2}{k_2^2} \tan^2 \theta + k_1 c_2 \dfrac{k_2^2 + a^2 \tan^2 \theta}{k_2^2} \dfrac{a^2}{k_1^2} \tan^2 \theta}$$

$$= \frac{k_1 k_2 a^2 \tan^2 \theta}{k_2 c_1 k_1^2 + k_2 c_1 a^2 \tan^2 \theta + k_1 c_2 k_2^2 + k_1 c_2 a^2 \tan^2 \theta}$$

$$= \frac{a^2 k_1 k_2 \tan^2 \theta}{(k_2 c_1 + k_1 c_2) a^2 \tan^2 \theta + k_1 k_2 (k_1 c_1 + k_2 c_2)}$$

Replace a with its equivalent $(k_1 c_1 + k_2 c_2)$ and divide by $\sin^2 \theta$.

$$k_\theta = \frac{k_1 k_2 (c_1 k_1 + k_2 c_2)}{(k_2 c_1 + k_1 c_2)(k_1 c_1 + k_2 c_2) \sin^2 \theta + k_1 k_2 \cos^2 \theta}$$

Replace c_1 and c_2 with their equivalent in terms of d_1 and d_2.

$$k_\theta = \frac{k_1 k_2 \left[\dfrac{d_1 k_1}{D} + \dfrac{d_2 k_2}{D} \right]}{\left[\dfrac{k_2 d_1}{D} + \dfrac{k_1 d_2}{D} \right]\left[\dfrac{k_1 d_1}{D} + \dfrac{k_2 d_2}{D} \right] \sin^2 \theta + k_1 k_2 \cos^2 \theta}$$

It has already been determined that

$$k_{max} = \frac{k_1 d_1 + k_2 d_2}{D}$$

and that

$$k_{min} = \frac{D}{\dfrac{d_1}{k_1} + \dfrac{d_2}{k_2}}$$

When these values are substituted in the equation for k_θ as derived above, the value of k_θ becomes

$$k_\theta = \frac{k_1 k_2 \, k_{max}}{\dfrac{k_1 k_2}{k_{min}} k_{max} \sin^2 \theta + k_1 k_2 \cos^2 \theta}$$

$$k_\theta = \frac{k_{max} \, k_{min}}{k_{max} \sin^2 \theta + k_{min} \cos^2 \theta} \qquad \text{(Eq. 3.14d)}$$

b. *Flow Nets in Anisotropic Soils*

Flow nets can be drawn in soils having different coefficients of permeability in two directions by altering the dimensions of the section through the structure and soil in such a manner that the distorted flow net can be drawn in the same manner as for isotropic soils. The section with the flow net can then be transformed back to its original correct shape.

Assume the flow is in a direction θ from the direction of k_{max} as shown in Figure 3.14d.

From Darcy's Law for laminar flow,

$$v_y = k_{min} \frac{\partial h}{\partial y}$$

$$v_x = k_{max} \frac{\partial h}{\partial x}$$

$$v_\theta = k_\theta \frac{\partial h}{\partial s}$$

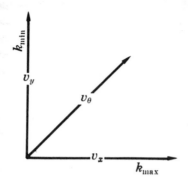

Figure 3.14d   Flow in anisotropic soil

If there is no volume change as the water flows through the soil,

$$\frac{\partial v_x}{\partial x} + \frac{\partial v_y}{\partial y} = 0$$

Inserting the values of v_y and v_x from Darcy's Law into the equation for zero volume change, the equation for volume change becomes

$$k_{max} \frac{\partial^2 h}{\partial x^2} + k_{min} \frac{\partial^2 h}{\partial y^2} = 0$$

If this equation can be altered in some way to make it conform to the Laplace equation $(\partial^2 h/\partial x^2) + (\partial^2 h/\partial y^2) = 0$, the soil may be treated as an isotropic material by applying the same transformation to the section through the soil as was used to make the no change equation conform to the Laplace equation.

The equation for no volume change can be put into the Laplace form as follows:

Divide the no volume change equation by k_{min},

$$\frac{k_{max}}{k_{min}} \frac{\partial^2 h}{\partial x^2} + \frac{\partial^2 h}{\partial y^2} = 0$$

Let $\dfrac{k_{max}}{k_{min}} = a^2$ and make this change in the equation.

$$a^2 \frac{\partial^2 h}{\partial x^2} + \frac{\partial^2 h}{\partial y^2} = 0$$

or

$$\frac{\partial^2 h}{\partial \left(\dfrac{x}{a}\right)^2} + \frac{\partial^2 h}{\partial y^2} = 0$$

Then let $x/a = X$ and $y = Y$. The equation then becomes

$$\frac{\partial^2 h}{\partial X^2} + \frac{\partial^2 h}{\partial Y^2} = 0$$

which is in the Laplace form.

Therefore, if the section is transformed so that $X = x/a$ or $x\sqrt{k_{min}/k_{max}}$, the transformed section can be treated as though the soil were isotropic, and a flow net drawn. The section with the flow net can then be transformed back to its original shape.

If it is desired to know the quantity of flow from the transformed section without transforming back to the original shape, a new k value, k, must be used, and k can be derived as follows:

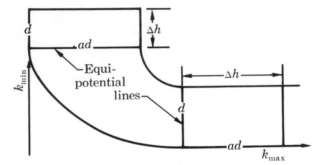

Figure 3.14e   Flow net for anisotropic soil

In the k_{min} direction

$$\Delta q = k_{min} \frac{\Delta h}{d} a \, d$$

In the k_{max} direction

$$\Delta q = k_{max} \frac{\Delta h}{ad} d$$

Δq is the same through all rectangles of the flow channel and Δh is the same between adjacent equipotential lines, so

$$k_{max} \frac{d}{a\,d} = k_{min} \frac{a\,d}{d}$$

$$k_{max} = k_{min} \, a^2$$

$$a = \sqrt{\frac{k_{max}}{k_{min}}}$$

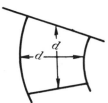

Figure 3.14f   Flow net in isotropic soil

In the flow net of squares in the transformed section

$$\Delta q = k \frac{\Delta h}{d} d$$

and, since Δq is the same in a flow channel of the transformed section as in the original section,

$$q = k \, \Delta h = k_{\min} \, \Delta h \, a$$

The value of k then is

$$k = a \, k_{\min} = k_{\min} \sqrt{\frac{k_{\max}}{k_{\min}}} = \sqrt{k_{\max} \, k_{\min}}$$

Therefore, if the section is transformed making all dimensions in the $k_{\max}$ direction $\sqrt{k_{\min}/k_{\max}}$ times their original length, the flow net is drawn as though the soil were isotropic. If the true flow net is desired, the section can be transformed back into its original shape. The flow can be estimated from the flow net by the use of a transformed value of k equal to $\sqrt{k_{\max} \, k_{\min}}$ in the equation

$$Q = \bar{k} \, h \frac{n_f}{n_e}$$

As an example of the flow of water through anisotropic materials, assume an impervious wall extending along an excavation to a depth of 25 ft below the bottom of a lake or river to within 20 ft of an inclined impervious layer as shown in Figure 3.14g. The coefficients of permeability are $k_{\max}$ parallel to the impervious layer $= 100 \times 10^{-4}$ cm sec$^{-1} = 200 \times 10^{-4}$ ft min^{-1}, and $k_{\min}$ perpendicular to the impervious layer $= 400 \times 10^{-4}$ cm sec$^{-1} = 800 \times 10^{-4}$ ft min^{-1}.

a. Draw a flow net for the flow of water from the lake into the excavation.

b. Determine the quantity of water required to be pumped per min per ft of wall in order to maintain a dry bottom of the excavation.

Solution:

Transform the section so that all dimensions in the k_{max} direction are

reduced by $\sqrt{\dfrac{k_{min}}{k_{max}}} = \sqrt{\dfrac{100 \times 10^{-4}}{400 \times 10^{-4}}} = \dfrac{1}{2}$. In the transformation, any

single point may be assumed as fixed and all other points projected in the k_{max} direction relative to this fixed point. In this particular case, the surface of the water at the wall is considered to be the fixed point and the soil and the structure transformed with reference to this fixed point.

To find the location of any point on the transformed section, project the point parallel to the k_{max} direction toward a line from the fixed point

perpendicular to the k_{max} direction a distance proportional to $\sqrt{\dfrac{k_{min}}{k_{max}}}$

from the original position of the point, in this case $\frac{1}{2}$. In this instance, any point a on the bottom of the excavation is projected along line a–b drawn parallel to k_{max} one-half the distance between point a and the intersection at b, with a line drawn through fixed point F perpendicular to k_{max}.

a. The flow net of squares on the transformed section is shown in Figure 3.14h. The true flow net is transferred back to the true section in Figure 3.14g. In a practical solution to such a problem, the true section and the transformed section are usually made on overlays on transparent materials.

b. The quantity of water flowing into the excavation per min per ft of wall is determined as follows:

$$\bar{k} = \sqrt{k_{max}\,k_{min}} = \sqrt{800 \times 10^{-4} \times 200 \times 10^{-4}} = 400 \times 10^{-4}\ \text{ft min}^{-1}$$

$$h = 25\ \text{ft},\, n_f = 3,\, n_e = 6$$

$$Q = 400 \times 10^{-4} \times 25 \times \frac{3}{6} = 0.50\ \text{cfm} = 3.4\ \text{gpm per ft}$$

REFERENCES

Anandakrishnan, M., and G. H. Varadarajulu, "Laminar and Turbulent Flow of Water Through Sand," *Journal Soil Mechanics and Foundations Division*, Proc. Am. Soc. C.E., Vol. 89, No. SM5 (September, 1963).

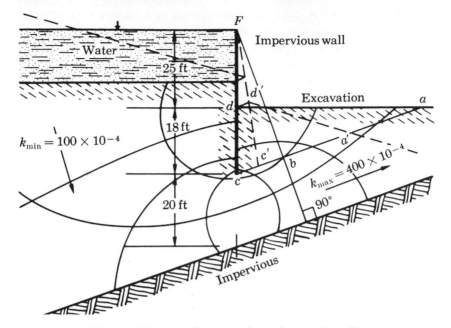

Figure 3.14g   **Flow net in anisotropic soil**

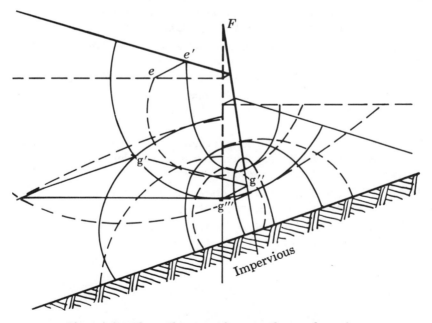

Figure 3.14h   **Flow net in transformed section**

Bertram, G. E., "An Experimental Investigation of Protective Filters," *Harvard University Soil Mechanics, Series No. 7* (January, 1940).

Casagrande, A., "Seepage Through Dams," *Journal New England Water Works Association* (June, 1937), and in *Contributions to Soil Mechanics 1925 to 1940*, Boston Society of Civil Engineers.

Casagrande, Leo, "Naerungsmethoden zur Bestimmung von Art und Menge der Sickerung durch geschüttete Dämme," Thesis, Technischule, Vienna (July, 1932).

Darcy, H., "Les Fontaines Publiques de la Ville Dijon," Dijon, 1856.

Forchheimer, P., "Zur Grundwasserbewegung nach isothermischen Kurvenscharen," *Sitzber. Kais. Akad. Wiss. Wien*, Abt. IIa, Vol. 126.

Hall, Howard P., "A Historical Review of Investigations of Seepage Toward Wells," *Journal Boston Society of Civil Engineers* (July, 1954).

Hammad, Hammad Y., "Seepage Under Dams," *Journal Soil Mechanics and Foundations Division*, Proc. Am. Soc. C.E., Vol. 89, No. SM4 (July, 1963).

Harr, Milton E., and Robert C. Deen, "Analysis of Seepage Problems," *Journal Soil Mechanics and Foundations Division*, Proc. Am. Soc. C.E., Vol. 87, No. SM5 (October, 1961).

Harr, Milton E., *Ground Water and Seepage*, New York: McGraw Hill Book Company, Inc., 1962.

Mansur, Charles L., and Rudy J. Dietrich, "Pumping Test to Determine Permeability Ratio," *Journal Soil Mechanics and Foundations Division*, Proc. Am. Soc. C.E., Vol. 91, No. SM4 (July, 1965).

Patel, V. J., A. V. Gopala Krishnayya, and K. L. Arora, "Mechanics of Inclined Filters in Earth Dams," *Journal Soil Mechanics and Foundations Division*, Proc. Am. Soc. C.E., Vol. 90, No. SM6 (November, 1964).

Samsioe, A. F., "Einfluss von Rohrbrunnen auf die Bewegung des Grundwassers," *Zeitung für Angewante Mathematik und Mechanik*, Vol. 11, No. 2 (April, 1931).

Schaffernach, F., "Erforschung der physikalischen Gesetze, nach welchen die Durchsickerung des Wassers durch Talsperre oder durch den Untergrund stattfindet," *Die Wasserwirtschaft*, No. 33, 1933.

Terzaghi, Karl, and R. B. Peck, *Soil Mechanics in Engineering Practice*, New York: John Wiley and Sons, Inc., 1948.

Weber, H., "Die Reichweite von Grundwasserabsenkungen mittels Rohrbrunnen," Berlin: J. Springer, 1928.

4

Settlement of Foundations

4.01 General

The term settlement is usually meant to apply to downward movement of a point in a structure with reference to its original position. Settlements may be caused by stresses which produce elastic deformation of the structural parts and of earth materials, volume decrease of the soil underneath a loaded area, plastic deformation of the soil with expansion of the soil laterally, failure of the soil and forcing of a portion of the soil outward and upward from under the loaded area, or by vibration of loose cohesionless materials. This chapter is concerned with settlements caused by volume change of the soil underneath the foundation. Settlements caused by overcoming the shear strength of the soil and forcing a portion of the soil from underneath the loaded area is treated in the chapter on Carrying Capacity of Foundations. Except for lightly loaded foundations on dry overconsolidated clay which may swell as water is absorbed by the dry clay, all foundations settle. The small, but sometimes significant, settlements caused by elastic deformation of structural materials are not treated in this chapter.

4.02   Settlements of Foundations on Cohesionless Soils

The shear strength of cohesionless materials is dependent upon the angle of internal friction and the pressure between the grains (effective stress). In order for settlement to occur in cohesionless soils without forcing the soil from under the foundation, the grains must slide on each other to positions which decrease the volume. Volume decrease can occur in a single grained structure only when the material is not in its densest state. Deformation due to movement of the grains in dense cohesionless material results in an increase in volume. Therefore, settlements of foundations on confined dense cohesionless materials are comparable to those which occur if the foundation is on rock.

The resistance to sliding of the grains is $s = \sigma \tan \phi$. The value of the internal friction angle ϕ depends upon the density of the soil, varying from 28° for loose, to 35° for dense, well rounded, uniform sand; and 38° for loose to 47° for dense, well graded, angular sand. The confirming pressure σ is provided by the weight of the overburden above the bottom of the footings. Therefore, static loads produce some settlement in loose and medium dense cohesionless soils, the amount depending upon the type of soil and the depth of the foundation.

Large and rapid settlements may be caused by vibration of loose cohesionless materials. Even fairly dense sands may experience such settlement to a lesser degree.

a.   Foundations on Gravel

Gravel is usually deposited in a fairly dense state. When placed far enough below the surface to prevent shear failure, foundations on gravel settle little due to static load. Any settlement will occur immediately upon application of the load. If the gravel is loose, sudden settlements may be caused by severe vibration. Almost any type of foundation can be used in dense gravel without fear of excessive settlement.

b.   Foundations on Sand

Static loads produce relatively small settlements of foundations in sand when placed at considerable depth below the surface. The same conditions that contribute to the carrying capacity of foundations on sand also contribute to the reduction of settlements. Medium and fine sands in natural deposits are often quite loose. Fairly large settlements of foundations may be caused by vibration of loose sand to a denser state. Settlements of foundations on dense sand placed at such depth as to be safe against failure in shear, are practically negligible.

As an example of settlement caused by vibration of a medium sand of medium density the following experience is cited:

A 20 ft by 72 ft mat for the reception of three gas compressors was installed on a 15 ft thick layer of medium sand of medium density in the Platte River Valley. The bottom of the mat was placed at the water table about 2.5 ft below the surface. Only two compressors were installed on the mat; one in the middle and one near the east end. No appreciable settlement was produced by the addition of the static load. During the first year, the end engine, No. 1, was run continuously at full capacity during the operating season. The middle engine, No. 2, because of mechanical difficulty, was run only a small portion of the time at partial load. At the end of the first year's operation, the outside edge of engine No. 1 had settled 1.7 in.; between the engines 1.9 in.; and the far edge of engine No. 2 had settled 1.0 in. The pattern of total settlement after six years of operation during the operating seasons, and the time of settlement relationship for the point of maximum settlement are shown in Figure 4.02a.

The ragged appearance of the time-settlement curve is probably due to the times at which the settlement measurements were taken. Some measurements were taken during the operating season, and others in the summer while the station was not operating. The reason for the smaller settlement of the far end of engine No. 2 was that the mat extended beyond engine No. 2 for the future reception of a third engine and compressor.

Thus, settlements of foundations on a thick layer of medium or loose sand may continue for a considerable time when there is continuous vibration. In the case cited above, the sand immediately under the mat probably was consolidated early in the settlement period. After the sand near the surface has become dense, the vibrations are transferred through it to the deeper sand, causing consolidation of the sand at depth and progressing deeper into the layer with the passage of time.

It is difficult to predict the amount of settlement to be expected of a foundation on sand. It depends upon the amount of vibration to which the sand is subjected, as well as the loading conditions and thickness of the sand layer. An estimate of the potential settlement can be obtained by determining the void ratio of the sand in place, the void ratio of the sand in its densest state, and the thickness of the layers that will contribute to the settlement. The density of the sand in place can be determined as described in Chapter I, Section 1.27d. The density of the sand in its densest state can be found by compacting a sample of the dry sand in a vessel of known volume V by tamping in layers and vibrating the sand, tapping the vessel as it is being filled, and determining the weight of

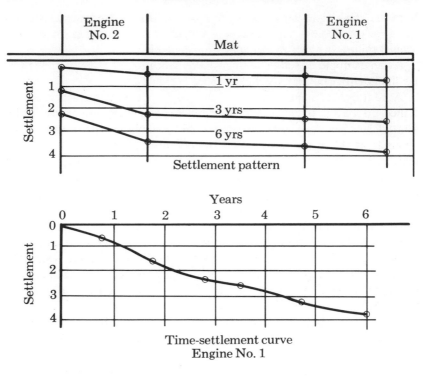

**Figure 4.02a   Settlement of compressor station
on medium sand**

the compacted sand. The volume of the solids in the sand sample, $V_s = \dfrac{W_s}{G_s}$, and the void ratio in the densest state $e_D = \dfrac{V - V_s}{V_s}$, when V is the volume of the vessel in which the sand was compacted, and G_s is the specific gravity of the sand solids, approximately 2.68. As an example, if the sand layer is 10 ft thick, the void ratio of the sand in place $e_n = 0.56$, and the void ratio in the densest state $e_D = 0.41$, the potential settlement produced by a severely vibrating load is

$$S = H\frac{e_n - e_D}{e_n} = 120\,\frac{0.56 - 0.41}{0.56} = 11.5 \text{ in.}$$

This analysis does not mean that the settlement will be 11.5 in., but that under a severely vibrating load it is possible for the settlement to be 11.5 in. Such analyses should not be used as an estimate of the expected settlement, but only as an aid to judgment.

Obviously, the method of preventing or reducing settlement of foundations on sand is to decrease the void ratio of medium or loose sand to a dense state, and to confine the sand under several feet of overburden.

Methods of compacting loose sands are described in Chapter 1, Section 1.27*b*.

c.   Foundations on Silt

As already mentioned in Chapter 2, Section 2.10, silt is often deposited in a very loose honeycomb structure which can be broken down under heavy pressure. Light loads which are not sufficient to destroy the structure of the silt produce comparatively little settlement. Heavy loads which break down the structure produce settlements out of proportion to the intensity of the pressure produced. Probably the most accurate method of estimating the expected settlement of a foundation on silt is the use of the results of a consolidation test. Useful information may also be obtained from a load test when properly interpreted. The performance of existing structures on the silt in the neighborhood should not be overlooked.

d.   Foundations on Loess

Although loess should not be classed as a strictly cohesionless soil, it is a loose deposit of cohesionless silt that is lightly cemented with a small amount of clay minerals, and usually with a small amount of calcium carbonate. Predicted settlement under load on loess may be estimated from a void ratio-pressure curve as shown in Figure 4.02*b*.

In Test No. 1, a specimen of a sample of Grant Co., Kansas loess in a consolidation ring was loaded in its dry state (natural water content) with the overburden pressure of 0.18 tons ft^{-2}, flooded, and subjected to a standard consolidation test. Test No. 2 was a specimen of the same sample loaded dry in increments up to 10 tons ft^{-2}, the load backed off to 3 tons ft^{-2}, flooded, and subjected to a standard consolidation test. As indicated by these void ratio-pressure curves, this loess could be loaded with pressures up to about 1 ton ft^{-2} with little or no appreciable settlement. A pressure of 3 tons ft^{-2} on the dry loess would produce little or no appreciable settlement but, if the loess were allowed to become saturated, settlement could amount to $[(0.78 - 0.65)/1.78]12 = 0.87$ in. per ft of thickness.

At the site where this sample of loess was taken, the layer of loess is about 22 ft thick. A load producing 6000 lb per sq ft over a large area could produce little settlement or settlements up to about 18 in., depending upon the amount of water fed to the underlying loess. At this site, a large natural gas compressor station was erected on a mat foundation on compacted fill, after removing the 22 ft of loess and compacting it

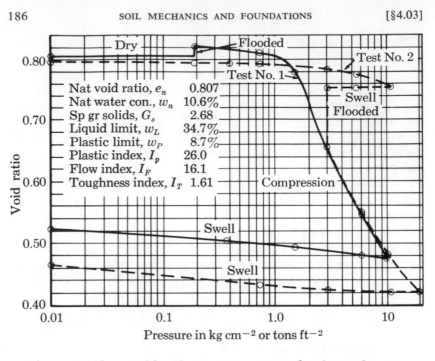

Figure 4.02b   Void ratio-pressure curves for Grant County Kansas loess

back into the excavation to a depth of 11 ft above the underlying caliche. The void ratio after compaction was 0.40. This procedure was considered necessary because several of the compressor units, which operate with a slight variation in speed, get in step and produce severely high impact loads. The station has operated for about 15 years with no distress caused by movements of foundations.

Fairly heavy structures which produce static pressures could be supported on this loess by means of a floating or compensated foundation in which all but about 1 ton per sq ft is compensated by removal of overburden. Because of the small rebound after removal of load, heave of the bottom of the excavation should present no problem in this soil.

4.03   Total Settlement of Normally Consolidated Clay

A normally consolidated clay is one that has been consolidated under its present overburden pressure and has never had a greater pressure applied to it.

In this discussion, settlement is assumed to be caused by consolidation of normally consolidated saturated clay produced by pressure greater than that caused by the present overburden.

Before a settlement analysis can be made, the thickness of the soil layers must be determined by exploration. For an accurate analysis, undisturbed samples of the different soil strata must be taken and a consolidation test made on a sample of each of the different soils. Usually, the soils underneath an area vary so much with depth that it is impractical to sample and test all the variations. Practically, only a few consolidation tests are made. Estimates are made of the properties of the soils not tested directly for compressibility. Aids to judgment in making these estimates of properties are natural void ratio, natural water content, liquid limit, and plastic limit. These index properties are used in comparison with the same properties of the tested samples.

The laboratory determined e-log p curve for a normally consolidated clay is curved to a point of tangency with the straight virgin portion of the curve at a point beyond the present overburden pressure. Because the soil in place is not recompressed, as the laboratory specimen was, when it is loaded in excess of the overburden pressure, the decrease in void ratio starts at the natural void ratio e_n. The e-p curve for the soil in place is the straight virgin curve from the natural void ratio. The laboratory determined curve is slightly below the curve for the soil in place. The laboratory sample was disturbed to the extent that it was relieved of its overburden pressure and recompressed. But the virgin portion of the laboratory curve is essentially parallel to the in place curve. The change in void ratio of the soil in place after consolidation under an increased pressure to p_2 is Δe_n

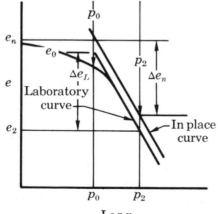

Figure 4.03a   Laboratory and in place e-log p curves for normally consolidated clay

as shown in Figure 4.03*a*. If the virgin portion of the laboratory curve is extended to an intersection with the preconsolidation (overburden) pressure p_0, the change in void ratio from p_0 to p_2 is Δe_L. Since Δe_n and Δe_L are equal, the laboratory determined curve can be used for estimating settlements of the soil in place. The values of e should not be taken directly from the laboratory curve, but should be computed on the basis of Δe, measured from the intersection of the straight virgin portion of the curve with the overburden pressure p_0 as shown in Figure 4.03*a*. The slope of the virgin curve is

$$C_c = \frac{e_0 - e_2}{\log \dfrac{p_2}{p_0}}, \text{ and } \Delta e = C_c \log \frac{p_2}{p_0}$$

A fairly accurate estimate of C_c can be made from a rational development made by Y. Nishida, $C_c = 0.54(e_n - 0.35)$. The void ratio of equal spheres in their densest state is 0.35. Clay grains are not spherical in shape, and the void ratio of clay in its denest state is less than 0.35. The authors have compared the values of C_c as determined from consolidation tests with those computed from the natural void ratio in the Nishida relationship for several overconsolidated clays in the southwestern part of the United States, several samples of compacted clays, some Chicago clays as reported by Peck and Reed in University of Illinois Bulletin 423, "Engineering Properties of Chicago Subsoils," and with a sample of Lake Agassiz clay from North Dakota. The Nishida formula gave slightly low values in almost all cases. A value of 0.3 instead of 0.35 in the formula gave somewhat better agreement. The relationship then becomes $C_c = 0.54(e_n - 0.3)$. The water content w_n for clays taken from below the water table (saturated clays) can also be used for estimating the slope of the virgin e-log p curve. Using 2.70 for G_s, the relationship becomes $C_c = 0.54(2.7w_n - 0.3)$. For normally consolidated clays, C_c can also be esti-

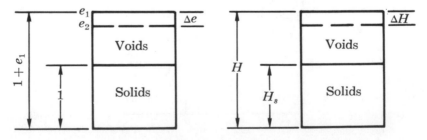

Figure 4.03b   Relationship between change in void ratio and settlement

mated from the imperical relationship based upon the liquid limit given by Terzaghi and Peck as $C_c = 0.009(w_L - 10)$, in which w_L is per cent water content at the liquid limit.

For greater accuracy in making a settlement analysis, thick strata of soils are divided into thin layers. Present overburden pressures p_1 and the corresponding e_1 must be determined or estimated for each layer. The average pressure on each layer produced by the added load is determined and added to p_1 to find the vaule of p_2. With the information described, the total settlement of a layer of clay under an added load can be computed.

The unit deformation of the clay layer is

$$\epsilon = \frac{e_1 - e_2}{1 + e_1} = \frac{C_c}{1 + e_1} \log \frac{p_2}{p_1}$$

The total settlement of a layer H thick is

$$\Delta H = H \frac{C_c}{1 + e_1} \log \frac{p_2}{p_1}$$

Example of Settlement Analysis:

Assume a soil profile consisting of two strata of homogeneous clays above an impervious layer and with a drainage layer of incompressible sand separating the strata as shown in the tabulation of Figure 4.03c. Undisturbed samples were taken from the positions shown, and consolidation tests made from which values of C_c were determined. The water table is 4 ft below the surface.

Assume that a very large area is to be loaded on the surface with a uniform load of 1500 lb per sq ft.

Physical properties of clay layers normally consolidated			
Upper layer		*Lower layer*	
One point on *e-p* curve		One point on *e-p* curve	
$e_c = 1.02$	$p_c = 1.0$ kg cm^{-2}	$e_c = 0.73$	$p_c = 1.6$ kg cm^{-2}
$G_s = 2.74$	$C_c = 0.36$	$G_s = 2.70$	$C_c = 0.24$

Solution:

The calculations are carried out on the tabulated form of Figure 4.03c in accordance with the following procedure:

a. Divide the upper and lower clay strata into convenient layers for the desired degree of accuracy. In the upper layer the water table is a convenient plane for division. The lower 13 ft stratum is arbitrarily divided into 6 ft and 7 ft layers.

b. Determine the average unit weight of the soil in each stratum. The unit weights are computed in column 5 of the tabulation.

c. Determine the overburden pressure p_1 at middepth of each layer. See column 6.

d. Compute the value of e_1 corresponding to the overburden pressure p_1 and record in column 8. These values of e_1 are computed from the

relationship $e_1 = e_c + C_c \log \dfrac{p_1}{p_c}$. The value of e_1 for $p_1 = 232$ lb ft^{-2} at middepth of the top layer is $e_1 = 1.02 + 0.36 \log \dfrac{2000}{232} = 1.02 + 0.33 = 1.356$. For practical purposes, 1 kg cm^{-2} = 1 ton ft^{-2} = 2000 lb ft^{-2}. The void ratio at middepth of the bottom layer, where $p_1 = 1493$ lb ft^{-2}, is $e_1 = 0.73 + 0.24 \log \dfrac{3200}{1493} = 0.73 + 0.0795 = 0.8095$.

e. Divide C_c by $1 + e_1$ and record in column 10. For the first layer

$$\frac{C_c}{1 + e_1} = \frac{0.36}{2.356} = 0.153$$

f. Multiply the value of $\dfrac{C_c}{1 + e_1}$ in column 10 by the thickness of the layer H and record in column 11. Because $\dfrac{C_c}{1 + e_1}$ is dimensionless, H can be in any units. ΔH will be in the same units.

g. Determine and record in column 12 the pressure produced at middepth of each layer by the added load. In this case, because the loaded area is large compared to the depth of the compressible layers, the increase in pressure Δp may be considered as constant for the full depth. Under a small loaded area, the total added load is distributed to a larger area at depth which makes the unit pressure Δp decrease with depth. Computation for determining pressure at depth under different loading conditions is discussed later in this chapter.

h. Add Δp to initial overburden pressure p_1 and record as p_2 in column 13.

i. Determine $\log p_2/p_1$ and record in column 14. p_2 and p_1 can be in any convenient units provided that they are both in the same units.

j. Multiply the values in column 14 by $H \dfrac{C_c}{1 + e_1}$ of column 11 to determine the contribution to settlement of the different layers. Record in column 15.

k. Add the contribution of the individual layers to obtain the total settlement produced by the added load.

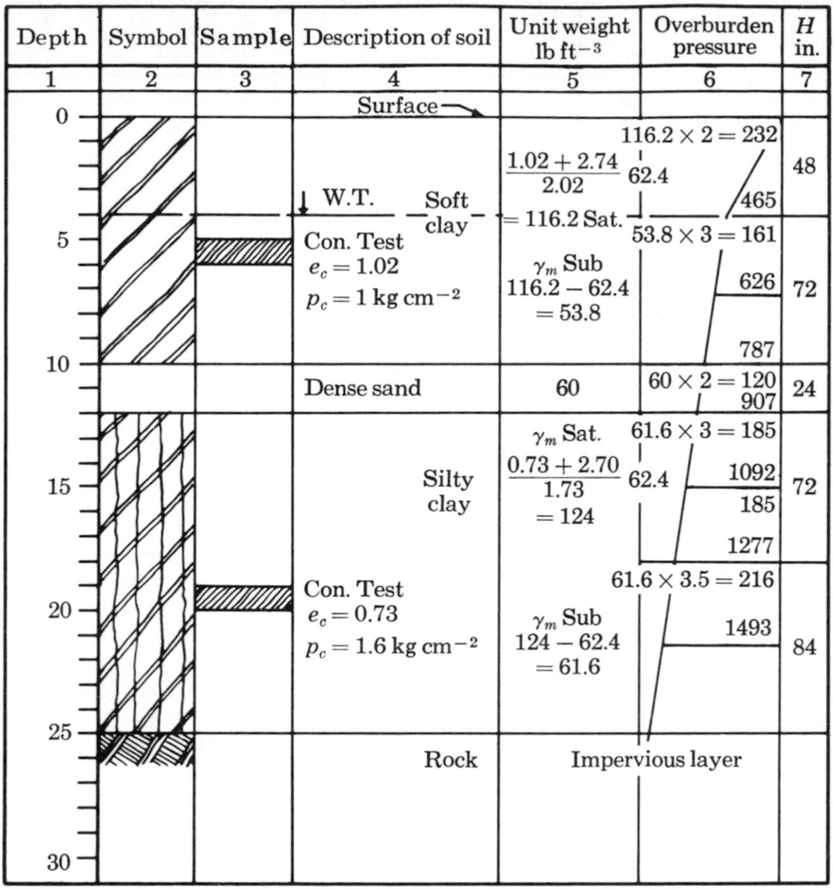

Depth	Symbol	Sample	Description of soil	Unit weight lb ft^{-3}	Overburden pressure	H in.
1	2	3	4	5	6	7
0			Surface→			
					$116.2 \times 2 = 232$	48
			↓ W.T. Soft clay	$\dfrac{1.02+2.74}{2.02}$ 62.4	465	
5		Con. Test	$= 116.2$ Sat.	$53.8 \times 3 = 161$		
		$e_c = 1.02$	γ_m Sub		626	72
		$p_c = 1\,\text{kg cm}^{-2}$	$116.2 - 62.4 = 53.8$			
					787	
10			Dense sand	60	$60 \times 2 = \dfrac{120}{907}$	24
				γ_m Sat.	$61.6 \times 3 = 185$	
15			Silty clay	$\dfrac{0.73+2.70}{1.73}$ 62.4	1092	72
				$= 124$	185	
					1277	
		Con. Test			$61.6 \times 3.5 = 216$	
20		$e_c = 0.73$		γ_m Sub	1493	84
		$p_c = 1.6\,\text{kg cm}^{-2}$		$124 - 62.4 = 61.6$		
25			Rock	Impervious layer		
30						

Sheet No. 1
Figure 4.03c Settlement analysis

This summation is the total estimated settlement after complete consolidation of all the layers. No consideration in this analysis has been given to the time required for the settlement to occur.

The preceding example of settlement analysis is for the simplest condition that could exist. It is presented here in order to illustrate how the computations for a settlement analysis can be organized. Often deposits of soft clays which will allow large settlements are fairly uniform over a large area. Usually, however, natural soil deposits are not as uniform as assumed in the example. A fill of uniform thickness applied over a very large area could provide the approximate loading conditions assumed in the example. The usual loading conditions consist of small areas of

e_1	C_c	$\dfrac{C_c}{1+e_1}$	$H\dfrac{C_c}{1+e_1}$	ΔP	p_2	$\log\dfrac{p_2}{p_1}$	$H\dfrac{C_c}{1+e_1}\log\dfrac{p_2}{p_1}$
8	9	10	11	12	13	14	15
Surface							
1.356		0.153	7.35	1500	1732	0.874	6.43
	0.36						
1.201		0.163	11.75	1500	2126	0.532	6.25
							(12.68)
0.842		0.130	9.36	1500	2594	0.374	3.50
	0.24						
0.809		0.133	11.18	1500	2993	0.302	3.38
							(6.88)
					Total settlement		19.56

Sheet No. 2
Figure 4.03c   **Settlement analysis**

different sizes, shapes, and distribution, supporting different total loads, sometimes applied at different depths beneath the surface. The determination of unit pressures at different points in the soil caused by loads on these small areas is discussed later in this chapter.

4.04   Settlement of Overconsolidated Clay

An overconsolidated clay is one that has been consolidated under greater pressure than that provided by its present overburden.

When such a clay is loaded to produce pressures greater than the present overburden pressure, it is subjected to recompression from its present overburden pressure to its preconsolidation pressure, and to consolidation for the first time under pressures greater than the preconsolidation pres-

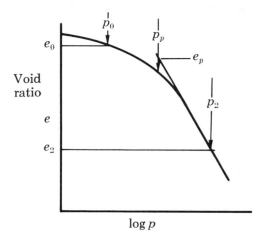

Void ratio

$\log p$

Figure 4.04a   Laboratory e-p curve for over-consolidated clay

sure. Therefore, in computing settlements based upon laboratory determined void ratio-pressure relationships, the change in void ratio used as a basis for computing the settlement should be taken directly from the curve instead of using the compression index C_c. The total settlement, in this case, should be computed as

$$\Delta H = H \frac{e_0 - e_2}{1 + e_0}$$

If the preconsolidation pressure is not much larger than the overburden pressure, and the added load produces pressures greatly in excess of the preconsolidation pressure, it may be sufficiently accurate to ignore the recompression and to estimate the settlement as though the clay were normally consolidated under the preconsolidation pressure. If this procedure is used, the computed settlement is

$$\Delta H = H \frac{C_c}{1 + e_p} \log \frac{p_2}{p_p}$$

As can be seen by reference to Figure 4.04a, this is equivalent to assuming that the consolidation from the added load begins at the intersection of the virgin curve extended back to the preconsolidation pressure, in which case not all the recompression has been neglected.

4.05   Settlement of Underconsolidated Clay

An underconsolidated clay is one that has been subjected to a load for an insufficient time to allow complete consolidation for the full depth of the layer. At time t after application of load Δp_1 to the overburden pressure p_0, the relationship between the pressure carried by the soil grains and that retained by the excess pore water pressure u with depth, is shown in Figure 4.05a. The degree of consolidation at time t and depth z is $(\Delta p_1 - u)/\Delta p_1$ and the pressure carried by the soil grains at time t and depth z is the overburden pressure p_0, plus the added pressure Δp_1 minus the excess pore water pressure u.

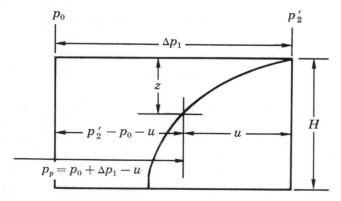

Figure 4.05a   Relation of stress in soil grains and pore water with depth at time t after start of consolidation under $p_0 + \Delta p$

In practice, two conditions of loading an underconsolidated soil may be experienced. In one case, the preload may be removed at time t before consolidation under the added load is complete. In this case, when Δp_1 is removed, the pressure in the pore water is relieved and the soil attempts to swell under the reduced load. The water is relatively incompressible and so does not expand when the pressure is relieved and the stress in the pore water changes from compression to tension, resisting the expansion of the clay. As water is drawn into the clay, the tension is relieved until the stress in the pore water becomes equal to the hydrostatic pressure; i.e., the excess pore water pressure u becomes zero. At this stage, the soil is an overconsolidated clay with the preconsolidation pressure varying with

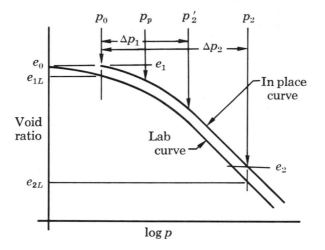

Figure 4.05b   e-log p curves for underconsolidated clay

depth. At depth z the preconsolidated pressure p_p is the overburden pressure p_0 plus the preload Δp_1 minus the excess pore water pressure u; i.e., $p_p = p_0 + \Delta p_1 - u$. If another load Δp_2 is added to the overburden pressure and left until complete consolidation is attained under the total pressure p_2, the settlement is measured by the change in void ratio e_1 to e_2 as measured on the in place curve or $e_{1L} - e_{2L}$ on the laboratory e-log p curve as shown in Figure 4.05b. The settlement after complete consolidation under pressure p_2 is

$$\Delta H = \sum H_z \frac{e_1 - e_2}{1 + e_1}$$

when H_z is the thickness of the increment at z depth into which the layer was divided for settlement computation. For each of the thickness elements, e_1 must be determined for each z depth from a degree consolidation curve as shown in Figure 4.05a.

The second case of loading an underconsolidated clay layer is experienced when an additional load is applied to the soil without removing the preload which has caused the partial consolidation. In this case, the settlement proceeds in the same manner as though the total load $\Delta p_1 + \Delta p_2$

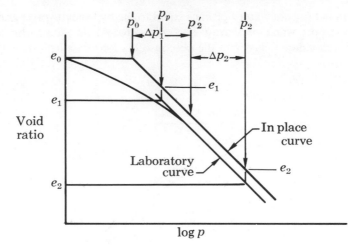

Figure 4.05c   e-log p curves for underconsolidated clay (settlement under load added to preload)

had been applied to the overburden pressure at the time the smaller preload Δp_1 was applied. In this case, the pore water pressure is not relieved and the clay does not expand, so there is no recompression. The settlement due to the addition of Δp_2 is the total settlement under $\Delta p_1 + \Delta p_2$ minus the settlement under Δp_1 at the time t after the preload Δp_1 was applied; i.e., when the additional load Δp_2 was applied.

4.06   Time-Settlement Relationship

The relationship between per cent consolidation U per cent and time factor T as determined from the consolidation equation is given in the following table.

U %	0	10	15	20	25	30	35	40
T	0.000	0.008	0.018	0.031	0.049	0.071	0.096	0.126
U %	45	50	55	60	65	70	75	80
T	0.159	0.197	0.238	0.287	0.342	0.405	0.477	0.565
U %	85	90	95	100				
T	0.684	0.848	1.127					

If the time factor T for a given layer of soil at a given time is known, the value of U per cent is known, and the settlement at time t is equal to U times the total settlement ΔH. The problem in time settlement analysis is to determine the value of T for a given time t or to determine the time for a given value of T.

From the consolidation equation $c_v = [k(1 + e)/\gamma_w a_v]$, in which k is the coefficient of permeability, and a_v is the slope of the e-p curve at e. Although k, e, and a_v change during the consolidation process, they change in such a manner that for practical purposes the ratio may be considered as constant. By definition $T = c_v(t/H^2)$. It will be observed that all of the involved properties of the soil are included in the value of c_v. Then, if c_v for the soil is known and the thickness of the soil layer is known, the relationship between T and t is known. In this case, H is the drainage thickness; i.e., the full thickness of a layer drained one side only, and one-half the thickness of a layer drained both sides.

The coefficient of consolidation c_v can be determined from one of the time-dial reading curves obtained from a consolidation test. The time-dial reading curve should be converted to a time-consolidation curve. A curve for one of the larger load increments and a fairly large deformation should be chosen for this purpose. From this curve, the time for some per cent consolidation can be determined. The time for 50 per cent consolidation is commonly used because it occurs in a steeper part of the curve and can be more easily determined than for much smaller or much larger values of U. 50 per cent consolidation occurs early enough so that the secondary consolidation has not appreciably distorted the curve, and late enough so that the percentage of error in reading the time, and dial readings after application of the increment of load, is much smaller than that for the earlier readings.

The value of H in the consolidation test is one-half the thickness of the specimen.

$$c_v = \frac{H^2 T}{t} \text{ for } U \text{ per cent} = 50, T = 0.2 \text{ (approximately)}$$

Then

$$c_v = \frac{0.2 H^2}{t_{50}}$$

For example, if the thickness of the specimen is 1 in. or 2.54 cm and if t_{50} is 1.2 min or 72 sec,

$$c_v = \frac{(0.2)(0.5^2)}{1.2} = 0.0416 \text{ in.}^2 \text{ min}^{-1} \text{ or } \frac{(0.2)(0.5^2)}{72} = 0.000695 \text{ in.}^2 \text{ sec}^{-1}$$

or

$$c_v = \frac{(0.2)(1.27^2)}{1.2} = 0.269 \text{ cm}^2 \text{ min}^{-1} \text{ or } \frac{(0.2)(1.27^2)}{72} = 0.0448 \text{ cm}^2 \text{ sec}^{-1}$$

Thus, the value of c_v can be obtained in any convenient units, but in its use these units must be preserved consistently.

Once c_v is known for the soil, a time-settlement curve can be prepared for a single layer of that soil during the consolidation period from the relationship $t = (H^2/c_v)T$. When two or more strata of the same or different soils contribute to the settlement, time-settlement curves must be prepared separately for each of the strata and the total settlement at a given time found by adding the settlements of the contributing layers at that time. In this sense, a stratum or layer of soil is a layer bound by drainage layers on both sides, or by a drainage layer on one side and an impervious layer on the other.

Example of Time-Settlement Analysis:

Assume the same soil and loading conditions as used for the example of total settlement in Section 4.03 and the following additional data.

Upper layer Height of specimen = 2.54 cm	Lower layer Height of specimen = 1.62 cm
$t_{50} = 4.6$ min	$t_{50} = 3.1$ min
$c_v = \dfrac{(0.2)(1.27^2)}{4.6} = 0.07 \text{ cm}^2 \text{ min}^{-1}$	$c_v = \dfrac{(0.2)(0.81^2)}{3.1} = 0.0423 \text{ cm}^2 \text{ min}^{-1}$
$c_v = \dfrac{0.07}{2.54^2} = 0.0108 \text{ in.}^2 \text{ min}^{-1}$	$c_v = \dfrac{0.0423}{2.54^2} = 0.00655 \text{ in.}^2 \text{ min}^{-1}$

Solution:

The settlement of a single stratum of clay at a given time or the time required for a certain amount of settlement to occur can be estimated from the parabolic relationship between U and T, provided that U is less than 60 per cent.

$$\frac{U_1^2}{U_2^2} = \frac{T_1}{T_2} = \frac{c_v \dfrac{t_1}{H_1^2}}{c_v \dfrac{t^2}{H_2^2}}$$

For the same soil c_v is constant, so the relationship may be written

$$\frac{U_1^2}{U_2^2} = \frac{t_1 H_2^2}{t_2 H_1^2}$$

Computation for a solution can be tabulated as follows:

Table 4.06a

		Upper layer $H = 60$ in. (drained 2 sides) $\Delta H = 12.68$ in., $\dfrac{H^2}{c_v} = 333{,}000$			Lower layer $H = 156$ in. (drained 1 side) $\Delta H = 6.88$ in., $\dfrac{H^2}{c_v} = 3{,}720{,}000$		
$U\%$	T	Settlement $U \times 12.68$	t min	t months	Settlement $U \times 6.88$	t min	t months
10	0.008	1.27	2,670	0.062	0.69	29,750	0.69
20	0.031	2.54	10,300	0.238	1.38	115,200	2.66
30	0.071	3.80	23,700	0.549	2.06	264,000	6.10
40	0.126	5.07	42,000	0.972	2.75	468,000	10.85
50	0.197	6.34	65,600	1.520	3.44	734,000	16.98
60	0.287	7.60	95,600	2.22	4.13	1,068,000	24.65
70	0.405	8.86	135,200	3.13	4.81	1,508,000	34.82
80	0.565	10.15	188,200	4.36	5.50	2,100,000	48.60
85	0.684	10.80	228,000	5.28	5.84	2,540,000	58.70
90	0.848	11.40	282,100	6.54	6.19	3,150,000	72.80
95	1.127	12.05	375,000	8.69	6.54	4,190,000	96.70

or, stated in words, the square of the degree of consolidation is directly proportional to the time and inversely proportional to the square of the thickness if drained one side or the square of one-half the thickness if drained two sides.

For example, the time required for 40 per cent consolidation or 5.04 in. settlement of the upper stratum of clay of the preceding example can be estimated by comparing the consolidation specimen with the stratum of clay from the parabolic relationship as

$$\frac{40^2}{50^2} = \frac{(t)(0.5^2)}{(4.6)(60^2)}$$

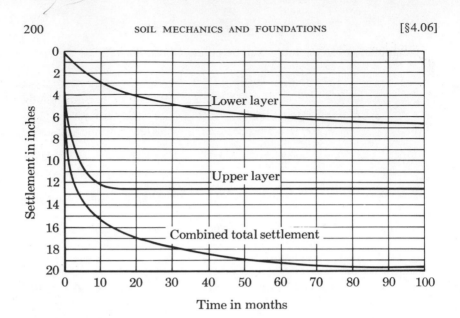

Figure 4.06a   Time-settlement curve

from which

$$t = \frac{1600(4.6)(60^2)}{2500\ (0.5^2)} = 42{,}400 \text{ min}$$

If the time required for 4 in. settlement is desired,

$$U = \frac{4}{12.68} = 31.6 \text{ per cent}$$

and

$$t = \frac{(31.6^2)(4.6)(60^2)}{2500\ (0.5^2)} = 26{,}500 \text{ min}$$

If the settlement at the end of 6 months is desired,

$$t = 259{,}200 \text{ min}$$

and

$$U = \sqrt{\frac{(2500)(0.5^2)(259{,}200)}{(4.6)(60^2)}} = 99 \text{ per cent}$$

or 12.5 in. settlement.

By comparison with values in Table 4.06a, it can be seen that this parabolic relationship gives quite accurate results for low degrees of consolidation, but for the 6 months calculation of settlement, there is considerable error, because at 6 months the degree of consolidation is considerably greater than 60 per cent. For degrees of consolidation greater than about 60 per cent, the relationship between U and T as given in the table at the beginning of this section must be used or, as a substitute, the approximate relationship $T = 1.781 - 0.933 \log (100 - U)$. For the 6 months settlement of the above illustration, the approximate relationship for T and degree of consolidation above 60 per cent may be used as follows:

$$T = T_2 \frac{tH_2^2}{t_2H^2} = \frac{(0.2)(259,200)(0.5^2)}{(4.6)(60^2)} = 0.784$$

and

$$\log (100 - U) = \frac{(1.781 - 0.784)}{0.933} = 1.069$$

$$100 - U = 11.7 \text{ and } U = 88.3 \text{ per cent}$$

$$\Delta H = 0.883 \times 12.68 = 11.2 \text{ in. settlement}$$

This value of the settlement of the upper layer at 6 months agrees fairly well with the settlement as computed by using the relationship between U and T listed in the table at the beginning of this section.

4.07   Unit Soil Pressures under Loaded Area

a.   Boussinesq Problem—Point Load on Surface of Semi-infinite Elastic Body

J. Boussinesq was the first to evaluate the stresses and deformations at a point in a semi-infinite elastic body caused by a concentrated load P applied to the surface of the body. As determined by Boussinesq, the vertical unit stress at any point x,y,z from coordinates through the point of application of the concentrated load to the surface is

$$\sigma_z = \frac{3P}{2\pi} \frac{z^3}{R^5} \qquad \text{(Eq. 4.07a)}$$

The terms in equation 4.07a are explained by reference to Figure 4.07a.

Equation 4.07a can be expressed in terms of r and z as

$$\sigma_z = \frac{3P}{2\pi} \frac{z^3}{(x^2 + y^2 + z^2)^{5/2}}$$

$$= \frac{3P}{2\pi} \frac{z^3}{(r^2 + z^2)^{5/2}}$$

$$= \frac{3P}{2\pi} \frac{1}{z^2 \left[\left(\dfrac{r}{z}\right)^2 + 1\right]^{5/2}}$$

This can also be expressed as

$$\sigma_z = \frac{P}{z^2} \frac{3}{2\pi} \left[\frac{1}{\left(\dfrac{r}{z}\right)^2 + 1}\right]^{5/2} \qquad \text{(Eq. 4.07b)}$$

If P_0 is made to represent the function of the dimensionless ratio $\dfrac{r}{z}$, then

$$\sigma_z = \frac{P}{z^2} P_0$$

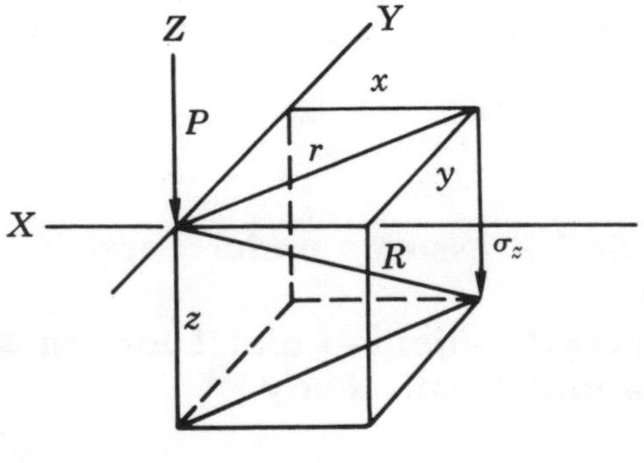

Figure 4.07a   Point load on surface of semi-infinite elastic body

Values of P_0 for values of $\dfrac{r}{z}$ were computed, tabulated, and published by Glennon Gilboy in the early 1930's. R. E. Fadum recomputed these influence values, which are published in the Appendix of *Theoretical Soil Mechanics* by Terzaghi.

Because σ_z is a function of only P, r, and z, curves can be drawn for a unit load P for different radii r, so that the value of σ_z for a unit P can be determined directly from the value of z and r. Such curves have been drawn for different values of r showing the unit pressures p_r^1 as depth z produced by a load of 1 kip at the origin. These curves drawn for $r = 0$, 10 ft, 15 ft, 20 ft, 30 ft, and 50 ft are shown in Diagram 4.07a. In order to determine the unit pressure p_r^1, it is only necessary to enter the diagram with the value of z in feet, pass horizontally to the curve for the proper value of r, and read up or down to the value of p_r^1. The vertical pressure produced by the total concentrated load equals $P \cdot p_r^1$. For values between those values of r for which the curves are drawn, the correct values of r may be interpolated between the two closest curves.

The magnitude of σ_z to a greater degree of accuracy can also be determined from the influence table prepared by Fadum.

As an example, assume that the unit vertical pressure is desired at a point 15 ft horizontally and 12 ft below the point of application of a concentrated load of 4 kips applied to the surface. From Diagram 4.07a the value of σ_z is determined as follows: From $z = 12$ ft pass horizontally to the curve for $r = 15$ ft, and read vertically to p_r^1 for 1 kip = 0.3 lb per sq ft. σ_z for $P = 4$ kips is $4 \times 0.3 = 1.25$ lb ft^{-2}. From the influence table prepared by Fadum, P_0 for $r/z = 15/12 = 1.25$ is found to be 0.0454. Then $\sigma_z = (4000/144) \times 0.0454 = 1.26$ lb ft^{-2}.

Values of σ_z obtained by the use of the curves on Diagram 4.07a are considered sufficiently accurate for practical purposes. It is obvious that a concentrated load cannot be applied to a point on the surface of a soil mass. It must be applied over some area. Therefore, near the surface at short distances from the center of application of the loaded area, values of σ_z determined for a point load are unrealistic. It will be shown later that the pressure at some distance from a loaded area is approximately the same as from the same total load applied at a point at the center of the loaded area.

b.   Uniformly Loaded Line of Finite Length— Boussinesq Solution

Foundations often consist of continuous footings supporting exterior or division walls which produce approximately uniform loads per lineal foot, and of interior independent footings supporting concentrated loads from columns. In estimating settlements produced by these line loads, it is necessary to determine the pressures produced by a uniformly loaded line.

The vertical unit pressure at a point at any depth z in a plane perpendicular to an end of the loaded line on the surface of a semi-infinite elastic body can be computed by the application of the Boussinesq solution as follows:

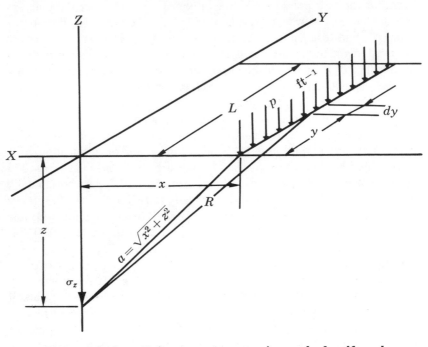

Figure 4.07b   Unit pressure opposite end of uniformly loaded line

The Boussinesq solution for a load p per ft applied to an infinitesimal length of line dy is

$$d\,\sigma_z = \frac{3\,z^3}{2\,\pi}\frac{p\,dy}{R^5} = \frac{3\,z^3}{2\,\pi}p\,\frac{dy}{(x^2 + z^2 + y^2)^{5/2}}$$

In this case, x and z are constants, so that the pressure produced by a loaded line of length L is

$$\sigma_z = \frac{3\,z^3}{2\,\pi}p\int_0^L \frac{dy}{(x^2 + z^2 + y^2)^{5/2}} \qquad \text{(Eq. 4.07c)}$$

Let $x^2 + z^2 = a^2$ (a constant) and $y = a\tan\alpha$. Then, $dy = a\sec^2\alpha\,d\alpha$, and equation 4.07c becomes

$$\sigma_z = \frac{3\,z^3}{2\,\pi}p \int \frac{a\,\sec^2\alpha\,d\alpha}{(a^2 + a^2\tan^2\alpha)^{5/2}} = \frac{3\,z^3}{2\,\pi}\frac{p}{a^4}\int \frac{\sec^2\alpha\,d\alpha}{(1 + \tan^2\alpha)^{5/2}}$$

$$= \frac{3\,p}{2\,\pi}\frac{z^3}{a^4}\int \frac{\sec^2\alpha\,d\alpha}{(\sec^2\alpha)^{5/2}} = \frac{3\,p}{2\,\pi}\frac{z^3}{a^4}\int \frac{d\alpha}{\sec^3\alpha}$$

$$= \frac{3\,p}{2\,\pi}\frac{z^3}{a^4}\int \cos^3\alpha\,d\alpha = \frac{3\,p}{2\,\pi}\frac{z^3}{a^4}\left[\sin\alpha - \frac{\sin^3\alpha}{3}\right]$$

Since $\tan\alpha = \dfrac{y}{a}$, $\sin\alpha = \dfrac{y}{\sqrt{a^2 + y^2}}$

So,

$$\sigma_z = \frac{3\,p}{2\,\pi}\frac{z^3}{a^4}\left[\frac{y}{a^2 + y^2} - \frac{y^3}{3(a^2 + y^2)^{3/2}}\right]$$

$$= \frac{p}{2\,\pi}\frac{z^3}{a^4}{}_0^L\left[\frac{a^2 + 2(a^2 + y^2)}{(a^2 + y^2)^{3/2}}\right]$$

$$= \frac{p\,z^3}{2\,\pi}\frac{L}{a^2\sqrt{a^2 + L^2}}\left[\frac{1}{a^2 + L^2} + \frac{2}{a^2}\right] \qquad \text{(Eq. 4.07}d\text{)}$$

When the equivalent value of a in terms of x and z are introduced, equation 4.07d becomes

$$\sigma_z = \frac{p}{z}\frac{1}{2\,\pi}\frac{\dfrac{L}{z}}{\dfrac{x^2}{z^2} + 1}\frac{1}{\sqrt{\dfrac{x^2}{z^2} + \dfrac{L^2}{z^2} + 1}}\left[\frac{1}{\dfrac{x^2}{z^2} + \dfrac{L^2}{z^2} + 1} + \frac{2}{\dfrac{x^2}{z^2} + 1}\right]$$

If, for convenience, $\dfrac{x}{z} = m$, and $\dfrac{L}{z} = n$, the equation may be written

$$\frac{z}{p}\sigma_z = \frac{1}{2\,\pi}\frac{n}{m^2 + 1}\frac{1}{\sqrt{m^2 + n^2 + 1}}\left[\frac{1}{m^2 + n^2 + 1} + \frac{2}{m^2 + 1}\right] \text{(Eq. 4.07}e\text{)}$$

If the function of m and n on the right side of equation 4.07e is called p_0, then $\sigma_z = (p/z)p_0$.

An influence table for values of p_0 in terms of m and n has been computed by R. E. Fadum and is published in the Appendix of *Theoretical Soil Mechanics* by Terzaghi. In using the influence table for determining p_0, it should be observed that m and n are not interchangeable. Diagram 4.07b gives values of p_0 for known values of m and n. Enter the diagram with the value of $L/z = n$, pass horizontally to the proper curve for $x/z = m$, and pass vertically up or down to the value of p_0.

If the stress is desired at a point below the surface offset from a point between the ends of the line, each part of the line must be considered as a separate loaded line, and the stresses found for the two parts added to obtain the stress produced by the entire loaded line. If the point at which the stress is desired lies beyond the end of the loaded line, the stress must be found for a loaded line extending to the perpendicular plane through the point, and the stress produced by a loaded line equal to the extension between the end of the line and the perpendicular plane must be subtracted from the stress found for the total extended line.

c. *Uniformly Loaded Rectangular Area—Boussinesq Solution*

Loads applied to the soil are normally distributed over an area. The Boussinesq solution is available for determining the vertical unit stress

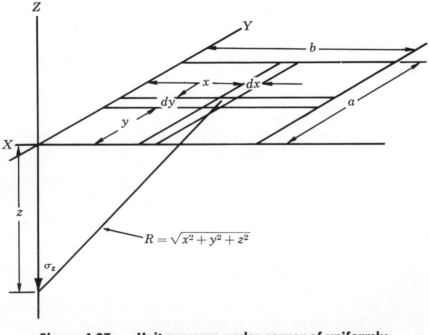

Figure 4.07c   Unit pressure under corner of uniformly loaded area

under a uniformly loaded area applied to the surface of a homogeneous elastic body of semi-infinite extent. A solution for determining the unit vertical stress under the corner of such a uniformly loaded rectangular area was made available by N. M. Newmark, by the integration of the relationship derived as follows:

For a uniform load of w per sq ft, the load on the elemental area $dy \cdot dx$ is $dw = w \, dy \, dx$, and the value of $d\sigma_z$ caused by this elemental load is

$$d\sigma_z = \frac{3 \, z^3}{2 \, \pi} \cdot \frac{w \, dx \, dy}{(x^2 + y^2 + z^2)^{5/2}}$$

The magnitude of σ_z for the entire rectangular area loaded with w per sq ft is

$$\sigma_z = \frac{3 \, z^3 \, w}{2 \, \pi} \int_0^a \int_0^b \frac{dx \, dy}{(x^2 + y^2 + z^2)^{5/2}}$$

In the first integration in the y direction, x and z are constants, in which case the result of the integration is the same as the result of integration for a loaded line, which leaves for the second integration

$$\sigma_z = \frac{3 \, w \, z^3}{2 \, \pi} \int_0^b \frac{a \, dx}{x^2 + z^2} \left[\frac{1}{(x^2 + a^2 + z^2)^{3/2}} + \frac{2(x^2 + a^2 + z^2)}{(x^2 + z^2)(x^2 + a^2 + z^2)^{3/2}} \right]$$

This second integration is long and difficult, but was accomplished by Newmark and found to be

$$\sigma_z = \frac{w}{4 \, \pi} \left[\frac{2abz\sqrt{a^2 + b^2 + z^2}}{z^2(a^2 + b^2 + z^2) + a^2b^2} \cdot \frac{a^2 + b^2 + 2z^2}{a^2 + b^2 + z^2} \right.$$

$$\left. + \tan^{-1} \frac{2abz\sqrt{a^2 + b^2 + z^2}}{z^2(a^2 + b^2 + z^2 - a^2b^2)} \right] \qquad \text{(Eq. 4.07)}$$

Equation 4.07f can be expressed in terms of the dimensionless ratios $m = \dfrac{a}{z}$ and $n = \dfrac{b}{z}$ as follows:

$$\frac{\sigma_z}{w} = \frac{1}{4 \, \pi} \left[\frac{2mn\sqrt{m^2 + n^2 + 1}}{m^2 + n^2 + 1 + m^2n^2} \cdot \frac{m^2 + n^2 + 2}{m^2 + n^2 + 1} \right.$$

$$\left. + \tan^{-1} \frac{2mn\sqrt{m^2 + n^2 + 1}}{m^2 + n^2 + 1 - m^2n^2} \right] \qquad \text{(Eq. 4.07g)}$$

In this relationship, m and n are interchangeable.

If the function of m and n which forms the right-hand member of Equation 4.07g be designated as w_0, the value of the vertical unit pressure at depth z under the corner of a uniformly loaded rectangular area can be written as $\sigma_z = w\, w_0$. Influence tables for w_0 for various values of m and n have been carefully calculated by R. E. Fadum and are published in the Appendix of *Theoretical Soil Mechanics* by Terzaghi. This is the usual form in which the relationship for σ_z, depth z, and dimensions of the loaded area a and b are expressed.

Another convenient form of the relationship for unit stress under the corner of a uniformly loaded rectangular area was used by W. Steinbrenner. The Steinbrenner curves are based upon the ratio of z/b and a/b. Values for plotting the Steinbrenner curves can be obtained from the influence values for w_0 in terms of m and n as follows:

For $z = 0$, $m = \infty$, and $n = \infty$, so for any ratio of a/b, $w_0 = 0.250$. For $z = b$ and $a = b$, $m = 1$ and $n = 1$, for which $w_0 = 0.175$. For $z = 2b$ and $a = b$, $m = 0.5$ and $n = 0.5$, for which $w_0 = 0.084$. Curves giving values of w_0 for all ratios of z/b and for any ratio of a/b can be drawn. Such Steinbrenner curves are included in Diagram 4.07c.

The stress under any point on the boundary or inside a loaded rectangular area is equal to the summation of the stresses produced under the corners of smaller rectangles which divide the total area, and whose corners meet at the point under which the stress is desired. The stress under a point outside a loaded rectangular area can be found by deducting the stresses from small rectangles required to complete a rectangle whose corner is at the point under which the stress is desired, from the

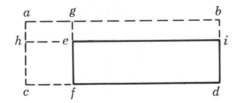

Figure 4.07d   Stress under point outside loaded area

stress produced by the total completed rectangle. For example, the stress under point a of Figure 4.07d for loaded rectangle $efdi$ is σ_z for the entire rectangle $abcd$, less σ_z at a for $acfg$ and σ_z at a for $abih$. Then, because σ_z at a for $aheg$ has been deducted twice, it must be added to the summation; i.e., $\sigma_{zefdi} = \sigma_{zacdb} - \sigma_{zacfg} - \sigma_{zabih} + \sigma_{zaheg}$.

d. *Uniformly Loaded Circular Area—Boussinesq Solution*

The unit vertical stress at depth z under the center of a uniformly loaded circular area applied to the surface of a semi-infinite elastic body can also be determined by means of the Boussinesq solution.

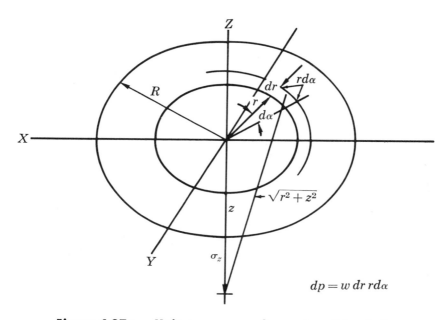

Figure 4.07e **Unit pressure under center of loaded circular area**

Applying the Boussinesq relationship

$$\sigma_z = \frac{3\,w}{2\,\pi}\,z^3 \int_0^R \int_0^{2\pi z} \frac{r\,d\alpha\,dr}{(r^2 + z^2)^{5/2}}$$

Integrating with respect to α and inserting limits

$$\sigma_z = \frac{3\,w\,z^2 2\pi}{2\,\pi} \int_0^R (r^2 + z^2)^{-5/2}\,r\,dr$$

Integrating with respect to r

$$\sigma_z = -\,w\,z^3 \int_0^R (r^2 - z^2)^{-3/2}\,r\,dr$$

Introducing the limits from 0 to R

$$\frac{\sigma_z}{w} = -z^3(R^2 + z^2)^{-3/2} + z^3(z^2)^{-3/2}$$

$$= 1 - \frac{1}{\left[\dfrac{R^2}{z^2} + 1\right]^{3/2}} = 1 - \left[\dfrac{1}{\dfrac{R^2}{z^2} + 1}\right]^{3/2}$$

Again, if the function of R and z on the right hand side of the equation be designated w_0, the magnitude of σ_z can be written $\sigma_z = w\,w_0$.

Influence tables for w_0 for stress under the center of a circular loaded area have been prepared and published in the Appendix of *Theoretical Soil Mechanics* by Terzaghi.

A curve showing the relationship between z, R and w_0 is in diagram 4.07e.

e.   *Westergaard Solution*

Soils such as varved clays which consist of multiple alternate thin layers of sand or silt and clay are reinforced against lateral deformation by the cohesionless sheets of silt. A. Casagrande suggested the problem of determining the stress in such a material to H. M. Westergaard, who obtained a solution for the extreme case in which the horizontal deformation is assumed to be zero. Influence tables for the Westergaard solution were also prepared by Fadum, using a value of Poisson's ratio equal to zero. Curves for the same loading conditions as for the Boussinesq solution are also presented for the Westergaard solution in Diagrams 4.07f, 4.07g, 4.07h, 4.07i, and 4.07j.

The Westergaard solution for the vertical stress caused by a load applied to the surface of a semi-infinite body, which follows Hooke's Law but is restrained from deforming laterally, is

$$\sigma_z = \frac{P}{2\pi} K \frac{z}{(x^2 + y^2 + K^2 z^2)^{3/2}}$$

in which $K = \sqrt{\dfrac{1 - 2\mu}{2(1 - \mu)}}$ and μ is Poisson's ratio for the softer material.

f.   *Comparison of Boussinesq and Westergaard Solutions*

In both the Bossinesq and the Westergaard solutions, the total stress produced on any horizontal plane below the surface must be equal to the total applied load plus the pressure produced by the overburden. The only difference between the two solutions lies in the distribution of the stresses below the surface. A comparison of the distribution of vertical stress on a horizontal plane 10 ft below the surface for a 1 kip load on the

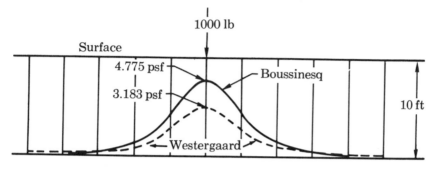

Figure 4.07f   Distribution of stress on horizontal plane—Boussinesq and Westergaard solutions

surface is shown in Figure 4.07f. Thus, it can be seen that the Westergaard solution indicates a lesser stress directly under the load than the Boussinesq solution, but distributes the total load over a larger area so that at some distance the Westergaard solution indicates a larger stress than the Boussinesq solution.

In general, neither of these solutions indicates the correct stress in a natural deposit of soil even when loaded on the surface. Even under ideal conditions, the soil is neither homogeneous nor completely elastic. Under no circumstance does the soil which contributes to settlement extend to an infinite depth. In a great many cases, usual with foundations, the load is not applied to the surface. Loaded areas on dense sand tend to produce higher stresses under the middle of the loaded area than are indicated by either the Boussinesq or the Westergaard solution.

Although neither the Boussinesq nor the Westergaard solution indicates the correct stress produced by loads applied to natural deposits of soil, they are nevertheless highly useful aids in analyzing settlements. Engineers often form a preference for one or the other in accordance with their own experience as to which has most often led to accurate prediction of settlements. Probably the Boussinesq solution is used most often.

g.   Approximate Estimate of Vertical Stress

An approximate estimate of the pressure in a soil mass produced by superimposed loads can be made by the simple assumption that the total load is distributed uniformly over an area defined by planes sloping from the edge of the loaded area at some angle α from the horizontal. The width of the area at z depth on which the load is assumed to be distributed is as shown in Figure 4.07g, and is equal to the width of the footing $2b$ plus 2 times $z \cot \alpha$.

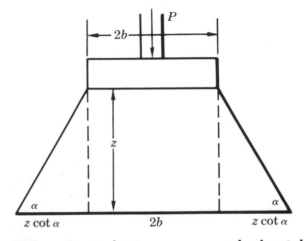

Figure 4.07g   Approximate pressure on horizontal plane

By comparison, for a total load of 1 kip per sq ft on a 4 ft square footing for z of 6 ft below the center of the bottom of the footing, the pressure by the Boussinesq solution is $1000 \times 0.037 \times 4 = 148$ lb ft^{-2}. If the distribution angle in the approximate solution is $60°$, the total load of 16,000 lb is distributed at 6 ft depth over $[4 + (2 \times 3.46)]^2 = 119$ sq ft. The unit pressure by the approximate method is $16,000/119 = 134$ lb ft^{-2}. Figure 4.07h shows a comparison with depth of the pressure computed by the approximate method and the Boussinesq solution. It may be seen that the crude method yields much smaller values of σ_z for shallow depths below the footing, but agrees quite reasonably when $z/2b > 1.5$. Thus, for compressible layers buried at considerable depth below the footing, the approximate method may be used as confidently as any other.

Under a flexible area, such as a large oil storage tank resting on the ground, a settlement analysis based upon the Boussinesq solution will undoubtedly yield a more accurate estimate of the settlement at the center of the tank than will one based upon the approximate solution. Also, the approximate solution cannot be used to estimate the differential settlement of a flexible area. However, if the load is applied by a very stiff slab, as in the case of an independent footing, the contact pressure is not uniform and the Boussinesq solution probably does not yield a more accurate

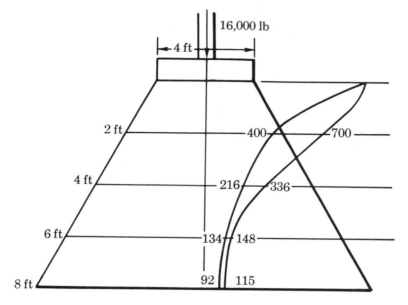

Figure 4.07h   Comparison of unit pressure under uniformly loaded area by Boussinesq solution and 60° distribution

estimate of the settlement than does the approximate solution because the rigid footing will not settle as much as is indicated by the Boussinesq pressure under the center of the flexible uniformly loaded area.

h.   Diagrams for Estimating Unit Vertical Pressure

Diagrams are presented which may be used for estimating the unit pressure produced by loads applied to the surface of a homogeneous semi-infinite elastic body by the Boussinesq and the Westergaard solutions. These diagrams are plotted from values taken from the influence tables prepared by R. E. Fadum. For most soils and loading conditions pressures determined by the use of these diagrams may be considered accurate enough for practical purposes, although they cannot be read as accurately as the influence values are computed. In most cases, extreme accuracy is not possible or necessary.

Seldom, if ever, do the soil and loading conditions conform to the assumptions upon which the Boussinesq and Westergaard solutions are based.

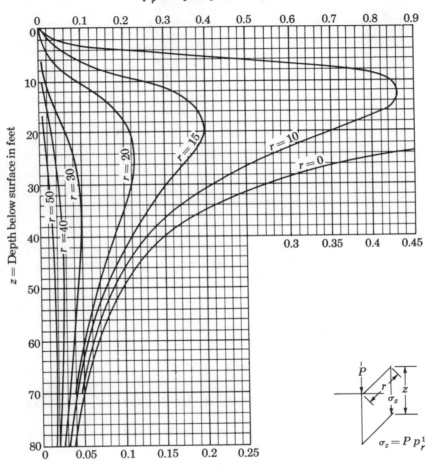

p_r^1 in lb per sq ft for 1 kip at $r = 0$

$z = $ Depth below surface in feet

p_r^1 in kg cm^{-2} or tons per sq ft for 1000 kip at $r = 0$

$\sigma_z = P\, p_r^1$

Diagram 4.07a   **Unit pressure at r distance and z depth caused by concentrated load at r = 0 —Boussinesq solution**

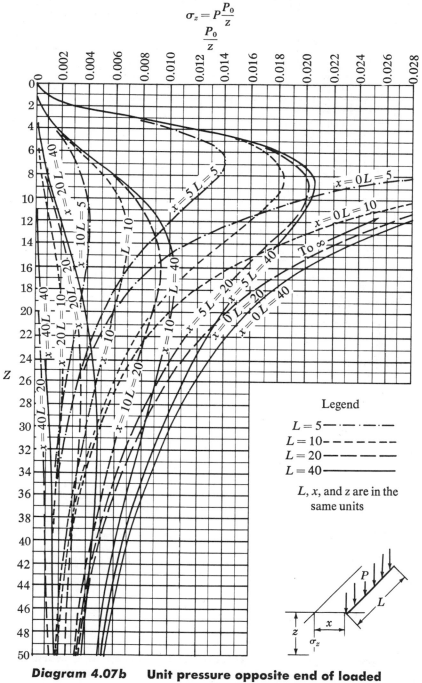

Diagram 4.07b   **Unit pressure opposite end of loaded line—Boussinesq solution**

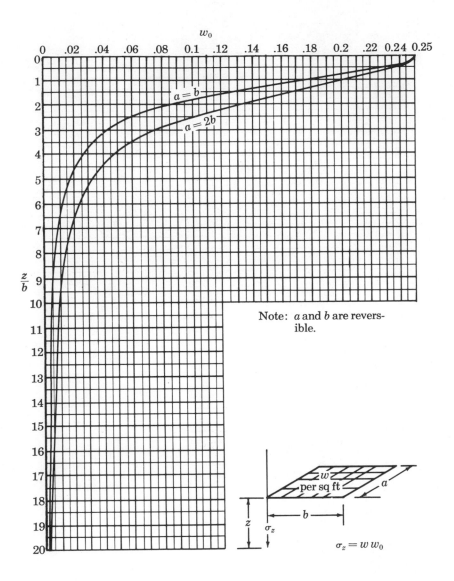

Diagram 4.07c   Unit pressure under corner of uniformly loaded rectangular area—Boussinesq solution

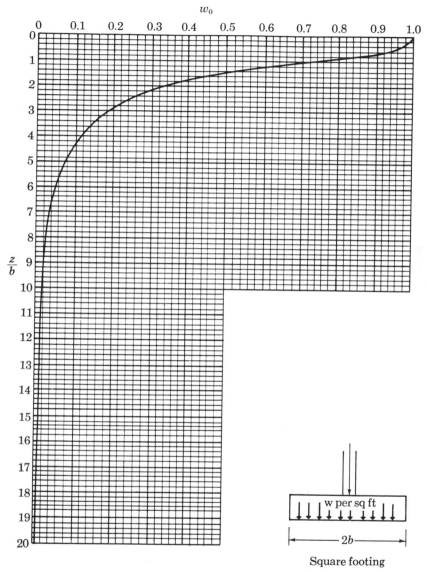

Diagram 4.07d   Unit pressure under center of uniformly loaded square area—Boussinesq solution

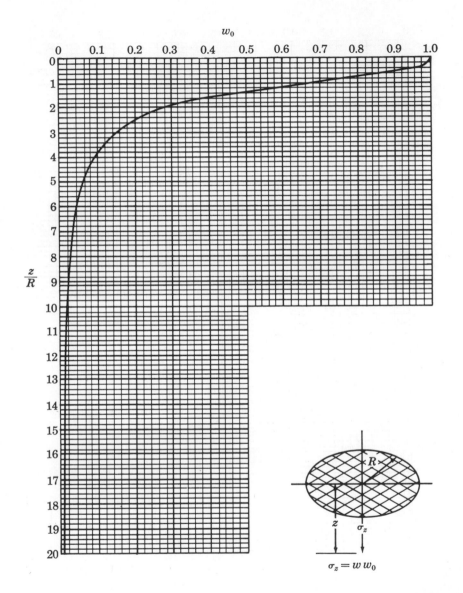

Diagram 4.07e   Unit pressure under center of uniformly loaded circular area—Boussinesq solution

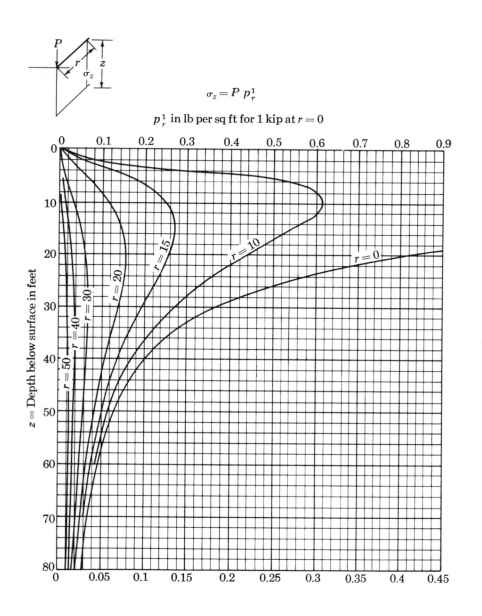

$$\sigma_z = P \, p_r^1$$

p_r^1 in lb per sq ft for 1 kip at $r = 0$

Diagram 4.07f   Unit pressure at *r* distance and *z* depth caused by concentrated load at *r* = 0 —Westergaard solution

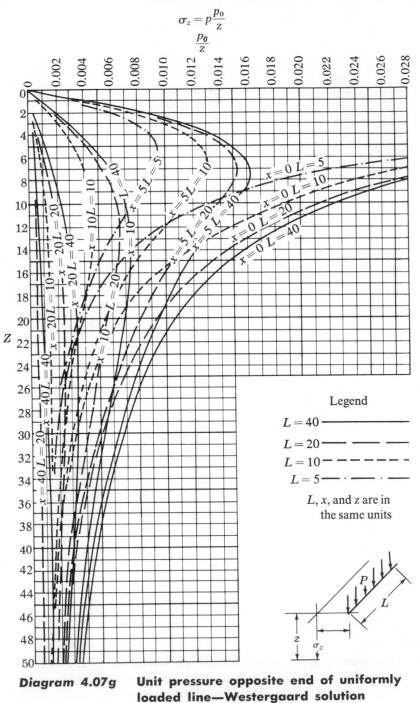

Diagram 4.07g   **Unit pressure opposite end of uniformly loaded line—Westergaard solution**

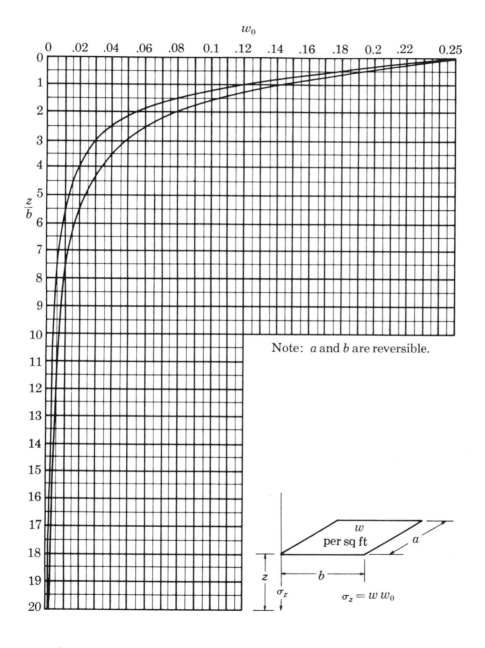

Diagram 4.07h   Unit pressure under corner of uniformly loaded rectangular area—Westergaard solution

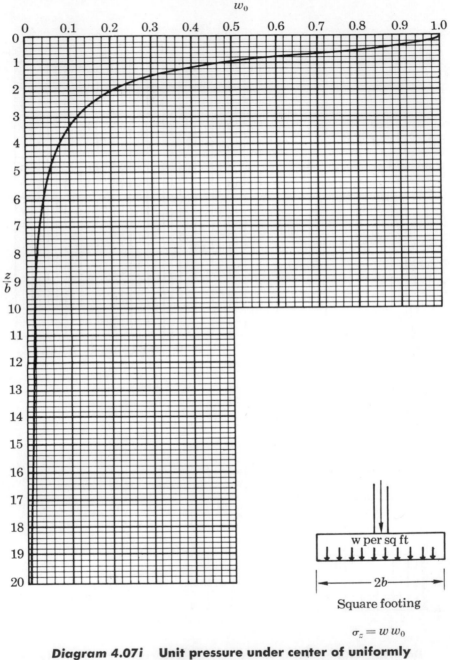

$$\sigma_z = w\,w_0$$

**Diagram 4.07i   Unit pressure under center of uniformly
loaded square area—Westergaard
solution**

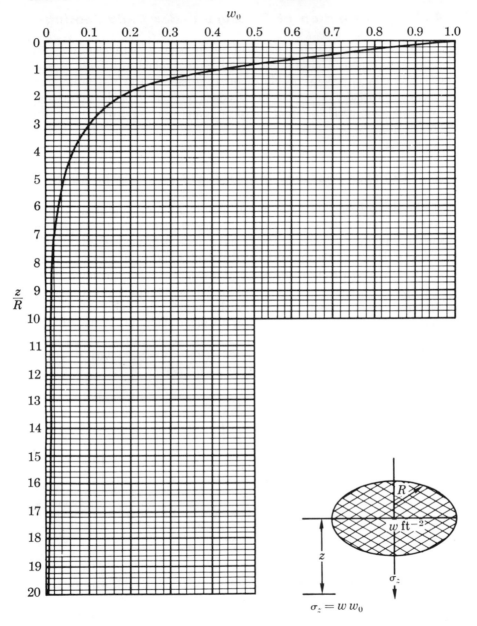

Diagram 4.07j   Unit pressure under center of uniformly loaded circular area—Westergaard solution

4.08   *Distribution of Pressure under Rigid Footing*

A rigid footing or slab under load produces equal settlement over the entire loaded area. Uniform contact pressure applied to a finite area of soil does not, in general, produce equal settlement over the entire area. Likewise, a rigid slab which forces equal settlement of the entire area does not, in general, produce uniform contact pressure over the entire area.

a.   *Contact Pressure under Rigid Footing in Sand*

The strength and the resistance to deformation of sand is dependent upon the contact pressure between the grains (effective stress). At the surface, sand has no shear strength and can be deformed readily. Under a rigid slab resting on the surface, the sand a short distance under the slab possesses a high shear strength and resistance to deformation because of the stress applied by the slab and the lateral confining stress resisting movement of the grains laterally. At the edge of the slab, no confining stress exists, and the grains are free to move laterally on the surface. Therefore, under a loaded rigid slab resting on the surface of sand, the contact pressure at the bottom surface of the slab is practically zero at the edge and much higher than average at the center, as shown in Figure 4.08*a*.

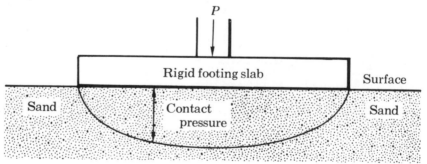

Figure 4.08a   Contact pressure under rigid slab on sand

If the rigid slab applies its load to the sand at some distance below the surface of the sand, the resistance to deformation at the edge of the slab may be fairly large, the magnitude depending upon the depth below the surface. But, in this case, the resistance to deformation is greater under the interior of the slab than at the edges. The distribution of contact pressure under the rigid slab on sand at depth is illustrated in Figure 4.08*b*.

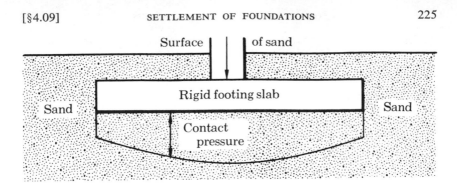

Figure 4.08b   Contact pressure under rigid slab in sand

b.   Contact Pressure under Rigid Footing on Clay

Clay, since it possesses cohesion or inherent shear strength, resists penetration of the edge of a rigid slab resting on the clay. As the clay at the edge of the slab is depressed, adjacent clay is dragged down by the shearing resistance of the clay. This resistance of the clay outside the loaded slab necessitates a high contact pressure around the edge of the rigid slab in order to produce uniform settlement.

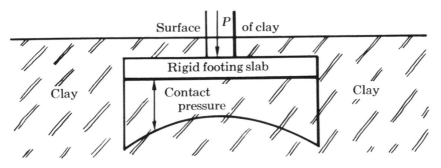

Figure 4.08c   Contact pressure under rigid slab on clay

4.09   Settlement of Flexible Uniformly Loaded Area

According to the Boussinesq solution, the distribution of stress under a uniformly loaded flexible area at some depth below the area is as shown in Figure 4.09a.

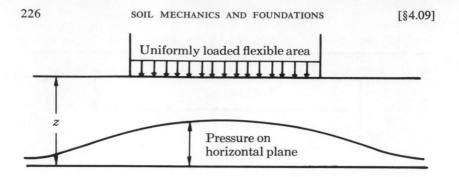

Figure 4.09a   Horizontal distribution of pressure under uniformly loaded flexible area

a.   Settlement of Uniformly Loaded Area on Sand

The resistance of sand to deformation is less at the edge of the loaded area than in the interior because, although the applied vertical pressure is the same over the entire area, the lateral confining pressure is less at the edges than in the interior. Therefore, the sand at the edge of the area yields and allows a greater settlement at the edges of the flexible area than at the interior. The settlement pattern for a uniformly loaded flexible area on sand is as shown in Figure 4.09*b*. The disparity between settlements at the edges and at the center decreases with increasing depth of footing.

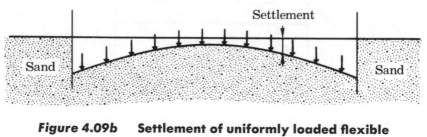

Figure 4.09b   Settlement of uniformly loaded flexible area on sand

b.   Settlement of Uniformly Loaded Flexible Area on Clay

Static pressure causes volume decrease of clay. Because the pressure at depth under the center of a uniformly loaded area is greater than that near the edges, the interior area settles more than that near the edges. The settlement pattern of a uniformly loaded flexible area is shown in Figure 4.09c.

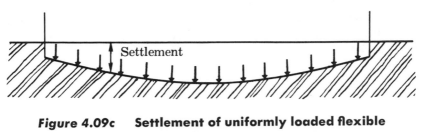

Figure 4.09c   Settlement of uniformly loaded flexible area on clay

4.10   Effect of Adjacent Loads Upon Settlement

If a load P_1 is placed upon the surface of a semi-infinite, elastic body, the pressure distribution at some depth a in a vertical plane through the load diminishes with distance from the load from a maximum under the load as shown in Figure 4.10a. When a second load P_2 is placed at a distance of $2a$ from the first, it produces additional stress in the material

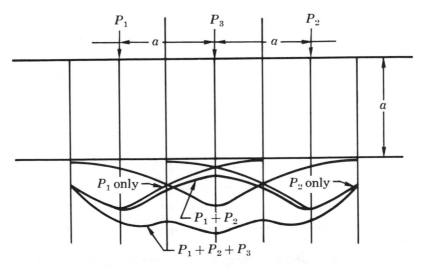

Figure 4.10a   Distribution of stress in vertical plane at depth a

under the first load. On clay the settlement of both will be greater than for either one alone, and the material between the loads will be compressed causing a settlement of the surface between the loads. Thus, if two heavily loaded structures covering small areas near each other are placed upon compressible soil away from the influence of other structures, they will lean toward each other as they settle. If a third load P_3 is placed between the first two loads, it will produce additional pressure and settlement of the other two loads, and will itself settle more than the outside loads.

4.11   *Effect of Size of Footing Upon Settlement*

Different size footings on compressible soil loaded to produce the same contact pressure will not settle equally. It is not possible to design a foundation on a thick layer of soft clay that will carry the column loads to earth with no differential settlement by adjusting the size of footings to the same or unequal contact pressures. The settlement of a footing on a

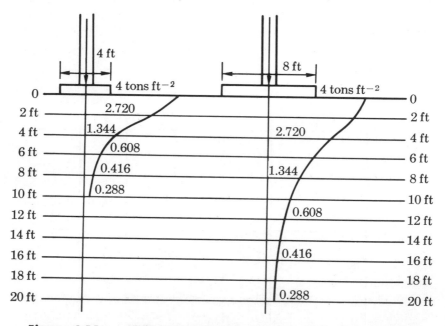

Figure 4.11a   **Unit pressure under center of flexible square area**

Contact pressure 4 tons ft⁻²
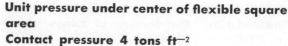

given layer of compressible soil is dependent upon the size of the footing, total column load, and the presence of adjacent added loads, as well as the contact pressure under the footing itself. In addition, the relationships are influenced by time.

Figure 4.11a shows the pressure at depth under footings of different sizes loaded to the same contact pressure. By reference to this figure, it can be seen that for the same contact pressure the pressure at some depth below the footings is greater under the larger footing than under the smaller one. This pressure distribution causes a greater deformation of the layers at the same depth under the larger footing than under the smaller one. Because of the greater deformation of the clay at depth below the larger footing, the total settlement of the larger footing will be greater than that of the smaller one loaded to the same contact pressure. The larger footing will continue to settle after the smaller one has stopped because, in the consolidation of the clay at depth, the pore water must travel from a greater depth under the larger footing.

4.12   Methods of Controlling Settlements on Compressible Soil

Settlements of foundations on compressible soils can be controlled within limits by one of the following methods.

a.   Floating Foundations

Theoretically, if an amount of soil exactly equal to the weight of the building is removed to form a basement, and the building load is distributed to the soil in such a manner that the state of stress in the soil beneath the foundation is not changed, no settlement would occur. If the foundation is placed on very compressible soil, this probably is the only method available for controlling total settlement. If the soil beneath the foundation is not uniform, differential settlements may occur even when this method is used.

A problem is encountered in the removal of the overburden for the reception of the building on very compressible soil because of the expansion of the soil when the overburden is removed. When the foundation, which usually is a stiffened raft type, is placed on the expanded soil in the bottom of the excavated area, the soil is not recompressed to its original volume. As the building load is added, the soil is recompressed proportional to the magnitude of the added stress. This recompression produces a distortion of the structure that has been placed early in the construction period. Because the unloaded soil near the center of the excavated area expands more than that near the edges of the excavation, the recompression of the expanded soil is equivalent to a differential settlement for the already completed portion of the structure. In extremely compressible soil, such as that existing in parts of Mexico City, it has been necessary to excavate the overburden as the building load is applied in order that at no time during construction is the state of stress in the soil changed by more than a small amount.

b. *Adjusting Footing Sizes*

Settlements can be controlled to some extent by adjusting the sizes of individual footings according to the loads carried and their position in the building. As illustrated in Figure 4.11a, a large footing loaded to the same contact pressure will settle more than will a small footing. Also, as shown in Figure 4.10a, a total load in the interior of a loaded area will settle more than will the same load at the edge of the area. Theoretically, one might increase the contact pressure under the outside columns to compensate for the difference in settlement because of their position and their difference in size. By properly adjusting the footing sizes, the higher compression adjacent to the bottom plus the lesser compression at depth under the small footings near the exterior of the building can be made equal to the lesser compression adjacent to the bottom plus the greater compression at depth under the larger footings.

But consolidation will take place first at the top of the layer and progress downward with time. This means that a given degree of consolidation of the soil just below the footings will be attained earlier than will the same degree of consolidation at depth, so that in the early settlement period, the smaller footings with the larger contact pressure will settle faster than will the larger footings. But as consolidation in the top part of the layer nears completion, the compression in the soil at depth will begin to contribute to the settlement and the larger interior footing will gain on the small ones until at some time the settlements of all footings will be equal again. After this time the interior larger footings will continue to settle faster than will the smaller outside ones, producing differential settlements in the opposite direction from those of the earlier period.

Therefore, although the differential settlements might be reduced by properly adjusting the sizes of footings, it is practically impossible to prevent differential settlements by this method.

c.　Distribution of Building Load over Site

Because total load as well as contact pressure is a factor in the settlement of footings, the building load can be distributed over the site in such a manner that the corners and exterior portions are loaded more heavily than the interior in the correct proportions to produce equal settlements over the entire area. This scheme requires the use of cantilevers and girders in the foundation system in order to distribute the load properly over the entire building area. Practically, this method of controlling differential settlements is open to the same objections as is that of controlling settlements by adjusting the contact pressures.

d.　Stiffened Slab or Frame

The foundation system can be designed stiff enough to redistribute the building loads to the footings so that differential settlements will be small enough for the structural frame and building parts to be able to assume the distortion without failure. As the stiffened frame deflects due to differential settlements, it transfers a portion of the load from the footings that settle most to those that settle least, thereby reducing the differential settlements.

The stiffening frame must be stiff and strong enough so that it will apportion the total building load to footings in such a manner as to limit differential settlement to values less than necessary to produce failure of the stiffening members. A series of several shallow members such as occurs in a multi-story building is more effective as a stiffening frame for distributing loads than is a single deep member. Differential settlements produce deformation or angle change in the members and, unless the frame is made sufficiently stiff and strong to materially reduce this deformation, it may fail and allow differential settlements as great as those that would occur without the stiffening frame. Increasing the stiffness of a single deep stiffening member could be detrimental.

The design of stiffening frames for reducing differential settlements is discussed later in this chapter. The design of stiffening slabs to prevent damage to residences and light buildings on active soils is discussed in the chapter on foundations on overconsolidated desiccated clays.

4.13　Settlement Analysis for Independent Footings of a Group

The difference in the analysis to determine the settlement of an independent footing of a group and that to determine the total settlement of a large area uniformly loaded as illustrated in Section 3.04 lies in the determination of the unit pressures under the footing produced by the footing itself and other footings of the group.

a.   Assumptions

An analysis for estimating the settlement of independent footings of a group can be made by applying the following assumptions.

(1) Pressures are determined by the Boussinesq or the Westergaard solution depending upon the nature of the soil. This assumption applies to a semi-infinite elastic soil mass loaded on the surface. Footings are usually placed at some distance below the surface of the soil, which makes the pressure determined for a surface load slightly in error.

(2) Pressure is assumed to be applied uniformly to the soil at the bottom of the column footing in determining the soil pressure at depths under the footings. This assumption is true only for a flexible footing uniformly loaded or for a footing of such stiffness as to deform the same as the unequal settlement produced by a uniform load on the surface. If the footing is rigid, the pressure distribution on clay is less at the middle and greater at the edges than average.

(3) Pressure under a footing of a group caused by loads on other footings of the group is computed as the summation of pressures caused by the other footings considered as point loads. Because other footings of the group are at some distance from the footing under consideration, this assumption does not produce an appreciable error.

(4) The settlement under a footing is assumed to be due to consolidation produced by the vertical pressure under the middle of the footing. This is the maximum vertical pressure under the footing on a horizontal plane below the footing and, therefore, probably indicates settlements slightly in excess of the actual settlement of the footing.

b.   Procedure for Settlement Analysis

(1) Determine depth, thickness and description of compressible soil layers below footings, taking undisturbed samples for testing. Determine elevation of the water table.

(2) Perform consolidation tests on undisturbed samples of compressible soil and prepare pressure-void ratio curves. Determine preconsolidation pressure p_p and compression indexes C_c. If it is not feasible to make consolidation tests, C_c can be estimated from the relationship $C_c = 0.54(e_n - 0.3)$.

(3) Divide the clay beds into layers of convenient thickness H for accuracy in the summation process. Compute the present overburden pressure p_1 at middepth of each clay layer.

(4) Determine the value of e_1 corresponding to the pressure p_1 and compute the value of $H[C_c/(1 + e_1)]$ for each layer.

(5) Determine the ratio of the depth from bottom of the footing to middepth of the clay layers to half the width and length of the footing. From the diagram for unit pressure under corner of uniformly loaded rectangular area, determine the unit pressure w_0 for unit contact pressure on the bottom of the footing. For round footings, determine the ratio of the radius of the footing R to the middepth of the layer z, and from the proper diagram determine the unit pressure w_0 for unit contact pressure at the bottom of the footing. Determine Δp for the load on the footing itself.

(6) Compute the contribution to pressure from other footings at r distance from the footing under consideration. Determine r. With r and z enter the diagram for unit pressure at r distance and z depth caused by concentrated load at $r = 0$ and determine p_r^1. Compute Δp as p_r^1 times the total load P on the distant footing.

(7) Determine the total Δp for each layer as the summation of the Δp for the footing's own load and the Δp's contributed by distant footings. Add this total Δp for each layer to the overburden pressure p_1 to determine p_2.

(8) Determine $\log p_2/p_1$ and multiply by $H[C_c/(1 + e_1)]$ for each layer to determine the contribution of each layer to the total settlement of the footing.

(9) Add the ΔH's for all layers to determine the total settlement of the footing.

c. Example of Settlement Analysis of Independent Footing of a Group

For the purpose of illustrating a method of settlement analysis for a single footing of a group of independent footings, an arrangement of footings is assumed as shown in Figure 4.13a. Sizes of footings are proportioned for a contact pressure of 2000 lb ft^{-2}. The footing loads are assumed to be applied independently, so that differential settlements have

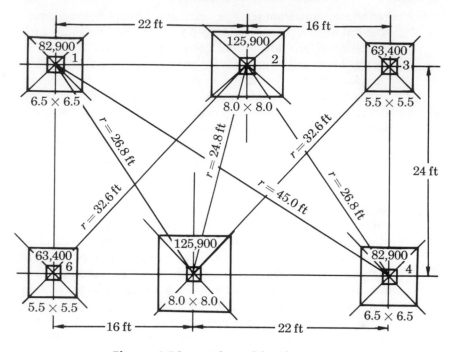

Figure 4.13a   Plan of footing group

no effect upon the applied loads. This same arrangement of footings is used later to illustrate the influence upon differential settlements of the stiffness of a structural frame supported on these footings.

The bottom of the footings is assumed to be 12 ft below the surface as shown in Figure 4.13b. The water table is assumed to be 15 ft below the surface. Properties of the soil as determined from consolidation tests are given under description of soil in Figure 4.13b. All of the derived properties are computed and recorded in columns 6 to 12 inclusive in the same manner described in Section 4.03.

The computations for this analysis are organized in Figure 4.13b. For the footing under consideration, columns 13, 14, and 15 are concerned with determining the pressures at middepth of the different layers into which the soil was divided. Values of w_0 were taken from the diagram for unit pressure under center of uniformly loaded square area. In this diagram, b is one-half the width of a square footing. Columns 16, 17, and 18 are concerned with determining the increase in pressure under the center of footing No. 5 caused by the load on footing No. 1. The unit vertical pressure at z depth and r distance, p_r^1, which is caused by a concentrated load of one kip, is taken from the diagram for unit pressure at r

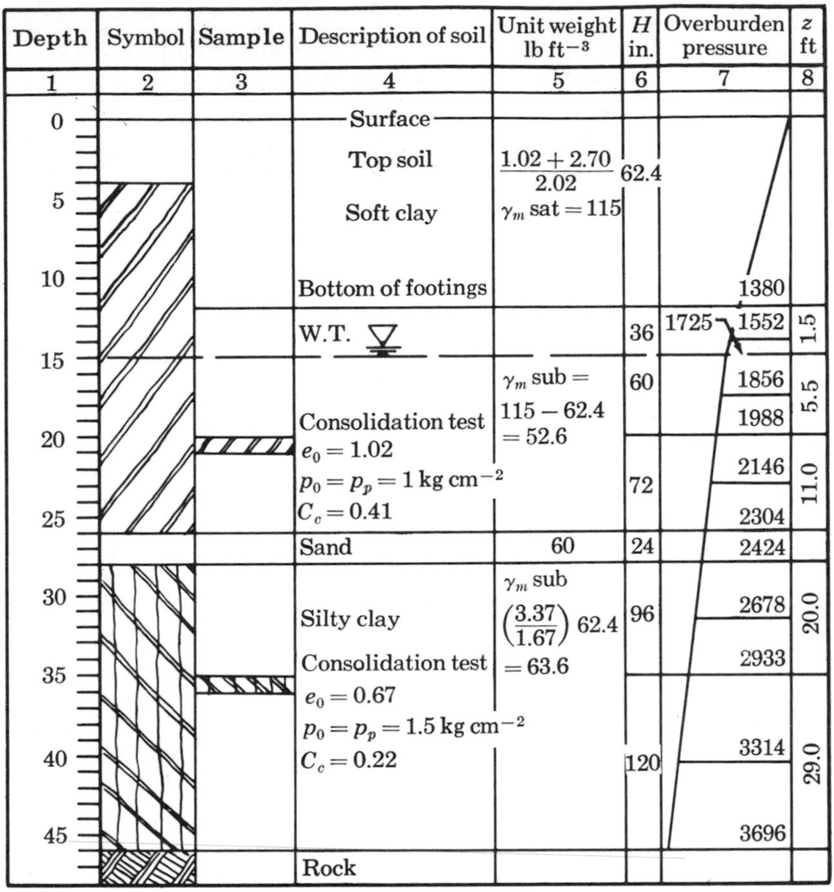

Depth	Symbol	Sample	Description of soil	Unit weight lb ft^{-3}	H in.	Overburden pressure	z ft
1	2	3	4	5	6	7	8
0			Surface				
5			Top soil	$\dfrac{1.02 + 2.70}{2.02}$ 62.4			
			Soft clay	γ_m sat $= 115$			
10			Bottom of footings			1380	
			W.T. ▽		36	1725 ⌐ 1552	1.5
15				γ_m sub $=$	60	1856	
20			Consolidation test	$115 - 62.4$		1988	5.5
			$e_0 = 1.02$	$= 52.6$		2146	
25			$p_0 = p_p = 1\,\text{kg cm}^{-2}$		72	2304	11.0
			$C_c = 0.41$				
			Sand	60	24	2424	
30			Silty clay	γ_m sub	96	2678	
				$\left(\dfrac{3.37}{1.67}\right)$ 62.4			20.0
35			Consolidation test	$= 63.6$		2933	
			$e_0 = 0.67$				
40			$p_0 = p_p = 1.5\,\text{kg cm}^{-2}$			3314	
			$C_c = 0.22$		120		29.0
45						3696	
			Rock				

Sheet No. 1

Figure 4.13b   Settlement analysis for independent footing

distance and depth z caused by a concentrated load at $r = 0$. Δp is the increase in pressure under the center of footing No. 5 for a concentrated load of 82.9 kip on footing No. 1, and is equal to $p_r^1\,P$. In the same manner, the contribution to pressure under the center of footing No. 5 is found for the remaining footings of the group.

Under summation is given the sum of all of the increases in pressure under footing No. 5 caused by its own load and the loads of all the other footings of the group. The total pressure under the center of footing No. 5 is the original overburden pressure plus the increase caused by the added footing loads. The contribution to settlement of one layer is $H[C_c/(1 +$

Footing No. 5   Size 8.0 × 8.0

C_c	e_1	$\dfrac{C_c}{1+e_1}$	$H\dfrac{C_c}{1+e_1}$	Footing No. 5 $w=2000\,\text{lbft}^{-2}$			Footing No. 1 $P=82.9\,\text{kip}$			Footing No. 2 $P=125.9\,\text{kip}$		
9	10	11	12	13	14	15	16	17	18	19	20	21
				$\dfrac{z}{b}$	w_0	Δp	r	p_r^1	Δp	r	p_r^1	Δp
0.41	1.065	0.198	7.14	0.37	0.98	1960	26.8	.008	0.6	24.8	.008	1.0
0.41	1.033	0.202	12.09	1.37	0.58	1160		0.01	0.8		0.01	1.3
0.41	1.008	0.204	14.70	2.74	0.22	440		0.04	3.3		0.05	6.3
0.22	1.511	0.087	8.40	5.00	0.08	160		0.11	9.1		0.13	16.4
0.22	1.491	0.088	10.60	7.25	0.04	80		0.14	11.6		0.15	18.9

Sheet No. 2

Figure 4.13b   **Settlement analysis for independent footing**

e_1)]$\log(p_2/p_1)$ and is recorded in column 34 of the tabulation. The total settlement of footing No. 5 is the summation of the contributions of all the compressible layers underlying footing No. 5.

d.   *Differential Settlement*

Following the same procedure as illustrated above, the total estimated settlement of footing No. 4 is 5.64 in. and that of Footing No. 6 is 5.00 in. Thus, the differential settlement between footings No. 4 and No. 5 is

Footing No. 5   Size 8.0 × 8.0   Contact pressure $w = 2000$

Footing No. 3 $P = 63.4$			Footing No. 4 $P = 82.9$			Footing No. 6 $P = 63.4$			Summation			
22	23	24	25	26	27	28	29	30	31	32	33	34
r	p_r^1	Δp	r	p_r^1	Δp	r	p_r^1	Δp	$\Sigma \Delta p$	p_2	$\log \dfrac{p_2}{p_1}$	ΔH
32.6	0	0	22	.005	0.4	16	.012	0.8	1963	3515	0.353	2.52
	.001	0		.018	1.5		0.05	3.2	1167	3019	0.210	2.54
	.019	1.2		0.08	6.6		0.24	15.2	473	2619	0.084	1.23
	.058	3.7		0.19	15.7		0.36	22.8	228	2906	0.035	0.29
	0.09	5.7		0.20	16.6		0.30	19.0	152	3466	0.019	0.20
											Total settlement	= 6.78

Sheet No. 3

Figure 4.13b   **Settlement analysis for independent footing**

$6.78 - 5.64 = 1.14$ in., and between No. 5 and No. 6 it is $6.78 - 5.00 = 1.78$ in.

For footings loaded to the same contact pressure, the pressure is the same immediately beneath all footings. At shallow depth the pressure produced by distant footings is small. Therefore, if the compressible layer is thin and lies near the bottom of the footings, even though the total settlement may be considerable, the differential settlement will be small. At depth the pressure under a large footing loaded to the same contact pressure is greater than the pressure at the same depth under a small footing. Therefore, the thicker the compressible layer contributing to the settlement, the greater will be the differential settlement compared to the total settlement.

If the compressible soil under the footings consists of a single thick layer of clay drained at the top surface only, the rate of settlement will be comparatively rapid in the early part of the settlement period as the clay near the top of the layer consolidates. The rate of settlement will decrease with time as the clay farther down in the layer contributes to the settlement. In the early part of the settlement period, differential settlement will be small and will increase with time. Therefore, footings on such a thick compressible layer may settle for considerable time, possibly for a year or more, before differential settlement becomes appreciable.

If the compressible soil is separated into thin layers of clay with drainage layers between the clay layers, both the total settlement and the differential settlements will occur simultaneously and at a comparatively rapid rate.

4.14   Settlement Due to Creep and Lateral Deformation

If a headless barrel of asphalt that breaks as a brittle material under sudden deformation is turned on its side and left for several months in warm weather, a considerable amount of the asphalt will have flowed out of the barrel onto the ground under the pressure of its own weight. After this very slow deformation or creep, the asphalt still breaks as a brittle material when subjected to sudden deformation. Clay soils will also creep under sustained stresses that exceed certain threshold stresses, which vary for different soils.

Clay consists of flat scale-like particles with negative charges existing on their broad surfaces. These charges attract the bipolar water molecules like tiny magnets holding a thin film about 10 Å thick as a solid layer of

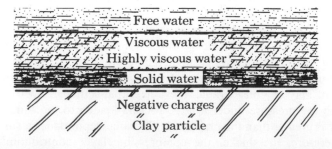

Figure 4.14a   Surface of clay particle with attached water

adsorbed water. Outside this solid adsorbed water layer, the viscosity of the water decreases with distance from the particle surface. This viscous layer, which is attached to the particle outside the adsorbed layer, is often called double layer water. The thickness of the attached water varies with the mineral in the clay particle, the pressure applied to the clay, and the temperature and availability of water.

If these clay particles are oriented with their broad surfaces parallel, they will be separated by the attached layers of water. Pressure forces some of the double layer water from between the particles. Evaporation

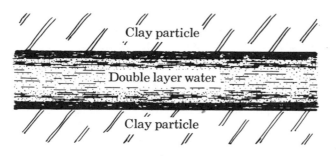

Figure 4.14b   Clay particles separated by double layer water

also removes some of the double layer water. In either case, the less viscous water is removed first leaving the more viscous water between the particles.

Newton discovered that if two plates are separated by a viscous liquid as shown in Figure 4.14c, the shearing resistance to movement of the particles relative to each other is proportional to the area A, inversely proportional to the thickness of the sheet of liquid d, and directly proportional to the velocity with which the plates are moved relative to each other v.

$$\frac{S}{S_1} = \frac{A\,v\,d_1}{A_1 v_1 d} \text{ or } s = \frac{v\,s_1 d_1}{d\,v_1}$$

If s_1 is the unit shear resistance for a velocity of 1 cm sec^{-1} and d_1 is 1 cm, then $s_1 d_1 / v_1$ is a constant designating the viscosity of the liquid η in g sec cm^{-2}, and the relationship can be written

$$v = \frac{s\,d}{\eta} \qquad\qquad \text{(Eq. 4.14a)}$$

Therefore, if shear stress is applied to clay with a parallel orientation as shown in Figure 4.14b (dispersed structure), the clay particles may

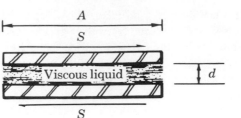

Figure 4.14c   Plates separated by viscous liquid

be displaced laterally relative to each other. The rate of this displacement
or creep, as indicated by Equation 4.14a, depends upon the applied shear
stress, the distance between the grains, and the viscosity of the double
layer of water between the grains. The thickness of the attached double
layer of water differs with different minerals. At zero pressure and ordinary
temperature, kaolinite has an attached layer of water about 400 Å thick
and montmorillonite has an attached layer 200 Å thick. The montmorillonite particle is so much thinner than is the kaolinite particle that the ratio
of attached water to soil mass is much greater in montmorillonite than in
kaolinite. Therefore, one might expect that, although montmorillonite is
much more compressible than kaolinite, creep might occur in kaolinite at
a lower shear stress than it would in montmorillonite. Consolidation due
to pressure and evaporation removes the less viscous water, thus reducing
the distance between particles and increasing the viscosity of the attached
water, and thus increasing the resistance to creep. Clays are usually deposited with a loose flocculent structure as shown in Figure 4.14d and
not with an oriented dispersed structure as illustrated above. When load is
applied to the clay with this loose flocculent structure and consolidation
occurs, the pressure becomes high at the points of contact, thus binding

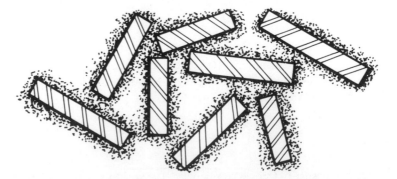

Figure 4.14d   Loose structure of clay

the particles at these points of contact with highly viscous water. Also, the applied pressure causes the particles to slip or creep past each other to positions of greater stability. Therefore, as consolidation occurs the resistance to creep increases.

Under the interior of a very large uniformly loaded area, the stress in the soil is uniform on a horizontal plane at any depth. When vertical stress is applied to a block of material causing a vertical deformation Δy, the

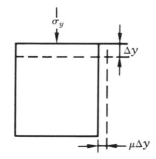

Figure 4.14e   Deformation of stressed block

material expands laterally against zero horizontal stress an amount equal to Poisson's ratio μ times Δy. This horizontal deformation could be prevented by a horizontal confining stress $\sigma_x = \mu \Delta y / E$. If the surrounding adjacent blocks of the same material are subjected to the same vertical stress, the adjacent blocks will attempt to expand the same as the first and the lateral stress required to prevent horizontal deformation is the same as the first. As shown in Figure 4.14f, these lateral stresses counteract each other and there is no lateral deformation of the stressed blocks. In this case, the vertical and horizontal stresses are principal stresses; i.e., $\sigma_z = \sigma_1, \sigma_x = \sigma_y = \sigma_2 = \sigma_3$. However, if the vertical stress on block 1 is greater than the stress on the adjacent block 3, the lateral deformation of

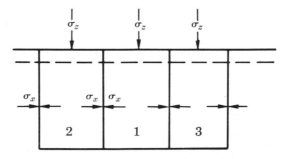

Figure 4.14f   Adjacent stressed blocks

block 1 will be greater than that of block 3. Because the lateral pressure from block 1 is greater than that required to prevent lateral deformation of block 3, lateral deformation will be produced in block 3 in a direction to reduce the lateral dimensions of block 3. In this case of gradually decreasing vertical stress in a horizontal plane the blocks are subjected to shearing stresses and the vertical and horizontal stresses are not principal stresses.

Therefore, under a small loaded area and under the edge of a large loaded area on compressible soil, where the vertical stress is decreasing with horizontal distance from the center, some lateral consolidation will occur and the soil will be subjected to shearing stresses tending to cause creep of the soil. Where the stresses are uniform over a horizontal plane, there can be neither lateral consolidation nor creep. That portion of the horizontal displacement under the edge of a loaded area caused by lateral consolidation is due to decrease in volume of the soil, and does not affect the soil on the surface adjacent to the loaded area. That portion of the lateral displacement caused by creep is due to movement of the soil particles out from under the loaded area, and results in a bulge or uplift of the soil adjacent to the loaded area.

The amount of horizontal consolidation and creep and their contribution to the total settlement are difficult to estimate. In an attempt to determine the influence of this lateral displacement upon settlements, Osterman and Lindskog of Sweden measured the horizontal displacements, vertical settlements, and pore water pressures at various depths in a 15 m thick layer of clay having a shear strength of about 0.1 kg cm^{-2}. The measurements were made at the edge of a 40 m long embankment of gravel 8.5 m wide and 1.5 m high, producing a surcharge of about 1.8 kg cm^{-2}. From the result of these observations, the settlement due to lateral displacement was estimated. At the beginning of the settlement period, lateral displacement of the clay accounted for most of the total vertical settlement. With the passage of time, the contribution of lateral movement to the total settlement decreased. At 100 days, the total settlement was about 18 cm and the contribution of lateral displacement was estimated at about 10 cm. At 500 days, the total settlement was 30 cm and the contribution of lateral displacement was about 14 cm. The maximum lateral movement of the clay occurred at a depth of about one-half the width of the loaded area.

The computed settlement of a long uniformly loaded line or of a uniformly loaded area is greatest in the middle and smallest at the ends or the corners. The effect of lateral displacement of soil by creep should increase the settlement at the edges of the loaded area thus tending to produce more nearly uniform settlements than those estimated on the basis of consolidation alone. However, in very compressible clay, such as much of the clay that underlies Mexico City, the actual settlement of long uniformly loaded walls closely follows the estimated settlement for consolidation alone. On the other hand, a large asphalt storage tank on very soft clay 12 ft thick settled by squeezing out some of the clay causing upheaval of the area outside the tank.

Settlement caused by creep or forcing soil from under a loaded area cannot be predictably controlled, because its magnitude and duration depend upon the excess stress above the creep strength and the rate of strength gain due to consolidation. Therefore, the stress that produces creep should be regarded as a limiting bearing capacity regardless of settlement considerations.

4.15 Upheaval of Bottom of Excavation

There exist two possible causes for heaving of soils: swelling and a slow plastic flow (creep). The latter cannot be tolerated, and must be avoided by cutting flat slopes, providing sheet piling, etc. Heave in the bottom of excavations must be tolerated because it is usually impossible to avoid. Therefore, an understanding of the swelling phenomenon is necessary in order to anticipate the problems associated with heaving.

When pressure is first applied to saturated clay, the pore water is subjected to pressure. As the pore water is forced out of the clay, the pressure is given over by the pore water to the soil stucture with a resulting volume decrease caused by elastic deformation of the clay particles, squeezing out of viscous attached water, slipping of soil grains to positions of greater stability, and, possibly, by compression of trapped gas. Since part of the deformation of the clay is elastic, and since, upon release of pressure, water is drawn back to the particles by the charges on their surfaces thus increasing the thickness of the attached water between the particles, when water is available the clay increases in volume when the pressure is released. This swelling occurs only as water is drawn back into the pores, making the rate of swelling after release of pressure essentially the same as that for consolidation under pressure.

Under the pressure of the overburden, the loosely deposited clay is compressed from its original void ratio e_0 to e_p as shown in Figure 4.15a. As discussed earlier, if an additional stress Δp is added to the overburden pressure p_p without relieving the pressure, the void ratio of the loaded soil is decreased from e_p to e_2, and

$$\Delta H = H \frac{e_p + e_2}{1 + e_p}$$

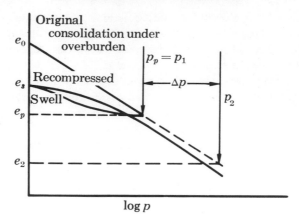

Figure 4.15a   Void ratio-pressure curve after complete consolidation

But if the overburden pressure is removed as occurs in the bottom of an excavated area and if water is available, as is the usual case in a consolidation test, after complete swelling the void ratio will increase from e_p to e_s, and heave in the bottom of the excavation will be

$$\Delta H = H \frac{e_s - e_p}{1 + e_p}$$

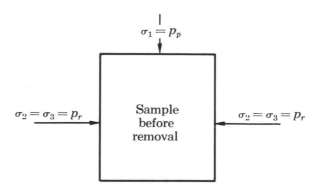

Figure 4.15b   Stress on soil in place

In a consolidation test, the sample is removed from its environment imposed by the overburden or a vertical stress of $\sigma_1 = p_p$ and horizontal stresses σ_2 and σ_3 equal to the earth pressure at rest p_r. After removal of the sample from its natural position, the external stresses are reduced to zero in all directions. With no additional water available, swelling of the sample is restricted by capillary stresses in the pore water as the soil attempts to expand. The specimen is placed in the consolidation ring while subjected to these capillary forces. If a vertical stress less than the stress produced by the capillary water is applied to the specimen in the ring and the specimen is flooded immediately, the specimen may swell against the applied stress. As soon as the applied stress becomes greater than the capillary stresses, consolidation occurs.

If the bottom of an excavation is at or near the water table so that water is available, the soil at the bottom of the excavation is free to expand under zero pressure. If the bottom of the excavation is above the water table but at a lesser distance than the capillary rise, capillary water hanging from the soil grains at the bottom of the excavation, as shown in Figure 4.15c, will offer a resistance to swelling equal to the weight of the

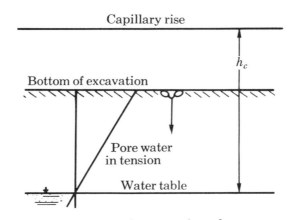

Figure 4.15c   Bottom of excavation above water table

capillary water between the water table and the bottom of the excavation. If the soil below the bottom of the excavation is a desiccated clay with a water content below the shrinkage limit, little swelling will occur until after water is made available, except for the small immediate elastic expansion due to removal of pressure. After water is available to the desiccated clay, the clay can expand a maximum amount.

In an excavation of limited dimensions in soft clay, the clay adjacent to the sides of the excavation is restrained from swelling by the weight of the overburden not removed and the shear strength of the clay. In the middle of the excavated area, the clay can swell practically to its fullest extent.

The greatest amount of upheaval will occur in very soft compressible clay where it is usually feasible to use a floating foundation such that the weight of the excavated overburden compensates for the weight of the building. The purpose of a compensated floating foundation is to apply the building load in such a manner that the state of stress in the soil is not changed, and to thus prevent settlement. But, after the application of

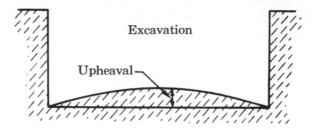

Figure 4.15d   Upheaval of bottom of excavation

the building load, the area in the middle of the excavation will settle under the uniformly reapplied overburden pressure an amount equal to $\Delta H = (e_s - e_p)/(1 + e_s)$, while next to the sides the settlement will be practically zero, thereby producing differential settlement. So, even though the weight of the excavated earth may compensate for the weight of the building, it may be necessary to provide a stiff foundation frame in order to control differential settlements.

If movement of the soil from below the bottom of the embankment is not restrained with sheet pile walls or other means, creep may have a considerable effect upon the amount of differential settlement which might be experienced.

4.16   Accuracy of Settlement Analysis

Any estimate of the settlement of structures on compressible soil depends upon so many unknown factors that the results of the computation can be only approximate. The accuracy of the estimate depends upon the knowledge of the dimensions and properties of the underlying materials. In those cases where the underlying soil is fairly homogeneous and uniform in thickness over the loaded area, with careful investigation and interpretation, it may be possible to predict settlements within 20 per cent of the actual settlements. As the arrangement of the deposits underlying the foundation becomes more complex, the ability to predict settlements becomes more remote. Under adverse conditions, predicted settlements based upon mathematical analysis may be as much as 100 per cent in error.

In the evaluation of settlement analysis, one should realize that the analysis is based upon idealized hypothetical conditions which may or may not closely resemble the actual conditions. Results obtained from the use of formulas should be evaluated on the basis of how closely the assumptions used in the derivation of the formulas fit the actual conditions.

Some of the conditions in which the assumptions used in the analysis are at variance with the existing conditons are as follows:

a. Applied Loads

Settlements are affected by the size and shape of the loaded area and by the distribution of the load over the area. Some compensation for these factors can be made in the computation of vertical pressures in the soil under the foundation. In the case of a building foundation, the ratio of dead to live loads and the length of time that live loads are applied influence the settlement. On compressible clays, live loads that remain for only short periods of time make little contribution to the settlement. However, on highly sensitive soils, such as honeycomb silts, a live load which produces collapse of the honeycomb structure may cause large and fairly rapid settlement when applied for only a short time.

Differential settlements are affected by the stiffness of the structure. Differential settlements in a stiff structure result in a redistribution of load to the foundation and a change from the settlement pattern based upon the assumption of a flexible structure which loads the parts of the foundation with a constant contact pressure throughout the settlement period.

b. Soil Pressures

Soil pressures determined by the Boussinesq or the Westergaard solutions are assumed to be those produced by the load applied to the surface of the loaded area, and it is assumed that the underlying soil is homogeneous, isotropic or ideally anisotropic, elastic, and limitless in extent laterally and in depth. These conditions are seldom met in practice. In the analysis, the vertical pressures, determined by the Boussinesq and Westergaard solutions, are usually assumed to be principal stresses. Under the center of a large uniformly loaded area the vertical stresses are nearly principal stresses, but near the edge of a loaded area vertical and horizontal shears are produced, making the principal stresses inclined toward the center of the loaded area somewhat greater than the vertical pressures.

c.   Homogeneity of Deposits

Soil deposits are seldom homogeneous for very great depths. Even a thick deposit of recently deposited clay may be very soft near the surface and increase in stiffness with depth caused by consolidation under the pressure of the overburden. On the other hand, the layer of clay deposited under similar conditions may be softer at depth than that near the surface because of a high pore pressure at depth which prevented consolidation. The clay near the surface may be much stiffer than that at depth because of consolidation by desiccation near the surface.

Often the underlying soil consists of layers of varying thicknesses and properties. Layers of sand interspersed with layers of clay not only contribute little to the settlement but, by being confined under an overburden, distribute the applied load over a larger area than would occur in homogeneous layer. If the sand layers serve as drainage layers, they increase the rate of settlement with time as well as reduce the total settlement. If the sand layers are lenses with no outlets and, therefore, do not serve as drainage layers, they may reduce the total settlement but affect the rate of settlement very little.

d.   Comparison of Laboratory Determined and In-Place Properties

Predicted settlements based upon laboratory determined properties of the underlying soils may be greatly in error if the laboratory determined properties do not correspond to the in-place properties of the soil from which the sample was obtained.

Removing a sample of soil from its original position results in more or less disturbance or partial remolding of a portion of the sample. At the very least, the state of stress in the soil sample is changed by removing the confining pressure of the overburden, and by a possible change of the pore water pressure from compression to tension as the sample attempts to swell under the reduced external pressure. In some soils, the structure may be broken to a considerable extent in the removal of the sample and the preparation of test specimens. If the sensitivity of the soil is appreciable, this partial remolding may affect the properties greatly. As shown in Figure 4.16a, the position in the sample from which the specimen was taken may be of significance because of disturbance near the edge of the sample.

Figure 4.16a shows the results of unconfined compression tests on specimens of the same sample of Boston blue clay taken from a drilled hole with a sampling spoon. Specimen No. 1 is from near the edge of

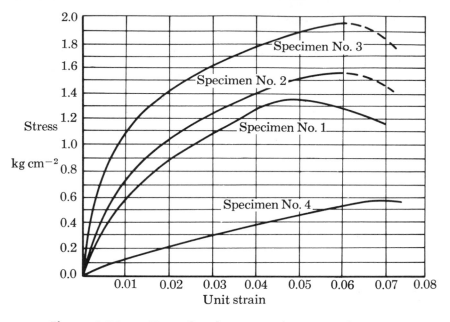

Figure 4.16a   **Unconfined compression tests of Boston blue clay**

the sample where the disturbance is greatest. Specimen No. 2 is from near the edge, but is nearer the center than is specimen No. 1. Specimen No. 3 is from the center of the sample. Specimen No. 4 is specimen No. 3 remolded and formed into a cylinder of approximately the same dimensions and with the same water content as No. 3. The sensitivity of this clay as indicated by these tests is about $1.89/0.55 = 3.4$.

Also, the manner of performing the laboratory tests influences the results. The time required to produce the same degree of consolidation under load is approximately proportional to the square of the thickness of the specimen. Thick specimens require much longer time for consolidation than thin ones and are, therefore, subject to greater influence of secondary compression.

In the consolidation test, the specimen is cut to fit snugly inside the consolidation ring in order to prevent lateral expansion. As the specimen is compressed, the lateral pressure against the sides of the ring produces friction between the ring and the specimen which resists deformation and carries a part of the applied load. The percentage of error caused by friction between the specimen and the ring is dependent upon the ratio of the contact area between the specimen and the ring and the cross sectional area of the specimen. Therefore, the thinner the specimen compared to its cross sectional area, the less is the error because of friction. In the

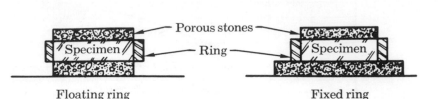

Floating ring   Fixed ring

Figure 4.16b   Floating ring and fixed ring consolidation test

floating ring consolidation test, both the top and bottom stones are small enough to slip into the ring so that the specimen is compressed toward the midheight from both top and bottom. In the fixed ring test, the bottom stone is larger than the specimen so that the compression of the specimen must occur between top and bottom. Therefore, less friction is produced in the floating ring test than in the fixed ring test. For some soils, the floating ring test cannot be used because the weight of the ring causes it to slip down from around the specimen before load is applied. The use of light weight plastic rings alleviates this tendency to slide down.

e.   Type and Condition of Soil

The variation between computed and actual settlements may be affected by the type and condition of the soil. The compressible soil may be inorganic or organic and may be normally consolidated, overconsolidated, or underconsolidated. Although it makes no difference to the building whether the settlement is due to primary consolidation or to secondary compression, the amount and rate of settlement is influenced by the type of soil and its condition at the time the load is applied, and this must be taken into consideration in making and interpreting the analysis.

(1)   Organic Soils

Settlements of highly organic soils are, to a considerable extent, due to secondary compression. In general, predicted settlements are computed on the basis of primary consolidation as determined by a consolidation test. If not properly made and interpreted, estimates of settlements of organic soils may be greatly in error. In estimating the settlement of organic soils, the decrease in volume should be computed from void ratios taken directly from the *e-p* curve of a properly performed consolidation test, and not computed from the value of the consolidation index C_c as is done for normally consolidated inorganic clays.

(2)   *Inorganic Soils*

On inorganic soils, secondary compression is generally of little consequence in producing settlements and, in settlement analyses, is usually ignored. However, some secondary compression does occur and may be of consequence during the life of the building. In inorganic clays, secondary compression occurs late in the settlement period. In thick layers of clay, secondary compression continues after primary consolidation at such a slow rate that its influence may be negligible. If the underlying soil consists of thin layers of clay interspersed with layers of sand, the settlement will occur at a rapid rate, with that portion of the settlement due to secondary compression occurring much earlier than it would in thick homogeneous strata of the same clay.

(3)   *Normally Consolidated, Overconsolidated, and Underconsolidated Clays*

Analysis for settlement of normally consolidated, overconsolidated and underconsolidated clays is discussed in Sections 4.03, 4.04, and 4.05, respectively. If the analysis for estimating settlements does not take into account whether the clay is normally consolidated, overconsolidated, or underconsolidated, the estimate of settlement is likely to be greatly in error.

Mathematical analysis at best is only an aid to the judgment in the design of a successful foundation and structure. The fact that settlements cannot be predicted with a high degree of accuracy need not detract from the usefulness of careful settlement analysis when interpreted intelligently. Even though the analysis is greatly in error percentagewise, it is important to know whether the settlement is likely to be a fraction of an inch, one or more inches, or one or more feet. But in the interpretation of the analysis, it is important for the designer to know the assumed conditions which yield the result of the analysis, how these assumed idealized conditions differ from the actual conditions, and the effect of these differences upon the result. But mathematical analysis is only one aid to the judgment. Other aids may be used to design successful foundations without the aid of mathematical analyses. Whether or not mathematical analyses can be made, all aids possible should be brought to bear upon the problem by the designer. Aids other than mathematical analysis are observation of existing structures, imagination, and experimentation.

4.17   Preloading

Under some conditions, such as those existing in very loose deposits, especially of organic soil such as peat, it is feasible to preconsolidate the deposit by preloading the building area for a long enough time to produce consolidation under the applied load. Such preloading usually consists in piling readily available soil materials on the site to produce a load somewhat less than, equal to, or greater than the weight of the structure to be erected on the site. After consolidation to the desired degree has been attained, the preload is removed and the permanent structure erected.

This preloading produces an overconsolidated soil. When the permanent structure is erected on the site, the settlement is restricted to that caused by recompression of the soil for that portion of the applied load which is less than the preconsolidation load. If the preload was equal to or larger than the load of the structure, and if the preload was retained long enough for complete consolidation of the soil, the entire settlement is restricted to that caused by recompression.

In saturated soils for which preloading is usually feasible, in addition to the cost and inconvenience of moving the preload on and off the site, a disadvantage of reducing settlements by preloading is the time required to produce consolidation. In very porous soil, such as peat, the time element may not be of considerable importance, but for clays of comparatively low permeability the time element may be a serious factor.

In order to know when the preload has accomplished its purpose so that it can be removed, the degree of consolidation produced by the preload must be known. The degree of consolidation at a given time after application of the preload can be estimated by computing the expected settlement with time and measuring the actual settlement. Probably, a more accurate method of estimating the degree of consolidation that has occurred at a given time is by measurement of pore water pressures at different depths in the compressible soil to be loaded by the permanent structure. The pressure of the pore water in excess of the hydrostatic pressure (excess pore pressure u) with depth can be plotted on a diagram such as shown in Figure 4.17a. As discussed in Section 4.05, the degree of consolidation at time t is the ratio of the area on the $\Delta p - u$ side of the curve to the total area of the rectangle $H\Delta p$. In this case, H is the thickness of the compressible layer when the layer rests on an impervious layer, so that all of the water squeezed out of the soil must flow to the

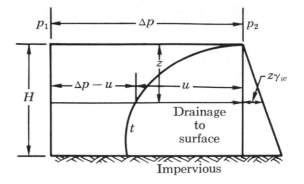

Figure 4.17a   Pore pressure at time t

surface in order to allow consolidation. If the layer is drained on both sides so that water can flow toward both top and bottom surfaces, H is one-half the thickness of the layer.

4.18   Sand Drains

As mentioned above, time is a serious factor in the consolidation of high void ratio clays by preloading. In order to reduce the time for consolidation, sand drains are sometimes used so that the pore water can drain laterally to the sand drains where it can flow to the surface through the permeable sand. The rate at which consolidation is produced is dependent upon the spacing of the sand drains. The ultimate solution would be to remove all the clay and replace it with sand or gravel. But if this were done, no preloading would be necessary. The sand drains, which

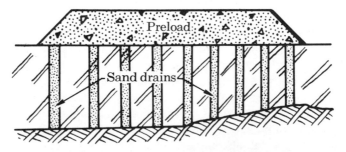

Figure 4.18a   Sand drains in loose clay

are constructed by pouring sand into drilled holes under the confining pressure of the surrounding soil act as incompressible piles. As the clay is consolidated by the preload, friction between the sand and the soil which is trying to slide down around the pile causes some of the preload to be carried by the sand piles and retards consolidation. The closer the sand piles are spaced, the greater will be the amount of preload carried by the piles and the less will be that applied to the clay to produce consolidation. If the sand drains are spaced too far apart, their effectiveness in draining the soil may be reduced to such an extent that they are practically useless in reducing the time for consolidation. Remolding of the clay next to the pile may reduce the permeability to such an extent that the pile is ineffective.

4.19   Settlement Analysis for Footings Supporting Continuous Frames

Except for extremely large total settlements, the structural engineer and the architect are usually more interested in differential settlements than in total settlements. In some cases, the architect may be more restricted as to differential settlements than is the engineer. Deformation that can be safely withstood by the structural frame may damage architectural materials and in other ways reduce the usefulness of the structure.

In the earlier portion of this chapter, methods were presented for estimating settlements of footings in which the applied loads are constant throughout the settlement period. This condition of loading assumes that the structural frame supported by the footings is completely flexible. Usually, the structural frame possesses at least some resistance to settlement deformation until after failure.

When loads are first applied to footings from a structural frame, there is no differential settlement, and the loads to each column footing can be determined. As differential settlement occurs, the structural frame is deformed. Force is required to distort the structural frame so that, as differential settlement occurs, the load carried by some columns is increased and that carried by others is decreased in such a manner that the summation of loads carried by all columns is always equal to the total building load. This redistribution of the building loads to the column footings changes the settlement pattern accordingly, so that differential settlements and the deformation of the frame are in equilibrium. Thus, the stiffness of the frame acts to reduce differential settlements and can be manipulated to control differential settlements.

There follows a method for estimating the settlement of column footings supporting continuous frames on normally consolidated clays. The method of analysis presented is long and tedious, but it is amenable to programing for computation by electronic computer. Probably this method can be shortened and improved, or a better method of analysis can be devised.

a.   *Method of Analysis for Estimating Differential Settlements*

The method of analysis presented here for estimating the settlement of individual footings supporting a loaded continuous frame is a combination of two methods of structural analysis for continuous frames in which there is settlement distortion and the method of settlement analysis as presented earlier in this chapter.

For convenience in writing relationships, the following symbols are used:

A subscript means in or on, such as ΔP_1 = change in load on Column No. 1. A symbol written at the top of another symbol like an exponent means due to, such as $\Delta P_2^{S_1=1}$ = change in load on Column No. 2 due to settlement of 1 in. in Footing No. 1, etc. Following these rules the following symbols are used:

S = Total settlement

S_1 = Total settlement of footing No. 1

S_1^P = Settlement of footing No. 1 due to the footing load for no deformation of the frame

$S_1^{\Delta P_1^{S_1}}$ = Settlement of footing No. 1 due to change in load on column No. 1 due to settlement of footing No. 1

Imagine an elastic continuous frame resting on independent column footings on an elastic soil mass. When a load is placed on the frame, it produces a deformation of the soil. Now consider that there are jacks in the columns just above the footings, and that as settlements of the footings occur, the jacks are extended the amount of the soil compression so that no settlement deformation of the frame occurs. Under these conditions, the column loads and the corresponding settlements (jack extensions) can be determined as outlined previously. Call this settlement of the footing with no settlement deformation of the frame S^P.

Now release one of the jacks until it assumes its original length; i.e., release the jack by an amount equal to the extension which was required to prevent deformation of the frame. This released jack extension will be taken up partly by deformation of the frame and partly by expansion of the elastic soil, thus raising the footing and lowering the column to a position of equilibrium depending upon the relative stiffnesses of the soil and the frame.

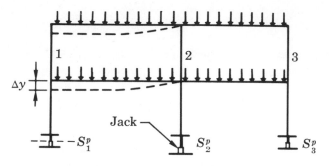

Figure 4.19a   Loaded continuous frame

The deformation of the frame produces a redistribution of load, changing the load on a column by an amount ΔP. The change from the computed settlement of column No. 1 in which the jack was released, S_1^P, is the settlement caused by the change in load on column No. 1 due to the settlement of column No. 1, $S_1^{\Delta P S_1}$, plus the settlement of column No. 1 caused by the change in load on column No. 2 due to the settlement of column No. 1 $S_2^{\Delta P S_1}$, plus the settlement of column No. 1 caused by the change in load on column No. 3 due to settlement of column No. 1 $S_{13}^{\Delta P S_1}$, etc.

So the actual settlement of footing No. 1 when the jack in column No. 1 only is released can be written as

$$S_1 = S_1^P + S_{11}^{\Delta P S_1} + S_{12}^{\Delta P S_1} + S_{13}^{\Delta P S_1}$$

$$S_1 = S_1^P + \Sigma S_1^{\Delta P S_1}$$

Then, if the jack in column No. 2 is released, the settlement of column No. 1 will be further changed due to the change in column loads which are produced by the accompanying deformation of the frame. The settlement of footing No. 1 with jacks released in column No. 1 and column No. 2 only is

$$S_1 = S_1^P + \Sigma S_1^{\Delta P S_1} + \Sigma S_1^{\Delta P S_2}$$

and, if all the jacks are released, the settlement in any footing can be written as

$$S_i = S_i^P + \Sigma S_i^{\Delta P S_i} + \Sigma S_i^{\Delta P S_1} + \Sigma S_i^{\Delta P S_2} \cdots + \Sigma S_i^{\Delta P S_n}$$

The settlement S_i^P caused by the column loads for an assumed flexible frame can be estimated as described earlier. But, the change in settlement caused by deformation of a frame possessing resistance to deformation cannot be determined until the changes in column loads due to differential settlements are known. However, the changes in column loads caused by a settlement of 1 in. in one column can be determined, and, from these changes in loads, the change in settlement caused by a frame deformation produced by a settlement of 1 in. in one column only can be determined. If a linear relationship between load and settlement is assumed, the change in settlement of footing No. 1 caused by the settlement of footing No. 2 is the settlement of footing No. 1 caused by a settlement of 1 in. in column No. 2 times the actual settlement of footing No. 2; i.e., $S_2 \Sigma S_1^{\Delta P\,S_2=1''}$. The effect of S_3 on the settlement of footing No. 1 is $S_3 \Sigma S_1^{\Delta P\,S_3=1''}$.

By following this procedure, an equation can be written for the settlement of any footing as follows:

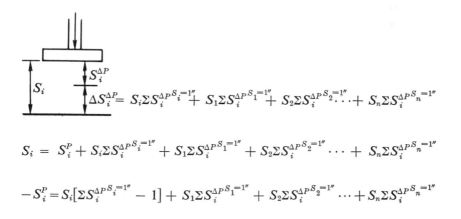

$$\Delta S_i^{\Delta P} = S_i \Sigma S_i^{\Delta P\,S_i=1''} + S_1 \Sigma S_i^{\Delta P\,S_1=1''} + S_2 \Sigma S_i^{\Delta P\,S_2=1''} \cdots + S_n \Sigma S_i^{\Delta P\,S_n=1''}$$

$$S_i = S_i^P + S_i \Sigma S_i^{\Delta P\,S_i=1''} + S_1 \Sigma S_i^{\Delta P\,S_1=1''} + S_2 \Sigma S_i^{\Delta P\,S_2=1''} \cdots + S_n \Sigma S_i^{\Delta P\,S_n=1''}$$

$$-S_i^P = S_i[\Sigma S_i^{\Delta P\,S_i=1''} - 1] + S_1 \Sigma S_i^{\Delta P\,S_1=1''} + S_2 \Sigma S_i^{\Delta P\,S_2=1''} \cdots + S_n \Sigma S_i^{\Delta P\,S_n=1''}$$

(Eq. 4.19a)

Equation 4.19a contains an unknown for each footing. A similar equation can be written for each footing in the group. This provides as many equations and as many unknowns as there are footings. The settlement of each footing can be determined by solving these equations simultaneously.

The details of the analysis can be carried out as outlined below: First, determine the column loads for no settlement deformation of the frame. Next, assume a settlement of 1 in. of one footing and determine the corresponding change in load for every column in the frame. Repeat this procedure for each column in the frame.

Now, choose one footing only, say No. 1, and determine the settlement due to the loaded flexible frame $S_1{}^P$. Then, determine the change in settlement of footing No. 1 due to ΔP for 1 in. settlement of column No. 1, then the change in settlement due to ΔP for 1 in. settlement of column No. 2, and so on until the effect upon footing No. 1 of 1 in. settlement of each footing has been determined independently. This provides all the information needed for setting up the equation for the settlement of footing No. 1. As shown later in the example, the computations for determining the constants and coefficients for forming the settlement equations can be organized and tabulated for convenience.

b.   Structural Analysis

Any method of structural analysis can be used for determining the column loads for no settlement deformation, and for determining the change in column loads caused by a change in elevation Δy in each bay of the structural frame. Moment distribution is used for this purpose in the example given herein. The sign convention used in this example calls the moment which bends a beam so that it will hold water as positive, and one which bends the beam so that it will not hold water as negative.

Figure 4.19b   Sign convention for moment in beams

For moments in columns, this same sign convention applies when the column is viewed from right to left as shown in Figure 4.19c. In the distribution, the column end moments are written above the column at the top, and below the column at the bottom as shown in Figure 4.19d, and the sign convention preserved. When the joint is balanced in equilibrium, the summation of moments at the right of the column must equal the summation of moments to the left of the column. In this case, the column may be considered as an equal sign. The carry over factor for straight prismatic members is $-\frac{1}{2}$, and their stiffness $M/\theta = 4EI/L = 4EK$. In carrying out the moment distribution, fixed end moments for the loading conditions are computed and written in their proper places on a section through the bent. Minus one-half of the proportional part of the unbal-

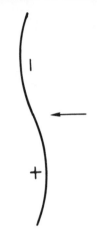

Figure 4.19c   Sign convention for moments in columns

anced moment is carried over to the opposite end of each member; i.e., $-K/2\Sigma K$ times the unbalanced moment at the joint is carried over to the opposite end of each member meeting at the joint. Then, $-K/2\Sigma K$ times the unbalanced moment due to carry over moments is carried over to the opposite end of each member. This step can be repeated to attain the degree of accuracy desired. These moments are added and balanced at the joints in accordance with $K/\Sigma K$ of the members meeting at the joint. End beam shears are computed from beam loads and end moments. The fixed end moments for beam rotation as shown in Figure 4.19e are plus and minus $6EI\Delta y/L_2$. The fixed end moments are computed for $\Delta y = 1$ in. and distributed to the frame as described above. The beam shears due to beam rotation are computed from the end moments; i.e., $\Delta V =$ difference in end moments divided by span length.

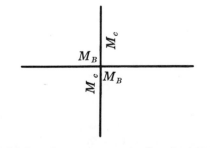

Figure 4.19d   Arrangement of moments at joints

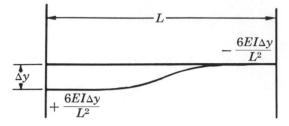

Figure 4.19e   Fixed end moments due to Δy

c.   Alternate Method of Settlement Analysis

As stated earlier, the method of settlement analysis described in Section 4.13 may be used for the purpose of determining the settlements of footings supporting a flexible frame. In the analysis for estimating settlements of footings supporting a frame possessing resistance to settlement deformation, it would be convenient to know the settlement produced by a column load of 1 kip so that the settlements could be determined simply by multiplying the settlement for 1 kip by the load on the column plus the change in column load due to settlement deformation.

Unfortunately, the ratio of pressure and void ratio after complete consolidation is not constant. The e-p curve for a normally consolidated clay has a constantly changing slope as shown in Figure 4.19f. For normally consolidated clay, the virgin $e - \log p$ curve is a straight line having

a slope of $C_c = \dfrac{\Delta e}{\log \dfrac{p_2}{p_1}}$. The slope of the e-p curve is $\dfrac{de}{dp}$, designated a_v

and called the coefficient of compressibility. The slope of the line from e_1 to e_2 is $\Delta e/\Delta p = \tan \alpha$. At some point between e_1 and e_2, the slope of the tangent to the e-p curve is the same as the slope of the secant line between e_1 and e_2. If it be assumed that the tangent and the secant are

parallel at $p_1 + \dfrac{\Delta p}{2}$, the value of Δe can be expressed as $\dfrac{de}{dp} \Delta p$. The e-p

curve is represented by the equation $e_1 - e = C_c \log \dfrac{p}{p_1}$ or $e = e_1 - C_c$

$\log \dfrac{p}{p_1}$. The slope of the e-p curve is $\dfrac{de}{dp} = \dfrac{d}{dp}(e_1 - C_c \log \dfrac{p}{p_1})$, and since

e_1 and p_1 are constants, $\dfrac{de}{dp} = -C_c \dfrac{1}{p} \log_{10} \xi = C_c \dfrac{0.434}{p}$. If the slope of the secant is assumed as equal to $\dfrac{de}{dp}$ at $p_1 + \dfrac{\Delta p}{2}$,

$$\Delta e = - C_c \frac{0.434}{p_1 + \dfrac{\Delta p}{2}} \Delta p \qquad \text{(Eq. 4.19b)}$$

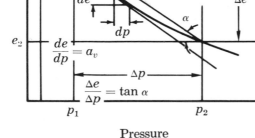

Void
ratio

Figure 4.19f   Void ratio–pressure curve

The error caused by assuming the slope of the secant to be the same as the slope of the tangent at $p_1 + \dfrac{\Delta p}{2}$ is evaluated later.

As shown by the settlement analysis of Figure 4.19b, except at considerable depth where the added stresses are quite low, most of the added stress in the soil is produced by the load on the footing itself. The settlement of a footing produced by the load on the footing itself without the contribution from distant loads is easily estimated, and the settlement per kip of column load $\Delta H/P^F$ determined. If this assumption is accepted, a curve showing the relationship between settlement per kip load on the footing $\Delta H/P^F$ and footing size can be drawn for a given soil condition as shown in Figure 4.19p. Such a curve is convenient if there are more than 4 or 5 footings of different sizes involved in the analysis.

Then, if it is assumed that the stress produced by distant loads causes settlement at the same rate as the stress from the footing load, the con-

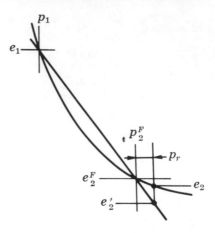

Figure 4.19g   **e-p curve with extension of secant from e_1 to e_2^F**

tribution to settlement of distant loads can be determined by multiplying the $\Delta P's$ produced by settlement of distant footings by the settlement rate $\Delta H/P^F$.

The use of this assumption introduces an error because e_2' is assumed located on an extension of the secant from e_1 to e_2^F instead of on the curve. Because the true e_2 on the curve is slightly larger than e_2' on the extension of the secant, settlements estimated by using this assumption are slightly larger than those found by using the true e_2 on the curve as was done in Section 4.13. If this assumption is accepted, a curve can be drawn for the contribution to settlement from distant loads. Because the slope of the secant between two different points on the e-p curve and the pressure at a given depth are dependent upon footing size, an accurate analysis requires a curve for each footing size. But, if the further simplifying assumption is accepted that the contribution to settlement from distant loads is the same for all footings as that for the average size footing, a single curve showing the relationship between distance r and settlement for 1 kip load $\Delta H/P_r$ can be drawn. The use of such a single curve reduces the labor of computation considerably. The use of this assumption of a constant contribution to settlement from distant loads for all footings results in values of settlement that are slightly less than those found by using the value of e_2 lying on the curve for footings larger than the size for which the curve was drawn and slightly greater for smaller footings.

Curves showing the relationship between size of footing and settlement per kip load and between distance and kip load are drawn for a given soil condition and apply to that condition and no other.

d. *Example of Settlement Analysis of Footings Supporting Continuous Frames*

Assume the structural frame loaded as shown in Figure 4.19h and determine the settlements of independent column footings resting on the soil shown in the example of Figure 4.13b at the same elevation as in the former example.

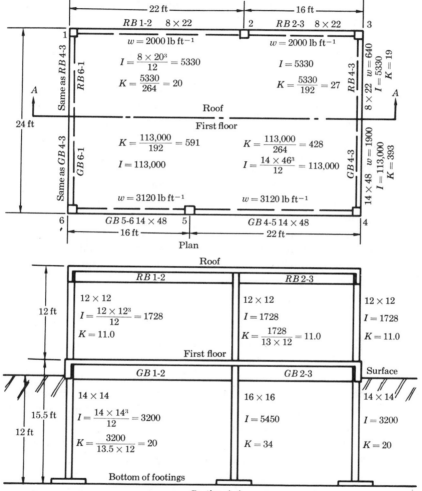

Figure 4.19h   Loaded continuous structural frame supported on independent column footings

(1)   *Example of Structural Analysis*

The structural part of the analysis consists of estimating the column loads for the loaded frame and determining the size of footings as done in Figure 4.19*i* and Figure 4.19*j*, and determining the change in column loads caused by settlement of each footing independently, as done in Figures 4.19*k*, 4.19*l*, and 4.19*m*.

In arriving at the values given, certain simplifying assumptions have been made in order to facilitate the analysis.

(a) Moments of inertia are computed for homogeneous rectangular sections. This assumption is probably a fairly accurate assumption for beams reinforced on the tension side only. Tees on the beams increase the stiffness somewhat as does compression steel either in beams or columns. For moment distribution this causes little error, but fixed end moments for beam rotation (not joint) computed for homogeneous rectangular sections are somewhat lower than actual fixed end moments for beams with tees and for beams and columns with compressive steel.

(b) Joints are assumed to rotate at the intersection of the axes of members meeting at the joint.

(c) The ends of columns are assumed to be fixed at the footings. Probably, the footings rotate slightly under the applied moments from columns. Also the columns are restrained somewhat by the pressure of the backfill around them.

(d) Sidesway or lateral deflection of the frame is neglected. The effect of sidesway can be included in the analysis and, under some conditions, might be important enough to be included.

(e) The effect of the floor framing between roof, floor, and grade beams is neglected. This slab construction may or may not have a negligible influence upon the resistance of the frame to settlement deformation.

(f) All calculations are by slide rule and no attempt is made to compute moments closer than the nearest ft kip.

Moments and shears are computed for the side bents in Figure 4.19*i* and for the end bents in Figure 4.19*j*. Column loads are computed by adding beam shears from all beams framing into each column and adding the weight of the column and its enclosing masonry.

If one should desire to follow the details of the computation or check the accuracy, the following explanations are given:

$$K = \frac{I}{L} = \frac{\text{in.}^4}{\text{in.}} = \text{in.}^3$$

$$FEM \text{ for } RB\ 1-2 = -\frac{wL^2}{12} = -\frac{2 \times 22^2}{12} = -81 \text{ ft kip}$$

COM to Col. No. 1 end of *RB* 1–2 is the unbalanced moment at Col.

No. 2 joint times $\dfrac{K}{2\Sigma K} = -\dfrac{88-43}{2} \times 0.34 = -6$. The sign of the

COM is easily determined by inspection; i.e., in order to balance the moments at column No. 2 joint, the balancing moments to the left of column No. 2 are positive and those to the right are negative, thus making the carry over moment to the column 1 end of the beam negative. The *COM's* are new fixed end moments which unbalance the joint again, so the effect of their distribution must be carried over as a new *COM*; i.e., the *COM* at column No. 1 end of *RB*1–2 as a result of the first carry over is

$$-\frac{26 - 1 + 15}{2} \times 0.34 = -2$$

The fixed end moments and the carry over moments are added and balanced at the joints. The unbalanced moment at Col. No. 1 at the roof joint is the difference in fixed end moments on opposite sides of the equality sign (column) or $-89 + 1 = -88$ too much on the right for equilibrium at the joint. This unbalanced moment rotates the joint to a condition of equilibrium; i.e., $\Sigma M = 0$. *RM* $1 - 2$ resists $0.65 \times 88 = 57$ ft kip and column No. 1 resists $0.35 \times 88 = 31$ ft kip. The signs of the

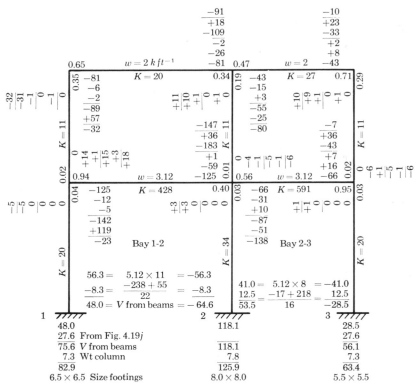

Figure 4.19i   **Horizontal members loaded—no settlement deformation—side bents held against sidesway**

balancing moments are such as to produce equilibrium at the joint, $\Sigma M = 0$, and are always positive on one side of the column and negative on the other.

Shears from beams are computed by adding to the simple shears the change in shear due to end moments. The simple beam shear is positive on the left and negative on the right and the change in shear due to end moments is the same along the entire length of the beam and is equal to the moment on the left subtracted from the moment on the right divided by the span length.

Footing loads are determined by adding the shears from all beams that frame into the column under consideration plus the weight of the column. Footing sizes are determined in this example on the basis of 2000 lb per sq ft. All footings are square.

Data for determining the change in column loads caused by 1 in. settlement of each column independently are computed in Figures 4.19h, 4.19i, and 4.19j. One distribution in each bent can be omitted by dis-

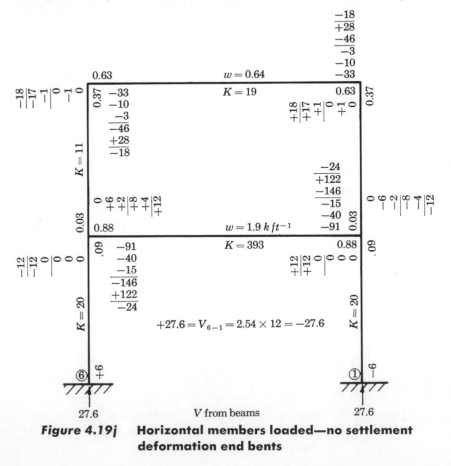

Figure 4.19j   **Horizontal members loaded—no settlement deformation end bents**

tributing *FEM* for 1 in. settlement deformation in each bay independently, instead of for settlement of each column. Shears for the shear deformation in the bays can be added to determine the effect of each column settlement.

As an example, the *FEM* for deflection Δy is

$$FEM = \frac{6EI\Delta y}{L^2} = \frac{6EK\Delta y}{L}$$

If E is lb in.$^{-2}$, I is in.^{4}, Δy is in., and L is in., the *FEM* is in. lb and

$$\frac{\text{in. lb}}{12} = \text{ft lb or } \frac{6EK\Delta y}{12L} = \text{ft lb. If } L \text{ is in ft, then } FEM = \frac{6EK\Delta y}{144L} = \text{ft lb}$$

when all factors are in. except L which is ft.

Using E for concrete as 3×10^6 lb in.$^{-2}$ and K as computed and listed

$$FEM = \frac{6 \times 3 \times 10^6 \times 1}{144} \frac{K}{L} = (1.25 \times 10^4) \frac{K}{L}$$

$$FEM = \frac{6EK\Delta y}{L} = \frac{6 \times 3 \times 10^6 \times K}{12L \times 12} = 1.25 \times 10^4 \times \frac{K}{L} = \text{ft lb}$$

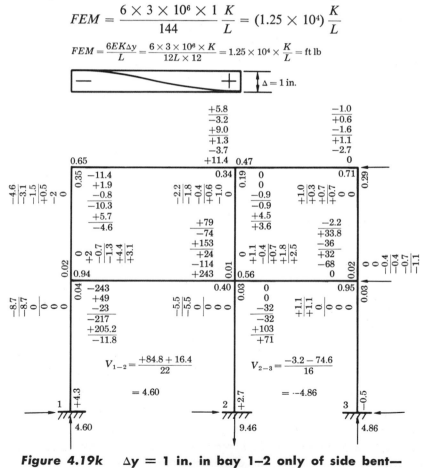

Figure 4.19k $\Delta y = 1$ in. in bay 1–2 only of side bent— held against sidesway

Fixed end moments are distributed to the frame for deflection in both bays of the side bents and in the end bents and bay shears computed as was done for loads on the frame. The distribution of these fixed end moments is done in Figures 4.19k, 4.19l, and 4.19m.

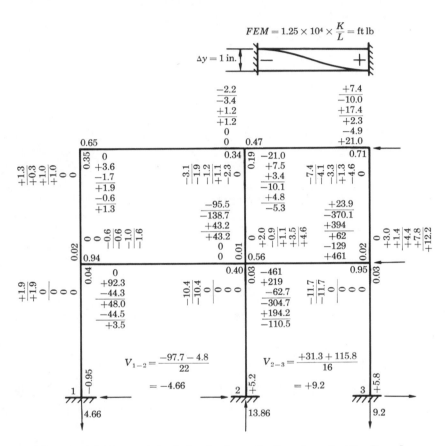

Figure 4.19l   Δy = 1 in. in bay 2–3 only of side bend—held against sidesway

The change in load on a column required to produce a settlement of 1 in. with no settlement of other footings, and the change in load on other columns of the frame caused by the settlement of the single footing, can be determined by adding the change in shears caused by the 1 in. settlement deformations in all the bents framing into the column under consideration. For example, the change in column loads caused by a settlement of 1 in. in Footing No. 1 only can be determined by combining the total bay shears found by the calculations for settlement deformations in Figures 4.19*k* and 4.19*m*. Change in load which reduces the load on a column is negative and vice versa.

$$\Delta P_1{}^{S_1=1''} = -4.60 - 2.26 = -6.86 \text{ kips}$$

$$\Delta P_2{}^{S_1=1''} = +4.60 + 4.86 = +9.46 \text{ kips}$$

$$\Delta P_3{}^{S_1=1''} = -4.86 \text{ kips}$$

$$\Delta P_6{}^{S_1=1''} = +2.26 \text{ kips}$$

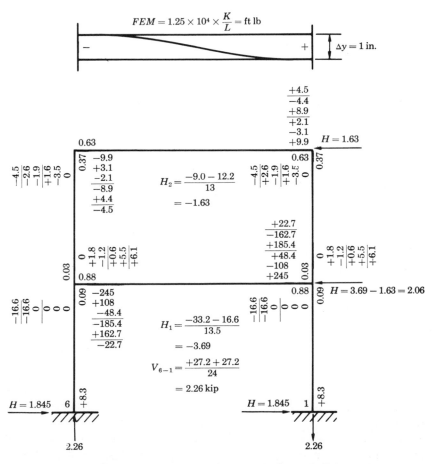

Figure 4.19m   Δy = 1 in. in end bents—held against sidesway

(2) *Example of Settlement Analysis*

The soil conditions are the same for this example as those for the example illustrated in Section 4.13, so the computations through column 12 of Figure 4.13 to determine $H \dfrac{C_c}{1 + e_1}$ are not repeated in the computation for settlement analysis, except column 8 for values of z and column 7 for values of p_1. Settlement is computed as

$$\Delta H = H \frac{0.434 \, C_c}{1 + e_1} \frac{\Delta p}{p_1 + \dfrac{\Delta p}{2}}$$

$H \dfrac{0.434 \, C_c}{1 + e_1}$ is a constant containing properties and dimensions of the soil only and, therefore, applies to any footing with its bottom at the depth for which the values are determined. These values are inserted in column 13 of the tabulation for settlement in Figure 4.19n.

In order to plot a curve showing the relationship between footing size and settlement per kip load on the footing itself, settlement analyses are made for four footing sizes neglecting the influence of distant footings in Figure 4.19n. The added stress in the soil for determining the settlement is found by multiplying the contact pressure by w_0 found for $\dfrac{z}{b}$ in Diagram 4.07d in Section 4.07. In this case, b is one-half the side of the footing. After the total settlement of a footing has been computed, the settlement is divided by the total load on the footing $\Delta H / P$. These four values of $\Delta H / P$ are plotted in Figure 4.19p to show the relationship between size of footing and settlement per kip column load.

Next, the settlements produced by a 1 kip load on distant footings are found. The influence of distant loads is practically independent of the size of the distant footing, but the relative contribution to settlement of a particular footing from a distant load depends upon the size of the particular footing. However, compared to the settlement caused by its own load, the contribution of a distant load to the settlement of a footing is small. A simplifying assumption is made that the contribution to settlement from distant loads is the same for all footings as for a footing of average size. Using these simplifying assumptions, the contribution to settlements for a 1 kip load at r distances of 10 ft, 20 ft, 30 ft, and 40 ft are computed in Figure 4.19o. These settlements caused by 1 kip column load at r distance are plotted in Figure 4.19q. The contribution from a distant column load can be determined by multiplying the settlement per kip load at r distance as found in Figure 4.19q by the total distant column load.

ΔH due to 2000 lb per sq ft on bottom of footing

p_1	z	$H\dfrac{0.434\,C_c}{1+e_1}$	4 ft − 0 in. × 4 ft − 0 in.					6 ft − 0 in. × 6 ft − 0 in.				
			$\dfrac{z}{b}$	w_0	Δp	$p_1+\dfrac{\Delta p}{2}$	ΔH	$\dfrac{z}{b}$	w_0	Δp	$p_1+\dfrac{\Delta p}{2}$	ΔH
7	8	13	14	15	16	17	18	19	20	21	22	23
$\dfrac{\text{lb}}{\text{ft}^2}$	ft	$\dfrac{\text{lb}}{\text{ft}^2}$		From Dia. IV	$\dfrac{\text{lb}}{\text{ft}^2}$	$\dfrac{\text{lb}}{\text{ft}^2}$	in.		From Dia. IV	$\dfrac{\text{lb}}{\text{ft}^2}$	$\dfrac{\text{lb}}{\text{ft}^2}$	in.
		Surface	$\dfrac{z}{2}$					$\dfrac{z}{3}$				
		Bottom of footings										
1552	1.5	3.10	0.75	0.87	1740	2422	2.22	0.50	0.95	1900	2502	2.34
1856	5.5	5.23	2.75	0.21	420	2066	1.06	1.83	0.38	760	2616	1.52
2146	11.0	6.35	5.5	0.06	120	2206	0.34	3.67	0.14	280	2286	0.78
2678	20.0	3.64	10.0	0.02	40	2678	0.05	6.67	0.04	80	2718	0.17
3314	29.0	4.59	14.5	0.02	40	3334	0.05	9.67	0.02	80	3354	0.11
Σ							3.72					4.92

$$\frac{\Delta H}{P} = \frac{\text{in.}}{k} = \text{in. per kip column load} = 0.116$$

$$\frac{\Delta H}{P} = 0.0683$$

Figure 4.19n   Settlement for isolated square footing

ΔH due to 2000 lb per sq ft on bottom of footing

p_1	z	$H\dfrac{0.434\,C_c}{1+e_1}$	8 ft – 0 in. × 8 ft – 0 in.					10 ft – 0 in. × 10 ft – 0 in.				
			$\dfrac{z}{b}$	w_0	Δp	$p_1+\dfrac{\Delta p}{2}$	ΔH	$\dfrac{z}{b}$	w_0	Δp	$p_1+\dfrac{p\Delta}{2}$	ΔH
7	8	13	24	25	26	27	28	29	30	31	32	33
$\dfrac{\text{lb}}{\text{ft}^2}$	ft	Surface	$\dfrac{z}{4}$	From Dia. IV	$\dfrac{\text{lb}}{\text{ft}^2}$	$\dfrac{\text{lb}}{\text{ft}^2}$	in.	$\dfrac{z}{5}$	From Dia. IV	$\dfrac{\text{lb}}{\text{ft}^2}$	$\dfrac{\text{lb}}{\text{ft}^2}$	in.
		Bottom of footings										
1552	1.5	3.10	0.37	0.98	1960	2532	2.37	0.30	0.985	1970	2537	2.40
1856	5.5	5.23	1.37	0.58	1160	2436	2.49	1.10	0.68	1360	2536	2.52
2146	11.0	6.35	2.75	0.21	420	2356	1.13	2.20	0.30	600	2446	1.56
2678	20.0	3.64	5.00	0.08	160	2758	0.21	4.00	0.115	230	2873	0.29
3314	29.0	4.59	7.25	0.04	80	3354	0.11	5.80	0.06	120	3374	0.16
Σ							6.31					6.93
$\dfrac{\Delta H}{P}$							0.0493					0.0346

Figure 4.19n   Settlement for isolated square footing

ΔH due to 1 kip at r Distance

z	Aver. $\frac{\Delta H}{\Delta P}$	1 kip at r = 10		1 kip at r = 20		1 kip at r = 30		1 kip at r = 40	
		Δp_{10}	ΔH_{10}	Δp_{20}	ΔH_{20}	Δp_{30}	ΔH_{30}	Δp_{40}	ΔH_{40}
8	34	35	36	37	38	39	40	41	42
Surface ft	in. ft² $\frac{kip}{}$ 6 × 6 $\frac{23}{21}$	lb ft⁻² $= \frac{kip}{ft^2 10^3}$ From Dia. I	$\frac{in.}{10^3}$ 35 × 34 Bottom of Footings	lb ft⁻² From Dia. I	$\frac{in.}{10^3}$ 37 × 34	lb ft⁻² From Dia. I	$\frac{in.}{10^3}$ 39 × 34	lb ft⁻² From Dia. I	$\frac{in.}{10^3}$ 41 × 34
1.5	1.23	0.08	0.098	0.006	0.064	0	0	0	0
5.5	2.00	0.40	0.800	0.030	0.060	0.003	0.006	0	0
11.0	2.79	0.85	2.370	0.110	0.307	0.020	0.031	0.005	0.014
20.0	1.34	0.69	0.925	0.215	0.288	0.060	0.080	0.020	0.027
29.0	1.37	0.48	0.590	0.216	0.296	0.093	0.127	0.040	0.055
$\frac{\Delta H}{P_r} = \frac{in.}{kip}$			0.04783		0.001015		0.000244		0.000096

Figure 4.19o   Contribution to settlement from distant loads

(3)   *Setting up Settlement Equations*

After the change in column loads for 1 in. settlement of each column, the relationship between settlement per kip load and footing size, and the relationship between distance r and contribution to settlement due to a 1 kip concentrated load at r distance have been determined, the necessary data are available for setting up the equations for settlement of each footing of the group supporting the continuous frame.

Computations for determining the constants and coefficients for setting up the settlement equations (Eq. 4.19a) are organized and tabulated in Figure 4.19r.

The first portion of the tabulation is concerned with determining the change in column load ΔP for each column caused by a settlement of 1 in. in each of the columns of the group. In column c of the tabulation, is listed the change in load on each column of the group produced by a set-

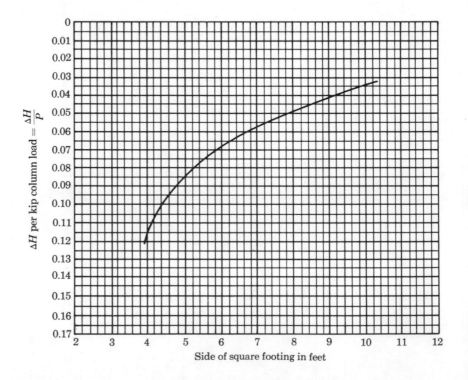

Figure 4.19p   Relation between footing size and settlement per kip column load

tlement of 1 in. in column No. 1. The change in load on column No. 1 due to a settlement of 1 in. in column No. 1 is −6.86 kip, and the change in load on column No. 2 due to a settlement of 1 in. in column No. 1 is 9.46 kip, etc. These values are found from Figures 4.19k, 4.19l, and 4.19m as described under d(1). The sum of the changes in load on all footings caused by the settlement of one footing must be equal to zero for equilibrium because the deformation of the frame caused by loads on the frame does not change the total load on the frame.

The second part of the tabulation is concerned with determining the settlement of footing No. 1, S_1^p, assuming all footing loads to be constant throughout the settlement period (flexible frame), and the contribution to settlement of column No. 1 for changes in all of the columns due to 1 in. settlement in each column. Distances from footing No. 1 are listed in the r column. Footing No. 1 is 0 distance from footing No. 1, footing No. 2 is 22 ft from footing No. 1, etc. The settlement per kip load in footing No. 1 is found for a 6.5 ft square footing on Figure 4.19p as 0.0625 in. The contribution to settlement of footing No. 1 for 1 kip load at 22 ft is found in Figure 4.19q as 0.0007 in., etc.

The settlement of footing No. 1, S_1^p, is the sum of the settlement from

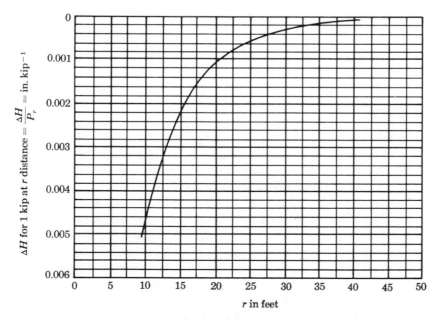

Figure 4.19q   Settlement produced by 1 kip load at r distance

its own load, 82.9 kip $\times$ 0.0625 = 5.185 in. plus the contribution to settlement of footing No. 1 of the load on column No. 2, 125.9 $\times$ 0.0007 = 0.088 in., etc.

The change in settlement of footing No. 1 due to change in load on all columns for a settlement of 1 in. in each column is found next. For instance, the change in settlement of footing No. 1 due to 1 in. settlement of footing No. 1 is $-$ 6.86 $\times$ 0.0625 = $-$ 0.429 in. and the change in settlement of footing No. 1 due to change in load on column No. 2 from 1 in. settlement of footing No. 1 is 9.46 $\times$ 0.0007 = 0.007 in., etc. The total change in settlement due to change in load on all columns from settlement of column No. 1 only is $\sum_1 S_1^{P^{S_1=1''}} = -0.421$ in., etc.

Because of the deliberate partial symmetry of the frame $S_1 = S_4$, $S_2 = S_5$, and $S_3 = S_6$, it is necessary to set up only three settlement equations which is done for footings No. 1, No. 2, and No. 3. The settlement equation for footing No. 1 is

$$(-0.421 - 1)S_1 + 0.565S_2 - 0.283S_3 + 0 + 0 - 0.001S_6 = -5.372$$

or $\quad -1.421S_1 + 0.565S_2 + (-0.283 - 0.001)S_3 = -5.372$

Tabulated computations for the solution of the three necessary settlement equations are performed in Figure 4.19s.

Differential settlements	
Without stiffening frame	*With stiffening frame*
$S_{1\text{-}2} = 6.436 - 5.372 = 1.064$	$S_{1\text{-}2} = 5.841 - 4.992 = 0.849$
$S_{2\text{-}3} = 6.436 - 5.160 = 1.276$	$S_{2\text{-}3} = 5.481 - 5.550 = 0.291$
$S_{1\text{-}6} = 5.372 - 5.160 = 0.212$	$S_{1\text{-}6} = 5.550 - 4.992 = 0.558$

From the analysis of the simple frame used in this example, one sees that where the frame is stiffest the differential settlement is reduced most, and that in certain unsymmetrical bays of a bent, in which the stiffness is much less than in other bays, the differential settlement may be increased because of the readjustment of loads to footings.

Although the labor of making such an analysis in the form presented here for a frame containing 4 or 5 bents or bays is not insurmountably great for some practical applications, the labor required for analyzing a large unsymmetrical frame with many columns makes the analysis practically prohibitive for application to any but simple frames. However, experience with such analyses for a few frames can serve as an aid to the judgment in the design of frames for control of differential settlements even though no rigorous mathematical analysis is made.

The method of analysis presented in this section is amenable, with some variation, to solution by electronic computer.

Footing No. 1 6.5 ft × 6.5 ft

a	b	c	d	e	f	g	h	r	$\dfrac{\Delta H}{P}$	S_1^P						
		ΔP due to S = 1 in. in Col.									S due to ΔP in column only					
Col. No.	Col. load kip	1	2	3	4	5	6				1	2	3	4	5	6
1	82.9	-6.86	9.26	-4.66	0	0	2.26	0	0.0625	5.185	-0.429	0.580	-0.292	0	0	0.141
2	125.9	9.46	-23.32	13.86	0	0	0	22	0.0007	0.088	0.007	-0.016	0.010	0	0	0
3	63.4	-4.86	14.06	-11.46	2.26	0	0	38	0.0001	0.006	0	0.001	-0.001	0	0	0
4	82.9	0	0	2.26	-6.86	9.26	-4.66	45	0.0001	0.008	0	0	0	-0.001	0.001	0
5	125.9	0	0	0	9.46	-23.32	13.86	26.8	0.0004	0.050	0	0	0	0.004	-0.009	0.005
6	63.4	2.26	0	0	-4.86	14.06	-11.46	24	0.00055	0.035	0.001	0	0	-0.003	0.008	-0.006
Σ		0	0	0	0	0	0	Σ		5.372	-0.421	0.565	-0.283	0	0	-0.001

Figure 4.19r **Construction of settlement equations**

Footing No. 2   8.0 ft × 8.0 ft

r	$\dfrac{\Delta H}{P}$	S_1^P	S due to ΔP in column only					
			1	2	3	4	5	6
22	0.0007	0.058	−0.005	0.007	−0.003	0	0	0.001
0	0.049	6.155	0.464	−1.141	0.679	0	0	0
16	0.0018	0.114	−0.009	0.025	−0.021	0	0	0
26.8	0.0004	0.033	0	0	0.001	−0.003	0.004	−0.002
24.8	0.0005	0.063	0	0	0	0.005	−0.012	0.007
32.6	0.0002	0.013	0	0	0	−0.001	0.003	−0.002
Σ		6.436	0.450	−1.109	0.656	0.001	−0.005	0.003

Footing No. 3   5.5 ft × 5.5 ft

r	$\dfrac{\Delta H}{P}$	S_1^P	S due to ΔP in column only					
			1	2	3	4	5	6
38	0.0001	0.008	−0.001	−0.001	0	0	0	0
16	0.0018	0.226	0.017	−0.042	0.025	0	0	0
0	0.0765	4.850	−0.372	1.074	−0.875	0.173	0	0
24	0.0005	0.045	0	0	0	−0.004	0.005	−0.003
32.6	0.0002	0.025	0	0	0	0.002	−0.005	0.003
45	0.0001	0.006	0	0	0	0	0.001	−0.001
Σ		5.160	−0.356	1.033	−0.085	0.171	0.001	−0.001

Figure 4.19r   Construction of settlement equations

Equation	$S_1 = S_4$	$S_2 = S_5$	$S_3 = S_6$	S^{PD}
1	−1.421	0.565	−0.284	−5.372
2	0.451	−2.114	0.659	−6.436
3	−0.185	1.034	−1.851	−5.160
2′	1.421	−6.661	2.076	−20.278
3′	−1.421	7.942	−14.218	−39.634
a = 1 + 2′	0	−6.096	1.792	−25.650
b = 3′ − 1	0	7.377	−13.934	−34.262
a′		−7.377	2.169	−31.039
c = a′ + b		0	−11.765	−65.301
			$S_3 = 5.550$	
a		−6.096	9.955	−25.650
		−6.096		−35.605
		$S_2 = 5.841$		
1	−1.421	3.300	−1.576	−5.372
	−1.421			−7.094
	$S_1 = 4.992$			
1	−7.093	3.300	−1.576	−5.369
2	2.251	−12.347	3.657	−6.439
3	−0.923	6.040	−10.273	−5.156

Figure 4.19s   Solution of settlement equations

e. *Accuracy of Analysis*

In addition to the inaccuracies caused by the assumptions listed in Section 4.13 and in Section 4.16, the following inaccuracies are introduced in the analysis for settlement of footings supporting a continuous frame by the use of the following assumptions:

1. The tangent to the e-p curve is assumed to be parallel to the secant from e_1 to e_2 at $p_1 + (\Delta p/2)$ for determining the settlement of a footing due to its own load only, and also for determining the contribution to settlement from distant column loads.

For footing No. 2 of the structure shown in Figure 4.13a, the analysis of Figure 4.13b based upon $\Delta e = C_c/(1 + e_1) \log p_2/p_1$ indicates a settlement of 6.55 in. due to its own load only without the influence of other footings of the group. The analysis of Figure 4.19n based upon $(0.434/p_1 + \frac{\Delta p}{2})\Delta p$ indicates a settlement of this footing without the contribution from other footings of the group equal to 6.436 in. resulting in an error of $6.55 - 6.436 = 0.114$ in. or $0.114/6.55 = 1.74$ per cent, which is insignificant.

2. The contact pressure is assumed to remain constant throughout the settlement period although the column loads change and the footing sizes do not.

After settlement of the footings supporting the frame, the load on column No. 2 is reduced by deformation of bay 1-2 an amount equal to $0.849 \times 9.46 = 8.09$ kip, and of bay 2-3 an amount equal to $0.291 \times 13.86 = 4.04$ kip. The column load on footing No. 2 after settlement is $125.9 - (8.05 + 4.04) = 113.4$ kip. The contact pressure on footing No. 2 is reduced to $\dfrac{113,400}{64} = 1770$ lb per sq ft. This change in contact pressure reduces the settlement caused by its own load from 6.436 in., as shown in Figure 4.19r, to 5.76 in., as shown in Figure 4.19t. The loads on the exterior footings are increased which produces a slightly larger contact pressure and resulting settlement of these footings. This assumption, therefore, indicates slightly larger differential settlements than the actual.

8.0 $\times$ 8.0		$w = 1770$ lb ft^{-2}	
w_0	Δp	$p_1 + \frac{\Delta p}{2}$	ΔH
0.98	1730	2417	2.22
0.58	1030	2371	2.27
0.21	370	2331	1.00
0.08	140	2748	0.18
0.04	70	3349	0.09
			$\Delta H = 5.76$ in.

Figure 4.19t   **Settlement of footing No. 2 for reduced contact pressure**

REFERENCES

Agerschau, Hans A., "Analysis of the Engineering News Pile Formula," *Journal Soil Mechanics and Foundations Division*, Proc. Am. Soc. C.E., Vol. 88, No. SM5 (October, 1962).

Aldrich, Harl P., "Precompression for Support of Shallow Foundations," *Journal Soil Mechanics and Foundations Division*, Proc. Am. Soc. C.E., Vol. 91, SM2 (March, 1965).

Boussinesq, J., "Application des Potentiels à l'Étude de l'Équilibre et du Mouvement des Solides Élastiques," Paris, Gauthier-Villard, 1885.

Casagrande, Leo, "Effect of Preconsolidation on Settlements," *Journal Soil Mechanics and Foundations Division*, Proc. Am. Soc. C.E., Vol. 90, No. SM5 (September, 1964).

Domenico, Patrick, and Glen Clark, "Electric Analogs in Time-Settlement Problems," *Journal Soil Mechanics and Foundations Division*, Am. Soc. C.E., Vol. 90, No. SM3 (May, 1964).

Fadum, Ralph E., "Influence Values for Estimating Stresses in Elastic Foundations," *Proc. Second International Conference on Soil Mechanics and Foundation Engineering*, Rotterdam, Vol. 3. Also mimeographed sheets *Graduate School of Engineering*, Harvard University, 1941.

Feld, Jacob, "Tolerance of Structures to Settlement," *Journal Soil Mechanics and Foundations Division*, Proc. Am. Soc. C.E., Vol. 91, No. SM3 (May, 1965).

Hardy, R. M., D. F. Ripley, and K. L. Lee, "Horizontal Movements Associated with Vertical Settlements," *Canada Associated Committee on Soil and Snow Mechanics*, National Research Council, Tech-Memo 72.

Horn, Harry M., and T. William Lambe, "Settlement of Buildings on MIT Campus," *Journal Soil Mechanics and Foundations Division*, Proc. Am. Soc. C.E., Vol. 90, No. SM5 (September, 1964).

Krizek, Raymond J., and Robert L. Kondner, "Settlement Caused by Footing Groups," *Journal Soil Mechanics and Foundations Division*, Proc. Am. Soc. C.E., Vol. 90, No. SM5 (September, 1964).

Lambe, T. William, "Methods of Estimating Settlements," *Journal Soil Mechanics and Foundations Division*, Proc. Am. Soc. C.E., Vol. 90, No. SM5 (September, 1964).

Leonards, G. A., *Foundation Engineering*, New York, McGraw-Hill Book Company, Inc., 1962.

Lo, K. Y., "Secondary Compression of Clays," *Journal Soil Mechanics and Foundations Division*, Proc. Am. Soc. C.E., Vol. 87, No. SM4 (August, 1961).

McKinley, Donald, "Field Observation of Structures Damaged by Settlement," *Journal Soil Mechanics and Foundations Division*, Proc. Am. Soc. C.E., Vol. 90, No. SM5 (September, 1964).

Newmark, N. M., "Simplified Computation of Vertical Pressures in Elastic Foundations," *Engineering Experiment Sta. Circular No. 24*, University of Illinois, 1935.

Nishida, Yoshichika, "A Brief Note on Compression Index of Soil," *Journal Soil Mechanics and Foundations Division*, Proc. Am. Soc. C.E., Vol. 82, No. SM3 (July, 1956).

Seed, H. Bolton, "Settlement Analysis, A Review of Theory and Testing," *Journal Soil Mechanics and Foundations Division*, Proc. Am. Soc. C.E., Vol. 91, No. SM2 (March, 1965).

Schiffman, Robert L., and Robert E. Gibson, "Consolidation of Nonhomogeneous Clay Layers," *Journal Soil Mechanics and Foundations Division*, Proc. Am. Soc. C.E., Vol. 90, No. SM5 (September, 1964).

Sowers, George F., "Fill Settlement Despite Vertical Sand Drains," *Journal Soil Mechanics and Foundations Division*, Proc. Am. Soc. C.E., Vol. 90, No. SM5 (September, 1964).

Steinbrenner, W., "Tafeln zur Setzungsberechnung," *Proc. International Conference on Soil Mechanics*, Cambridge, Mass., 1936.

Terzaghi, Karl, *Third Texas Conference on Soil Mechanics and Foundations*, University of Texas, Austin, 1940.

Wahls, Harvey E., "Analysis of Primary and Secondary Consolidation," *Journal Soil Mechanics and Foundations Division*, Proc. Am. Soc. C.E., Vol. 88, No. SM6 (December, 1962).

Wallace, George B., and William C. Otto, "Differential Settlement at Selfridge Air Force Base," *Journal Soil Mechanics and Foundations Division*, Proc. Am. Soc. C.E., Vol. 90, No. SM5 (September, 1964).

Westergaard, H. M., "A Problem of Elasticity Suggested by a Problem in Soil Mechanics: Soft Material Reinforced by Numerous Strong Horizontal Sheets," *Contributions to Mechanics of Solids*, S. Timoshenko 60th Anniversary Volume, Macmillan, New York, 1938.

Yoshimi, Y., and J. O. Osterberg, "Compression of Partially Saturated Cohesive Soils," *Journal Soil Mechanics and Foundations Division*, Proc. Am. Soc. C.E., Vol. 89, No. SM4 (July, 1963).

5

Carrying Capacity of Foundations

5.01   *General*

Carrying capacity is the ability of the foundation to support its super-imposed load without causing failure or rupture of the supporting soil. Failure of the soil is always accompanied by excessive settlement and often causes collapse of the structure. Failures of soils under foundations have been classified as local shear failures and general shear failures.

Although foundations are often designed on the basis of carrying capac-ity, probably, in most cases, the criterion for design should be settlement. Often excess settlements, especially differential settlements, occur under conditions providing a fairly high factor of safety against failure just as in the case of deflection of beams and other members of a structure. Failures may be produced fairly rapidly by overcoming the ultimate shear strength of the soil along a surface of failure, or very slowly by creep of very soft clays from under a loaded area without a defined failure surface.

a.   Relationship of Stresses at a Point in a Stressed Body

Failure in a material is produced by surpassing the ability of the material to withstand (a) normal stress, (b) shearing stress, (c) a combination of normal and shearing stresses, (d) deformation, or (e) energy. Whichever factor or combination of factors causes the failure, stress is involved. It is, therefore, necessary to know the relationship which exists between normal and shearing stresses acting on planes through a point in a stressed body, and to be able to determine the maximum normal stress and the maximum shear stress or the combination of shear and normal stresses on any plane through the point and the orientation of the planes upon which these stresses act.

The relationship between stresses on different planes through a point in a stressed body which must exist for equilibrium can be shown by means of a free body as illustrated in Figure 5.01a.

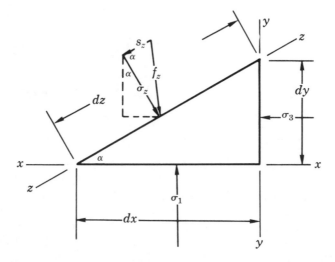

Figure 5.01a   **Stresses at a point in a stressed body**

Assume planes x-x and y-y are planes of zero shear acted upon by the major principal stress σ_1 and the minor principal stress σ_3. Writing $\Sigma H = 0$, $\sigma_3 dy + \tau_z dz \cos \alpha - \sigma_z \sin \alpha = 0$ and $\Sigma V = 0$, $\sigma_1 dx - \tau_z dz \sin \alpha - \sigma_z dz \cos \alpha = 0$ and substituting for dx and dy, $dx = dz \cos \alpha$ and $dy = dz \sin \alpha$, and solving simultaneously, the following relationships are obtained:

$$\sigma_z = \frac{\sigma_1 + \sigma_3}{2} + \frac{\sigma_1 - \sigma^3}{2} \cos 2\alpha \qquad \text{(Eq. 5.01}a\text{)}$$

$$\tau_z = \frac{\sigma_1 - \sigma_3}{2} \sin 2\alpha \qquad \text{(Eq. 5.01}b\text{)}$$

b. Circle of Stress

Since these equations are parametric equations of a circle, Otto Mohr and Müller Breslau suggested at different times that the relationship between stresses on different planes through a point could be represented graphically by means of a circle. In this relationship, the principal stresses (maximum and minimum normal stresses) act upon planes of zero shear at 90° to each other. Another relationship exists in which the sum of the normal stresses acting on any pair of 90° planes through the point is a constant. Müller Breslau's circle of stress has a diameter of $\sigma_x + \sigma_y = \sigma_1 + \sigma_3$. Mohr's circle of stress has a diameter of $\sigma_1 - \sigma_3$. For a great

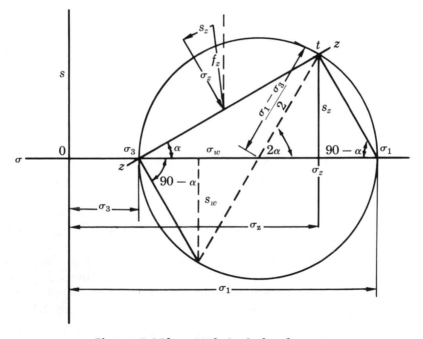

Figure 5.01b Mohr's circle of stress

many problems in mechanics, the Müller Breslau circle of stress is more convenient than Mohr's, but for use in soil mechanics, Mohr's circle is the more useful because it can be combined with diagrams for the relationship between stress and failure of a material.

To construct a Mohr circle of stress for two dimensional stress conditions, two perpendicular axes are laid off. Values of σ are measured along one axis, usually horizontal but not necessarily so, and the unit shear s or τ on the other. All stresses are measured from the origin, positive to the right and upward. When σ_3 and σ_1 are laid off along the σ axis, the circle of stress is defined such that $R = (\sigma_1 - \sigma_3)/2$. Stresses on any other plane through the stressed point can be found by passing a line through point $(0, \sigma_3)$ parallel to the plane to an intersection with the circle. The coordinates of this point of intersection represent the normal and shearing stresses on the plane. In Figure 5.01b, line z-z is drawn through point $(0, \sigma_3)$ parallel to plane z-z of Figure 5.10a. The distance from the intersection of line and circle normal to the σ axis represents the value of the shear stress on plane z-z, and the distance from the origin to the foot of the shear line represents the value of the normal stress σ_z acting on the plane z-z.

Proof:

From the geometry of Figure 5.01b,

$$\tau_z = \frac{(\sigma_1 - \sigma_3)}{2} \cos 2\alpha \qquad \text{(Eq. 5.01}b\text{)}$$

and

$$\sigma_z = \sigma_3 + \frac{(\sigma_1 - \sigma_3)}{2} + \frac{(\sigma_1 - \sigma_3)}{2} \cos 2\alpha$$

$$\sigma_z = \frac{(\sigma_1 + \sigma_3)}{2} + \frac{(\sigma_1 - \sigma_3)}{2} \cos 2\alpha \qquad \text{(Eq. 5.01}a\text{)}$$

If σ_x, σ_y, and τ_{xy} are known the circle of stress for this state of stress is defined and σ_3 and σ_1 become known. The angles between the x and y planes and the planes of the principal stresses are determined by lines from $(0, \sigma_1)$ and $(0, \sigma_3)$ to the intersections of τ_{xy} and the circle. But the orientation of these planes depends upon the direction and magnitude of the shear and the magnitude of the normal stresses. When the σ axis is parallel to the x plane, if the shear is plotted from σ_x, 0 in the direction of the shear on the left of the block; i.e., positive if upward and negative if downward, the plane upon which σ_1 acts is parallel to a line drawn from σ_x, τ_{xy} to σ_1, 0, and the plane upon which σ_3 acts is parallel to a line from σ_x, τ_{xy} to σ_3, 0.

Further discussion of the use of Mohr's circle of stress in the solution of problems in soil mechanics is included in this and later chapters.

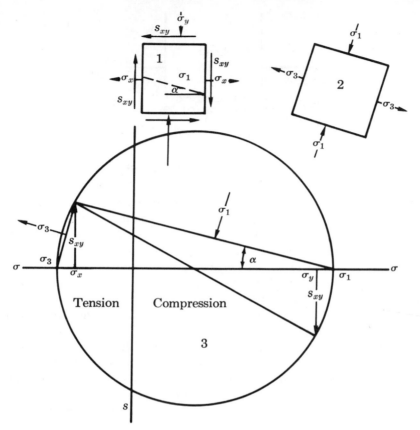

Figure 5.01c   Mohr circle of stress and orientation of planes

5.02   Local Shear Failure

Local shear failure occurs in unsaturated loose soils. An applied load compacts the soil directly under the footing as the footing settles after overcoming the slight shear resistance of the soil along the edge of the footing. In this case, there is very little displacement of the soil grains except as required to produce the volume change under the loaded area. Lateral displacement is probably insignificant as compared with the displacement due to consolidation. This is the same type of failure that occurs in the compaction of soil under a sheepsfoot roller. Local shear failure is really a settlement problem rather than one concerning carrying

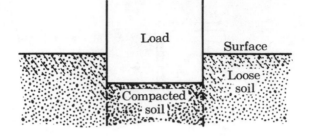

Figure 5.02a   Local shear failure

capacity. As the loose soil is compacted, the resistance to settlement increases. When properly interpreted, a load test on loose unsaturated soil can be an aid to the judgment in the design of foundations on such soils. But it should be realized that the soil affected by the test on a small area is a relatively thin layer immediately beneath the loaded area.

Perhaps some help can be obtained from two load tests on different size areas from which a relationship between contact pressure and shear resistance around the periphery of the test areas can be obtained for a given settlement. One test area, perhaps 1 ft square, is loaded to produce the allowable settlement. Another test area, perhaps 2 ft square, is loaded to produce the same allowable settlement. If the load on an area A_1 and periphery L_1 required to produce the settlement S is P_1, and the load on area A_2 and periphery L_2 required to produce the same settlement is P_2, the relationship between periphery shear s and contact pressure q can be written

$$sL_1 + qA_1 = P_1 \text{ and } sL_2 + qA_2 = P_2$$

from which s and q are found to be

$$q = \frac{P_1L_2 - P_2L_1}{A_1L_2 - A_2L_1}$$

and

$$s = \frac{P_1A_2 - P_2A_1}{A_2L_1 - A_1L_2}$$

Then, presumably, footings designed for a shear resistance around the periphery of s and contact pressure of q will settle an amount equal to S. However, this same relationship between q and s may not hold for footings of different sizes carrying heavier loads.

Under some conditions, improved economy and better foundation conditions can be achieved by removing the loose material and compacting it back into place than by using piers or piles extending through the loose material to a more firm stratum. As an example, in Southwest Kansas a large gas compressor station was to be erected on a 22 ft thick layer of windblown silt containing a small amount of montmorillonite and having a void ratio of approximately 1.0. The 22 ft layer of silt was removed and compacted to a void ratio of 0.4 to a depth of 11 ft above the caliche layer underlying the silt. A thick concrete mat for the reception of the compressor blocks was cast on the compacted fill. This compacted fill distributed the load to the caliche layer over the entire area and provided a better foundation at considerably lower cost than could have been achieved with concrete piers. Under other conditions, the removal and compaction of the loose material might not have been feasible.

5.03 General Shear Failure

In general shear failure, little or no volume change is produced by the load, but the soil is forced out and upward from under the loaded area along a surface of failure as shown in Figures 5.03a and 5.03b.

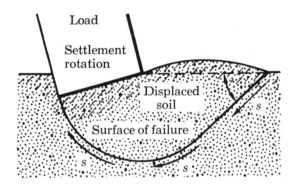

Figure 5.03a   One sided general shear failure

Saturated soils always fail in general shear. Excessive settlement, and usually, collapse, occur as a result of general shear failure. Settlements occur in saturated soils without failure due to squeezing the pore water out and allowing a volume change.

The failure may be one sided as shown in Figure 5.03a, in which case there will be settlement and rotation; or the failure may be two sided as shown in Figure 5.03b, in which case there may be no tilting but only settlement. Two sided failures usually occur in deep pier type foundations and one sided failures in shallow foundations. The deeper the footing is located below the surface, the steeper the surface of failure will be in case of failure. For a load applied on or near the surface as shown in Figure

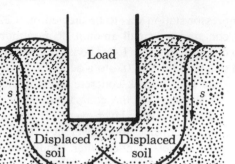

Figure 5.03b   Two sided general shear failure

5.03a, the failure surface probably resembles a spiral cylinder approximating a circular cylinder and a tangent plane. A fairly accurate analysis for estimating the carrying capacity of footings on or near the surface is available in the Krey ϕ-circle method. Other approximate methods are available.

5.04   Methods of Analysis for Estimating Carrying Capacity

Although it is not strictly accurate, the methods of analysis for estimating the carrying capacity of foundations are based upon the assumption that the shear strength of the soil can be expressed by the Coulomb equation $s = c + \sigma \tan \phi$, in which s is the shear strength, c is that part of the shear strength due to cohesion, σ is the normal pressure between the grains, and ϕ is the angle of internal friction.

a.   Krey ϕ-Circle Method of Analysis

In the Krey ϕ-circle method of analysis for estimating the carrying capacity of foundations, it is assumed that the soil is isotropic and uniform to a depth below the failure zone, and that the shear strength is represented by the Coulomb equation. The failure surface is assumed as a cylinder and a tangent plane ABC.

The graphical solution for estimating the carrying capacity of a footing near or on the surface is illustrated in Figure 5.04a.

Since there is no shear stress on the surface outside the loaded area, the stresses normal and parallel to the surface at the surface are princi-

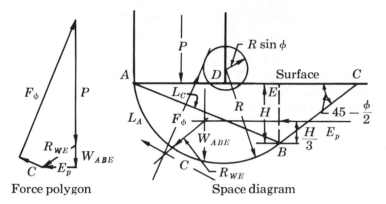

Force polygon   Space diagram

Figure 5.04a   Krey ϕ-circle method for carrying capacity of footing on surface

pal stresses. In passive earth pressure, the parallel stress is the major principal stress and the normal stress is the minor principal stress. Therefore, the surface of failure meets the surface at an angle $45 - \dfrac{\phi}{2}$. If the triangular wedge of earth between a vertical plane at the tangent to the cylindrical portion of the assumed surface of failure and the plane portion is assumed to produce a resistance to horizontal movement of the wedge ABE equal to the passive earth pressure E_p against the vertical plane EB, the wedge of soil ABE is in equilibrium under the passive earth pressure E_p against the surface EB, its own weight W_{ABE}, the resultant cohesion along failure surface arc AB, the resultant of normal force N and friction along arc AB, which is F_ϕ, and the load on the footing P.

The direction of the plane portion of the failure surface is known. The value and line of action of forces E_p, W_{ABE}, and C are known or can be determined, and the direction of F_ϕ can be determined on the space diagram. These values and directions can be determined as follows:

For a material for which the shear strength is expressed as $s = c + \sigma \tan \phi$, the relationship between principal stresses at a point in a stressed body is $\sigma_1 = 2c \tan\left(45 + \dfrac{\phi}{2}\right) + \sigma_3 \tan^2\left(45 + \dfrac{\phi}{2}\right)$, and the failure plane makes an angle of $45 + \dfrac{\phi}{2}$ with the plane of the major principal stress σ_1 and $45 - \dfrac{\phi}{2}$ with the plane of the minor principal stress σ_3. Because the shear stress at the surface outside the loaded area is zero, stresses normal and parallel to the surface are principal stresses and, since in this case the vertical stress is the minor principal stress, the angle between the surface and the surface of failure is $45 - \frac{\phi}{2}$. The center of rotation is near the corner of the loaded area. From this information, an assumed failure surface can be drawn and the load P that would just cause failure along that surface determined.

If imminent failure throughout the mass EBC is assumed, the value of the passive earth pressure on the plane EB can be determined as follows:

At depth z, $\sigma_3 = \gamma_e z$ and $\sigma_1 = 2c \tan\left(45 + \frac{\phi}{2}\right) + \gamma_e z \tan^2\left(45 + \frac{\phi}{2}\right)$.

$$E_p = \int_0^H \left[2c \tan\left(45 + \frac{\phi}{2}\right) + \gamma_e z \tan^2\left(45 + \frac{\phi}{2}\right) z \right] dz = 2cH \tan\left(45 + \frac{\phi}{2}\right)$$

$+ \frac{\gamma_e H^2}{2} \tan^2\left(45 + \frac{\phi}{2}\right)$. Under these conditions, the resultant pressure E_p acts above the lower third point and is horizontal.

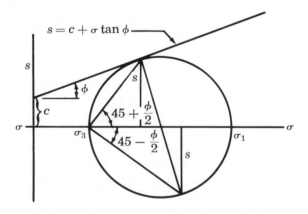

Figure 5.04b   Mohr's circle of stress and rupture line

W_{ABE} is equal to the unit weight of the soil times the volume of the wedge ABE, acts through the centroid of ABE. E_p and W_{ABE} are plotted on the equilibrium polygon, and their resultant R_{EW} is found and drawn through the intersection of E_p and W_{ABE} on the space diagram.

The moment of the cohesion is $cL_A R$ and the resultant cohesion C is parallel to the chord L_C and its moment about the center of rotation is $C \cdot$ arm $= cL_A R$. The cohesion over a small length of arc ΔL_A is $c\Delta L_A$ and its component parallel to the chord L_C is $c\Delta L_A \cos \alpha$. But, $\Delta L_A \cos \alpha = \Delta L_C$, and the summation of $\Delta L_A \cos \alpha$ over the full length of the arc is $\sum \Delta L_A \cos \alpha = L_C$. Therefore, $C = cL_C$ and the moment of the cohesion

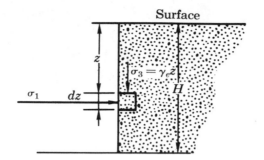

Figure 5.04c   Passive earth pressure

about the center of rotation is $C \cdot \text{arm} = cL_C \cdot \text{arm} = cL_A R$, making the arm of the resultant C equal to $(L_A/L_C)R$.

The value of $C = cL_C$ is plotted parallel to the chord at $(L_A/L_C)R$ distance from the center of rotation and its value and direction are plotted on the force polygon.

The arc AB is also subjected to a normal force N and a frictional resisting force $N \tan \phi$. The rotational resisting moment of the frictional part of the resisting moment over the elemental length of arc is $R\Delta N \tan \phi$. The moment of the normal ΔN is zero. Instead of using ΔN and ΔN

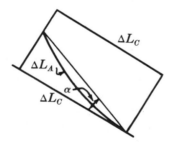

Figure 5.04d   Projection of ΔL_A on chord L_C

$\tan \phi$ their resultant ΔF_ϕ may be used. The moment of the resisting friction on an element of arc is $\Delta F_\phi \cdot \text{arm} = R\Delta N \tan \phi$ and, since $\Delta N = \Delta F_\phi \cos \phi$, the moment about the center of rotation is $\Delta M_F = \Delta F_\phi \cdot \text{arm} = R\Delta N \tan \phi = R\Delta F_\phi \cos \phi \tan \phi = R\Delta F_\phi \sin \phi$. The moment arm for ΔF_ϕ is, therefore, equal to $R \sin \phi$.

Since every elemental ΔF_ϕ has a moment arm equal to $R \sin \phi$; i.e., every element is tangent to a circle whose center is at the center of rotation and whose radius is $R \sin \phi$, one might assume that the resultant F_ϕ

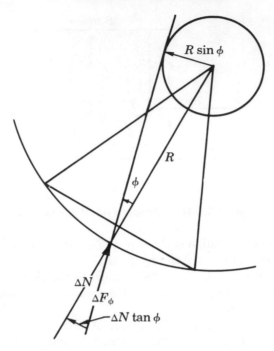

Figure 5.04e   Normal and frictional forces acting on element of arc L_A

must be tangent to the $R \sin \phi$ circle. This assumption that the resultant F_ϕ is tangent to the $R \sin \phi$ circle is not quite true. Corrections for this error were computed by D. W. Taylor and found to be practically insignificant except for arcs having large central angles.

R_{WE}, C, and F_ϕ are in equilibrium and, therefore, are concurrent forces. So, the direction of F_ϕ is determined by drawing a line on the space diagram from the intersection of R_{WE} and C to a tangent to the $R \sin \phi$ circle. The force F_ϕ can then be drawn on the force polygon to an intersection with the vertical line representing P. This closure of the force polygon determines the value of P which produces imminent failure along the investigated surface of failure.

b.   Sliding Wedge Method

Considerable effort and time are required in order to determine the weight and center of gravity of the volume of soil represented by the area ABC in the Krey ϕ-circle method of analysis. An easier but less accurate method of analysis for surface and near surface loaded areas is available by assuming that the failure surfaces are plane. The failure plane makes an angle of $\left(45 + \dfrac{\phi}{2}\right)$ with the plane of the major principal stress. Then, if under the footing the major principal stress is assumed to be vertical and its plane horizontal, the surface of failure AB makes an angle of $\left(45 + \dfrac{\phi}{2}\right)$ with the horizontal. This tacitly assumes that the surface of contact between soil and footing is frictionless and cohesionless. At the unloaded surface, the major principal stress is horizontal and the failure plane makes an angle of $\left(45 - \dfrac{\phi}{2}\right)$ with the horizontal. If it is assumed that failure occurs along these planes instead of along a spiral surface, a simple graphical method is available as shown in Figure 5.04f.

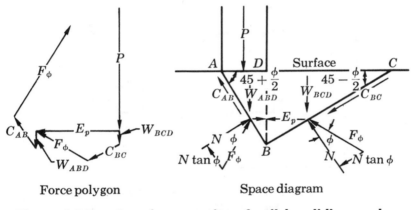

Force polygon   Space diagram

Figure 5.04f   Carrying capacity of soil by sliding wedge method for surface load

The load and the weight of the wedge ABD force the wedge down the slope against the surface BD. The forces acting in equilibrium on wedge ABD are P, W_{ABD}, C_{AB}, N_{AB}, $N \tan \phi$, and E_p. The forces in equilibrium on wedge DBC are E_p, W_{DBC}, N_{BC}, $N \tan \phi$, and C_{BC}. The resultant of N and $N \tan \phi$ is F_ϕ making an angle of ϕ with the normal force N, and can be used instead of N and $N \tan \phi$ in the analysis. In the analysis, forces are usually computed for one foot of length of the loaded area AD.

c.   Principal Stress Method

If it is assumed that there is imminent failure throughout the mass of soil affected by the footing load, that the effects are limited to the soil directly under the footing to a depth equal to the footing width, and that the principal stresses act vertically and horizontally within this region, then an approximate analysis can be made by considering the equilibrium of an element of the soil at middepth of the mass under consideration.

At B in Figure 5.04g, σ_3 is the minor principal stress and σ_h is the major. At A the minor principal stress is σ_h and the major is σ_1. σ_1 is equal to the contact pressure q plus the weight of the soil between the bottom of the footing and point A.

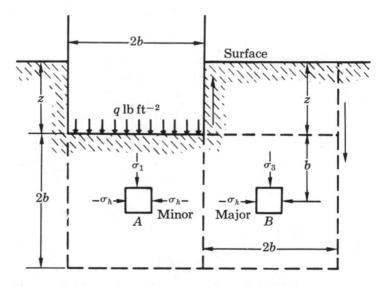

Figure 5.04g   Carrying capacity of footing—principal stress method

If σ_h is transmitted horizontally through the soil from A to B, the failure conditions at A and B are as shown in Figure 5.04h.

The relationship between major and minor principal stresses σ_h and σ_3

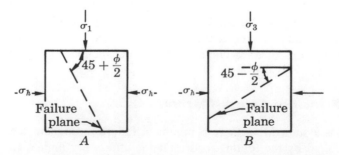

Figure 5.04h   Failure conditions at points A and B

and σ_1 and σ_h can be shown and expressed as in Figure 4.04i. The relationship between major and minor principal stresses at B can be stated as

$$\sigma_\text{h} = 2c \tan\left(45 + \frac{\phi}{2}\right) + \sigma_3 \tan^2\left(45 + \frac{\phi}{2}\right)$$

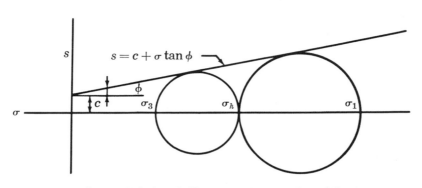

Figure 5.04i   Failure stresses at A and B

At A the stress relationship is $\sigma_1 = 2c \tan\left(45 + \frac{\phi}{2}\right) + \sigma_h \tan^2\left(45 + \frac{\phi}{2}\right)$. If c and ϕ and σ_3 are known, σ_1 can be easily computed. The contact pressure q is $\sigma_1 - \gamma_e b$, when γ_e is the unit weight of the soil.

The most highly indeterminate part of the analysis is the determination of σ_3. In order for σ_h at B to produce failure, the soil above B must be deformed upward to overcome the frictional resistance along surfaces CD and EF.

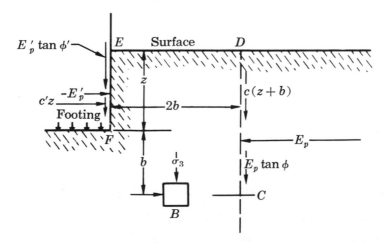

Figure 5.04j   Forces resisting σ_3

The resistance along CD is $c(z + b)$ plus the friction of the earth pressure $E_p \tan \phi$. The friction along EF is the earth pressure E_p' against EF times the tangent of the angle of friction between wall and soil ϕ'. If the wall is rough so that imminent failure is produced in the adjacent soil, some additional resistance to movement of the pier or wall downward may be provided by the cohesional part of the shear strength of the adjacent soil. This adjacent soil is likely to be backfill and, if not compacted, may load the footing instead of resisting settlement. σ_3 is unit pressure and, if all of the factors mentioned above are considered, is equal to

$$\sigma_3 = \gamma_e(z + b) + \frac{c(z + b)}{2b} + \frac{E_p \tan \phi}{2b} + \frac{E_p' \tan \phi'}{2b} + \frac{c'z}{2b}$$

An advantage of the principal stress method is that it can be applied equally conveniently to shallow or deep footings or piers and that the earth above the bottom of the footing may be considered as overburden with no shear strength or as possessing any value of c, ϕ, c', and ϕ' either equal to or less than those values for the soil below the bottom of the footing. In using the principal stress method of analysis for estimating the carrying capacity of footings or piers, it is wise not to depend upon any formula for estimating σ_3, but to use the judgment in estimating the values of the forces resisting upward movement of the wedge of earth. If the designer believes that the passive earth pressure E_p or E_p' will not be realized under working conditions, he may use active earth pressure or earth pressure at rest. In a good many cases, especially for independent footings with backfill around the columns, undoubtedly E_p' and c' should be ignored, and possibly also the earth pressure above the bottom of the footing. Possibly, a smaller value of E_p and ϕ should be used for the upper portion of surface DC.

In studying problems of carrying capacity of footings or piers under given conditions, several analyses can be made rather quickly for comparison of different soil conditions above and below the bottom of the footings. In general, the principal stress method yields more conservative and safer results than other methods when applied to estimating the carrying capacity of footings.

5.05   Carrying Capacity of Footings on Sand

Sand has no cohesion so its shear strength may be expressed as $s = \sigma \tan \phi$. With reference to Figure 5.04j

$$\sigma_3 = \gamma_e(z + b) + \frac{E_p \tan \phi}{2b} + \frac{E_p' \tan \phi'}{2b}$$

If E_p' be neglected,

$$\sigma_3 = \gamma_e(z + b) + \frac{\gamma_e(z + b)^2 \tan^2\left(45 + \frac{\phi}{2}\right) \tan \phi}{4b}$$

and

$$\sigma_h = \gamma_e(z + b) + \frac{\gamma_e(z + b)^2 \tan^2\left(45 + \frac{\phi}{2}\right) \tan \phi}{4b} \tan^2\left(45 + \frac{\phi}{2}\right)$$

and

$$\sigma_1 = \gamma_e(z + b) + \frac{\gamma_e(z + b)^2 \tan^2\left(45 + \frac{\phi}{2}\right) \tan \phi}{4b} \tan^4\left(45 + \frac{\phi}{2}\right)$$

From a study of this relationship it is readily apparent that the carrying capacity of footings in sand as measured by contact pressure increases greatly with depth. For example, for a sand whose $\phi = 40°$ and whose $\gamma_e = 100$ lb ft^{-3}, the relationship becomes

$$\sigma_1 = 100(z + b) \tan^4 65° + \frac{100(z + b)^2 \tan 40° \tan^6 65°}{4b}$$

$$\sigma_1 = 2000(z + b) + 1990 \frac{(z + b)^2}{b}$$

For a footing 4 ft wide ($b = 2$) the carrying capacity in lb ft^{-2} for different depths is listed below on the last line of each column.

$$b = 2 \text{ ft}$$

Term \ Depth	$z = 0$	$z = 2$	$z = 4$	$z = 6$	$z = 8$
$2090\,(z + b)$	4180	8360	12540	16720	20900
$1990\,\dfrac{(z + b)^2}{b}$	3980	15920	35820	63680	99500
σ_1	8160	24280	48360	80400	120400
$\gamma_e b$	200	200	200	200	200
q	7960	24080	48160	80200	120200

Thus, it is apparent that the contact pressure which causes failure of clean sand increases rapidly with increase in depth below the surface of the sand.

The effect of footing width on contact pressure at failure is not so pronounced as is the effect of depth. For example, in the same sand as assumed for the example above, and at a depth of 4 ft, the contact pressures at failure for different widths of footings are listed below.

$$z = 4 \text{ ft}$$

Term \\ Width	$b = 1$	$b = 2$	$b = 4$	$b = 6$
$2090 (z + b)$	10450	12540	16720	20900
$1990 \dfrac{(z + b)^2}{b}$	49750	35820	31840	33200
σ_1	60200	48360	48500	54100
$\gamma_e b$	100	200	400	600
q	60100	48160	48160	53500

For footings in the usual range of sizes, this method of analysis indicates that the contact pressure at failure is little influenced by footing width in clean sand, except for footings at or near the surface.

A test load on a 1 ft square footing applied on the surface of the sand assumed for the above examples should fail for $z = 0$ and $b = 0.5$ at about

$$q = \sigma_1 - 50 = 2090(0.5) + 1990 \left(\frac{0.25}{0.5} \right) - 50 = 1880 \text{ lb ft}^{-2}$$

So, one can readily see the gross error in assuming that the test load at failure on a 1 ft square footing on the surface of sand is the contact pressure at failure for any size footing at any depth below the surface.

5.06   Carrying Capacity of Footings on Clay

If load is applied very slowly to a soft plastic clay allowing consolidation to occur between load increments, the clay gains shear strength as consolidation occurs, which causes the rupture line for clay to indicate an increase in strength with stress somewhat similar to the rupture line for sand. Immediately upon deposition, clay has practically no shear strength, but after consolidation under its overburden the clay possesses some inherent shear strength c. Generally, but not always, loads are applied to the clay after it has gained some strength. When the load is applied rapidly, as is usually the case with man made structures, the clay does not have time to consolidate appreciably under the added load and does not gain much strength with increase of load.

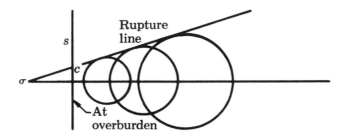

**Figure 5.06a   Rupture line for plastic clay
Slow application of load**

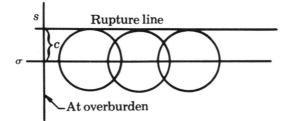

**Figure 5.06b   Rupture line for plastic clay
Rapid application of load**

If load is applied to fat plastic clay without allowing time for consolidation of the clay as the load is applied, the shear strength of the clay may be assumed as $s = c$, c being the shear strength attained under previously applied pressure. The shear strength of such soft clays can be increased by preloading for a long enough time for the clay to consolidate under the added load.

For normally consolidated clays and loads applied rapidly enough so that consolidation under the added load does not occur, the contact pressure at failure as determined by the principal stress method of analysis is as follows:

$$\sigma_3 = \gamma_e(z + b) + \frac{c(z + b)}{2b}$$

$$\sigma_h = 2c \tan 45° + \left[\gamma_e(z + b) + \frac{c(z + b)}{2b} \right] \tan^2 45°$$

$$\sigma_1 = 2c \tan 45° + 2c \tan^3 45° + \gamma_e(z + b) \tan^4 45° + \frac{c(z + b)}{2b} \tan^4 45°$$

Since $\tan 45° = 1$,

$$\sigma_1 = 4c + \gamma_e(z + b) + \frac{c(z + b)}{2b}$$

In order to show the relationship for contact pressure at failure, width of footing and depth for footings on clay in which $s = c = 1000$ lb ft^{-2}, the same analyses are made for clay as were made for sand. The results are recorded below.

$$b = 2 \text{ ft}$$

Term \ Depth	$z = 0$	$z = 2$	$z = 4$	$z = 6$	$z = 8$
$4c$	4000	4000	4000	4000	4000
$\gamma_e (z + b)$	200	400	600	800	1000
$\dfrac{c(z + b)}{2b}$	500	1000	1500	2000	2500
σ_1	4700	5400	6100	6800	7500
$\gamma_e b$	200	200	200	200	200
q	4500	5200	5900	6600	7300

If the inherent strength of the clay does not increase with depth, the contact pressure at failure increases somewhat with depth.

Thus, at the same depth, the contact pressure at failure in soft clay decreases slightly with increase in width of footings. Settlements in soft clays increase with size of footings at the same contact pressure.

Usually, in a normally consolidated deposit of clay, the shear strength increases with depth because of the greater overburden at depth. However, this is not always the case. High pore water pressure may prevent consolidation of the clay under its overburden in which case the shear strength does not increase with depth and may even be less at depth than it is near

$$z = 4 \text{ ft}$$

Width \\ Term	$b = 1$	$b = 2$	$b = 4$	$b = 6$
$4c$	4000	4000	4000	4000
$\gamma_e (z + b)$	500	600	800	1000
$\dfrac{c(z + b))}{2b}$	2500	1500	1000	835
σ_1	7000	6100	5800	5835
$\gamma_e b$	100	200	400	600
q	6900	6900	5400	5235

the surface. Clay near the surface may be considerably stronger than that at depth because of consolidation due to desiccation near the surface.

The initial strength of some clays is dependent upon the length of time that the clay has been subjected to the applied pressure after primary consolidation has been completed. After the pore water pressure has been reduced and pressure between the grains has driven out all but highly viscous water at the points of contact, a high initial shear strength is built into the clay. Remolding the clay at the same water content reduces the shear strength of the clay. Such a sensitive clay may be capable of supporting relatively heavy stresses until the stress at some point overcomes the high initial shear strength. The remolding along the failure surface reduces the shear strength causing rapid progressive failure.

For loads quickly applied on the surface of saturated clay, the Swedish circle method proposed by W. Fellenius (based on the earlier work of K. E. Petterson and S. Hultin) in the early part of the twentieth century is simpler than the ϕ-circle method developed by Krey. For soft clays in which for practical purposes ϕ is zero, the assumption that the surface of failure is cylindrical is accurate enough for a great many practical purposes. The center of rotation of the cylindrical surface, which offers the least resistance to rotation for surface loads on soil whose $\phi = 0$, is located at about $0.85b$ above an edge of the loaded area as shown in Figure 4.06d. An advantage of this method of analysis over the Krey ϕ-circle method is that the weight of the cylindrical sliding wedge acts through the center of rotation and need not be considered in the analysis. Therefore, the resistance to rotation consists only of the moment of the cohesion along the cylindrical surface about the center of rotation.

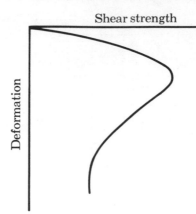

Shear strength

Deformation

Figure 5.06c   Stress-strain curve for sensitive clay

The driving moment about the center of rotation is Pb and the resisting moment is the surface of arc AC times the unit cohesion c. With the center of rotation at $0.85b$ above the edge of the loaded area, the radius of the cylindrical surface is $2.2b$. The angle at the center between the two extreme radii is $2 \tan^{-1}(2/0.85) = 2 \times 67 = 134°$. The length of arc $AC = 2.2b2\pi(134/360) = 5.15b$. Then, $Pb = 5.15b2.2bc$ and $P = 11.3bc$.

For a footing 4 ft wide applied to the surface of a soil possessing a

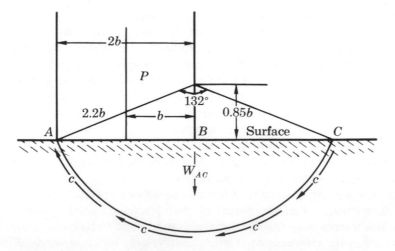

Figure 5.06d   Cylindrical failure surface in soft clay

shear strength $c = 1000$ lb ft^{-2}, the carrying capacity as determined by this simple cylindrical sliding surface method is

$$P = 11.3 \times 2 \times 1000 = 22,600 \text{ lb}$$
$$q = \frac{22,600}{4} = 5640 \text{ lb ft}^{-2}$$

This value of the carrying capacity compares with 4500 lb ft^{-2} as determined by the principal stress method. The principal stress method yields more conservative values than other methods of analysis in almost all cases.

5.07   Failure Due to Creep of Clay

Creep may be defined as that property of a material which allows it to be deformed very slowly under sustained stress, without rupture, without elastic rebound, and without volume change. A plastic material can be deformed rapidly, without rupture, without elastic rebound, and without volume change. Creep of plastic materials usually occurs under considerably lower sustained stress than that required to produce failure under rapid deformation. The creep strength of clays may vary from 25 to 90 per cent of the strength resisting rapid deformation as determined by a laboratory quick test. Special long time testing techniques are required in order to determine accurately the creep strength of clays.

Creep of the soil from under a loaded area is accompanied by a gradual upheaval of the soil adjacent to the loaded area. Just as in the case for preventing sudden failure due to excessive load on the soil, upheaval due to creep can often be reduced or prevented by applying a fill or berm on the surface adjacent to the loaded area. By this method, the shear stress can be reduced to an intensity that is less than that required to produce creep. Soft clays of low sensitivity may flow out from under the loaded area without showing any well defined surfaces along which deformation has occurred. Creep failures of some soils, especially highly sensitive clays, often occur along fairly well defined planes.

A method of analysis for estimating the weight of a fill or berm placed adjacent to a loaded area to prevent creep of a fairly thin layer of soft clay from under the edge of the area is illustrated in Figure 5.07a.

On a plane AB at the edge of the loaded area, the earth pressure on the side under the loaded area is the active earth pressure which is resisted by the passive earth pressure on the opposite side. If it is asumed that no vertical and horizontal shear stresses exist on the vertical plane AB

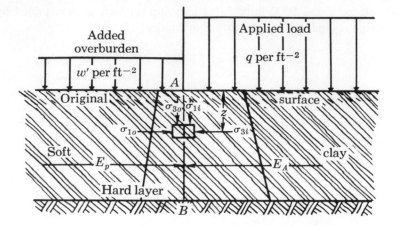

Figure 5.07a   Earth pressure at edge of loaded area on soft clay

(which is not true), the vertical stress on an element of soil at depth z on the active pressure side of the plane is the major principal stress $\sigma_1 = q + \gamma_e z$, and the horizontal minor principal stress, when $c' =$ creep strength, is

$$\sigma_{3i} = -2c' \tan 45° + (q + \gamma_e z) \tan^2 45°$$

On the passive pressure side of the plane the vertical and minor principal stress is $\sigma_{3o} = w' + \gamma_e z$ and the horizontal passive pressure is

$$\sigma_{1o} = 2c' \tan 45° + (w' + \gamma_e z) \tan^2 45°$$

At the same depth z, the active earth pressure on the load side of the plane is resisted by the passive earth pressure on the side away from the loaded area so

$$-2c' + q + \gamma_e z = 2c' + w' + \gamma_e z$$

from which the required weight of the berm is found to be

$$w' = q - 4c' \qquad \text{(Eq. 5.07a)}$$

The berm or added overburden should be extended from the edge of the loaded area a distance greater than the thickness of the soft layer or the width of the loaded area. The weight of the added overburden may be reduced gradually with distance from the loaded area.

One might reason that the analysis for creep could be made by assuming a cylindrical failure surface as illustrated in Figure 5.06d and loading the wedge to prevent rotation. In the cylindrical failure surface method, little or no plastic deformation is assumed to exist within the rotating wedge so that failure occurs only along the surface of failure. In the case of general shear failure of a sensitive clay, this assumption is probably not unreasonable. But, in the case of creep of a clay of low sensitivity, plastic deformation may occur throughout the mass of soil affected without a definite surface of failure.

5.08   Bearing Capacity of Piles

Piles may transfer their load to ground by friction along their sides and by resistance of the point to penetration into the material on which they rest. The ratio of the portion of the load carried by friction to that carried by end bearing depends upon the soil conditions and the nature of the pile used. If the point resistance allows so little vertical movement of the pile that the shearing deformation of the soil around the pile is not sufficient to develop the shearing resistance of the soil adjacent to the sides of the pile, practically all of the load is transferred by end bearing. If the point bearing allows considerable movement of the pile, the material along the sides of the pile is deformed sufficiently to develop its shear strength, in which case most of the load is transferred by friction along the sides of the pile. In some cases in which the pile is driven through very loose material to a hard stratum, the loose material may later consolidate to a smaller volume and, by friction along the sides of the pile, load the pile in end bearing with a load larger than its superimposed load.

No reliable theoretical relationships and resulting formulas have been devised which can estimate the bearing capacity of a pile with sufficient accuracy to be of much practical value. The only reliable method of determining the bearing capacity of a single pile is by means of a test load on the pile. Once the load carrying capacity of a pile has been determined with relation to resistance to driving in a given soil condition, piles driven to the same resistance in that same soil condition may be presumed to have a bearing capacity equal to that determined by the load test.

Many engineers require that contractors attempt to drive point bearing and point friction piles to so-called refusal. In attempting to achieve refusal, piles are often damaged by over-driving, especially when using a drop hammer. Over-driving may result in breaking the pile as shown in Figure 5.08a, splitting, or otherwise damaging and reducing the carrying capacity of the pile.

Load tests on piles are usually conducted by driving the pile to the estimated permissible penetration under the last blow of the hammer and loading in about the same manner as described for a load test in

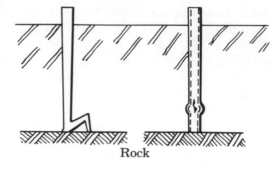

Rock

Figure 5.08a   **Piles damaged by over-driving**

Chapter 1. The frictional resistance of piles, especially those driven into soft clay, is sometimes estimated by means of a pull-out test. The pull-out test is probably a better measure of the frictional resistance than a compression test because most of the influence of possible point resistance is eliminated.

5.09   Dynamic Pile Formulas

Although it is quite generally known that dynamic pile formulas for estimating the bearing capacity of a single pile are based upon the erroneous assumption that the same conditions of loading apply for rapidly repeated dynamic loadings as apply for static loading of the pile, these dynamic pile formulas are still used to a considerable extent with some degree of confidence by a great many engineers because, other than experience, there is nothing much better that is economically feasible for small jobs. These formulas are simple to use and they yield definite values which give a sense of security to the designer. But, if the designer knows that the formula does not tell the truth, it may be used as an aid to the judgment when combined with experience.

Some of these dynamic formulas are quite simple, like the Engineering News formula, and others, like the Hiley formula, are quite complex. The difference in all of these formulas depends upon the evaluation of the energy losses that occur during the driving operation. Since none of the assumptions used in determining these energy losses apply to the pile supporting a static load, the simplest formula is as reliable as the more complicated ones.

Symbols used in the pile formulas listed below are as follows:

W_h = Weight of pile driver hammer
W_p = Weight of pile
H = Height of fall of hammer
L = Length of pile
E_l = Energy loss
E = Modulus of elasticity of pile material
A = Area of pile
P = Bearing capacity of pile—Static force required to produce penetration of the pile
Δz = Permanent penetration of the pile under the last blow of the hammer
$\Delta z'$ = Total penetration of the pile under the last blow of the hammer including permanent penetration plus rebound

Dynamic formulas are based upon the assumption that the force P on the pile which forces it through a penetration Δz under a single blow of the hammer is constant throughout the penetration so that the work done in producing the penetration is $P\Delta z$. Because of energy losses, not all of the work performed by the falling hammer is effective in producing penetration of the pile. The work of the falling hammer $W_h H$ can be equated to the work used in producing penetration of the pile plus the energy losses E_l.

$$W_h H = P\Delta z + E_l \qquad \text{(Eq. 5.09a)}$$

The energy losses that are commonly considered in the development of dynamic pile formulas are one or more of the following:

1. An energy loss equal to the penetrating force times the rebound of the pile due to elastic rebound of the soil and the pile. An attempt is sometimes made to measure this loss in the field by drawing a line along a straight edge fastened to the pile, marking on a board that is held stationary against the straight edge as the pile is struck with the hammer. The resulting graph appears somewhat like the curve of Figure 5.09a. The loss from this elastic deformation is $P(\Delta z' - \Delta z) = E_l$.

2. The energy loss is due to the elastic deformation of the pile, in which case

$$E_l = \frac{P^2 L}{2AE}$$

3. All or part of the energy loss is equivalent to the Newtonian loss due to direct central impact. The Newtonian impact loss was deter-

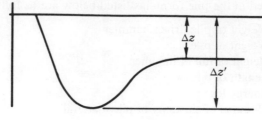

Figure 5.09a   Graph showing penetration and rebound of pile from one blow

mined for a falling body striking another body that can be moved without restraint other than inertia, such as a body A weighing W_A falling free to strike a second body B weighing W_B as illustrated in Figure 5.09b. If the bodies are perfectly elastic, after impact when B comes to its original position, A will have been driven back to its original position, or one might say that the coefficient of restitution is unity and there has been no loss of energy due to impact. If the bodies were perfectly inelastic, the entire energy expended by the falling body would be dissipated in producing plastic deformation of the bodies and the coefficient of restitution would be zero.

Newton established for the energy loss due to impact of two bodies, such as described above, the relationship

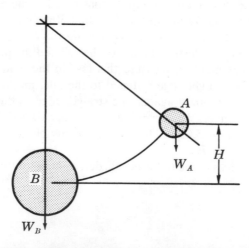

Figure 5.09b   Newtonian experiment for energy loss from impact

$$E_l = W_A H \frac{W_B(1 - n_e^2)}{W_A + W_B}$$

in which n_e is the coefficient of restitution. For perfectly elastic bodies $n_e = 1$ and $E_l = 0$. For perfectly inelastic bodies, $n_e = 0$, and

$$E_l = W_A H \frac{W_B}{W_A + W_B}$$

When applied for use in a pile formula, the weight of the falling hammer is designated W_h, the weight of the pile W_p, and the height of fall of the hammer H. In the pile formulas, the Newtonian loss is stated as

$$E_l = W_h H \frac{W_p(1 - n_e^2)}{W_h + W_p}$$

When applied to a pile being struck by a hammer, the conditions are quite different from those for which Newton established his relationship for energy loss due to impact of two bodies. The long pile is restrained along its entire length and is not deformed in the same manner as the spheres of Newton's experiment.

4. Some formulas include other losses which are not easy to define, such as brooming of the pile head, energy absorbed by a pile cap, etc.

About 1820, Weisbach proposed a formula for the carrying capacity of a single pile by assuming that the entire energy loss is equal to the elastic deformation of the pile, which causes the formula to take the form

$$W_h H = P\Delta z + \frac{P^2 L}{2AE}, \text{ from which the Weisbach formula is derived.}$$

$$P = \sqrt{\frac{2W_h AEH}{L} + \left(\frac{\Delta z\, AE}{L}\right)^2} - \frac{\Delta z\, AE}{L} \qquad \text{(Eq. 5.09}b\text{)}$$

About the same time that Weisbach proposed his formula, Eytelwein proposed a formula equating the energy loss to the Newtonian energy loss assuming perfectly inelastic bodies for which $n_e = 0$. For this case, the relationship is $W_h H = P\Delta z + W_h H \dfrac{W_p}{W_h + W_p}$, from which Eytelwein's formula is derived.

$$P = \frac{W_h H}{\Delta z + \dfrac{W_p}{W_h} \Delta z} \qquad \text{(Eq. 5.09}c\text{)}$$

About 1850, Sanders proposed a pile formula in which it is assumed that the bodies are perfectly elastic, in which case the energy loss is zero making the Sanders formula

$$P = \frac{W_h H}{\Delta z} \qquad \text{(Eq. 5.09}d\text{)}$$

A. M. Wellington proposed a pile formula, which was published by the Engineering News and is commonly known as the Engineering News formula, in which the factor $(W_p/W_h)\Delta z$ of the Eytelwein formula was replaced by a constant c_p. The Engineering News formula is, therefore,

$$P = \frac{W_h H}{\Delta z + c_p} \qquad \text{(Eq. 5.09}e\text{)}$$

The value of c_p is dependent upon the type of hammer, the type of pile, and the type of soil into which the pile is driven. Wellington devised the formula to apply to wood piles and a drop hammer for which case he proposed a value of $c_p = 1$. This value of $c_p = 1$ was based upon experience with driving wood piles with a drop hammer into the Chicago clay. The value of $c_p = 0.1$ for a steam hammer was suggested on the spur of the moment without rational analysis or experience, but it has been used by engineers with confidence.

Some engineers use a relationship based upon the measured penetration and rebound determined in the field, as illustrated in Figure 5.09a, as a criterion for the bearing capacity of a single pile. In this case, the energy loss is considered to be the force producing penetration of the pile times the rebound of the pile from the maximum penetration produced by a blow of the hammer,

For this case
$$E_l = P(\Delta z' - \Delta z)$$
$$P = \frac{W_h H}{\Delta z'} \qquad \text{(Eq. 5.09}f\text{)}$$

Some formulas have been proposed which include energy losses from the Newtonian impact, loss due to elastic deformation of the pile, and additional losses absorbed by a pile cap, brooming of the pile head, etc. The most recent of these all-inclusive formulas was proposed by A. Hiley in 1930. Such formulas are of the form

$$W_hH = P\Delta z + W_hH \frac{W_p(1 - n_e^2)}{W_h + W_p} + \frac{P^2L}{2AE} + E_{ls} \quad \text{(Eq. 5.09g)}$$

In this relationship, the engineer is free to exercise his own judgment as to the value of n_e and E_{ls}.

As already stated, these dynamic formulas have value only as calibrated by load tests. For this purpose, the simplest of the formulas is as valuable as the most complicated.

5.10   Floating Piles—Static Pile Formulas

Because the dynamic relationships that exist during driving of a pile are not the same as the relationship that exists when the pile is at rest supporting its static load, attempts have been made to relate the static bearing capacity of the pile to the shear strength of the soil into which the pile is driven. When a pile is driven into a cohesive soil, the structure of the soil adjacent to the pile is destroyed by remolding with an accompanying loss of strength. So long as the pile is kept in motion preventing consolidation of the disturbed adjacent soil, the resistance to driving is relatively light. After the driving has stopped and the pile is allowed to stand still long enough for the surrounding soil to consolidate and perhaps for some thixotropic action to occur, the resistance to penetration is increased to such an extent that usually several blows of the hammer are required to start movement of the pile after the resumption of driving. The consolidated clay adjacent to the pile has a greater strength than the soil in its original condition.

When the pile is driven into saturated clay, the adjacent clay is subjected to heavy pressure which is carried by the pore water. This increase in pore water pressure in the clay near the pile forces migration of the pore water into the undisturbed clay farther away from the pile which results in consolidation of the clay adjacent to the pile and a resulting increase in shear strength. As the pile is being driven, the remolding of the adjacent clay reduces the shear strength adjacent to the pile as shown at A in Figure 5.10a. After being allowed to stand for a considerable length of time, the consolidated clay adjacent to the pile attains a high strength as shown at B in Figure 5.10a. If the surface of the pile is not smooth or lubricated, failure of the soil will occur a short distance away from the pile, and the bearing capacity will depend upon the shear strength of the soil instead of upon the coefficient of resistance between the soil and the surface of the pile. When the pile is pulled, the stronger consolidated clay adjacent to the pile clings to it and is pulled out.

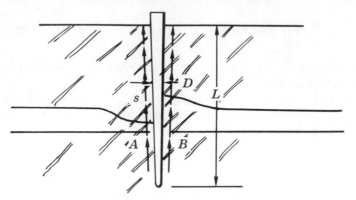

Figure 5.10a   Floating pile illustrating shear strength of clay during driving and after consolidation of disturbed adjacent clay

For a pile driven into soft clay, the point resistance is usually neglected and the bearing capacity is stated as the contact surface of the pile times the shear strength of the soil.

$$P = s\pi DL \qquad\qquad (Eq. 5.10a)$$

The shear strength of the clay can be estimated from laboratory tests, or from shear vane tests in the field, but the only reliable determination must be made by a load test on the pile or a pulling test.

The carrying capacity of a group of floating piles is not necessarily equal to the number of piles times the carrying capacity of an individual pile. The group may fail as a group and not as individual piles.

If the carrying capacity of a single pile is $P_1 = s\pi DL$ and that of a group acting as individual piles is $P_N = Ns\pi DL$, the carrying capacity of the group acting as a unit should be made at least equal to the capacity of the total number of single piles in the group. The carrying capacity of the group acting as a unit is $P_N = 2(A + B)sL$. If a is the critical center to center spacing of the piles, $A = (n_A - 1)a$ and $B = (n_B - 1)b$. Equating the carrying capacity of the group as individual piles to that of the group as a unit, the following relationship is derived:

$$2\,[(n_A - 1)a + (n_B - 1)b]\,sL = Ns\pi DL \qquad (Eq. 5.10b)$$

If the pile group is square,

$$n_A = n_B \text{ and } a = \frac{N\pi D}{4n - 4}$$

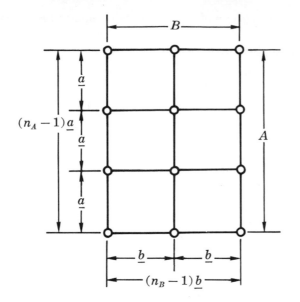

Figure 5.10b   Group of floating piles

Theoretically, if the piles are spaced as much as or more than a distance apart, the group would fail as individual piles, and if the piles were spaced less than a distance apart, the group would fail as a unit around the periphery of the group. This analysis ignores the bearing capacity of the soil under the group, which may offer some support.

Floating piles should be used with caution. Displacement piles driven into soft sensitive clay or silt may reduce the shear strength of the clay by remolding and initiate a substantial amount of consolidation. Settlement of structures resting on floating piles may be greater than that for the same structure on a properly designed foundation without the piles.

5.11   Point Friction Piles

As stated earlier, point friction piles are those that are driven through soft material into a layer of sand or other good bearing material below. The carrying capacity of point friction piles depends almost entirely upon the resistance along the contact surface in the bearing stratum and a small amount of end bearing. If the stratum is sand, the pile cannot be driven far into it unless the sand is very loose.

The carrying capacity of a point friction pile can be estimated as follows:

The average pressure against the pile required to cause failure of the sand is

$$\sigma_1 = \sigma_3 \tan^2 \left(45 + \frac{\phi}{2} \right)$$

In this case σ_3 is the weight of the overburden above the midpoint of the penetration into the sand $\sigma_3 = \gamma_e \left(z + \frac{L}{2} \right)$. The total horizontal pressure of the sand at failure against the pile is the passive earth pressure $E_p = \pi DL\sigma_1$, and the total resistance to penetration is

$$P = E_p \tan \phi = \pi DL\gamma_e \left(z + \frac{L}{2} \right) \tan^2 \left(45 + \frac{\phi}{2} \right) \tan \phi \quad \text{(Eq. 5.11a)}$$

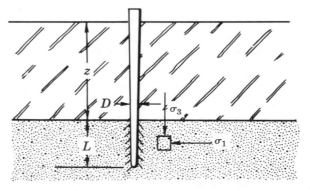

Figure 5.11a   Point friction pile

Since the penetration into the sand is relatively small, $L/2$ may be neglected without serious error. This approximation ignores the point resistance which makes the analysis err on the safe side. The load in this case is the failure load and not the design or safe load.

The load carried by the pile point by friction may be equal to, greater than, or less than the superimposed load on the pile. If the material through which the pile is driven to reach the sand layer is loose, it may consolidate after being remolded by the pile to a smaller volume than its original volume and load the pile by friction along the sides of the pile. If the material is such that it is not reduced in volume after driving the piles, the settlement allowed by the point resistance may be sufficient to develop a small amount of resistance along the pile above the sand.

In general, a group of point friction piles carries its load to the sand as individual piles and the piles can be spaced closer together than the critical spacing for floating piles.

5.12   Point Bearing Piles

The point bearing pile, which is driven through soft material to rock, transfers its load entirely by end bearing. The carrying capacity of a point bearing pile may usually be considered as the capacity of the pile as a short column. Lateral restraint offered even by quite soft material is sufficient to prevent buckling of the pile.

5.13   Batter Piles

To support loads having horizontal components, batter piles are often driven at such an angle that the resultant load is axial to the pile. The carrying capacity of these slanting piles is determined in the same manner as already discussed.

5.14   Piles and Poles Subjected to Horizontal Loads

There are a good many situations in which piles or poles are subjected to horizontal loads applied above the surface of the ground in which the pile is embedded. Examples are wind and earthquake forces on pile supported structures, wave forces against exposed parts of marine piles and against structures supported on these piles, and anchor pulls on piles used for the anchorage of earth retaining structures. The distinction between a pile and a pole is not easily made, but, generally, poles function as an integral part of the superstructure and provide foundation as well. Poles are usually not embedded as deeply as piles. Poles for telephone and power lines are subjected to horizontal forces when the lines change direction, the poles supporting outdoor signs must resist the wind loads, and the poles that constitute a part of the structural frame for small buildings and shelters must also resist wind forces.

Sometimes the piles may be considered individually, while at other times group action occurs; and in some cases the pile acts freely, while in other cases its action is constrained by the presence of a pile cap or other restraining influence. The whole question of pile movement and the distribution of the lateral resisting pressure on the side of the pile is a complex one that has been the subject of many theoretical and experimental investigations. The behavior depends on the characteristics of both the pile and the soil. M. T. Davisson and Shamsher Prakash (1963) have thoroughly reviewed the results of previous studies of the behavior of laterally loaded poles and have interpreted these from the viewpoint of modern soil mechanics.

The scope of this section does not permit a full discussion of the various procedures and theories pertaining to this problem. However, Bengt B. Broms (1965) has suggested simple procedures for the design of laterally loaded piles. His procedures are based on the assumptions that short piles fail as a result of simple rotation or translation, according to whether the top of the pile is free or restrained, and that long piles fail as a result of the development of one or two plastic hinges, according to whether the top of the pile is free or restrained. Broms cautions that, as yet, there is not sufficient experience to indicate whether or not the procedures are generally reliable. Therefore, the design parameters should be assigned values as unfavorable as could probably exist. The suggested procedures are in reasonable agreement with others that have been proposed and with the limited amount of observational data available.

The basis for Broms' analysis is that the lateral resistance of the pile is dependent upon the lateral resistance of the soil or upon the strength of the pile in bending.

In a cohesive soil having a shear strength equal to c_u as determined by undrained triaxial or shear test, Broms assumes that the soil reaction against the pile is zero to a depth of $1\frac{1}{2}$ times the pile diameter D below the surface and is a maximum at that depth and equal to $9c_uD$. This soil reaction is assumed to be constant to the center of rotation of the pile or point of maximum moment at some depth f below the surface. Below the center of rotation, the soil reaction acts in the same direction as the

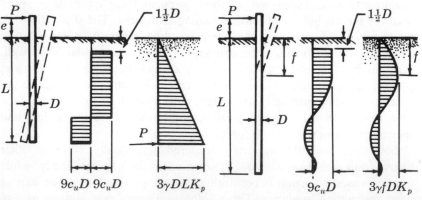

(a) Short Cohesive   Cohesionless (b) Long   Cohesive Cohesionless

Figure 5.14a   Failure modes for free piles—After Bengt B. Broms

applied load. The center of rotation must be located so that the horizontal soil reaction against the pile must equal the applied force P, and so that the summation of moments about the point is equal to zero.

In cohesionless soil, the soil reaction is assumed to be three times the triangular passive pressure distribution having a pressure intensity equal to $3\gamma_e DfK_p$ at the depth f where maximum moment occurs. K_p is the coefficient of passive earth pressure, $\tan^2\left(45 + \dfrac{\phi}{2}\right)$. These pressure distributions are shown in Figures 5.14a and 5.14b.

Failure of the piles is assumed to occur when the maximum moment under the load of the soil reaction and the applied load reaches the capacity of the pile at the section of maximum moment.

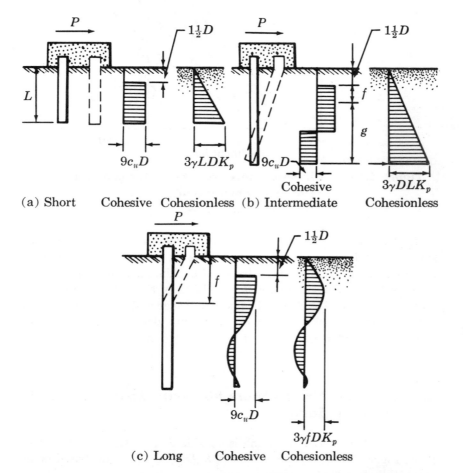

(a) Short   Cohesive Cohesionless (b) Intermediate   Cohesionless

(c) Long   Cohesive   Cohesionless

Figure 5.14b   Failure modes for piles with restrained end—After Bengt B. Broms

The design procedures for piles subjected to lateral loads are made quite simple by the use of charts prepared by Broms. These charts are shown in Figures 5.14c to 5.14f inclusive and 5.14h and 5.14i.

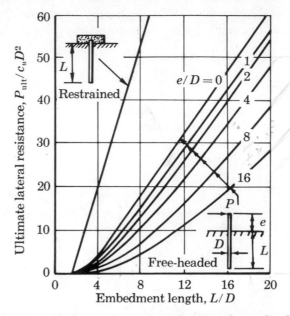

Figure 5.14c   Ultimate lateral resistance for cohesive soils related to embedment length—After Bengt B. Broms

The design procedures suggested by Broms are illustrated by two simple examples which also serve to define the parameters employed in the design charts. It is assumed that local buckling does not occur in the piles. In both examples, a steel H pile, 12 in. x 12 in. at 53 lb per ft is used, and the lateral load is applied perpendicular to the major axis of the cross section. $E = 29 \times 10^6$ psi, $I = 394.8$ in.^{4}, depth $= 11.78$ in., yield strength $= 33,000$ psi, $S = 67.0$ in.^{3}, $b = 12.046$ in.

a.   Example No. 1—Short Pile with Restrained End in Dense Sand

The pile has an L/D of 8 and is considered as restrained at its top. From Figure 5.14d, it is found that $P/K_pD^3\gamma_e = 97$. Thus, based upon properties of the soil,

$$P = 97 \ K_pD^3\gamma_e = 97(4.2)(1)^3(115) = 47,000 \text{ lb (ultimate)}$$

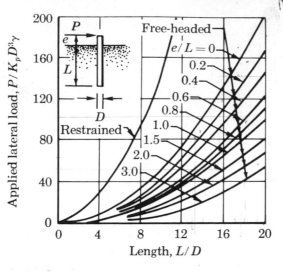

Figure 5.14d   Ultimate lateral resistance for cohesionless soils related to embedment length— After Bengt B. Broms

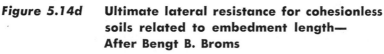

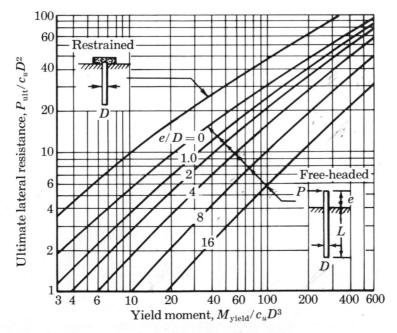

Figure 5.14e   Ultimate lateral resistance for cohesive soils related to yield moment— After Bengt B. Broms

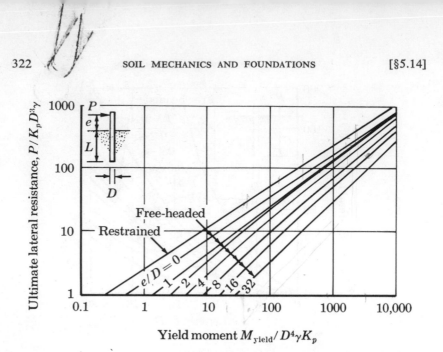

Figure 5.14f **Ultimate lateral resistance for cohesionless soils related to yield moment— After Bengt B. Broms**

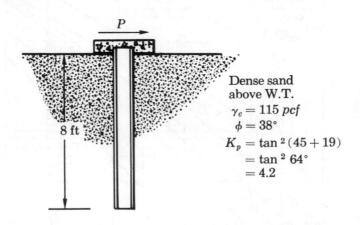

Dense sand above W.T.

$\gamma_e = 115 \ pcf$

$\phi = 38°$

$K_p = \tan^2(45 + 19)$

$\quad = \tan^2 64°$

$\quad = 4.2$

Figure 5.14g **Short H pile subjected to horizontal load at surface**

As to the sufficiency of the pile itself, Broms indicates that for cylindrical pipe piles the (plastic) yield moment can be taken as $M_{yield} = 1.3 \ f_y \ S$. For H piles, the yield moment can be taken as $1.1 \ f_y \ S_{max}$ for flexure around the major axis and 1.5 $f_y S_{min}$ for flexure around the minor axis. In this example,

$$M_{yield} = \frac{1.1(33,000)(67)}{12} = 203 \text{ ft kip}$$

$$\frac{M_{yield}}{D^4 \gamma_e K_p} = \frac{203,000}{(1)^4(115)(4.2)} = 420$$

From Figure 5.14*f*,

$$\frac{P}{K_p D^3 \gamma_e} = 100$$

Then,

$$P = 100(4.2)(1)^3(115) = 48,300 \text{ lb (ultimate)}$$

The safe load for use in design should probably not exceed 50 per cent of the smaller of the ultimate load estimates found above.

Suppose that a lateral load of 20 kips is applied to the top of the pile. The lateral deflection at the ground surface may be found by using Figure 5.14*i*. The coefficient of lateral subgrade reaction n_h, following K.

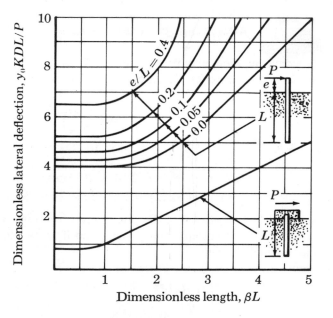

Figure 5.14h   **Lateral deflections at ground surface for cohesive soils—**
After Bengt B. Broms

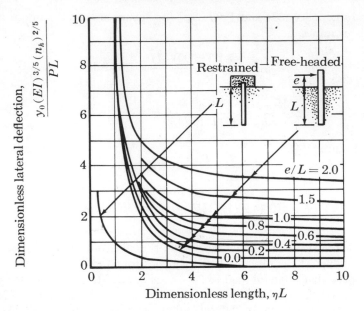

Figure 5.14i   **Lateral deflections at ground surface for cohesionless soils— After Bengt B. Broms**

Terzaghi's recommendation, may be estimated as 7, 21, and 56 tons ft^{-3} for loose, medium, and dense sands, respectively. The coefficient

$$\eta \text{ is } \sqrt[5]{\frac{n_h}{EI}}. \text{ In the example, } \eta = \sqrt[5]{\frac{56\left(\dfrac{2000}{1728}\right)}{29 \times 10^6(394.8)}} =$$

$$= \sqrt[5]{56.6 \times 10^{-10}} = 2.24 \times 10^{-2} \text{ in.}^{-1}$$

$$\eta L = 0.0224(8)(12) = 2.15 \text{ (dimensionless)}$$

According to Broms, if $\eta L < 2.0$, the pile behaves as an infinitely stiff member, subject only to translatory movement, and if $\eta L > 4.0$, the pile behaves as an infinitely long member.

From Figure 5.14i,

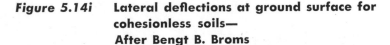

$$\frac{y_0(EI)^{3/5}(n_h)^{2/5}}{PL} = 0.5 \quad \text{chart gives} \quad 0.35$$

$$y_0 = \frac{0.5(20,000)(96)}{(29 \times 10^6 \times 394.8)^{3/5}\left(56 \times \dfrac{2000}{1728}\right)^{2/5}} = \frac{0.96}{(1.083)(5.3)} = 0.17 \text{ in.} \quad \times \frac{0.35}{0.50} = 0.119$$

(handwritten: 0.35 above 0.5(20,000)(96); .119)

lateral movement at ground surface.

b.   *Example No. 2—Long Pile with Free End in Cohesive Material*

Assume that the soil in this example is a moderately over-consolidated clay. The field vane shear strength is 0.5 tons ft^{-2}, and the coefficient of vertical subgrade reaction for a 1 ft by 1 ft plate is 70 tons ft^{-3}. The ratio L/D is 20, and e/D is 4.

From Figure 5.14c,

$$\frac{P_{ult}}{c_u D^2} = 47, \text{ from which}$$

$$P_{ult} = 47(1000)(1)^2 = 47,000 \text{ lb}$$

based upon the strength of the soil.

The resistance of the pile is estimated as follows: M_{yield} is the same as in Example No. 1

$$\frac{M_{yield}}{c_u D^3} = \frac{203,000}{1000(1)^3} = 203$$

From Figure 5.14e,

$$\frac{P_{ult}}{c_u D^2} = 28 \text{ from which}$$

$$P_{ult} = 28(1000)(1)^3 = 28,000 \text{ lb}$$

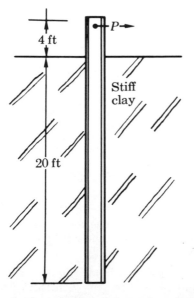

Figure 5.14j   Long H pile subjected to horizontal load at top end

After taking into consideration the considerable uncertainty usually present in the value adopted for c_u, an allowable load of $P = 10,000$ lb would not appear to be excessive.

In order to determine the approximate lateral deflection at the ground surface when a load of 10,000 lb acts laterally at a distance $e = 4$ ft above the surface of the ground, Figure 5.14h is used. Broms suggests that the coefficient of horizontal subgrade reaction for a long pile can be estimated from the coefficient of vertical subgrade reaction determined from a plate bearing test using a plate of side or diameter B, from the relationship $k_h = 0.4 \, k_0 D/B$, where D is the diameter or width of the pile. It has been assumed that k_0 is constant with depth, which is usually a conservative assumption. In this example

$$k_h = \frac{0.4\,(70)(1)}{1} = 28 \text{ tons ft}^{-3}$$

Then

$$\beta = \sqrt[4]{\frac{k_h \, D}{4 \, E I}} = \sqrt[4]{\frac{28 \left(\dfrac{2000}{1728}\right)(12)}{4 \times 29 \times 10^6 \, (394.8)}} = 0.96 \times 10^{-2} \text{ in.}^{-1}$$

$$\beta L = 0.0096(20)(12) = 2.3$$

According to Broms, piles for which $\beta L > 2.25$ may be considered as relatively long piles. From Figure 5.14h, using $\dfrac{e}{L} = \dfrac{4}{20} = 0.2$,

$$\frac{y_0 k D L}{P} = 7.2$$

$$y_0 = \frac{7.2(10,000)}{28 \left(\dfrac{2000}{1728}\right)(12)(20)(12)} = 0.77 \text{ in.}$$

lateral movement at ground surface.

REFERENCES

Agershau, Hans A., "Analysis of Engineering News Pile Formula," *Journal Soil Mechanics and Foundations Division*, Proc. Am. Soc. C.E., Vol. 88, No. SM5 (October, 1962).

Balla, Arpad, "Bearing Capacity of Foundations," *Journal Soil Mechanics and Foundations Division*, Proc. Am. Soc. C.E., Vol. 88, No. SM5 (October, 1962).

Broms, Bengt B., "Allowable Bearing Capacity of Initially Bent Piles," *Journal Soil Mechanics and Foundations Division*, Proc. Am. Soc. C.E., Vol. 89, No. SM5 (September, 1963).

Broms, Bengt B., "Lateral Resistance of Piles in Cohesionless Soils," *Journal Soil Mechanics and Foundations Division*, Proc. Am. Soc. C.E., Vol. 90, No. SM3 (May, 1964).

Broms, Bengt B., "Design of Laterally Loaded Piles," *Journal Soil Mechanics and Foundations Division*, Proc. Am. Soc. C.E., Vol. 91, No. SM3 (May, 1965).

D'Appolonia, Elio, and John A. Hribar, "Load Transfer in a Step Taper Pile," *Journal Soil Mechanics and Foundations Division*, Proc. Am. Soc. C.E., Vol. 89, No. SM6 (September, 1963).

D'Appolonia, Elio, and J. P. Romualdi, "Load Transfer in End Bearing Steel H Piles," *Journal Soil Mechanics and Foundations Division*, Proc. Am. Soc. C.E., Vol. 89, No. SM2 (March, 1963).

Davisson, M. T., and H. L. Gill, "Laterally Loaded Piles in a Layered Soil System," *Journal Soil Mechanics and Foundations Division*, Proc. Am. Soc. C.E., Vol. 89, No. SM3 (May, 1963).

Davisson, M. T., and Shamsher Prakash, "A Review of Soil-Pole Behavior," *Highway Research Record, No. 39*, Highway Research Board, 1963, pp. 25-48.

Francis, Arthur J., "Analysis of Pile Groups with Flexural Resistance," *Journal Soil Mechanics and Foundations Division*, Proc. Am. Soc. C.E., Vol. 90, No. SM3 (May, 1964).

Hu, George C. Y., "Variable Factors Theory of Bearing Capacity," *Journal Soil Mechanics and Foundations Division*, Proc. Am. Soc. C.E., Vol. 90, No. SM4 (July, 1964).

Johnson, Sidney M., "Determining the Capacity of Bent Piles," *Journal Soil Mechanics and Foundations Division*, Proc. Am. Soc. C.E., Vol. 88, No. SM6 (December, 1962).

Kenney, T. Cameron, "Pore Pressures and Bearing Capacity of Layered Clays," *Journal Soil Mechanics and Foundations Division*, Proc. Am. Soc. C.E., Vol. 91, No. SM4 (March, 1965).

Klohn, Earle J., "Pile Heave and Redriving," *Journal Soil Mechanics and Foundations Division*, Proc. Am. Soc. C.E., Vol. 87, No. SM4 (August, 1961).

Klohn, Earle J., and J. T. Hughes, "Buckling of Long Unsupported Timber Piles," *Journal Soil Mechanics and Foundations*, Proc. Am. Soc. C.E., Vol. 90, SM6 (November, 1964).

Kondner, Robert L., "Friction Pile Groups in Cohesive Soil," *Journal Soil Mechanics and Foundations Division*, Proc. Am. Soc. C.E., Vol. 88, No. SM3 (June, 1962).

Krizek, Raymond J., "Approximation for Terzaghi's Bearing Capacity Factors," *Journal Soil Mechanics and Foundations Division*, Proc. Am. Soc. C.E., Vol. 91, No. SM2 (March, 1965).

Lysmer, J., and F. E. Richart, "Dynamic Response of Footings to Vertical Loading," *Journal Soil Mechanics and Foundations Division*, Proc. Am. Soc. C.E., Vol. 92, SM1 (January, 1966).

Meyerhof, G. G., "Load Carrying Capacity of Concrete Pavements," *Journal Soil Mechanics and Foundations Division*, Proc. Am. Soc. C.E., Vol. 88, No. SM3 (June, 1962).

Meyerhof, G. G., "Penetration Tests and Bearing Capacity of Cohesionless Soils," *Journal Soil Mechanics and Foundations Division*, Proc. Am. Soc. C.E., Vol. 82, No. SM1 (January, 1956).

Nordlund, R. L., "Bearing Capacity of Piles in Cohesionless Soils," *Journal Soil Mechanics and Foundations Division*, Proc. Am. Soc. C.E., Vol. 89, No. SM3 (May, 1963).

Spillers, William R., and Robert D. Stoll, "Lateral Response of Piles," *Journal Soil Mechanics and Foundations Division*, Proc. Am. Soc. C.E., Vol. 90, No. SM6 (November, 1964).

Yoshimi, Yoshiaki, "Piles in Cohesionless Soil Subject to Oblique Pull," *Journal Soil Mechanics and Foundations Division*, Proc. Am. Soc. C.E., Vol. 90, No. SM6 (November, 1964).

6

Foundations on Overconsolidated Desiccated Clay

6.01 General

Throughout the world there exist areas of surface clays in climates in which there are alternating dry and wet periods. In such climates, the surface clays are subjected to cycles of desiccation and saturation. The capillary forces in the drying clay have subjected the clay to preconsolidation pressures which produce overconsolidation to considerable depths. Some of these clays have been preconsolidated by heavy overburden, sometimes much greater than the preconsolidation produced by desiccation, which has been removed by erosion.

Structures erected on these overconsolidated desiccated clays have suffered extensive damage because of expansion of the clays upon increase in water content. This chapter is concerned with the effect of climate upon the volume change of clays, the effect of the construction of a building upon a deposit of clay upon the water content of the clay, the effect of volume change of the clay upon the building, and with methods of reducing damage caused by swelling clays.

6.02   Compressibility of Clay

When compressive stress is applied to saturated clay which is confined laterally, deformation and volume change are produced. Volume change of the saturated clay can occur only as the incompressible water is forced out. As pressure is applied to the soil structure some of the double layer water is forced out from between the grains against the pull of the electromagnetic field surrounding the soil grains, the elastic soil particles are bent and deformed, the soil particles slide to new positions of greater stability among themselves, and entrapped gas is compressed or forced out. Upon release of pressure, if free water is available, the magnetic field reclaims the attached water to the soil grains and the elastic particles rebound to their original shapes resulting in an elastic rebound of the soil mass. As shown in (1) of Figure 6.02a, when a load p_1 is applied to a layer of clay L thick which has never been previously loaded, part of the deformation produced is inelastic, ΔL_i, and part is elastic, ΔL_e. Upon release of load, the layer expands the elastic portion ΔL_e of the total deformation as shown at (2).

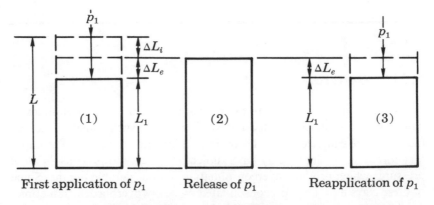

First application of p_1 Release of p_1 Reapplication of p_1

Figure 6.02a   Deformation of clay

A second application of the compressive load p_1 after the elastic recovery, as shown at (3), produces a deformation slightly larger than the elastic recovery ΔL_e. Removal of the second application of load allows an elastic recovery not quite equal to the deformation caused by the second application. Each application seems to produce a slight additional rearrangement of the soil grains and a slight increase in permanent deformation. But this reduction in volume with each application of load cannot continue indefinitely. Eventually, after the load has been repeated often enough, the deformation will be entirely elastic.

6.03   Shrinking and Swelling of Clay

When free water is available on the surface of saturated clay, the tension in the pore water is zero. When evaporation begins, menisci are formed in the surface pores as shown in Figure 6.03a and a tensile stress is produced in the pore water equal to $u = 0.152/R_B$, when R_B is the radius of the meniscus formed at position B. This tension is transmitted throughout the soil mass making the radius of the menisci in all of the pores at the surface equal to R_B. The pores at the surface are subjected to a compressive stress equal to the total stress produced by the stressed pore water. This load on the soil grains produces a deformation or shrinkage of the clay in the same manner as if this stress were applied from a superimposed load. Further evaporation causes a receding of the menisci

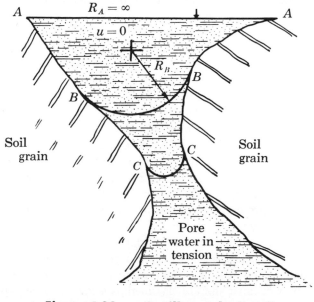

Figure 6.03a   Capillary tube in soil

to the smallest portion of the largest connecting pore as at C in Figure 6.03a. At this stage, the greatest pore water tension and corresponding compression in the soil will be developed. The clay will have attained its maximum shrinkage. At this shrinkage limit, the clay, for practical purposes, is still saturated.

When free water is supplied to the surface of the saturated clay at the shrinkage limit, the menisci on the surface are destroyed, the tension in the pore water is relieved, and the clay is free to swell through the elastic portion of the deformation caused by the pore water stress. Completely drying out the soil below the shrinkage limit produces little additional shrinkage. When water is admitted to the surface of dry clay menisci are formed in the pores pulling the water into the clay. The reaction of the menisci against the soil grains near the surface and the pressure of the compressed air in the pores causes disintegration of the structure of the clay on the surface, sometimes with almost explosive force. A piece of brick-like clay when dropped into a glass of water will quickly disintegrate into a pile of soft individual clay particles which can be readily shaken into suspension.

6.04   Properties of Desiccated Clay

The following discussion is not meant to imply that all desiccated clays have the properties described below. A great many of the clays that have been exposed to innumerable repetitions of drying and wetting are fissured, making them break easily along well defined cleavage planes. In general, these clays possess high shear strength as measured by their carrying capacity under foundations. In unconfined compression, they crumble easily, making it impractical to determine their shear strength by unconfined compression tests.

Excavated vertical banks in most of these clays stand so long as the moisture content does not change. Drying causes them to crumble along cleavage planes and to slough off into the excavation. Wetting of the dry clay causes disintegration of the clay structure and collapse of the embankments. Occasionally, in excavations, clays are found in which the crack patterns are preserved by dust which fell into the cracks when they were open during dry weather.

Some of these clays have been consolidated under several hundred feet of overburden which has since been removed by erosion. Some of the overconsolidated clays resemble shale more than they do clay, and are called shale by workmen and are classified as shale by some exploration companies. These clays disintegrate rapidly when immersed in water and form a suspension when shaken slightly.

6.05   Spring Analogy

Except for the time factor, the action of desiccated clays under conditions of loading and moisture conditions can be illustrated fairly accurately with a spring analogy.

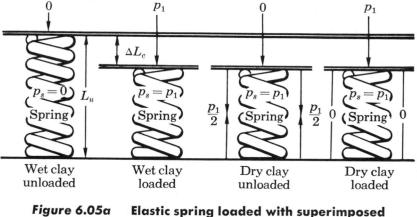

Figure 6.05a   Elastic spring loaded with superimposed load and with tie downs

Assume an elastic spring of unloaded length L_u in which a superimposed load p_1 produces a deformation ΔL_e as shown in Figure 6.05a. If the spring is tied down with tension members having a modulus of elasticity many times that of the spring and of such length that the deformation of the spring is ΔL_e, loading the tied down spring with a superimposed load less than p_1 causes very little additional deformation of the spring. The tension in the tie wires is reduced with little deformation and the compression in the spring remains approximately p_1. If the tie wires are cut, some rebound of the spring will occur. The greater the applied load on the spring when the tie wires are cut, the less will be the elastic rebound.

Clay at the shrinkage limit may be considered as an elastic spring tied down by the tensile stress in the capillary pore water. Applying free water to the surface of the clay eliminates the tension in the pore water and allows the clay to expand as water is drawn into the pores.

6.06   Relationship between Load and Swelling

The pressure applied to the clay by the pore water in tension is dependent upon the effective pore diameter of the clay. As seen from the spring analogy, if the clay is dry and loaded to the same pressure as the pressure that produced the shrinkage, the clay cannot swell against this pressure when free water is applied to the soil.

The pressure p_s to which the clay has been subjected by capillary pore water can be estimated from a swelling and consolidation test, or by a test in which external pressure is applied just sufficient to prevent expansion of the clay. The expansion of a layer of clay against an applied pressure can be estimated by the use of the swelling index C_s as determined from a consolidation test. If the natural void ratio e_n is known, e_1 to which the clay will swell against an applied pressure p_1 which is less than p_s can be estimated from the relationship $e_1 = e_n + C_s \log p_s/p_1$. The method of estimating the relationship between pressure and swelling by the use of the swelling index C_s is not likely to be accurate because the $e - \log p$ swelling curve is usually not straight and because the structure of the clay may be somewhat changed by the higher pressure applied in the consolidation test before the clay is allowed to swell.

Several series of tests have been performed in the Soil Mechanics Laboratory at Oklahoma State University in an attempt to determine the relationship between pressure and amount of swelling of undisturbed Permian clays which have been preconsolidated by overburden to pressures up to about 30 tons per sq ft. In these tests, specimens of samples from the same test pit were placed in consolidation rings, allowed to dry

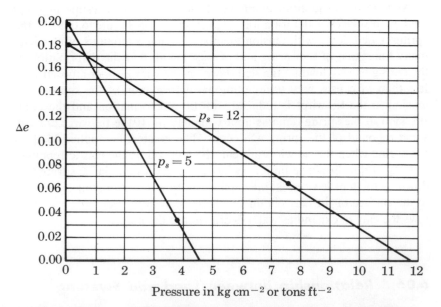

Figure 6.06a   Relationship between pressure and swelling for two overconsolidated desiccated clays

out, and the space between the dried out specimen and ring was filled. The specimens and rings were arranged for fixed ring consolidation tests. Each specimen was loaded to a different pressure varying from small intensity to greater than the preconsolidation pressure from desiccation. The specimens were then flooded and the amount of swelling was measured for each loading condition. Wide scattering of points made the results of the tests inconclusive. However, for specimens for which the same p_s is indicated, points indicating the ratio of change in void ratio Δe to pressure p_1 follow approximately a straight line relationship as shown in Figure 6.06a.

6.07   Relationship between Vertical and Horizontal Swelling

The discussion of the preceding section deals with swelling of clays when confined against lateral deformation. This is the condition that usually prevails under foundations where the clay is restrained against horizontal deformation by the surrounding clay which is subjected to the same restraining pressure. However, the horizontal expansion of clays often produces serious damage to buildings. Some examples of damage produced by horizontal expansion of overconsolidated desiccated clays are described later in this chapter.

By a process of reasoning from a knowledge of the properties of clay particles, one is led to believe that if a mass has a random structure it is likely to expand as much horizontally as vertically and to exert as much pressure horizontally as vertically whether the mass of clay has been compacted by nature or by artificial means. One would also expect a clay with a horizontal parallel (dispersed) structure to swell more than one

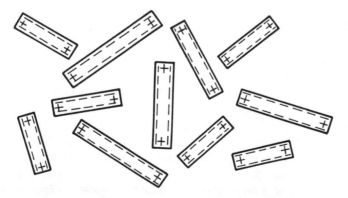

Figure 6.07a   Random structure of clay

having a random structure. In the case of a random structure, many edges
of the particles carrying positive charges are adjacent to the broad surfaces carrying negative charges which causes the edges to be held to the
broad surfaces by the attractive forces of the unlike charges and to inhibit
the formation of thick layers of water between the grains. This reasoning
has been vindicated experimentally by a considerable number of investi-
gators.

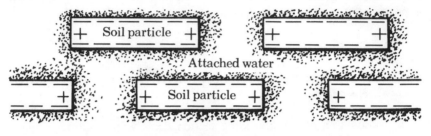

Figure 6.07b   Dispersed structure of clay

In a series of tests for measuring the vertical and horizontal swelling of
some highly overconsolidated desiccated clays in the undisturbed and in
the artificially compacted states made at Oklahoma State University, it was
found that in all cases the horizontal swelling was greater than the vertical
swelling under zero or very light confining pressures. These tests indicate
that for clay specimens compacted by kneading in the Harvard compaction apparatus (which simulates the kneading action of a sheepsfoot roller)
the vertical and horizontal swelling were nearly equal at optimum moisture content and, for specimens compacted under static pressure, the
horizontal expansion slightly exceeded the vertical. Swelling of specimens
compacted by all methods exceeded that of undisturbed specimens by a
fairly large margin. Specimens compacted by dynamic compaction (standard Proctor) swelled slightly more than those compacted by static pressure. These tests seem to indicate that dynamic compaction produces a
structure which more nearly approximates the structure of undisturbed
clay that has been compacted by static overburden pressure than does
compaction by kneading.

The question of the exact relationship between relative amounts of
swelling in horizontal and vertical directions for zero confining pressures
is somewhat academic, except as it may be indicative of the pressure-
deformation relationship. There are so many conditions which affect the
amount of expansion of clays with increase in water content and the pressure required to prevent swelling that experience with the clay and climate
in an area is probably more important than the results of experimentation
on clays of another region made under laboratory conditions which

may not duplicate field conditions. But it is useful to know that, generally, overconsolidated desiccated clays swell both vertically and horizontally against fairly high pressures, and that the same clay when compacted artificially swells considerably more than when undisturbed in a natural deposit.

6.08   Effect of Climate on Surface Clays

Some clays, especially those containing montmorillonite, are more susceptible to volume change due to change in water content than others, but all clays are affected to some extent. Clays near the surface are affected by climatic conditions.

a.   State of Stress in Pore Water

Free water in soil may exist at zero stress, in compression, or in tension. The stress to which the soil grains are subjected depends upon the state of stress in the pore water.

At the water table, the stress in the pore water is zero and exerts no force upon the soil grains. Below the water table, the water is in compression under the hydrostatic head and exerts no stress in the soil grains, except for the reduction in unit weight by the buoyant effect of submersion. The unit weight of the soil below the water table is less by the unit weight of water than the unit weight of the saturated soil not submerged. The pressure between the grains (effective pressure) due to the overburden pressure is reduced because of submersion of the soil below the water table.

Above the water table, the soil may be saturated by capillary water hanging from the soil grains. The pressure between the grains of the soil in the capillary fringe is produced by the weight of the soil and the weight of the capillary water hanging in tension from the grains. The tension in the capillary water may vary from zero at the water table to the full head of the capillary rise at the top of the zone, even though the capillary rise does not extend to its maximum possible height.

If there were no free water on the surface, and there were no evaporation from the surface, and if the surface were less than the maximum capillary rise above the water table, the entire layer of clay above the water table would be saturated with capillary water in tension hanging from the grains near the surface. The pressure on the soil grains in this area would be that produced by the saturated weight of the overburden. In

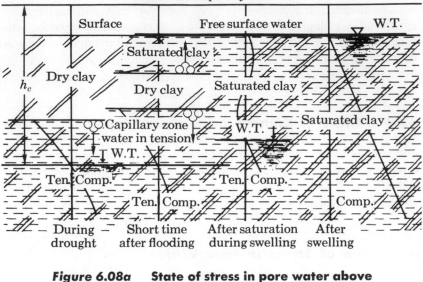

Figure 6.08a   **State of stress in pore water above water table**

this case, the menisci at the surface are not fully developed because there is no evaporation and no flow of water.

b.   *Effect of Climate*

During a drought, evaporation from the surface lowers the top of the capillary fringe toward the water table until, for a given deposit of clay, equilibrium is reached between the rate of evaporation and the distance to the capillary moisture. The dry clay above the capillary zone is subjected to the maximum shrinkage pressure. The menisci in the pores at the top of the capillary fringe are fully developed producing a tension in the water equal to the maximum capillary rise. The forces forming the menisci are the weight of the water in the pores below the top of the fringe and the water table, and the resistance to flow of water through the soil between the water table and the top of the capillary fringe where the evaporation is occurring. The tension in the water is reduced to zero at the water table. The clay in the capillary fringe is subjected to the full pressure of the capillary rise at the top of the fringe and to lesser pressures as the resistance to flow becomes less until at the water table the clay is subjected to the pressure of the overburden only.

After a rain, the free water on the surface is pulled into the pores of the surface clay downward toward the capillary zone above the water table. At the same time, since evaporation from above has ceased, the capillary water begins to rise to meet the capillary water coming down from above. At the front of these advances of capillary water, the soil is subjected to pressure equal to the maximum capillary rise. The tension in the water is in equilibrium with the pressure between the grains and the resistance to movement of water through the pores of the soil.

After the two advancing capillary zones meet and there is free water on the surface, the capillary tension in the pore water throughout the mass of soil between the water table and the surface is relieved, and the clay can begin to swell against the reduced pressure. After the clay has had time to expand as much as it can against its overburden pressure, the stress in the pore water becomes equal to the hydrostatic pressure and equilibrium is established between the expansive force of the clay and the reduced overburden pressure of the submerged soil. The amount of swelling for a given clay is smaller at depth where the overburden pressure is greater.

6.09   Time Required for Swelling

When the two capillary zones first meet, the water throughout the soil mass above the water table does not immediately change to the hydrostatic pressure from the surface. As the pressure between the grains is reduced the soil begins to expand, but it can do so only as water is drawn into the enlarged pore spaces. Movement of water through the pores is resisted by the very low permeability of the clay. The expanding soil creates tension in the water which prevents immediate expansion.

The time required for complete swelling of a layer of clay after free water is provided on the surface, depends upon the coefficient of permeability of the clay and the distance through which the water must be drawn through the soil. After the surface of dry clay is ponded, the clay on the surface can expand immediately. At some distance below the surface, the clay can begin to swell after it has become saturated and can continue to do so only as water is drawn from the supply at the surface through the intervening clay. The time required for swelling to occur depends upon the distance from the surface of application of water.

If a 5 ft thick layer of dry Pauls Valley clay is flooded on the surface and water can get into the clay from the top only, approximately 2 years would be required for complete expansion of the 5 ft layer. A layer of this clay 10 ft thick would require about 8 years for complete expansion.

Because of the long time required after ponding for expansion of the

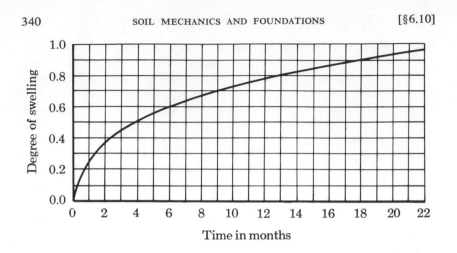

Figure 6.09a   Relationship between time and degree of swelling at different elapsed times after application of water to surface of a 5 ft layer of clay

clay to occur, clay exposed to the weather in some climates is never allowed to swell because the wet periods do not last long enough. Clay is not necessarily fully expanded because it is saturated.

6.10   Effect of Building on Surface Clays

When a building is erected on a clay layer, evaporation from the surface is retarded. If the water table is at a distance below the building less than the maximum capillary rise, the soil below the building attains a high degree of saturation with capillary water drawn up from below. Since there is little evaporation under the building, the clay immediately under the building will be subjected only to the weight of the pore water hanging from the top soil grains and the building load. If this pressure is less than the maximum pressure capable of being produced by capillary tension in the water, swelling of the clay can occur against this reduced pressure. This expansion of the clay can occur even during a dry period, due simply to the presence of the building.

After equilibrium is reached between swelling and load, and free water is admitted to the surface outside the building, the stress in the pore water is changed from tension to compression and the pressure between the grains is reduced to the submerged weight of the overburden and the

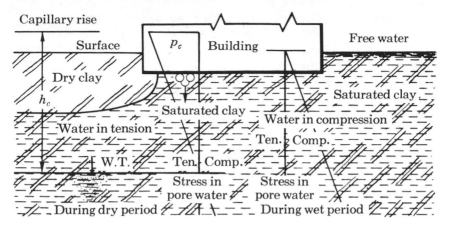

Figure 6.10a   Effect of building on water content of clay

weight of the building. This reduced pressure allows swelling of the clay under the building unless the building load is equal to the maximum pressure previously produced by the capillary forces.

Once equilibrium has been established between load, the distance to the water table, and the climate, the clay under the interior of the building will probably remain stable until conditions are changed to upset the equilibrium, such as by a leaking water line. Around the periphery of a building which loads the soil to pressures less than the maximum capillary pressure, changes in climate and application of water to the surface may cause periodic swelling and shrinkage of clay under shallow exterior footings.

6.11   Effect of Swelling on Buildings

As one would expect, an enormous amount of damage has been done to light buildings on shallow foundations on expansive clays in a climate of long dry periods and intermittent wet periods by the volume change of the clays as the water content is changed. Heavy multi-storied buildings, if otherwise structurally sound, stand indefinitely with little or no damage, except to the lightly loaded portions like floor slabs on the ground. Unless special precautions are taken to eliminate the effect of expanding clay, light one story buildings are often badly damaged by differential uplift as the volume of the clay changes.

In some areas, where the water table is normally high and the clay is continuously saturated, severe damage has been caused by shrinkage of the clay when exposed to an unusual drought which has occurred for the first time since construction of the buildings.

a.   *Examples of Damage from Expanding Clays*

Some specific examples of damage to buildings are described to illustrate the type and cause of damage produced by expansive clays and a cooperative climate. These examples are all concerned with the highly overconsolidated Permian clays of Oklahoma.

(1) During the dry period of the early nineteen thirties, narrow pavements on the east side of the Oklahoma State University campus were widened by laying a new concrete slab alongside the old pavement. The new slab eventually rose about 2 in. above the old slab and has remained so.

(2) During the same period, a number of utility tunnels were constructed on the Oklahoma State University campus. The tops of the tunnels were laid flush with the ground and are used for sidewalks. Adjacent sidewalks were laid directly on the ground alongside the tunnel tops as shown in Figure 6.11a. Swelling of the clay between the bottom of the tunnel and sidewalks has raised the sidewalks above the tunnel tops from 2 to 3 in. These sidewalks remain permanently high because evaporation of water from the clay underneath the sidewalks and tunnels has been retarded.

(3) Also during the early thirties an addition to the Animal Husbandry Building was erected on the Oklahoma State University campus. The exterior brick walls were supported on deep grade

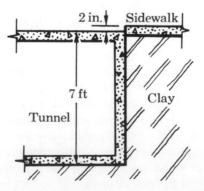

Figure 6.11a   Section through tunnel and sidewalk

beams and independent footings about 7 ft below grade as shown in Figure 6.11b. The floors of the corner areas back of the tiered seats around the arena are concrete slabs laid on excavated clay about 3 ft below grade. The upper structural slabs forming the floor in the corners back of the tiered seats of the arena were cast integrally with concrete lintel beams in the wall over the windows.

Rooms were formed with 4 in. tile partitions in the corners back of the seats. The tile partitions were supported on the ground floor slab and wedged tight against the structural slab above. The clay between the slab and the bottom of the footings swelled against the slab and, acting through the tile partitions, lifted the floor slab above the exterior brick wall. The exterior brick wall was lifted off the grade beam as shown at A in Figure 6.11b for a distance of about 8 ft at the partitions. This crack was

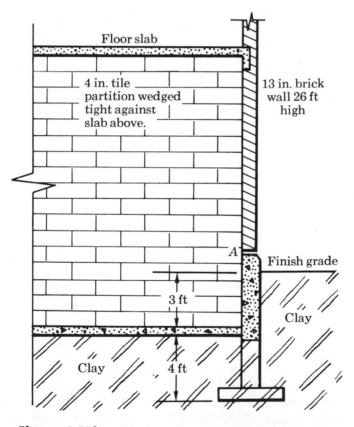

Figure 6.11b   Section through exterior wall of animal husbandry arena

large enough that one could look through it from the inside and
see automobiles pass in the street. The floor slabs in the middle
of the rooms were lifted about 3 in. more than at the partitions.
The partitions were badly broken by the uplift of the expanding
clay as shown in Figure 6.11c.

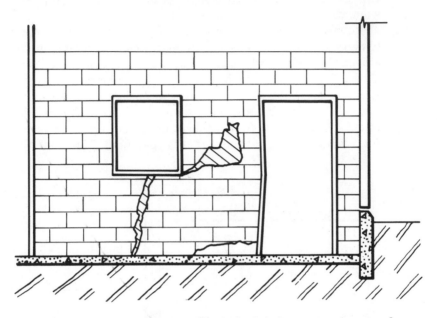

**Figure 6.11c   Tile partition forming corner room of
animal husbandry arena**

The water table under this building is more than 50 ft below
the surface.

(4) Whitehurst Hall on the campus of Oklahoma State University was
erected in 1927 on a site where the water table is only about 16 ft
below the surface. The building is supported on a structural frame
on independent column footings. The ground floor is a slab-on-
ground independent of the structural frame. A few years after
completion of the building, the floors in the middle of rooms on
the ground floor were 2 to 3 in. higher than they were next to
the partitions which rested on the slabs. Partitions were badly
broken, and few doors in the first story could be closed.

During the summer of 1937, when the ground outside the
building was so dry that shrinkage cracks 2 in. and more in width
had formed in the surface, the ground floor was removed. The
clay under the slab was completely saturated so that the clay

could be remolded into soft mud. There were no leaking water lines. A new slab was placed on the saturated clay. There has been no noticeable movement of the new slab.

(5) A boys' dormitory was constructed on the campus of Oklahoma State University during 1939-40. The building is four stories in height supported on a concrete structural frame on independent column footings located about 14 ft below the surface. The basement is about 8 ft below the surface and the water table is more than 50 ft below the surface.

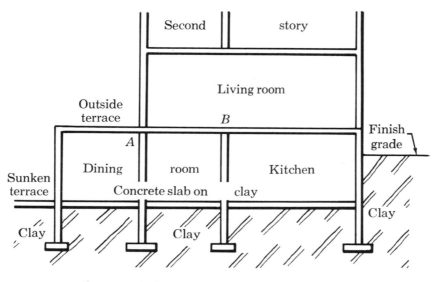

Figure 6.11d   Section through Cordell Hall

When the basement was excavated, the clay was dry, hard and shale-like. As soon as possible after the basement walls were erected, the basement floor was placed on the dry clay. At the end of the construction period about a year later, floor drains that had been installed 2 in. lower were found to be $5\frac{1}{2}$ in. higher than the reference point for elevation of the basement floor at the outside wall. Eight years after its installation this floor was still moving upward.

Another damaged condition in this dormitory was caused by uplift of lightly loaded columns supporting the first floor only in the middle of the living room as shown at B in Figure 6.11d. These single story columns are on footings at the same depth as the other footings, and the contact pressures are approximately the same. The total load on one of the small footings is so much less than the load on the main footings that the expanding clay below the footings has lifted the lightly loaded columns producing a ridge in the living room floor 3 inches higher than the floor at the exterior walls.

The outside terrace which loads the clay less than the main building was lifted, causing the terrace floor to slope toward the building.

(6) In south central Oklahoma, a one story commercial building was constructed on a continuous foundation about 3 ft wide and 4 ft below the surface. The exterior walls are of brick 13 in. thick and about 20 ft high. The floor is a concrete slab laid on the clay at grade. A water line was installed in a shallow trench inside the building about 30 ft from and parallel to the north wall.

A leak in the water line fed water to the clay under the floor and the continuous footing under the west wall. The expanding clay adjacent to this line lifted the floor slab several inches above other portions of the floor, pushing a partition through the ceiling. The west wall was lifted in this area producing a large crack as shown in Figure 6.11e.

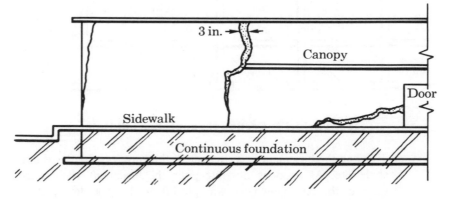

Figure 6.11e   Elevation west wall of commercial building

(7) In making additions to water service lines in Tulsa, Oklahoma, the lines, where they crossed the street at each residence site, were laid in trenches and backfilled with sand rather than clay in order to prevent damage to pavements from subsequent settling of backfill.

The sand fed water to the clay adjacent to the sides of the trench causing it to swell earlier than did the clay farther away. This action produced a hump on each side of each line with a depression over the trench.

(8) A type of damage common to light buildings on shallow continuous foundations is caused by tilting of footings and walls outward. This tilting is caused by the clay under the inside edge of the footing gaining moisture and expanding, while the clay under the exterior edge remains dry and compressed. This tilting is sometimes aided and sometimes caused by lateral swelling of compacted clay fill.

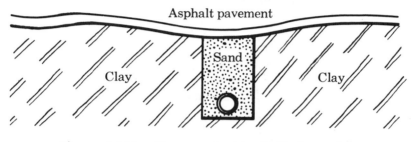

Figure 6.11f   Pavement at backfilled trench

In order to stiffen the exterior walls to prevent cracking from unequal uplift, monolithic concrete was used for these walls in a one story school building in south central Oklahoma. The exterior walls were supported on a continuous foundation about 30 in.

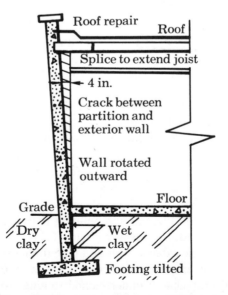

Figure 6.11g   Section through monolithic concrete wall

wide and 3 ft below the surface. As the clay under the building gained moisture, it expanded under the inside of the footing tilting the exterior walls along their middle portions. The connecting walls at corners prevented rotation at the ends. Roof joists were pulled out of their seats making it necessary to extend them with splices as shown in Figure 6.11*g*.

Brick walls that are tied at the roof line and supported on shallow continuous footings are sometimes cracked horizontally by rotation of the footings as shown in Figure 6.11*h*.

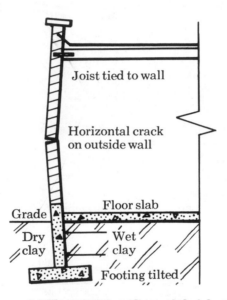

Figure 6.11h   Section through brick wall

(9) Another example of damage to buildings caused by the combination of climate and properties of clay is a fairly recently erected college building in southwestern Oklahoma. This building has a steel frame supported on a drilled and underreamed pier and grade beam type foundation. The footings were placed about 16 ft below the surface for vertical stability. On the south side of a portion of the building, the outside wall of the first story was placed about 4 ft inside the exterior building line, leaving the exterior columns exposed, as shown in Figure 6.11*i*. This panel wall was supported on the exterior wall of a pipe tunnel running parallel to the wall. This exterior tunnel wall, carrying the panel wall, was supported on pier and underreamed footings to the same depth as the footings under the main columns.

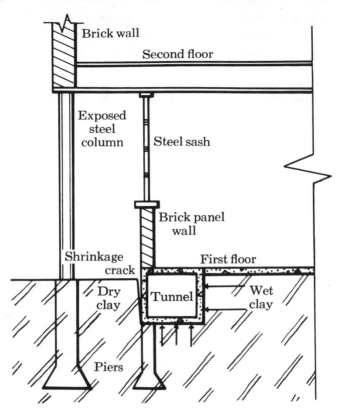

Figure 6.11i   **Section through south wall of building**

The clay outside the building was dried out by sun and wind and was somewhat protected by the overhang of the second story. A broken water line under the building fed water to the clay, which accelerated the rate of swelling. The swelling clay on the inside of the building forced the tunnel outward and upward which wrecked the panel wall to such an extent that it had to be torn out and rebuilt.

(10) A church in southwestern Oklahoma finished in 1957 is supported on grade beams on piers and belled footings cast in drilled and underreamed holes. The footings are about 16 ft below the surface. Care was taken to provide a void under the grade beams to prevent uplift from expanding clay. Each of the exterior piers is loaded with about 75,000 lb. Several low interior brick partitions are supported in the same manner as the exterior walls, but on smaller footings. The heavy exterior walls have suffered no

damage but the inside partitions have been cracked by uplift of
the cast in place piers. As the clay expanded, the friction and
the shear strength of the clay were sufficient to lift the piers against
the light partition loads.

(11) A grade beam cast in a trench in clay supporting an 8 in. brick
wall under the stadium at Oklahoma State University was anchored at each end to the columns supporting the main structure.
Expanding clay under the grade beam created enough pressure to
break the beam and lift the wall.

(12) A combination dormitory, school, and recreation building at an
institution in southern Oklahoma has a pier and belled footing
type of foundation with grade beams for the exterior walls. The
grade beams were cast in trenches in which the clay had been
loosened in the bottom, so that consolidation of the loose clay
could compensate for expansion of the undisturbed clay below.
The grade outside the building is 1 to 2 ft lower than the floor. The

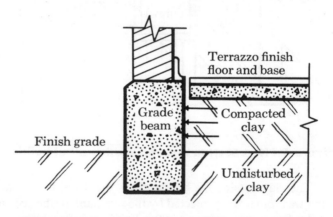

**Figure 6.11j   Floor slab on compacted clay fill
between grade beams**

floor was cast on a compacted clay fill between grade beams. The
terrazzo cove base was supported on the grade beams and on
beams supporting the partitions. The floor slab was cast independent of the beams and base so that uplift of the floor slab
would not crack the base. There is very little evidence of damage caused by vertical expansion of the clay. The finish floor and
the cove base are still at approximately the same elevation, but
the fairly thin layer of compacted clay has swelled horizontally,

pushed the grade beams outward, and caused a crack about $\frac{1}{2}$ in. wide between the floor and the cove base. Horizontal cracks have also been produced in the brick wall at the top of windows by the wall rotation and restraint at the roof line.

Another identical building was built a year later from the same plans and by the same contractor about 100 yards from the building described above. In this building, the grade beams were cast on a layer of hay in the bottom of the trenches and the fill under the floor between the grade beams was made of sand. No evidence of distress could be found in a recent examination of this building.

6.12   Methods of Preventing Damage from Expanding Clays

As stated earlier, in climates subject to long dry and intermittent wet periods, the clays near the surface have been dried out and shrunk. Unless ponded for several years, they remain shrunken even though they become saturated near the surface during wet periods. From consideration of the cause of shrinking and swelling of clays and the condition of surface clays exposed to variable climatic conditions, three methods of preventing damage to buildings constructed on clays which are at or below the shrinkage limit are suggested.

(1) The clay may be loaded with a unit pressure approximately equal to the compression produced by the capillary water which produced the shrinkage.

(2) The building may be supported on footings at a depth below the surface and near enough to the water table that the water content of the clay is not affected by climatic changes. Precautions must be taken to prevent damage to the building by uplift on parts of building by expansion of the clay between the footings and grade beams, floors, and other parts of the building at grade.

(3) A mat or platform of sufficient stiffness and strength to support the building load without excessive deflection for any possible distribution of supporting pressure under the slab may be laid on the surface of the clay, and the building constructed on the stiffened slab.

Each of these methods has advantages and disadvantages. A method which might be suitable under one set of conditions might not be suitable under other conditions.

a. *Preventing Damage with Heavy Pressure*

As seen from the spring analogy in Section 6.05, when dry clay is loaded to a pressure equal to the pressure produced by capillary forces, negligible deformation is produced and there can be no expansion of the clay under this pressure when capillary forces are released. This suggests a method of preventing damage due to uplift of expanding clay by applying heavy superimposed loads. Unfortunately, this cannot be done except for heavy buildings or other structures. The pressure required to prevent swelling varies for different clays over a fairly wide range. The Permian clays of Oklahoma require from 3.5 to 4.5 tons per sq ft to prevent expansion. Experience has shown that pressures from 5000 to 8000 lbs per sq ft have contained the expansion to amounts that do not cause damage to buildings.

A 20 story building is required to produce an average pressure of 5000 lb per sq ft. This pressure can be achieved with a grain storage elevator. The size of footings can easily be adjusted for any design contact pressure, thereby preventing expansion of the clay immediately below the footing. At depth below the footing, the load is distributed over an area larger than the footing which reduces the unit pressure on the clay. The relationship between depth and unit pressure under the center of flexible square footings loaded with uniform contact pressures is illustrated in Chapter 4, Figure 4.11*a*. This figure shows that the clay 4 ft below a 4 ft square footing can swell approximately twice as much as the same clay 4 ft below an 8 ft square footing loaded to the same unit contact pressure.

Small footings carrying light loads can be expected to be lifted by expanding clay more than would large footings carrying heavy loads even though both are designed for the same contact pressure. An example of this occurrence is given in the description of damage to a boys' dormitory in Section 6.11(5). Adjusting the spacing and loads so that all footings under the structure carry the same load and are the same size helps to prevent unequal uplift and resulting damage. But, if the footings are near the surface, unequal uplift may occur because the clay under the building gains moisture at a different rate and maintains a more nearly constant moisture content than does the clay around the periphery of the building.

If the footings can be placed near enough to the water table that the reduced pressure below the footings occurs in clay that is continuously saturated, adjusting the footing sizes for a high contact pressure can be successful in preventing unequal uplift or settlement.

The above discussion applies only to clays that have been overconsolidated by desiccation. For normally consolidated saturated clays, design pressures are governed by considerations related to the theory of consolidation.

b. *Preventing Damage with Deep Footings*

Clay at a considerable distance below the surface does not swell and shrink as much as does clay near the surface. The clay at depth, being closer to the water table and farther from the source of evaporation at the surface, is less affected by climatic changes than is surface clay. Also, expansion of the clay because of increase in water content is inhibited by the pressure of the overburden. The depth to stable clay depends upon the climate and the distance to the water table as well as upon the character of the clay.

Damage from uplift of the footings can be reduced by placing them at considerable distance below the surface. Footings placed in a basement area the same distance below the original surface are subject to greater uplift than are footings carrying the same load outside the basement area where they have the help of the overburden in preventing uplift. Lightly loaded footings should be placed nearer the water table than heavily loaded ones in order to prevent uplift. Footings in a basement area also should be placed closer to the water table than those under a building with no basement. In one instance, a 4 story building had its footings 12 ft below the original surface and 5 ft below an excavated and unfloored utility space. This area remained continuously inundated from street drainage which seeped into the area during rains. After being exposed to this condition for 8 years, the space was deepened by removing 3 ft of clay and covering the area with a concrete floor slab. This change in conditions caused some slight additional cracking of partitions in the upper stories of the building.

Placing independent footings at depths of up to 30 ft in hard desiccated clay can be done quite economically by casting piers and belled footings in drilled and underreamed holes. But placing the footings at depths where the clay is stable may not be a solution to the uplift problem. One of the major problems in using these deep footings is to prevent damage caused by expansion of the clay between the footings and the parts of the buildings at grade. If proper precautions are not taken to prevent it, damage due to expansion of surface clay may be about as great as if the footings were placed near the surface. Some precautionary measures which may be taken to prevent damage from this cause are described below.

6.13 *Uplift on Piers*

The pier and belled footing cast in a drilled and underreamed hole is in reality a cast in place pile with an enlarged base. If the clay is dry or below the shrinkage limit when the pier is cast, it will subsequently swell both laterally and vertically and exert pressure against the sides of the pier and uplift along the pier. This uplift force along the surface of the pier is limited by friction along the pier surface, by the shear strength of the clay, and by the expansive force of the clay. Without precautions for reducing the friction between clay and concrete of the pier, it is probable that the shear strength of the clay will be the governing factor. The uplift pressure is greatest near the top of the pier where the clay expands most. In some cases, uplift has been sufficient to pull the pier in two at the top of the bell.

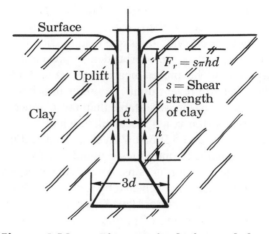

Figure 6.13a   Pier cast in desiccated clay

If the clay in which the pier is cast has a shear strength of 1 ton per sq ft, the uplift pressure along the sides of a minimum 12 in. diameter pier with a contact length above the bell of 12 ft, could be $F_r = 3.14 \times 12 \times 1 = 37.7$ tons. If the bell were made 3 times the diameter of the pier, the equivalent contact pressure with no side friction would be 9,500 lbs ft^{-2}. For a 30 in. diameter pier under the same conditions as the example above, the load required to prevent uplift by side friction is 94.2 tons. The contact pressure with no uplift for this load is 4,250 lbs per sq ft on the bottom of the footing. Usually, architects and engineers like to design these piers and footings on the basis of contact pressure on the bottom of the footing only, as though they were independent footings.

In the Permian clays of Oklahoma, heavily loaded cast in place piers and belled footings have generally proven satisfactory. Uplift of lightly loaded piers and footings, such as those supporting residences and other one story buildings, structural floor slabs for one story only, and partitions only, have allowed considerable damage from uplift by friction. Based on present knowledge and experience, it is believed that the following criteria can be used for the design of successful foundations of cast in place pier and belled footing units.

a. Use as high contact pressure as is consistent with carrying capacity of the soil.

b. Use bell three times diameter of pier for maximum anchor.

c. Use smallest pier compatible with load and bell size in order to keep surface area minimum.

d. Extend reinforcement into bell to within 4 inches of bottom in order to anchor pier to bell.

For lightly loaded piers, the frictional resistance along the surface of the piers should be reduced to a negligible amount so that the clay as it swells cannot exert uplift. Uplift from frictional force has been reduced successfully by drilling an oversized hole for the pier and casting the pier in a form 4 in. smaller in diameter than the hole. The space around the pier can be filled with a material of low shear strength or possibly left open and a collar formed at the top to prevent surface soil from filling the open space. The space around the pier should not be filled with sand. Sand confined under pressure has a high shear strength.

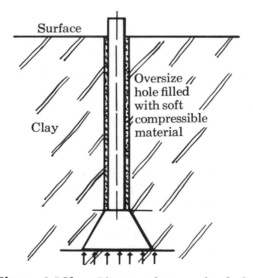

Figure 6.13b   Pier cast in oversize hole

Sometimes the oversize hole is drilled to the entire depth and the bell is formed at the bottom of the oversize hole. The bell is filled with concrete to extend a slight distance into the pier above the bell and the casing for the pier is pushed a short distance into the fresh concrete in order to prevent concrete from rising into the space around the outside of the casing. When using this procedure, care should be exercised to see that the casing is not let into the hole before the concrete has been placed in the bell; otherwise a shaft may be cast with no footing. This has been done with serious results.

In some areas, the use of cast in place piers and belled footings has not been successful in desiccated clays on slopes. When the clay on the surface of the slope becomes saturated during wet periods, it swells normal to the slope, and when it dries it shrinks vertically causing the surface

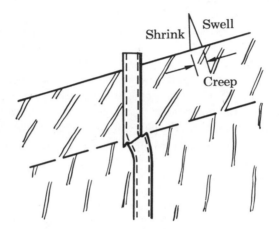

Figure 6.13c **Pier on slope of desiccated clay**

clay to creep slowly down the slope as it is subjected to many cycles of wetting and drying. Piers cast in desiccated clays on slopes have been broken by the shearing force of the creeping clay. In San Antonio, Texas, where this phenomenon has occurred, the creeping blanket of surface clay is reported to extend to depths of about 5 ft. In this area, light residences are usually placed on stiffened structural slabs cast on the surface.

The reader should be warned that these criteria apply only to the design of pier and belled footings cast in hard overconsolidated clays. They do not apply to piers designed to transmit loads through soft clays to a hard stratum below.

6.14   Uplift under Grade Beams

Grade beams cast in contact with desiccated clay are sometimes broken by uplift pressure of expanding clay. A grade beam 10 inches wide may be subjected to uplift pressure as high as several thousand lb per ft. Even if the grade beam were reinforced to resist this pressure, the uplift on the supports might cause as much damage as if the beam were allowed to break. Provision should be made for a void under grade beams into which the clay can expand without exerting uplift pressure.

Attempts have been made to create a void under grade beams by excavating 12 to 18 in. below the bottom of the grade beam and allowing the soil to fall back into the trench in a loose condition. A layer of sisalkraft paper was spread along the bottom of the trench to prevent concrete from filling the voids in the loose soil. In some cases, this loosening of the clay has been successful when used experimentally in preventing damage from uplift, but in others it has not. In a few cases, packed hay or straw has been used in the bottom of trenches and covered with roofing felt or sisalkraft for reception of the concrete. When the clay begins to expand, it compresses the hay, but before the clay has had time to swell enough to cause damage, the hay will have disintegrated to provide the required void. Spraying the hay with a solution of ammonium nitrate hastens its disintegration. The use of hay or straw under grade beams has not always been successful in preventing uplift on the bottom of grade beams, probably because of insufficient hay or straw to provide sufficient void into which the clay can swell. It is not a practical method of solving the uplift problem.

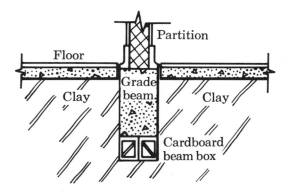

Figure 6.14a   Partition on grade beam

The use of collapsible cardboard beam boxes is a much more practical and sure method of preventing uplift under grade beams than any of the methods mentioned above. These cardboard boxes are shipped flat and are folded to form a hollow box of the proper dimensions for the purpose. The cardboard is treated to prevent immediate disintegration and to remain strong enough to support runways for concrete buggies long enough for concrete to be placed and harden. These cardboard beam boxes are produced commercially in Kansas and Texas.

In order to prevent damage to partitions, they may be placed on grade beams supported on the main piers or columns as shown in Figure 6.14a instead of on floor slabs resting on the ground.

6.15   Structural Slabs on Desiccated Clay

The only sure method of providing a stable floor at ground level over desiccated clay is to provide a structural floor system supported on the structural frame with an excavated space below the slab into which the clay can swell upon gaining moisture.

The greatest item of cost in using a structural floor slab at ground level is the extra excavation and forming. The removal of forms in a restricted space is a large item of cost. The use of a structural floor system using the earth as forms for beams and slabs does not eliminate damage due to swelling of the dry clay underneath. Unless the floor system is designed for uplift pressures of several thousand lb per sq ft, the swelling clay underneath may break the members of the floor system. If they are designed strong enough to resist the swelling, the building may be lifted, pulling the piers or columns loose from their footings.

Several methods have been devised for casting the structural floor system on forms that lie directly on the clay and disintegrate after a short period leaving a space for expansion of the clay.

a.   Structural Slab on Loosened Soil

One method for forming the slab which has been used experimentally is to loosen the clay to a depth of 1 ft to 18 in. and to form the loose soil in windrows to make a form for joists.

In order for this method to be successful, the depth of the loosened clay must be adjusted to existing conditions. The volume decrease of the loosened soil must be equal to or greater than the volume increase of the undisturbed clay below the loosened material. Sand should not be used as form material above the undisturbed clay because sand is relatively incompressible and would transfer the pressure to the bottom of the slab in undiminished intensity.

This method of forming with loosened soil to receive the floor slab might be successful under proper conditions but generally should be considered as unreliable. During construction of the loose fill, the soil may

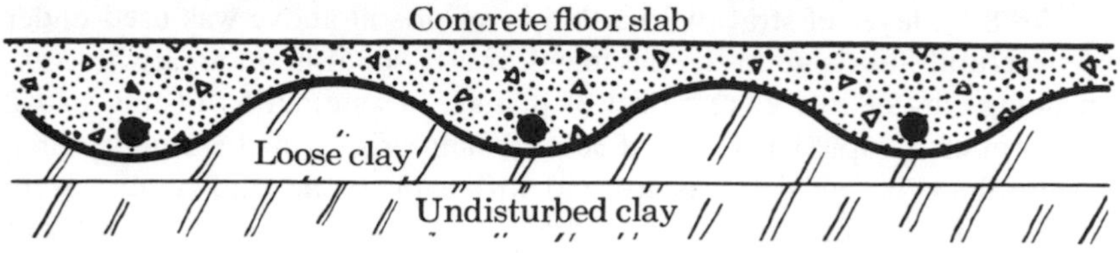

Concrete floor slab

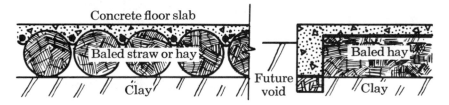

Figure 6.15a   **Structural slab on loosened clay**

be compacted until it will itself swell as much as, or more than, the undisturbed soil. A successful use of this method of forming for a structural slab over desiccated clay is as likely to be accidental as to be the result of planning.

b.   *Structural Slab on Baled Straw*

Another method of forming on desiccated clay was used experimentally by Professor Dean Irby of the Technical Institute of Oklahoma State University. This method consists of excavating deeply enough to form the

Concrete floor slab

Figure 6.15b   **Structural slab on baled straw form**

area solid with baled hay or straw laid end to end and side by side. These bales are covered with roofing felt or sisalkraft. The depressions between the bales are forms for joists. The hay or straw is sprayed with ammonium nitrate to accelerate disintegration of the straw. Under a test slab used as the entrance to a testing laboratory, Professor Irby found that after 8 months, a 3 in. void existed under the bottom of the slab.

Professor Irby has found that the hay or straw supports runways for concrete buggies satisfactorily. In order to keep the covering over the straw smooth, a small amount of concrete must be placed in the depression between bales 2 or 3 joists ahead of the placing of concrete.

The hay increases the fire hazard and makes the construction site look like a feed lot. The aesthetic value of rotting hay under the floor is questionable. The hay also probably attracts termites.

An 8 in. layer of straw with a thin layer of soil above was used under a structural floor slab in the basement of a hospital in an area where expanding clay causes a great deal of damage. Examination of this slab 2 years after completion revealed several hair cracks in the laundry area where the concrete slab was covered with asphalt tile, and rather severe uplift and cracking around a floor drain in a service entrance. No odor of rotting straw could be detected.

c. Structural Slab on Fiberboard Forms

An effective method of providing void spaces under slabs and beams into which the clay can expand without producing uplift pressure is by the use of waterproofed cardboard forms of sufficient strength to support the fresh concrete and which later disintegrate. The cardboard forms are shipped flat and are folded into shape during installation.

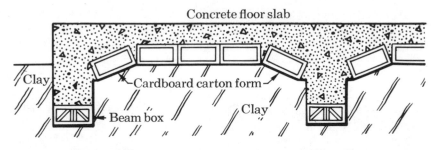

Figure 6.15c   **Structural slab on fiberboard forms**

Such cardboard forms are used extensively in the middle western United States where the problem of uplift is acute. A disadvantage of the use of these collapsible forms in basements is produced because the structural slab must be supported at the exterior basement walls. Often exterior beams are formed and the cardboard forms laid and the concrete placed before the basement walls are formed and cast above the exterior beams.

When the basement floor is formed and cast before the basement walls are erected, the collapsible forms are exposed to the weather during construction of the floor, and the banks of the excavation are susceptible to sloughing or sliding into the excavation. During a prolonged rainy period, the exposed cardboard forms become weakened and collapse or become badly deformed before concrete is placed. This disadvantage can be alleviated to some extent by extending the basement walls a sufficient distance below the slab to form a shelf or slot on which the slab can be formed and

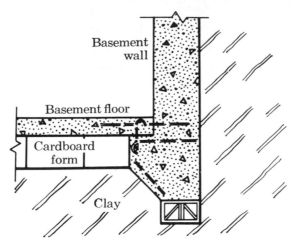

Figure 6.15d   Joint at basement wall and floor

cast after enough of the superstructure has been erected to protect the forms against damage by rain.

Sometimes a cardboard form is placed under the basement wall. Under a heavy wall this precaution is probably not necessary and possibly is ineffective because the beam box may be crushed by the weight of fresh concrete in the heavy wall. Investigation has shown that beam boxes have been crushed when used under concrete basement walls.

d.   Structural Slab on Sonotube Forms

Another method of forming on clay used experimentally and successfully by Professor Irby consists of excavating the area about 4 in. below the bottom of the concrete joists and covering the area with split Sonotubes laid side by side to provide forms for joists as shown in Figure 6.15e. The bottom of the space between the two halves is filled with sand about 3 in. deep. The joist steel and concrete are placed to form a reinforced concrete floor slab supported on the grade beams. After a short time, the Sonotubes disintegrate, the sand runs out from under the joists, and a void is formed into which the clay can swell without exerting pressure on the bottom of the slab. Short lengths of reinforcing steel can be driven into the clay between Sonotube forms to support reinforcing steel in the joists and to hold the forms in place.

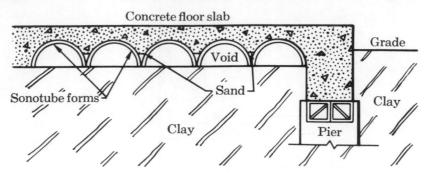

Figure 6.15e   Structural slab on Sonotube forms

6.16   Non-Structural Slabs on Undisturbed Desiccated Clay

Sometimes it is neither economically nor structurally feasible to support the ground floor on the structural frame. Where floor slabs must be placed on the surface of desiccated clays, there are precautions that may eliminate or reduce the damage from swelling.

Partitions, furred spaces, and other parts of the structure that are tied to the building proper should be supported on the structural frame with beams and brackets as illustrated in Figure 6.14a. If the floor slabs are cast free of the partitions and other parts of the building, they can be raised and broken without damaging other parts of the building. After these slabs have been in place for several years and the volume of the clay has reached equilibrium for the conditions imposed, the old broken slabs can be removed and new ones installed with some assurance that the new slab will remain fixed as long as the conditions under the slab remain constant.

Sometimes some of the swelling can be induced in the clay before the slab is laid by flooding the surface as soon as possible at the beginning of construction and waiting as long as possible to place the slab. The area is usually excavated 6 to 8 in. below the bottom of the slab and filled with coarse gravel or crushed stone as soon as possible after drain lines that are to be below the floor have been installed. The area is then flooded to within 1 or 2 in. of the top of the stone fill. These attempts to swell the clay before placing the slab are usually not successful, especially in basements where the overburden has been removed. The period of flooding seldom lasts long enough to produce more than a small percentage of the total swelling that may occur under the changed conditions that occur after the slab is placed. Drilling holes 6 ft deep and 6 ft apart in the basement area and filling with sand before flooding has been used without complete success.

Sometimes consolidation of carelessly compacted clay fill under a slab on the ground compensates for the swelling of undisturbed clay below the fill. In the senior author's early experience, the ground floor of a school building on active clay was laid on undisturbed clay at one end and on a fill of 1 ft to 18 in. at the other. The soil from the end below the original grade was hauled by wheelbarrow to make the fill at the opposite end and dumped with no compaction other than that required to work the fill material into place. A year after completion of the building, partitions resting on the slab on undisturbed clay were broken and distorted until none of the doors could be opened or closed. At the end of the building where the slab was on the poorly compacted fill, there occurred no evident damage.

Some builders believe that the use of coarse broken stone or gravel fill under slabs will reduce the uplift pressure of expanding clay by providing void spaces into which the clay can flow as it expands. Tests have shown that the hard, overconsolidated Permian clays of Oklahoma when saturated will flow into the voids of crushed stone when subjected to pressures of approximately 30 tons per sq ft. Certainly, under the light pressures of floor slabs, the clay does not enter the pores of the crushed stone enough to prevent uplift and cracking of slabs. The practical purpose of a layer of coarse material under a slab is to act as a drainage medium and to keep capillary water from the slab.

6.17   Stiffened Slabs on Ground

The method of preventing damage to light buildings on expansive clay by placing them on slabs or frames strong and stiff enough to transmit the building loads to the soil without excessive deflection is used extensively in some areas where the soil and climatic conditions are exceptionally bad. Various means of stiffening the slabs have been proposed. The most widely used method of stiffening consists of a slab cast integrally with stiff beams placed several feet apart in two directions. Some use cross beams of varying cross section below the slab.

The design of these stiffened slabs is based to a considerable extent upon experience and judgment. Mathematical analysis is difficult and highly in-

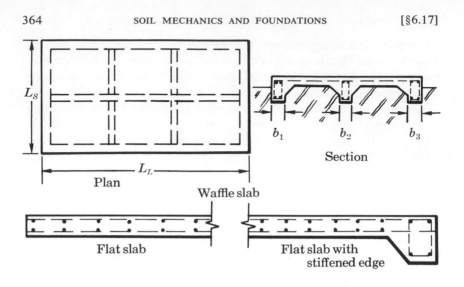

Figure 6.17a   Typical stiffened slabs

determinate. If the distribution of contact pressure were known, a rational analysis could be made for specific building loads which would be useful in the design of stiffened slabs. Unfortunately, the slab placed on desiccated clay may at some periods be supported almost entirely around the periphery of the slab and at other times over a portion of the interior.

The Building Research Advisory Board of the National Academy of Sciences has recently completed a report formulated by a special committee. The report *Design Criteria for Residential Slabs-on-Ground* was submitted to the Federal Housing Administration. The report proposes design criteria for four types of slabs on ground.

Type I   —Unreinforced floating slabs
Type II —Reinforced floating slabs
Type III—Stiffened slabs
Type IV—Structural slabs

This discussion is concerned only with Type III—Stiffened Slabs as proposed in the report — and parallels the report to a considerable extent but not in all respects.

Because at some periods the slab may be supported along the edges and at other times in the interior, it is necessary to design the slab so that it can resist either condition without excessive deformation or distress. The superimposed dead and live loads of the structure can be estimated in the same manner as for the design of any other supporting structure. The distribution of supporting pressure of the soil on the bottom of the slab is highly indeterminate. In order to obtain a mathematical relationship which may be of some aid to the judgment, some rather far-fetched hypothetical assumptions have been accepted in the analysis which follows.

Some of the assumptions used in the analysis of stiffened slabs on ground are as follows:

(1) The weight of the superstructure and slab is distributed uniformly over the entire area of the slab. This is a simplifying assumption which, with additional effort, may be avoided.

(2) The supporting pressure is uniformly distributed over the proportional part of the total area at the two ends or in the middle of the slab as illustrated in Figure 6.17b. This assumption is probably rather far-fetched. As the soil dries out from the periphery during a drought, it may shrink in varying degrees with distance from the edges of the slab, possibly leaving the slab unsupported at the edges and with a gradual increase in pressure toward the middle. During a prolonged wet period, the opposite condition may

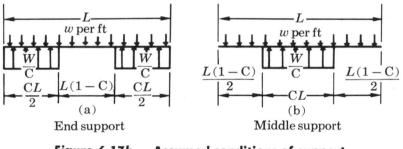

(a)
End support

(b)
Middle support

Figure 6.17b   **Assumed conditions of support for slab-on ground**

prevail. What the true critical supporting condition will be during the life of the slab in a given climate and soil can only be imagined. But, in the absence of more accurate knowledge, imagination is an important aid to the judgment. If the ratio C of supporting area to total area is well chosen, this assumption will in general lead to adequate designs.

(3) The ratio C of support area to total area is assumed to be constant for all sizes of slabs and to be dependent upon the average plastic index I_p of the underlying soil to a depth of several feet and upon the duration and frequency of prolonged droughts and wet periods. The ratio C is undoubtedly not a constant for all sizes of slabs. During drought, the soil is dried out for a certain distance from the slab somewhat independent of the size of the

slab. Probably the width of the supporting area at the edge is more nearly constant than the ratio. However, this type of slab is generally used for small residential slabs for which the assumption that the ratio C is a constant probably does not cause serious error.

These factors and their use are discussed in detail later.

a.   *Climatic Rating or Weather Constant, C_w*

The climate rating C_w to be used in conjunction with the soil properties in determining the ratio C of supporting area to total area probably depends upon several indeterminate factors, such as frequency and duration of dry and wet periods, depth to water table, humidity during periods of no rainfall, possibility of leaking water or sewer lines under the slab, the presence of trees and shrubs adjacent to the slab, etc. Because the most important of these factors is duration of drought, and because it is the simplest to determine, values of C_w are assigned on the basis of drought duration alone. The values given in the table below are little better than guesses based upon some experience and should be used only as a rough guide. Each designer should be guided by his experience in his own area.

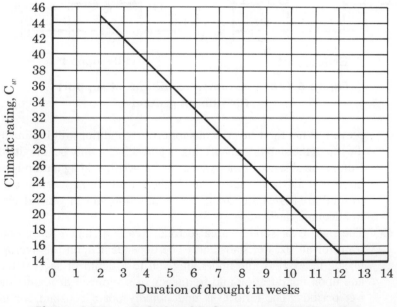

Figure 6.17c   Relationship between climatic rating and duration of drought

In the BRAB report values of C_w are assigned to designated areas on a map of the 48 states of continental U.S.A.

The relationship between duration of drought and climatic rating C_w as shown in the diagram of Figure 6.17c is made solely for the purpose of translating duration of drought into the climatic rating values used in the BRAB relationship between C_w and C.

b.   Soil Properties and Support Index, C

The plasticity index was considered to be a good indication of the activity of the clay. Therefore, the plasticity index and the climatic rating were made the criteria for estimating the proportionate part of the contact area that carries the building load. Because the rate at which swelling of the clay below the surface is dependent upon the permeability of the soil, and because permeability is to a large extent dependent upon grain size, the activity number, which is the ratio of plastic index to percentage of soil grains smaller than 0.002mm $A = I_p/$ per cent < 0.002, is probably a better criterion for the selection of C than the plastic index alone.

The relationship for plastic index, climatic rating, and support index is shown in Figure 6.17d. The relationship shown indicates that, for the most favorable climatic rating, $C_w = 45$, the support area is not affected for soils having a plastic index less than 50 (soils of low compressibility ML), and under extremely unfavorable climatic conditions the ratio of

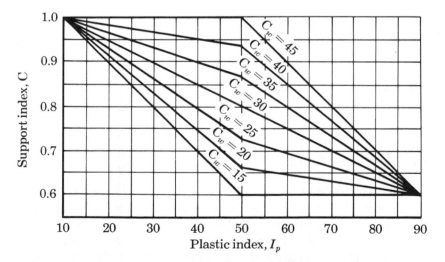

Figure 6.17d   Relationship between climatic rating C$_w$ and support index C from BRAB report

support area to total area decreases rapidly for these soils to a minimum support area of 0.6. It also indicates that, under the most favorable condition of climate and in the most active soil, the support area is never less than 0.6 of the total area.

c. Permissible Deflection

The slab must not only be of design strong enough to support its load without distress to the materials used, but must also be stiff enough so that deflection will be limited to an amount that will not cause damage to the structure supported on the slab. Recommended permissible maximum deflections given in U. S. Department of Commerce, National Bureau of Standards, BMS 109, Strength of Houses (Washington, 1948), was accepted by the committee and are listed in Table 6.17a.

Table 6.17a

Design Factors for Stiffened Slabs
to Minimize Utility Damage to Superstructure
Due to Slab Deflection and Superimposed Load

Type of construction	Maximum permissible deflection	$\dfrac{\Delta}{L}$
Wood frame—wood exterior and interior	1 in 200	$\dfrac{1}{200}$
Wood frame—masonry veneer plaster board interior	1 in 300	$\dfrac{1}{300}$
All masonry, plaster on lath interior	1 in 330	$\dfrac{1}{330}$
Wood frame—stucco exterior plaster on lath interior	1 in 360	$\dfrac{1}{360}$

d. Design Load

The slabs should be designed for full live and dead loads of the structure supported by the slab plus the weight of the slab. If the dead load is assumed to be distributed uniformly over the slab area, the total load of the structure should be increased for design purposes by about 33 per cent. In the absence of more accurate information, the slab might be designed for a uniform live load of 40 psf and a dead load equal to the weight of exterior walls and partitions to enclose an average size room divided by the area of the room plus the weight per sq ft of the roof construction. For example, assume a one story residence with brick veneer exterior walls, wood stud and plasterboard partitions, plasterboard ceiling, and wood roof rafters and solid 1 in. decking with asphalt shingle roof. Assume 8 ft ceiling height and 15 ft by 15 ft average size room.

Assume the following weights of materials:

Brick veneer wall	50 psf
Partition	15 psf
Ceiling	10 psf
Roof	12 psf

For a 15 ft by 15 ft corner room, weights are

Exterior walls	30 by 50 by 8	12,000 lb
Partitions	30 by 15 by 8	4,800 lb
Ceiling	15 by 15 by 10	2,250 lb
Roof	15 by 15 by 12	2,700 lb
	Total weight	21,750 lb

$$\text{Av. Uniform Load} = \frac{21,750}{15 \times 15} = 96 \text{ psf}$$

Live Load 40 psf on floor plus 20 psf on roof = 60 psf
Design load

Dead load = 96 by 1.33 = 128		
Live load		60
Total		168 psf

To this superimposed load must be added the weight of the slab.

e.   *Analysis*

The designer of these stiffened slabs on ground should make his own assumptions to conform to what he considers best fits the existing conditions. In the following suggested method of analysis, the following assumptions are made for rectangular waffle slabs. These assumptions are, generally, not true, which should be considered in interpretation of the analysis.

1. Moments of inertia and moments are computed for the entire cross section of the slab; i.e., across Section *A-A* for the long dimension and across Section *B-B* for the short dimension.

2. In case of projections from the rectangular plan, as shown in Figure 6.17e, the rectangle formed by the projection and the contiguous portion of the main rectangle is considered as another rectangle of dimensions L'_L and L'_S and treated in the same manner as the main rectangle.

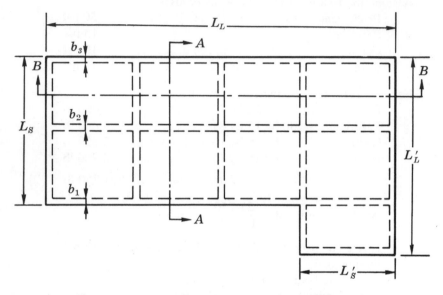

Figure 6.17e   Plan of rectangular waffle slab

3. The supporting area is considered to be concentrated at the two ends or at the middle of the span being considered. This assumption ignores the support along the edge normal to the assumed support area.

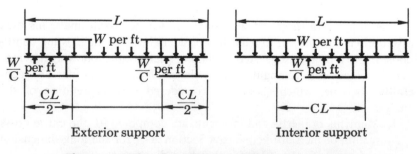

Figure 6.17f   Possible conditions of support

4. The contact pressure over the supporting area is assumed to be uniform.
5. The building load on the slab is assumed to be distributed uniformly over the area of the slab.

In this analysis, the slabs are designed to limit deflection to that recommended in Table 6.17a. Therefore, the steps in the analysis follow the order listed below.

1. Determine the highest plasticity index I_p for the soil to a depth of about 10 ft or to rock.
2. Find C factor for I_p and the climatic rating of the area from Table 6.17b.
3. Determine moment of inertia I which limits deflection for both conditions of loading to permissible $\dfrac{\Delta}{L}$ of Table 6.17a.
4. Determine dimensions of the beam sections to provide the required moment of inertia.
5. Determine the moment for the loading condition.
6. Determine the reinforcing steel required in top and bottom of beams.
7. Design slabs for two way reinforcement.

(1)   *Required Moment of Inertia*

For the edge supported condition, the required moment of inertia can be determined from the relationship for deflection. The following development is based upon the geometry of deformation (area moments).

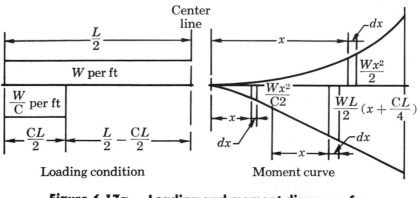

Loading condition   Moment curve

Figure 6.17g   Loading and moment diagrams for edge support

Because of symmetry, the deflection can be determined as though the member were a cantilever from the midspan.

Since E and I are constant,

$$\Delta\,EI = \int_0^{\frac{CL}{2}} \frac{W\,x^2}{C\,2}\, x\,dx + \int_0^{\left(\frac{L}{2}-\frac{CL}{2}\right)} \frac{WL}{2}\left(x + \frac{CL}{4}\right)\left(x + \frac{CL}{2}\right) dx$$

$$- \int_0^{\frac{L}{2}} \frac{W\,x^2}{2}\, x\,dx$$

$$= \frac{5}{384}\,W\,L^4\,(1 - 1.2C + 0.2C^3)$$

$$I = \frac{5}{384}\,\frac{W\,L^4}{E\,\Delta}\,(1 - 1.2C + 0.2C^3)$$

$$= \frac{5}{384}\,\frac{W\,L^3}{E(\Delta/L)}\,(1 - 1.2C + 0.2C^3)$$

The total load in the long direction across the section, W_L, is equal to the unit load per sq. ft, w, times the distance across the section, L_S, or $W_L = w\,L_S$.

Therefore, in the long direction

$$I_L = \frac{5}{384}\,\frac{w\,L_S L_L^3}{E(\Delta/L)}\,(1 - 1.2C + 0.2C^3)$$

and in the short direction

$$I_S = \frac{5}{384}\,\frac{w\,L_L L_S^3}{E(\Delta/L)}\,(1 - 1.2C + 0.2C^3)$$

If w is in lb ft^{-2}, L is in ft, E is in lb in^{-2}, and I is in in.^{4}, the relationships become

$$I_L = \frac{5 \times 144}{384}\,\frac{w\,L_S L_L^3}{E(\Delta/L)}\,(1 - 1.2C + 0.2C^3)$$

$$= \frac{w\,L_S L_L^3}{E(\Delta/L)}\,1.875\,(1 - 1.2C + 0.2C^3)$$

$$= \frac{w\,L_S L_L^3}{E(\Delta/L)}\,F_E(C) \qquad\qquad \text{(Eq. 6.17}a\text{)}$$

and

$$I_S = \frac{w\,L_L L_S^3}{E(\Delta/L)}\,F_E(C) \qquad\qquad \text{(Eq. 6.17}b\text{)}$$

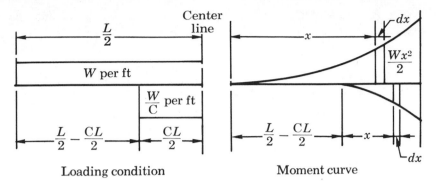

Figure 6.17h   Loading and moment diagrams for center support

For the support area in the middle portion of the slab (during drought), the value of I can be estimated as follows:

$$EI\Delta = \int_0^{\frac{L}{2}} \frac{W x^2}{2} x \, dx - \int_0^{\frac{CL}{2}} \frac{W x^2}{C 2} \left(x + \frac{L}{2} - \frac{CL}{2}\right) dx$$

$$I = \frac{3}{384} \frac{W L^4}{E \Delta} (1 - 1.33C^2 + 0.33C^3)$$

$$= \frac{3}{384} \frac{W L^3}{E(\Delta/L)} (1 - 1.33C^2 + 0.33C^3)$$

Using load per sq. ft w instead of load per ft

$$I_L = \frac{3}{384} \frac{w L_S L_L^3}{E(\Delta/L)} (1 - 1.33C^2 + 0.33C^3)$$

and

$$I_S = \frac{3}{384} \frac{w L_L L_S^3}{E(\Delta/L)} (1 - 1.33C^2 + 0.33C^3)$$

When w is in lb ft^{-2}, L is in ft, E is in lb in.$^{-2}$, and I is in in.^{4}, these relationships become

$$I_L = \frac{3 \times 144}{384} \frac{w L_S L_L^3}{E(\Delta/L)} (1 - 1.33C^2 + 0.33C^3)$$

$$= \frac{w L_S L_L^3}{E(\Delta/L)} 1.13 (1 - 1.33C^2 + 0.33C^3)$$

$$= \frac{w L_S L_L^3}{E(\Delta/L)} F_C(C) \qquad \text{(Eq. 6.17c)}$$

and

$$I_S = \frac{w L_L L_S^3}{E(\Delta/L)} F_C(C) \qquad \text{(Eq. 6.17d)}$$

The functions of C, $F_E(C)$ and $F_C(C)$ have been evaluated and the relationship between $F(C)$ and C plotted in Figure 6.17i.

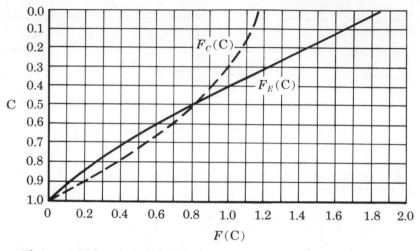

Figure 6.17i **Relationship between proportionate support area C and function of C for edge support F_E (C) and center support F_C (C)**

(2) Moments

Beams must not only be of such size as to limit deflection but must resist the imposed moment without exceeding the allowable stresses of the materials.

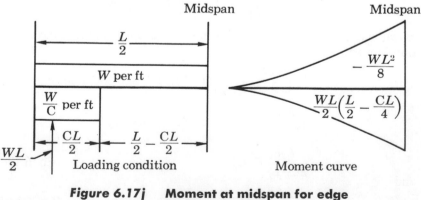

Loading condition

Moment curve

Figure 6.17j **Moment at midspan for edge loading condition**

As illustrated in Figure 6.17*j*, the moment at midspan for the edge loading condition is

$$M = \frac{WL}{2}\left(\frac{L}{2} - \frac{CL}{4}\right) - \frac{WL^2}{8} = \frac{WL^2}{8}(1 - C) \quad \text{(Eq 6.17e)}$$

For the center loading condition, as illustrated in Figure 6.17*k*, the negative moment is

$$M = -\frac{WL^2}{8} + \frac{WL}{2}\left(\frac{CL}{4}\right) = -\frac{WL^2}{8}(1 - C) \quad \text{(Eq. 6.17e)}$$

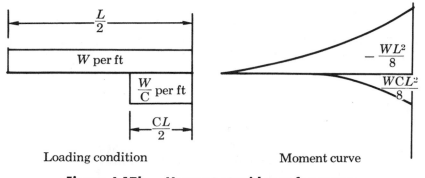

Loading condition   Moment curve

**Figure 6.17k   Moment at midspan for center
loading condition**

Thus, the maximum positive and negative moments for both loading conditions are equal, which indicates that the same area of steel should be used in top and bottom of beams.

(3)   *Size of Beams or Depth of Slab*

In order to limit deflection to that permissible for the type of super-structure, the moment of inertia of the beams or slab must be not less than that determined for deflection,

$$I_L = \frac{w\,L_S L_L^3}{E(\Delta/L)}\,F(C), \text{ when } w = \text{lb ft}^{-2},\, L = \text{ft and } E = \text{lb in.}^{-2}$$

$$I_L = \text{in.}^{-4}$$

For a rectangular reinforced concrete beam the moment of inertia is approximately equal to that of a rectangular homogeneous beam of the same size; i.e., $I = (bd^3/12)$. From this relationship, the dimensions of the minimum size beams that will control deflection can be determined. In the case of the waffle slab, b is the width of all of the beams in the section for which I was determined. For section $A - A$ of Figure 6.17e, $b = b_1 + b_2 + b_3$. For a flat slab on the ground, $b = L$.

The moment of inertia of a rectangular reinforced concrete beam about the neutral axis is

$$I_{kd} = \frac{b(kd)^3}{3} + nA_s(d - kd)^2$$

$$= \frac{bd^3}{3} k^3 + npbd^3(1 - k)^2$$

$$= bd^3 \left[\frac{k^3}{3} + np(1 - k)^2 \right]$$

For $E_s = 3 \times 10^7$ lb in.$^{-2}$ and $E_c = 3 \times 10^6$ lb in.$^{-2}$, $n = 10$. Using $n = 10$ and $k = 0.4$, the relationship becomes $I_{kd} = bd^3 (0.021 + 3.6p)$.

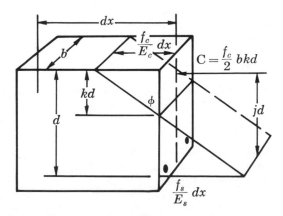

Figure 6.17l   Deformation of rectangular beam

For the minimum size beams as determined from $I = (bd^3/12)$, the ratio of area of steel to area of concrete $p = (A_s/bd)$ required to make these beams provide the required I can be found from the relationship $0.021 + 3.6\, p = (1/12) = 0.0833$ from which $p = 0.0173$ or 1.73 per cent. If more or less steel than this percentage is used, the moment of inertia will be slightly different from $(bd^3/12)$. But, if the beams are made such that

$$\frac{bd^3}{12} = I = \frac{w\, L_s L_L^3}{E(\Delta/L)} F(C)$$

and the percentage of steel made not less than 1.73, they will be stiff enough to limit deflection to the (Δ/L) chosen.

Obviously, if the properties of the concrete and steel are such that k is not equal to 0.4 and n is not equal to 10, the relationship will be slightly different from that given above, but the use of these values for most concretes and steels probably introduces less error than the erroneous assumption that the concrete below the neutral axis is not stressed (cracked section up to the neutral axis).

With the minimum value of I determined and value of b chosen, the corresponding values of d and p can be determined from the relationship

$$\frac{I}{b} = d^3 (0.021 + 3.6\,p) \qquad \text{(Eq. 6.17}f)$$

Thus, when I and b are known, the required value of d for a given ratio of steel to concrete or the required p for a given d can be determined.

It may be necessary to increase the size of the beams in order to prevent the materials from being over stressed because of moment or shear.

The relationship which must exist between working stress in the concrete f_c and the stress in the steel f_s for conservation of plane section is as shown by the geometry of Figure 6.17l.

$$\frac{f_c dx}{E_c kd} = \left(\frac{f_c}{E_c}\,dx + \frac{f_s}{E_s}\,dx\right) kd$$

or

$$f_s = f_c \frac{n(1-k)}{k}$$

For $n = 10$ and $k = 0.4$, f_s must equal $15f_c$.

If the ratio of stress to strain up to the working stress of concrete is constant, the applied moment M resisted by the concrete section is

$$M = \frac{f_c}{2}\,b\,kd\,jd$$

from which

$$f_c = \frac{2M}{b\,kd\,jd}$$

When $k = 0.4$, and $j = 0.867$, $kj = 0.347$ making

$$f_c = \frac{2M}{0.347\,b\,d^2}$$

For a given value of f_c and b, the value of d as determined by stress is

$$d = \sqrt{\frac{2M}{0.347\,b\,f_c}} \qquad \text{(Eq. 6.17}g)$$

f. *Example*

Assume a slab as shown in Figure 6.17e to support a building with brick veneer exterior walls and partitions of plasterboard on wood studs. The dimensions of the slab are $L_S = 20$ ft, $L_L = 40$ ft, $L_L' = 28$ ft and $L_S' = 10$ ft. The plastic index of the soil is 42. The longest drought on record in the area is 9 weeks. Allowable stresses $f_c = 1300$ psi, $f_s = 19,500$ psi.

Solution:

From Figure 6.17c, the climatic rating $C_w = 24$
From Figure 6.17d, the support index $C = 0.77$
From Table 6.17s, $(\Delta/L) = 1/300$
From example in Section 6.17d, $w_{D+L} = 168$ psf
Assume weight of slab $= 100$ psf
$w = 268$ psf
From Figure 6.17i, the larger $F(C)$ for C of 0.77 is $F_C(C) = 0.44$
From Equation 6.17c

$$I_L = \frac{268 \times 20 \times 40^3 \times 300}{3 \times 10^6} 0.44 = 15,100 \text{ in.}^4$$

Make beams 12 in. wide, $b = 36$ in.
Minimum beam for deflection

$$d = \left[\frac{15,100 \times 12}{35}\right]^{\frac{1}{3}} = 17.2 \text{ in.}$$

Moment in long dimension

$$M_L = \frac{268 \times 20 \times 40^2 \times 12}{8}(1 - 0.77) = 2,960,000 \text{ in. lb}$$

Minimum d for moment

$$d = \sqrt{\frac{2 \times 2.96 \times 10^6}{0.347 \times 36 \times 1300}} = 19.1 \text{ in.}$$

Make beams 12×23, $d = 20$ in.

$$\frac{I}{b} = \frac{15.100}{36} = 420$$

From Equation 6.17f, $p = \dfrac{420 - (0.021 \times 20^3)}{3.6 \times 30^3} = 0.00875$

The area of steel required to limit deflection to $(1/300) L_L = A_s = 0.00875 \times 12 \times 20 = 2.1$ in.^{2} in the top of each beam and in the bottom of each beam.

The area of steel required to resist moment in the long dimension,

$$A_{sL} = \frac{2.96 \times 10^6}{19,500 \times 0.867 \times 20} = 8.75 \text{ in.}^2$$

Since there are 3 beams across the long dimension, each beam should receive $8.75/3 = 2.92$ in.^{2} in the top and the same amount in the bottom. Since the beams in the short dimension are the same size and since w is the same in both directions, the total area of steel in the short dimension is

$$A_{sS} = A_{sL}\frac{L_S}{L_L} = 8.75\left(\frac{20}{40}\right) = 4.38 \text{ in.}^2$$

Five beams cross the short dimension, therefore, each beam should receive $4.38/5 = 0.88$ in.^{2} of steel in the top and the same amount in the bottom. This amount of steel may have to be increased to meet minimum requirements of the building code in force in the area. The two beams in the L_L' direction should receive the greater amount of steel required for moment and deflection found in the analysis of the L_L' by L_S' portion of the slab.

The L_L' by L_S' portion of the slab should be analysed in the same manner as a slab 28 ft long with 4 beams and 10 ft wide with 2 beams.

Stirrups should be used in the beams and other requirements of good design adhered to.

Slabs between beams should be designed for the maximum upward contact pressure and for the maximum dead and live load.

REFERENCES

Bozozuk, M., "Soil Shrinkage Damages Shallow Foundations at Ottawa," *Canada Engineering Journal*, Vol. 45, No. 7, 1962.

Building Research Advisory Board, National Academy of Sciences, "Design Criteria For Residential Slabs On Ground," *Report No. 30 to Federal Housing Administration*, Washington, D.C., 1965.

Conference, "Theoretical and Practical Treatment of Expansive Soils," *Golden Colorado: Quarterly of the Colorado School of Mines*, Vol. 54, No. 4 (October, 1959).

Hamilton, J. J., "Volume Changes in Undisturbed Clay Profiles in Western Canada," *Canada Geotechnical Journal*, Vol. 1, No. 1 (September, 1963).

Jennings, J. E., and J. E. Kerrick, "Heaving Buildings and Associated Economic Consequences with Particular Reference to Orange Free State Goldfields," *Civil Engineering in South Africa*, Vol. 4, No. 11 (November, 1962).

Lambe, T. William, "Soil PVC Meter—The Character and Identification of Expansive Soils," *Washington, D. C.: Technical Studies Report FHA-107*, Federal Housing Administration (December, 1960).

Matthes, R. K. Jr., and H. D. Bowen, "Water Vapor Transfer in Soil by Thermal Gradients and Its Control," *Trans. Am. Soc. Agric. Engrs.*, Vol. 6, No. 3, 1963.

Parcher, J. V. and Ping-Chuan Liu, "Some Swelling Characteristics of Compacted Clays," *Journal Soil Mechanics and Foundations Division*, Proc. Am. Soc. C.E., Vol. 91, No. SM3 (May, 1965).

Seed, H. B., J. K. Mitchell, and C. K. Chan, "Studies of Swell and Swell Pressure Characteristics," *Highway Research Bulletin No. 313*, Highway Research Board, 1962.

Seed, H. B., Richard J. Woodward, Jr., and Raymond Lundgren, "Prediction of Swelling Potential for Compacted Clays," *Journal Soil Mechanics and Foundations Division*, Proc. Am. Soc. C.E., Vol. 88, No. SM3 (June, 1962).

Warkentin, P., and M. Bozozuk, "Shrinking and Swelling Properties of Two Canadian Clays," *Canada Associated Committee on Soil and Snow Mechanics*, National Research Council, Tech-Memo 72.

7   Earth Pressures

7.01   *General*

The solution of many practical problems in the field of foundation engineering and general construction requires a knowledge of the pressures which may be exerted by the earth. Principal among the problems is the design of various earth retention structures, such as retaining walls, bulkheads, and temporary sheathing for the support of vertical cuts. In other kinds of problems, such as the design of anchorages in the earth, the capability of the soil to resist forces which tend to rupture it must be evaluated.

In the first instance, the shearing resistance of the soil acts in conjunction with the retention structure to oppose the gravitational forces and surcharges which tend to displace the soil mass downward. In the second case, the shearing resistance of the soil acts in conjunction with the gravitational forces and surcharges to oppose the tendency toward upward displacement arising from pulls exerted on the anchor. Thus, there are formed two classes of problems involving quite different magnitudes of the pressures which act on surfaces of contact between the structure and the soil mass. No difficulty is posed in identifying a particular problem as belonging, generally, to one or the other of the two classes. In either case, however, the determination of the pressure is complicated by a variety of factors and can only be accomplished inexactly.

The manner in which the structure yields or deforms often cannot be accurately predicted. The nature of the accompanying soil deformations and the pattern formed by the potential or actual surfaces of failure are uncertain. Frictional forces acting along surfaces of contact between the structure and the soil generally must be surmised on the basis of crude tests, or must be estimated. The influence of conditions at lateral boundaries may be difficult to analyze. The selection of the soil properties to be used in the analysis or design (particularly where cohesive soils are involved) is usually marked by a certain degree of arbitrariness, and may fail to take into account the influence of time and environment on the soil properties. Together, the preceding factors influence the magnitude, direction, and position of the resultant force exerted by the earth against the structure. Dependable solutions to the problems may, therefore, depend as much upon experience and the exercise of good judgment as upon the application of the principles of mechanics. However, only the latter can be taught in a formal way, and its importance as a vital part of the whole scheme should not be underestimated. Those principles constitute the primary subject of this chapter.

a.   Initial State of Stress

An element of a soil mass which is in a state of elastic equilibrium is acted on by stresses which cannot produce failure so long as the soil properties and loads remain unchanged. The initial relationships among the principal stresses are influenced by the soil characteristics and by the manner in which the soil has arrived at its present position. For example, the ratio of major principal stress to minor principal stress at a point in a mass of sand is likely to differ from that at a similar point in a mass of clay. In natural soils, the principal stress ratio will be governed by the nature of the sedimentation processes which have produced the soil and by the stress history of the formation, differing according to the degree of overconsolidation. In artificial fills and backfills, the method and intensity of compaction will affect the ratio.

Consider a point at depth z in a semi-infinite mass of soil having an effective unit weight γ_e. The effective stress on the horizontal plane is due to the weight of the overburden and is equal to $\gamma_e z$. The stress on the vertical plane (considering a two dimensional state of stress) is given as $K_0 \gamma_e z$, in which K_0 is termed the *coefficient of earth pressure at rest*. In the usual case, K_0 will be smaller than unity and the state of stress on the element is represented by a Mohr's circle such as No. 1 in Figure 7.01a.

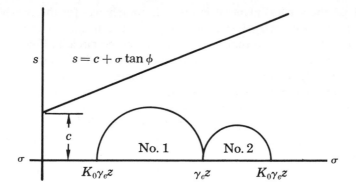

Figure 7.01a   Earth pressure at rest

In the case of a heavily overconsolidated or intensively compacted soil, the stress on the vertical plane may exceed that on the horizontal plane due to overburden. Then K_0 will exceed unity, and the corresponding "at rest" state of stress is represented by a Mohr's circle such as No. 2.

The at rest condition always represents a state of equilibrium because the conditions for failure are not satisfied. If the strength of an isotropic soil truly corresponds to the strength line $s = c + \sigma \tan \phi$, only stress circles which are tangent to this line indicate states of stress that will produce failure. Of course, no stress circle may cross the line, as this would depict an impossible state of stress. An infinite number of circles may be drawn through $\sigma = \gamma_e z$ which neither cross the strength line nor are tangent to it. Any such circle represents a condition of elastic equilibrium and could correspond to some particular at rest state of stress.

If the soil is permitted (or forced) to deform by varying the normal

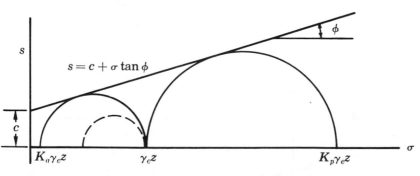

Figure 7.01b   Plastic equilibrium

stress on the vertical plane, it is possible to achieve, for the overburden pressure $\gamma_e z$, two states of stress that represent an unstable condition. For an initial state of stress represented by the dashed circle in Figure 7.01b, a sufficient reduction of the horizontal pressure results in a state of stress represented by the full circle on the left, whereas a sufficient increase of horizontal pressure results in the state of stress represented by the full circle on the right. Both of these states of stress correspond to a condition of plastic equilibrium, and imply a continued yielding at unaltered stress. The circle on the left is said to represent an *active* state of plastic equilibrium while the one on the right represents the *passive* state. The pressures on the vertical plane for these two conditions are, respectively, $K_a\gamma_e z$ and $K_p\gamma_e z$, in which K_a is the *coefficient of active earth pressure* and K_p is the *coefficient of passive earth pressure*. Any attempt to reduce the horizontal pressure below $K_a\gamma_e z$ or to increase it above $K_p\gamma_e z$ must result in a relatively sudden failure of the soil.

b.   *Active Earth Pressure*

An element of soil acted on by the major and minor principal stresses, σ_1 and σ_3, is first assumed to be in elastic equilibrium. If the minor principal stress σ_3 acting horizontally is decreased while σ_1 remains constant, the Mohr's circle will increase in size until it reaches a point of tangency with the strength line, as in Figure 7.01c. For the resulting state of plastic

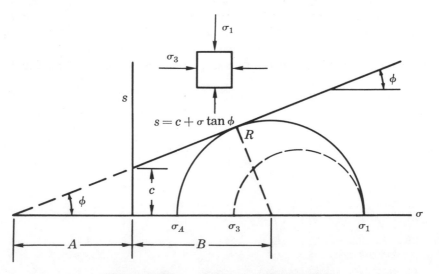

Figure 7.01c   Active earth pressure

equilibrium, the minor principal stress will have been reduced to σ_A, the active earth pressure, which is the smallest horizontal pressure consistent with equilibrium.

The relationship between σ_A and σ_1 depends upon the soil properties. A derivation of the relationship may be made rather simply from the geometry of Figure 7.01c. The radius R of the stress circle may be expressed in two ways:

$$R = \frac{1}{2}(\sigma_1 - \sigma_A), \text{ and } R = (A + B)\sin\phi$$

Since $A = \dfrac{c}{\tan\phi}$ and $B = \dfrac{1}{2}(\sigma_1 + \sigma_A)$, an equilibration of the two expressions for R gives

$$\frac{1}{2}(\sigma_1 - \sigma_A) = \left[\frac{c}{\tan\phi} + \frac{1}{2}(\sigma_1 + \sigma_A)\right]\sin\phi$$

from which

$$\sigma_A = -2c\,\frac{\cos\phi}{1 + \sin\phi} + \sigma_1\frac{1 - \sin\phi}{1 + \sin\phi}$$

In the United States, the expression commonly appears in a trigonometrically altered form:

$$\sigma_A = -2c\tan\left(45 - \frac{\phi}{2}\right) + \sigma_1\tan^2\left(45 - \frac{\phi}{2}\right) \quad \text{(Eq. 7.01a)}$$

If the nature of the soil, load application, and drainage conditions justify an analysis based on the assumption that $\phi = 0$ (a horizontal strength line) Equation 7.01a reduces to $\sigma_A = \sigma_1 - 2c$. On the other hand, for a cohesionless soil, the equation becomes

$$\sigma_A = \sigma_1\tan^2\left(45 - \frac{\phi}{2}\right)$$

c.   *Passive Earth Pressure*

If, instead of reducing the horizontal pressure as in the preceding section, the pressure is increased, the size of the Mohr circle will at first decrease as the magnitude of σ_3 approaches that of σ_1. When the pressure on the vertical plane exceeds that on the horizontal, the positions of the principal stresses will have been reversed. The horizontal stress is now the major principal stress; and its ultimate magnitude, σ_P, for a state of plastic equilibrium, is the passive earth pressure.

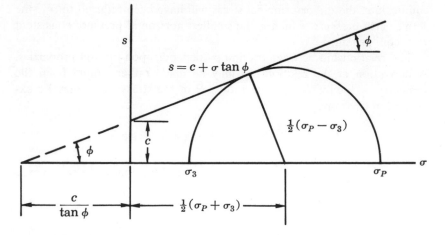

Figure 7.01d   Passive earth pressure

From the geometry of Figure 7.01d, two expressions for the radius of the Mohr circle may again be written and equated. The resulting expression

$$\frac{1}{2}(\sigma_P - \sigma_3) = \left[\frac{c}{\tan\phi} + \tfrac{1}{2}(\sigma_P + \sigma_3)\right]\sin\phi$$

may be solved for the passive earth pressure.

Thus,

$$\sigma_P = 2c\tan\left(45 + \frac{\phi}{2}\right) + \sigma_3\tan^2\left(45 + \frac{\phi}{2}\right) \quad \text{(Eq. 7.01b)}$$

For purely cohesive or purely cohesionless soils, Equation 7.01b may be reduced to simpler expressions in the same manner as was done for Equation 7.01a.

d.   Orientation of Planes

In connection with the study of equilibrium of soil masses it is necessary, as will be discussed later, to make some assumption with regard to the configuration of the slip surface which marks the boundary between that part of the mass that will be involved in any slide and that which will remain stationary. It is sometimes helpful, in this respect, to study the orientation of potential failure planes in various elements of the mass, particularly those elements adjacent to boundaries.

For any element within the mass, a known or assumed state of stress may be fully represented by a Mohr circle plot. If the stress components acting on any two planes of known orientation are specified, the stresses acting on every plane passing through the point (element) are uniquely determined. Conversely, the orientation of a plane subjected to a specified (compatible) set of conditions; e.g., limiting equilibrium, may be found. A useful concept for the visualization or graphical study of orientation of planes is that of the "pole" of the Mohr circle. To introduce this concept, refer to Figure 7.01e.

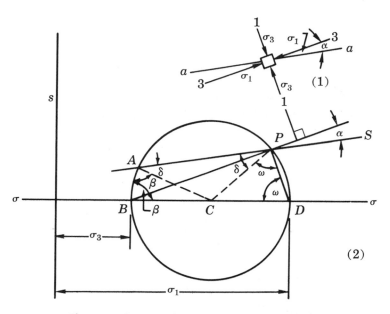

Figure 7.01e   The pole of Mohr's circle

Suppose an element to be acted on by the principal stresses σ_1 and σ_3 such that the major principal plane, 1-1, and the minor principal plane, 3-3, are oriented as shown in Figure 7.01e(1). Through the point D representing the major principal stress σ_1 in Figure 7.01e(2) pass a line parallel to the plane 1-1. This line intersects the Mohr circle at a point P having the special property that any line PA passing through P will intersect the circle at a second point A whose coordinates, σ_A, τ_A, correspond to the stresses on the plane a-a passing through the stressed element parallel to PA. In order to prove the truth of this statement, it is necessary only to show that the central angle BCA of the Mohr's circle is equal to twice the angle α between the planes a-a and 3-3. Note that the sum of the interior angles of the quadrilateral $BAPD$ must be 2π. Denote $CBA = CAB = \beta$, $CPA = CAP = \delta$, and $CPD = CDP = \omega$. Then, $2\beta + 2\delta + 2\omega = 2\pi$, from which

$$\beta + \delta + \omega = \pi \qquad (1)$$

Now

$$CPA + CPD = \pi - SPD, \text{ or } \delta + \omega = \pi - \left(\frac{\pi}{2} - \alpha\right) \qquad (2)$$

Thus,

$$\beta + \frac{\pi}{2} + \alpha = \pi \qquad \text{from (1) and (2)}$$

or

$$2\beta + 2\alpha = \pi$$

From this, by reference to the isosceles triangle BCA, it is readily deduced that the central angle BCA must equal 2α.

An element in active plastic equilibrium under horizontal and vertical principal stresses within a soil mass having the strength properties $s = c + \sigma \tan \phi$ is illustrated in Figure 7.01f(1). A line through the point σ_1 on the Mohr circle, parallel to the horizontal plane on which σ_1 acts, intersects the circle at the point P_A coincident with σ_3. P_A is the "active"

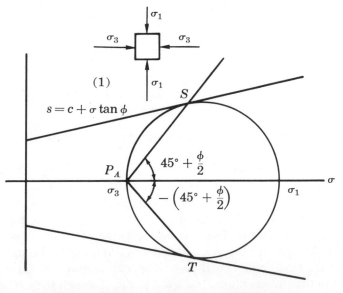

Figure 7.01f   Limiting equilibrium

pole of the circle. Lines through this pole to the points S and T, where the circle is tangent to the strength lines, define the orientation of failure surfaces within the stressed element. The lines $P_A - S$ and $P_A - T$ make angles of $45° + \dfrac{\phi}{2}$ and $-\left(45° + \dfrac{\phi}{2}\right)$ respectively with the horizontal. These two lines, therefore, intersect at $90° + \phi$.

As a general illustration, using the sign convention that treats compressive stress and counterclockwise shear stress as positive quantities, suppose that the planes of the major and minor principal stresses are to be determined when the given state of stress is as shown in Figure 7.01g(1), where $\sigma_y > \sigma_x$. The Mohr circle is plotted from the given stresses as shown in Figure 7.01g(2). Now, a line drawn horizontally

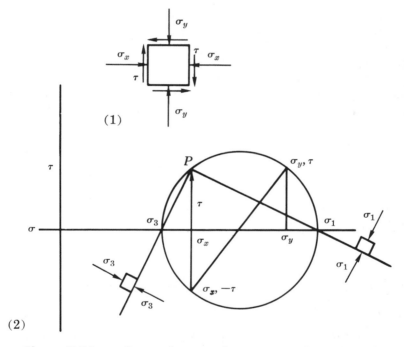

Figure 7.01g   General state of stress (two dimensional)

from (σ_y, τ) or vertically from $(\sigma_x, -\tau)$ determines the pole P. A line drawn from P through the point $(\sigma_1, 0)$ establishes the orientation of the plane of the major principal stress, and a line from P through the point $(\sigma_3, 0)$ establishes the orientation of the plane of the minor principal stress. The importance of this concept as a means for rapid visualization of the orientation of planes will be apparent in subsequent sections.

7.02   Classical Earth Pressure Theories

Section 7.01 deals with active and passive earth pressures in a rather general, and even abstract, way. Attention was centered on the state of stress at a point, primarily without attempting to arrive at any conclusions regarding the force necessary to retain or disrupt large masses of soil. Yet, it is the latter with which engineers are mainly concerned. From time to time during the past 200 years, engineers have addressed themselves to the problem with the result that significant progress has been made toward an understanding of the theoretical aspects of earth pressures. The work of Coulomb, Rankine, Rebhann, Poncelet, Culmann, Engesser, and others, provided tools for the solution of certain kinds of earth pressure problems. In engineering practice, difficulties arose in the application of the theories because of a lack of appreciation of the essential nature of the assumptions which had been made in formulating the theories. Differences in observed and predicted earth pressures led some engineers to regard the theories as useless. Others intuitively recognized that such differences had to be expected when the real problem and the theoretical problem lacked compatibility. It remained for Terzaghi in modern times, to clear away much of the misunderstanding which had arisen. His theoretical and experimental work, together with that of Tschebotarioff, has especially shown the importance of the influence of the manner in which a wall yields.

The earth pressure theories of Rankine and Coulomb have been particularly important in the history of earthwork construction. Under appropriate conditions, the use of these theories is still justified. The following sections discuss these theories and their applications.

a.   Rankine's Theory of Earth Pressure for Cohesionless Materials

W. J. M. Rankine dealt with a mass of homogeneous, isotropic, cohesionless material of semi-infinite extent; i.e., occupying all space on one side of a plane and none on the other. The plane is presumed to be represented by the ground surface. An essential (implied) assumption of the Rankine theory is that the entire mass is deformed uniformly, either by elongation or contraction, in a direction parallel to the plane. The so-called Rankine states of stress are those corresponding to deformations of sufficient magnitude to produce a condition of plastic equilibrium throughout the mass.

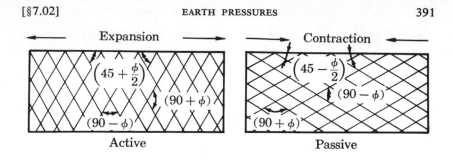

Figure 7.02a   Rankine states of plastic equilibrium

Figure 7.02a illustrates the pattern of slip surfaces (infinite in number) consistent with the two specified kinds of deformation of the mass. The principal planes are vertical and horizontal.

If a section of cohesionless soil having the strength property $s = \sigma \tan \phi$, H thick, and bounded by frictionless planes is permitted to expand horizontally as shown in Figure 7.02b, an active state of stress is produced throughout the mass of soil. In this case the vertical stress is the major

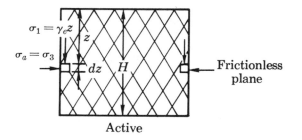

Figure 7.02b   Rankine active state of stress

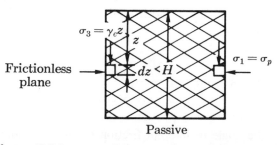

Figure 7.02c   Rankine passive state of stress

principal stress and the horizontal stress is the minor. The unit horizontal stress at any depth z is, therefore

$$\sigma_a = \sigma_3 = \gamma_e\, z \tan^2\left(45 - \frac{\phi}{2}\right)$$

and the stress on an element dz thick is

$$dE_a = \sigma_a dz = \gamma_e\, z \tan^2\left(45 - \frac{\phi}{2}\right) dz$$

and

$$E_a = \int_0^H \gamma_e\, z\left(45 - \frac{\phi}{2}\right) dz = \gamma_e \frac{H^2}{2} \tan^2\left(45 - \frac{\phi}{2}\right) \qquad \text{(Eq. 7.02a)}$$

If the same section of soil under the same conditions is subjected to horizontal compressive stress as shown in Figure 7.02c, a passive state of stress is produced and the vertical stress is the minor principal stress and the horizontal stress is the major. Therefore, the horizontal stress is

$$\sigma_p = \sigma_1 = \gamma_e\, z \tan^2\left(45 + \frac{\phi}{2}\right)$$

and the stress on an element dz thick at depth z is

$$dE_p = \sigma_p\, dz = \gamma_e\, z \tan^2\left(45 + \frac{\phi}{2}\right) dz$$

and the total pressure against H is

$$E_p = \gamma_e \frac{H^2}{2} \tan^2\left(45 + \frac{\phi}{2}\right) \qquad \text{(Eq. 7.02b)}$$

Rankine also considered cohesionless masses having sloping surfaces. In this case, the stress on a vertical plane acts parallel to the ground surface, so that the vertical plane is no longer a principal plane. Rankine derived an expression for the horizontal component of the stress on a vertical plane at depth z, which can be written in the form

$$\sigma_h = k\gamma_e z, \text{ where } k = \cos^2 i\, \frac{\cos i - \sqrt{\cos^2 i - \cos^2 \phi}}{\cos i + \sqrt{\cos^2 i - \cos^2 \phi}}, \, i \text{ being the slope}$$

angle and ϕ the angle of internal friction of the cohesionless material. The pattern of slip surfaces and stress trajectories can be most readily studied by reference to the Mohr-Coulomb diagrams.

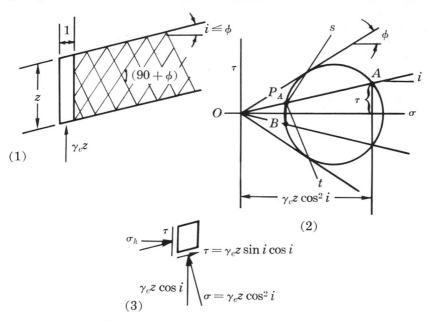

Figure 7.02d   Active plastic equilibrium in infinite slope

An element of the mass having unit width and a depth z from the surface is shown in Figure $7.02d(1)$. Since the position of the element along the infinite slope is arbitrary, the resultant stresses acting on the two vertical faces must be equal, opposite, and collinear; and the resultant force on the inclined base must equal the weight $\gamma_e z$ of the soil column. The unit stresses acting on an element of soil at the base are indicated in Figure $7.02d(3)$. If the mass is expanded parallel to the slope, the stresses acting on the vertical face undergo a reduction in magnitude until the limiting conditions shown in Figure $7.02d(2)$ are reached. Point A on the Mohr circle represents the stresses on the inclined base, and OA to some scale is equal to $\gamma_e z \cos i$. P_A is the (active) pole, and point B represents the components of stress on the vertical plane. The slip surfaces are oriented in the directions $P_A s$ and $P_A t$.

The passive state attained by contraction along the slope may be similarly analyzed. Figure $7.02e$ shows the Mohr-Coulomb diagram for the passive case and the corresponding sets of slip surfaces, which are parallel to the lines $P_P s$ and $P_P t$. The pronounced difference in the magnitude of σ_h for the active and passive cases is quite apparent when it is recognized that, for a given depth z, the points A in Figures $7.02d$ and $7.02e$ represent identical stresses.

From the geometry of the Mohr-Coulomb diagrams representing the Rankine state in cohesionless soil, it is clear that the orientation of the

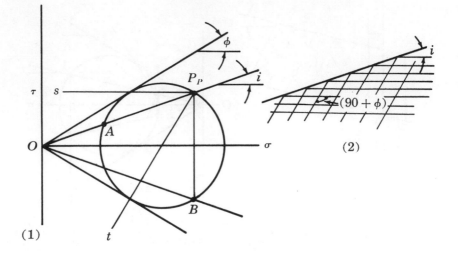

Figure 7.02e   **Passive plastic equilibrium in infinite slope**

slip surfaces is independent of depth. Since the surfaces are planar, Equations 7.01a and 7.01b show, also, that the pressure on the vertical plane is a linear function of the depth. From this, it follows that the position of the resultant stress on any vertical plane may be found.

b.   *Plastic Equilibrium in Cohesive Soils*

The behavior of a semi-infinite mass of cohesive soil, subjected to the same conditions of deformation as were used above for cohesionless masses, may also be analyzed. Cohesive soils possess some strength that is independent of the normal pressure acting on any plane. This of course implies a capability for resisting tensile stresses, even though the wisdom of relying on this capability in long term stress situations may be open to question.

For cohesive masses having horizontal surfaces, the active and passive poles in the Mohr-Coulomb diagram lie on the σ axis, Figure 7.02f. The orientation of the failure surfaces is $P_A s$ and $P_A t$ for the active case (2), and $P_P s$ and $P_P t$ in the passive case (3). These imminent failure surfaces occur at angles of $\left(45 + \dfrac{\phi}{2}\right)$ and $\left(45 - \dfrac{\phi}{2}\right)$ with the planes of the principal stresses, which in this case are parallel and normal to the surface. As in the case of cohesionless soils, these imminent failure surfaces are

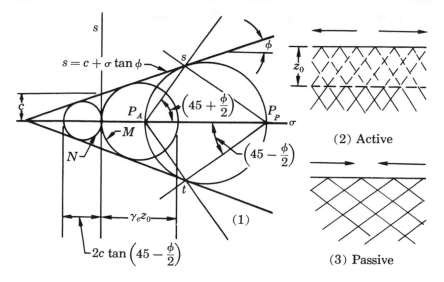

**Figure 7.02f   Plastic equilibrium of cohesive mass
(horizontal surface)**

plane surfaces since the orientation is the same for every position of the
Mohr circle.

In the active case there is some depth z_0 for which the stress σ_a on the
vertical plane must be zero. The depth z_0 may be established from the
geometry of the diagram (1) by considering the circle M corresponding
to a vertical stress $\gamma_e z$ and a horizontal stress $\sigma_a = 0$. In the general rela-
tionship, $\sigma_a = -2c \tan\left(45 - \dfrac{\phi}{2}\right) + \sigma_1 \tan^2\left(45 - \dfrac{\phi}{2}\right)$, when σ_a is set
equal to zero and σ_1 set equal to $\gamma_e z_0$, the resulting expression for z_0 is
found to be

$$z_0 = \frac{2c}{\gamma_e \tan\left(45 - \dfrac{\phi}{2}\right)} = \frac{2c}{\gamma_e} \tan\left(45 + \dfrac{\phi}{2}\right) \qquad \text{(Eq. 7.02}c\text{)}$$

For every $z < z_0$ the stress on the vertical plane is tensile. At the surface,
where $\sigma_1 = \gamma_e z = 0$, the general relationship shows that $\sigma_a = -2c \tan$
$\left(45 - \dfrac{\phi}{2}\right)$, the minus sign indicating tension. The circle N in Figure
6.02f represents the state of stress at the surface. That part of the active
pressure due to the weight of the soil, $\gamma_e z \tan^2\left(45 - \dfrac{\phi}{2}\right)$, varies linearly

with depth and is always positive. The part due to cohesion, $-2c \tan$ $\left(45 - \dfrac{\phi}{2} \right)$, is independent of the depth (i.e., constant) and is always negative.

If the surface of the mass is not horizontal, two possibilities are to be considered. The slope angle i may be less than or equal to ϕ, as for cohesionless soil; or i may exceed ϕ, which is not possible in cohesionless masses. Figure 7.02g illustrates the case where $i \leq \phi$.

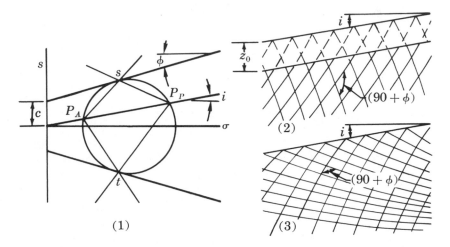

Figure 7.02g   Cohesive mass with sloping surface $i \leq \phi$

In the active case, at a certain depth z in the slope the stress is represented by the Mohr-Coulomb diagram, Figure 7.02g(1), for which the active pole lies on the slope line i. As the depth z varies, the manner in which the Mohr circle moves horizontally along the σ axis may be easily visualized. The lines P_As and P_At, representing the orientation of the failure surfaces change direction as the circle is displaced. The slope of P_As decreases as the circle moves from left to right, while the (negative) slope of P_At increases. At depth z_0, P_A coincides with the origin, and both P_As and P_At make angles of $\left(45 + \dfrac{\phi}{2} \right)$ with the horizontal. This result indicates that the failure surfaces must be curved in somewhat the manner illustrated (exaggerated) in Figure 7.02g(2). The pattern shown above depth z_0 is not likely to develop since in this tension zone failure is more likely to develop on surfaces approximating the minor principal planes.

For the passive case, the behavior of the lines P_Ps and P_Pt may be similarly imagined as the circle is displaced along the σ axis. P_Ps must be flatter and P_Pt steeper as displacement to the right occurs. The corresponding failure surfaces are shown, again with exaggerated curvature, in Figure $7.02g(3)$.

If the slope angle i exceeds ϕ, the failure surfaces become strongly curved. A critical depth z_c exists at which one set of failure surfaces for both the active and passive states is parallel to the surface. Below this depth, the conditions for plastic equilibrium cannot be satisfied because of the impossible stress components that would be required on some planes.

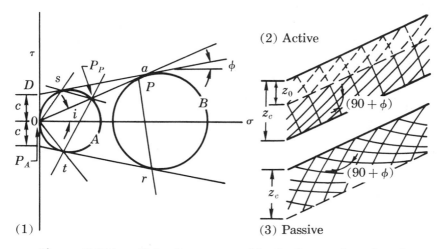

Figure 7.02h   Cohesive mass with sloping surface $i > \phi$

The circle A may be used to represent the active state of stress at depth z_0 or the passive state at the surface, and lines drawn from the respective poles through the points of tangency s and t describe the orientation of the associated failure surfaces. To investigate what happens with increasing depth z, let us recall that coordinates of every point on the line Oa represent the stress components σ and τ acting on a plane parallel to the surface at depth z. Point a is the intersection of the slope line Oa with the strength line Da. It may be observed that through every point of Oa, except at a itself, two circles may be drawn that are tangent to the strength lines. One of these circles (the left) represents the active state of plastic equilibrium, and the other represents the passive state at the same depth. It is further apparent that as the point moves along Oa the two circles, active and passive, must approach each other more and more closely, until they finally become coincident in the circle B when the point reaches a. Thus the active and passive states of stress are identical at some depth z_c where the normal stress on a plane parallel to the surface is represented by the abscissa of point a. Points beyond a on the slope line represent intolerable states of stress for the material under consideration. From the geometry of the diagram, it is easily shown that

$$\sigma_a = \frac{c}{\tan i - \tan \phi}$$

The approximate pattern of failure surfaces above the depth z_c is illustrated in Figure 7.02h(2) and (3).

c.   Coulomb's Theory

Nearly 200 years ago, C. A. Coulomb considered the problem of the earth pressure acting on retaining walls. His analytical solution of the problem employs the calculus for determination of the minimum and maximum pressures consistent with the equilibrium of a soil mass bounded by a wall, the ground surface, and a lower planar surface extending upward from the toe of the wall to intersect the ground surface. The procedure is generally referred to as the *sliding wedge analysis*, and the most significant assumption is that the sliding surface is a plane. The static equilibrium of the wedge under the action of external forces is considered, without regard to internal stresses or deformation of the wedge of earth.

A general solution to the earth pressure problem as developed by Coulomb is stated in Equation 7.02d.

$$E_a = \frac{1}{2} \gamma_e H^2 \left[\frac{csc\ \theta \sin (\theta - \phi)}{\sqrt{\sin (\theta + \delta)} + \sqrt{\dfrac{\sin (\phi + \delta) \sin (\phi - i)}{\sin (\theta - i)}}} \right]^2 \qquad \text{(Eq. 7.02}d)$$

The general solution for the Coulomb sliding wedge relationship is tedious

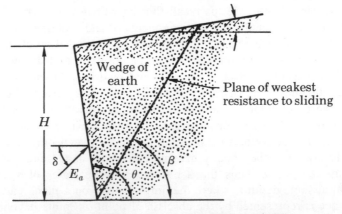

Figure 7.02i   Coulomb sliding wedge

to obtain, unwieldy to use, and its use is limited to those cases where the surface of the backfill is plane. Consequently, the graphical solutions presented later in this chapter are generally employed. The graphical solutions are quite simple to construct, are not much complicated by unusual configurations of the backfill surface, and give a "feeling" for the problem which is especially helpful to the inexperienced. The principles involved in the Coulomb analysis may be demonstrated by selecting a problem in which the boundary conditions are kept as simple as possible. For example, consider an embankment of cohesionless soil with a horizontal surface, retained by a smooth (frictionless) vertical wall. The forces acting on a wedge of the soil adjacent to the wall in the active case are shown in Figure 7.02j(1), and the equilibrium force polygon in Figure 7.02j(2).

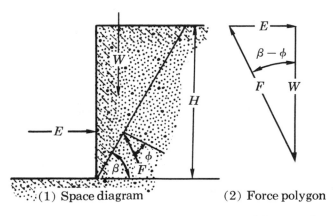

(1) Space diagram   (2) Force polygon

Figure 7.02j   Coulomb sliding wedge and force polygon

The weight of the wedge, W, is equal to its volume times the unit weight γ_e. For unit thickness,

$$W = \frac{1}{2} \gamma_e H^2 \cot \beta$$

From the force polygon,

$$E = W \tan (\beta - \phi) = \frac{1}{2} \gamma_e H^2 \cot \beta \tan (\beta - \phi) \tag{1}$$

The derivative of (1) is

$$\frac{dE}{d\beta} = \frac{1}{2} \gamma_e H^2 [\cot \beta \sec^2 (\beta - \phi) - \tan (\beta - \phi) \csc^2 \beta]$$

Setting this derivative equal to zero, it is found that

$$\frac{\tan (\beta - \phi)}{\sec^2 (\beta - \phi)} = \frac{\tan (90 - \beta)}{\sec^2 (90 - \beta)}$$

for which the general solution is $\beta - \phi = 90 - \beta$, making $\beta = \left(45 + \dfrac{\phi}{2}\right)$. This solution indicates that the force E attains its maximum value E_z in the active case when $\beta = \left(45 + \dfrac{\phi}{2}\right)$. Substituting these values in (1),

$$E_a = \frac{1}{2}\,\gamma_e H^2 \cot\left(45 + \frac{\phi}{2}\right)\tan\left(45 + \frac{\phi}{2} - \phi\right)$$

$$E_a = \frac{1}{2}\,\gamma_e H^2 \tan^2\left(45 - \frac{\phi}{2}\right) \qquad\text{(Eq. 7.02e)}$$

In a similar analysis for the passive case, in which the frictional component of F acts to oppose motion upward along the inclined plane, a minimum value, E_p, for E is found to exist when $\beta = \left(45 - \dfrac{\phi}{2}\right)$, in which case

$$E_p = \frac{1}{2}\,\gamma_e H^2 \tan^2\left(45 + \frac{\phi}{2}\right) \qquad\text{(Eq. 702f)}$$

For this simple case, the active and passive earth pressures correspond with those found by Rankine (Equations 7.02a and b) for cohesionless soils.

7.03   Wall Characteristics

a.   Friction

The angle of friction between the wall and the soil depends upon the kind of material used for the wall, and upon the nature of the backfill soil. It varies also with wall roughness or finish. The extensive investigation of Potyondy (1961) represents the bulk of what is known about soil-wall interaction. Table 7.03a summarizes the recommendations given by Potyondy, expressed in terms of the coefficients f_ϕ, f_c, and f_c max, defined as shown in the table. The use of f_c max is recommended for purely cohesive soils, where the strength is independent of the normal stress. The angle of obliquity, δ, must of necessity have a value between 0 and the angle of internal friction, ϕ, of the backfill soil.

The obliquity of the resultant force between wall and soil will, of course, vary as the wall yields, approaching a limiting obliquity as failure impends. For the usual concrete wall construction for the retention of cohesionless soil, it is probably reasonable to assume $\delta = \phi$. The pattern of the slip sur-

Table 7.03a
Proposed Coefficients of Skin Friction between Soils and Construction Materials—after Potyondy

$$f\phi = \delta/\phi,\quad fc = \frac{c_a}{c},\quad fc\max = \frac{c_a\max}{c\max};\text{ without factor of safety}$$

Construction material		Surface finish of construction material	Sand 0.06<D<2.0 mm Dry Dense $f\phi$	Sand Sat. Dense $f\phi$	Cohesionless silt 0.002<D<0.06 Dry Dense $f\phi$	Sat. Loose $f\phi$	Sat. Dense $f\phi$	Cohesive granular soil 50% Clay + 50% Sand Consist. I. =1.0–0.5 $f\phi$	fc	Clay D≤0.06 mm Consist. Index: 1.0–0.73 $f\phi$	fc	$fc\max$
Steel	Smooth	Polished	0.54	0.64	0.79	0.40	0.68	0.40	—	0.50	0.25	0.50
Steel	Rough	Rusted	0.76	0.80	0.95	0.48	0.75	0.65	0.35	0.50	0.50	0.80
Wood		Parallel to grain	0.76	0.85	0.92	0.55	0.87	0.80	0.20	0.60	0.40	0.85
Wood		At right angles to grain	0.88	0.89	0.98	0.63	0.95	0.90	0.40	0.70	0.50	0.85
Concrete	Smooth	Made in iron form	0.76	0.80	0.92	0.50	0.87	0.84	0.42	0.68	0.40	1.00
Concrete	Grained	Made in wood form	0.88	0.88	0.98	0.62	0.96	0.90	0.58	0.80	0.50	1.00
Concrete	Rough	Made on adjusted ground	0.98	0.90	1.00	0.79	1.00	0.95	0.80	0.95	0.60	1.00

faces and the magnitude of the resultant pressure against the wall are influenced by the wall friction. The most conservative results (i.e., greater active pressure E_a and smaller passive pressure E_p) are associated with $\delta = 0$. If there is good reason to suppose that $\delta < \phi$, and economic objections to assuming $\delta = 0$, it may be practicable to devise simple experiments to assist in establishing a reliable value for δ applicable to the situation.

The imaginary vertical plane utilized in the Rankine analysis yields in such a way that it remains, in the case of a mass with a horizontal surface, a principal plane; and in any case obliquity of the resultant force on the plane does not alter as yielding occurs. Coulomb's wedge analysis places no such restriction on the direction of the resultant, but is limited by the assumption that the slip surface is plane. Because both theories are based on assumptions which, at least to some extent, are at variance with the truth, it is important to discover under what conditions the theories can be useful in earth pressure problems.

b.   *Yielding*

The manner in which a wall yields when acted on by earth pressure has a powerful influence upon the distribution of the pressure against the wall. Some kinds of walls that are frequently used to retain earth are illustrated in Figure 7.03*a*.

Walls of the first four types may be generally classified as free standing walls. Movement may occur in the form of rotation about some point in the plane, or as translation resulting from slippage along the base. It

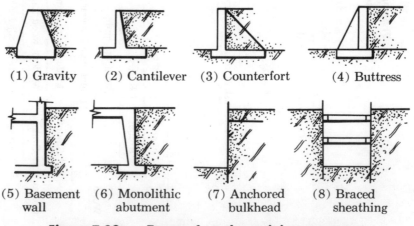

(1) Gravity   (2) Cantilever   (3) Counterfort   (4) Buttress

(5) Basement   (6) Monolithic   (7) Anchored   (8) Braced
     wall   abutment   bulkhead   sheathing

Figure 7.03a   Types of earth retaining structures

is conceivable that movements of this type produced on a large enough scale, may be capable of permitting certain parts of the soil mass to achieve a condition of plastic equilibrium as supposed by Rankine. The remainder of the wall types shown in Figure 7.03a impose such different restrictions on the mode of deformation that the magnitude and, especially, the distribution of pressure against the wall will be vastly altered from those that could be found using the methods of Rankine or Coulomb. The solution of such problems is most often accomplished empirically, although theoretical approaches are also helpful in certain cases.

Preliminary consideration of the free standing wall is simplified by considering the wall as a plane, or series of planes, along which the soil is restrained. If the plane OA in Figure 7.03b rotates about its base O to

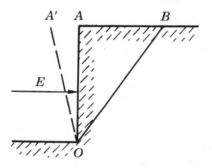

Figure 7.03b   Rotation about base

a new position OA' it is possible for the triangular mass OAB to expand uniformly in the horizontal direction; i.e., the same unit deformation throughout the mass OAB. If no frictional (tangential) force is developed along OA, the mass can, if sufficiently deformed, pass into an active state of plastic equilibrium. The earth pressure E decreases to the value E_a, according to Rankine, and a continuous slip surface OB will form at an angle of $\left(45° + \dfrac{\phi}{2} \right)$ with the horizontal ground surface. Similarly, for opposite rotation of OA it could be concluded that E will attain a magnitude E_p and that the slip surface OB will intersect the ground surface at $\left(45° - \dfrac{\phi}{2} \right)$.

If wall friction exists, rotation may still produce a relatively uniform horizontal strain. In this case, however, principal planes adjacent to the wall are no longer horizontal and vertical but rotate from these positions as the frictional drag along the wall increases. Consequently, failure surfaces that form in the vicinity of the wall will no longer be inclined to the horizontal at an angle of $\left(45° \pm \dfrac{\phi}{2} \right)$. The influence of this fact on the configuration of the slip surface that develops between O and B will be examined in the next section.

7.04   Slip Surfaces

In Figure 7.03b planes coinciding with the surface AB, for each element along AB, are principal planes; and slip surfaces must form angles of $\left(45° \pm \dfrac{\phi}{2} \right)$ with AB, according to the active and passive conditions. On the other hand, OA is not a principal plane if frictional forces act along it. Although at A an infinitesimal element is apparently subjected to incompatible boundary conditions, we may imagine that, in general, some sort of transition zone exists in which slip surfaces curve so as to satisfy the directional requirements at both boundaries.

Figure 7.04a illustrates the effect of wall friction on the configuration of that potential failure surface OCB extending from the toe of the wall to the ground surface. In connection with the sketches in Figure 7.04a, the algebraic sign for the angle of wall friction δ is taken as positive if the frictional component on OA acts upward in the case of active pressure or downward in the case of passive pressure. Thus, $+\delta$ describes the usual directions associated with active and passive earth pressures, while $-\delta$ describes a direction of resultant earth pressure only rarely encountered, and always in unusual situations. For rotation of the wall away from the soil (active), the surface tends to subside, with wall friction acting upward to resist soil subsidence. For rotation toward the soil (passive), the surface tends to rise, which is resisted by a downward drag on the face of the soil.

The failure wedge of $OABC$ in Figure 7.04a(1,2) consists of one part OAC, in which the influence of wall friction is manifested by a curvature of the failure surfaces, and another part, ACB, that may be called a Rankine zone. The slope of the tangent to OC at point O, the base of the wall, is obtained from 7.04a(3). The slope of failure surfaces at points on the wall above O are just the same as at O, since the scale of the Mohr-Coulomb diagram can be chosen to correspond to any depth z (N.B. — True only for cohesionless soil for which the strength line passes through the origin). There are, of course, two sets of slip surfaces intersecting each other at $90° \pm \phi$ throughout the wedge. Our particular interest is in the set of surfaces comprising OCB (or $OC'B'$ if δ is negative)

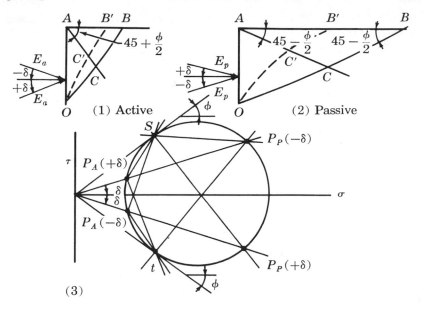

Figure 7.04a   Influence of wall friction on shape of slip surface

and providing a continuous failure surface from the base of the wall to the surface of the ground.

In Figure 7.04a(3), the active and passive poles of the Mohr circle are shown for both positive and negative angles of wall friction. The slope of a tangent to OC or OC' at O is readily found by drawing a line from the appropriate pole to s (in the active case) or to t (in the passive case). Thus, for example, the slope of OC at O is given by the line $P_A(+\delta)s$ in the active case (1), and by $P_P(+\delta)t$ in the passive case (2). The slopes of OC' are similarly found.

The important thing to be noted here is that in the active case the surface OCB (or $OC'B'$) does not deviate much from a plane, even though δ may be quite large. Thus, the use of Coulomb's analysis in which a plane is assumed, is a reasonable procedure for finding the active earth pressure of a cohesionless soil against a retaining wall that is more or less free to rotate about a point on its base. E_a found in this manner differs by only a few per cent from that obtained from an analysis employing the surface OCB. In the passive case, for small angles of wall friction, the curvature of OC and the consequent error in a Coulomb analysis for E_p are of no practical significance. However, if δ exceeds about $\phi/3$, the error begins to be excessive, leading to unnecessarily large values of E_p as δ approaches ϕ.

In such cases, use of one of the methods discussed later in this chapter is preferable.

7.05   Earth Pressure for Cohesionless Materials

a.   Plane Slip Surface

As pointed out in the preceding section, a satisfactory solution for the active earth pressure acting against a wall may be obtained by assuming a plane slip surface provided that (1) a cohesionless backfill is involved, (2) the wall can yield by rotation about its base, and (3) the properties of the backfill are known. If the angle is small (Terzaghi suggested an upper limit $\delta = \phi/3$) the passive earth pressure may be found similarly. There is no compelling theoretical reason why cohesive backfills could not also be treated in this manner. However, the observed curvature of slip surfaces in cohesive soils, the difficulty of determining properties appropriate for use in the field, and the gross changes in properties with variation of moisture content argue powerfully against placing too much reliance on *any* theoretical approach to the problem.

When a plane slip surface is assumed, the problem may be solved analytically using Coulomb's method with equations or by making successive trials involving different failure surfaces. However, graphical solutions are generally preferred because of the greater ease with which variations in surface and wall configuration and surface loading can be handled. Graphical solutions usually, but not always, utilize implicit trial and error procedures organized so as to proceed very quickly. In the following sections, three graphical procedures are shown, each of which may, in appropriate problems, possess advantages over the others. The procedure of Poncelet gives a unique solution (also shown analytically by Rebhann), whereas the methods of Culmann and Engesser are essentially trial and error. In the interest of clarity, the mechanics of the procedures will be presented as a sequence of steps, first for active, then for passive earth pressure. In all cases, ϕ is the angle of internal friction of the soil and ψ is the angle that the resultant earth pressure E makes with the vertical.

(1)   Poncelet's Procedure

In Figure 7.05a, OA represents the face of contact between wall and soil, and AB is the constantly sloping surface of the backfill. The procedure is as follows:

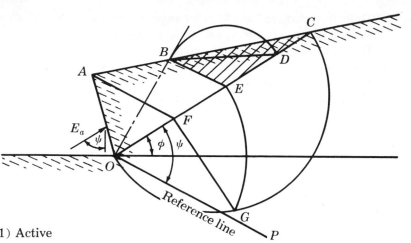

(1) Active

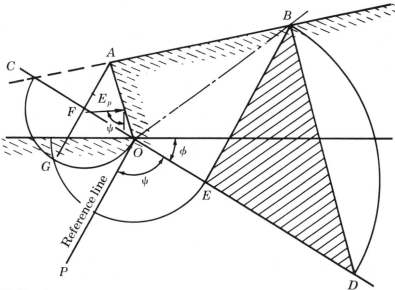

(2) Passive

Figure 7.05a   Poncelet's procedure

(a)   *Active Pressure*

  1. Draw the line OC from the toe of the wall to the surface of the backfill at angle ϕ above the horizontal.

2. Draw the reference line *OP* at an angle ψ with the ϕ line *OC*. Construct a semi-circle having *OC* as its diameter.
3. Draw line *AF* parallel to the reference line.
4. Construct *FG* perpendicular to the diameter *OC*.
5. Swing arc *GE* having radius *OG* (i.e., center at *O*).
6. Draw line *EB* parallel to reference line.
7. Swing arc *BD* having radius *EB* (i.e., center at *E*).
8. Draw line *BD*.
9. Compute: E_a = Area of triangle *BED* according to scale of drawing times unit weight of soil. If the area of triangle *BED* is ft² and γ_e is lb ft⁻³, the resultant pressure is lb per lin. ft of wall.

(b)   *Passive Pressure*

The steps are identical to those given above for the active pressure, except that ϕ is laid out in the opposite direction from the horizontal necessitating an imaginary extension *AC* of the backfill surface. The final computation produces the passive earth pressure E_P. A visual comparison of the relative sizes of the triangles *BED* in the two cases illustrates the great difference in E_a and E_p. The failure surface *OB*, in both cases, divides the soil mass *OABE* into two equal parts. The necessity for fulfilling this requirement was established by Rebhann.

The Culmann and Engesser procedures consist of plotting curves for the values of E_a and E_p for a number of assumed earth wedges from which the maximum value of E_a and the minimum value of E_p can be measured. These procedures are applications of simple statics as illustrated in Figure 7.05*b*.

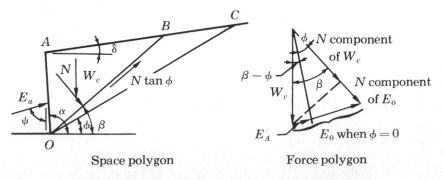

Space polygon   Force polygon

Figure 7.05b   Active pressure for wedge OAB on surface OB

From this static relationship, an algebraic equation for E in terms of ϕ, α, ψ, δ, β, H, and γ_e can be derived in which β is the only variable. The first derivative of this equation set equal to zero gives the maximum value of E_a for the conditions imposed. The Coulomb equation is quite long and complicated making the graphical solution generally preferable.

(2)   Culmann's Procedure

Culmann's graphical solution is shown in Figure 7.05c for the problem previously solved by Poncelet's method.

(a)   Active Pressure

1. Draw the line OC from the toe of the wall at angle ϕ above the horizontal.
2. Draw the reference line OP at an angle ψ with the ϕ-line OC.
3. Draw the rays OD, OD', etc. These may be drawn arbitrarily; however, to facilitate subsequent computation and plotting of the W components it is helpful to lay out $AD = DD'$, etc., forming a series of wedges of equal mass.
4. Compute the weight of OAD and lay out as O-1 along the line OC, choosing any convenient force scale. Compute the weight of ODD' and lay out similarly as 1-2. Thus the weight of OAD' is represented by O-2. Continue until the weights of every trial wedge bounded by OA, the backfill surface, and a ray have been laid out as O-1, O-2, O-3, etc.
5. Through the points 1, 2, 3, etc., draw lines parallel to the reference line OP.
6. Mark the points of intersection of these lines with their corresponding rays; i.e., the point at which the line from 1 intersects OD, the point at which the line from 2 intersects OD', etc.
7. Through these points of intersection, draw the smooth curve OFM.
8. The active earth pressure E_a is now represented by the maximum distance EF, parallel to the reference line, from the line OC to the curve OFM. The magnitude is determined from the same force scale factor used to lay out the forces O-1, O-2, O-3, etc. The position of the failure plane OFB is also determined. Although in the illustration, Figure 7.05c(1), EF coincides with one of the trials the coincidence is accidental. Every trial represents the construction of a force polygon equivalent to that shown in Figure 7.02j(2). The critical polygon for which E attains its maximum value E_a is sketched as $E'O'F'$ in Figure 7.05c(1).

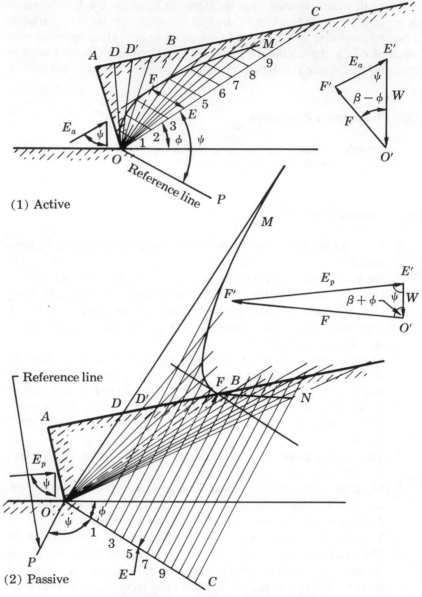

Figure 7.05c   Culmann's procedure

(b)   *Passive Pressure*

1. Draw the line OC from the toe of the wall at angle ϕ below the horizontal, Figure 7.05c(2).

2.
3.
4.
5.
6.
{ Same as for active case above, except that the first ray OD is drawn so that the angle POD is somewhat less than 180°. Thus, the weight of wedge OAD, represented by O-1, is usually greater than that of each subsequent increment.

7. Through the points of intersection found in 6, draw the smooth curve MFN.

8. The passive earth pressure E_p is represented by the minimum distance EF, parallel to the reference line, from the line OC to the curve MFN. The corresponding critical force polygon is also shown in Figure 7.05c(2). The failure surface is OFB. The position of F on OFB (in this case falling about at the backfill surface) is an accident of scale choice, depending both on dimensional scale and force scale.

(3)   Engesser's Procedure

The procedure suggested by Engesser may be laid out in different ways. That shown in Figure 7.05d is quite convenient. Whatever the method, the result desired is the envelope described by a series of lines whose position and direction vary for each trial. In Figure 7.05d, the active and passive pressures, E_a and E_p, act at the same angle to the wall (same δ and same ψ) as in Figures 7.05a and 7.05c. To avoid clutter, these factors are not shown in Figure 7.05d.

(a)   Active Pressure

1. Draw the line OC from the toe of the wall at angle ϕ above the horizontal, and extend it downward to the left as OC'.

2. Draw the reference line OP at an angle ψ with the ϕ-line OC.

3. Draw the rays OD, OD', etc. representing arbitrary trial failure surfaces (remarks under Culmann procedure apply).

4. On OC' lay out, to an appopriate scale, the weights of the soil wedges defined by the various trial surfaces. Thus O-1 is the weight of soil wedge OAD, O-2 the weight of wedge OAD', etc.

5. Through each of the points 1, 2, 3, 4, etc., draw a line parallel to the respective trial surface. Thus 1-1' is parallel to OD, 2-2' is parallel to OD', etc. These lines define the smooth envelope $C'E$ 1' of Figure 7.05d(1).

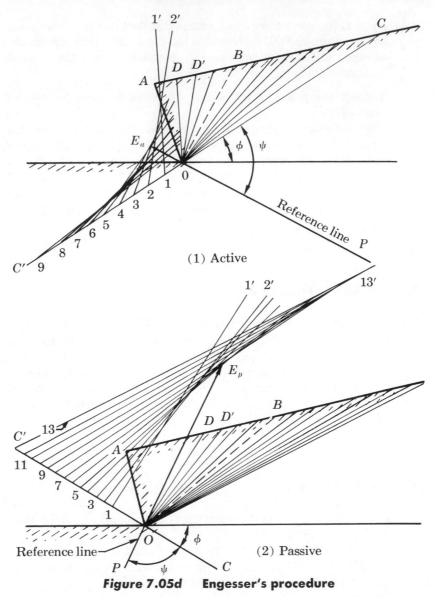

Figure 7.05d   Engesser's procedure

6. The active pressure E_a is determined by scaling OE, a continuation of PO. In the direction OE, this is the maximum possible distance to any tangent of the envelope. The direction of the failure surface OB corresponds to the slope of the tangent to the envelope $C'E1'$ at E. In the example, this is approximated by the fourth trial. The critical force polygon nearly corresponds to $O4E$, and is the same polygon as $E'O'F'$ in Figure 7.05d(1).

(b)   *Passive Pressure*

1. Draw the line *OC* from the toe of the wall at angle ϕ below the horizontal, and extend it upward to the left as *OC'*.

2. ⎫
3. ⎪ Same as for active case, except that the first trial surface *OD* is
4. ⎬ drawn so that angle *POD* < 180°. The envelope defined at the con-
5. ⎪ clusion of step 5 is the curve 1 *E* 13'.
   ⎭

6. The passive pressure E_p is found by scaling *OE*, a continuation of *PO*. In the direction *OE*, this is the minimum possible distance to any tangent of the envelope. The direction of the failure surface *OB* corresponds to that of the tangent to the envelope at *E*. In the example, this is approximated by the sixth trial. The critical force polygon nearly corresponds to *O6E*, and is the same polygon as *E'O'F'* in Figure 7.05c(2).

b.   Curved Slip Surface

In Section 7.04, the influence of wall friction on the slope of the slip surface was noted. When the angle of friction between soil and wall is not negligible, it is advisable to compute the passive pressure of cohesionless soil on the basis of a slip surface having some assumed curvature. Slip surfaces in cohesive soils are almost always observed to be curved. The configuration of curved slip surfaces has been the subject of theoretical and experimental studies that have demonstrated the difficulty of arriving at a mathematical formula which exactly describes the surface. In order to be of practical use, the slip surface assumed in the analysis must be one that is in reasonable conformity with those observed in failures, and it must also be one that enables a fairly simple analysis of the problem. Two curves fulfilling these requirements, which have been widely used, are the *circular arc* and the *logarithmic spiral*. Neither choice appears to possess a clear advantage over the other. In either case, it is generally assumed that a portion of the slip surface (that in an assumed Rankine zone) is planar. The usual procedure consists of making at least three trials involving different locations of the assumed slip surface, and deducing from these the minimum (E_p) value corresponding to a critical location. The work can be accomplished graphically or by analytical solution of the equations of equilibrium.

(1)   Circular Arc

The circular arc method lends itself more readily to graphical solution than does the spiral method. For a discussion of the friction circle (ϕ-

circle) method which is used here, refer to Chapter 5. The procedure is illustrated in Figure 7.05e, and involves the use of a space diagram and a force polygon, both drawn to scale in the case of a graphical solution. In the example, the backfill surface is horizontal, and the assumed Rankine zone is symmetrical. If the surface slopes, the Rankine zone must be defined in accordance with the principles illustrated in Figure 7.02e.

The passive earth pressure E_p is assumed to act at the lower third point of the wall at a known angle δ (positive wall friction) with a normal to the wall. The line AC is laid out from the top of the wall at an angle $\left(45 - \dfrac{\phi}{2}\right)$ below the horizontal surface. A trial arc OB is laid out by selecting an arbitrary point B, on the line AC, and laying out angle ABP equal to ϕ so that the radius is perpendicular to the tangent BE. The center of the arc, P, is determined by making $r = PO = PB$, which is usually done by trial although it may be done geometrically by erecting a perpendicular at mid-point of the chord OB.

The equilibrium of the soil mass $OADB$ is considered. The mass is acted on by its own weight W_e, through the center of gravity; the force

$$E_{P1} = \frac{1}{2}\, \gamma_e H_1^2\, \tan^2\left(45 + \frac{\phi}{2}\right)$$ acting horizontally at the lower third point of H_1; the unknown resultant F of the normal and frictional components on OB; and the force E_p of unknown magnitude on the face OA.

The line of action of E_{p1} is extended on the space diagram to intersect the line of action of W_e. The direction of the resultant R is determined from the force polygon, and its line of action is laid out through the intersection of the lines of action of E_{p1} and W_e. The line of action of E_p is extended to intersect the line of action of R. For the force system to be concurrent, as required, the line of action of F must pass through the intersection of R and E_p. In addition, F must be (approximately) tangent to a circle centered at P, of radius $r \sin \phi$. With the direction of F thus established, the force polygon can be completed and the magnitude of E_p determined. The magnitude of E_p is then plotted to some scale above the point D (i.e., $E_p = D2$).

Other trials are made similarly to yield as many points, 1, 2, 3, etc. as are necessary to define a smooth curve 1-2-3 that includes a low point (minimum). The required E_p is scaled from the drawing, and the critical slip surface is defined by the requirement that point B must fall on AC directly below the minimum point of curve 1-2-3. In general, it will not coincide with any of the trials.

(2)   Logarithmic Spiral

If the curved part of the trial failure surface is approximated by a logarithmic spiral, the procedure for solving the problem is fundamentally

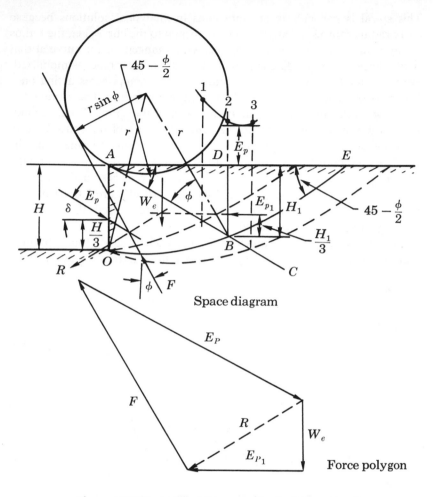

Figure 7.05e   Circular arc (φ-circle) method cohesionless soil

the same as that just used in the case of the circular arc. From a graphical standpoint the problem is complicated by the necessity for laying out the spiral, a task more difficult than that of constructing a circular arc. The particular spiral used in these solutions has the relationship

$$r = r_0 e^{\theta \tan \phi} \qquad\qquad \text{(Eq. 7.05a)}$$

in which

r = radius of spiral
r_0 = starting radius (for $\theta = 0$)
e = base of natural logarithms
θ = angle between r_0 and r
ϕ = angle of internal friction of soil

This spiral is particularly advantageous in analytical solutions because every radius r forms the angle ϕ with a normal to the curve; i.e., the radius to any point makes an angle of $90 - \phi$ with a tangent to the curve at that point. Since, for impending slip, the full frictional resistance is mobilized, every resultant dF of the normal and frictional components acting on a length ds of the curve must be directed along a radius. The resultant F of all forces dF must also act along a radius of the spiral. Thus, the moment of F taken with respect to the center (origin) of the spiral is zero.

In the solution of the problem, it will be necessary to determine the weight of soil under consideration and the position of its center of gravity. This may be done by arithmetical computation; or, as is sometimes easier, the properties of the various trial sections $OADB$ (Figure 7.05a) may be found mechanically. If the computational method is used, the properties of a log spiral sector are needed.

The area of the sector shown in Figure 7.05f is easily found by integration when dA is set equal to $\frac{1}{2}r^2 d\theta$. From this and from Equation 7.05a,

$$A = \int_{\theta=0}^{\theta=\theta_1} \tfrac{1}{2}\, r_0^2\, e^{2\,\theta\,\tan\,\phi}\, d\theta$$

from which

$$A = \frac{r_1^2 - r_0^2}{4\,\tan\,\phi} \qquad\qquad \text{(Eq. 7.05b)}$$

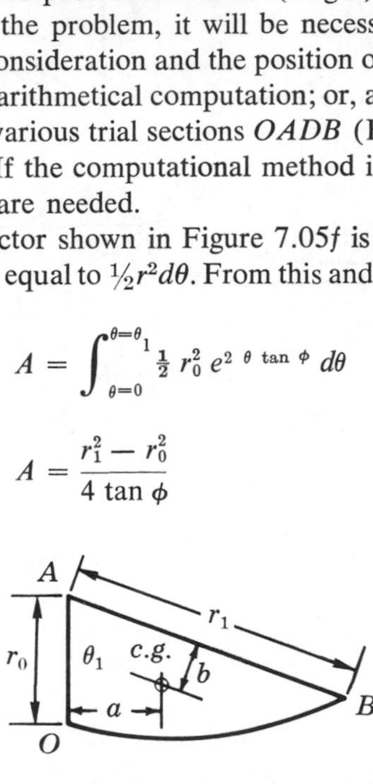

Figure 7.05f   Log spiral sector

The centroidal distances, a and b, have been given by Hijab as follows:

$$a = \frac{4}{3}r_0\,\frac{\tan\theta}{9\tan^2\phi + 1}\times\frac{\left(\dfrac{r_1}{r_0}\right)^3(3\tan\phi\sin\theta - \cos\theta) + 1}{\left(\dfrac{r_1}{r_0}\right)^2 - 1} \qquad \text{(Eq. 7.05c)}$$

$$b = \frac{4}{3}r_0\,\frac{\tan\phi}{9\tan^2\phi + 1}\times\frac{\left(\dfrac{r_1}{r_0}\right)^3 - 3\tan\phi\sin\theta - \cos\theta}{\left(\dfrac{r_1}{r_0}\right)^2 - 1} \qquad \text{(Eq. 7.05d)}$$

Hijab expressed these results in the form of dimensionless ratios, and presented tables and charts to facilitate their rapid determination. Generally, the properties of the spiral sector must be combined with those of two triangles to arrive at the needed weight and centroidal location. For example, in trial 1 (dashed) in Figure 7.05g, the spiral sector OKB' must be combined with triangles OAK and $B'AD'$.

If a mechanical procedure is used to find the centroid of the sliding wedge, the entire section $OADB$ may be treated. For example, suppose that each trial section $OADB$ is traced on uniformly thick cardboard, paper, acetate, etc. The section may be accurately weighed and the weight multiplied by an appropriate scale factor to find the weight of the soil;

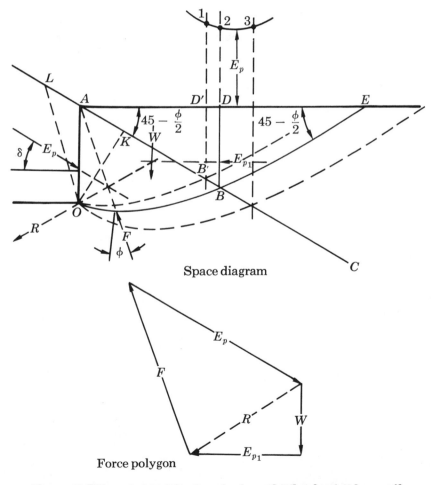

Space diagram

Force polygon

Figure 7.05g   Logarithmic spiral method cohesionless soil

and it may be suspended from a pin hole near each corner, in turn, tracing from the pin vertical lines that will intersect at the center of gravity.

Figure 7.05g shows that the solution for E_p is done in much the same way as for when a circular arc is assumed. However, the force F, instead of being tangent to a friction circle, is directed toward the center of the spiral. In the illustration, the solution for the second trial is shown, for which the center of the spiral is at A. For trials 1 and 3, respectively, the center of the spiral was at K and L. For every trial, the center must be on the line AC so that the spiral may pass smoothly to its tangent BE. The direction of F is fully determined by the positions of the center of the spiral, and of the intersection of R and E_p.

It is necessary to have a special template or pattern for each value of ϕ used in these analyses. For sands, ϕ will usually fall between 25° and 40°. In Figure 7.05h, four spirals have been drawn for possible use by the reader. The $r_0 = 1$ shown on the $\theta = 0$ line is merely for computational purposes, as r_0 may have any value. *Any* radius of the spiral may be designated r_0 for purposes of plotting the spiral onto a drawing. Thus the initial radii AO, KO, and LO for the three trials of Figure 7.05g all correspond to different positions of the $\phi = 30°$ spiral.

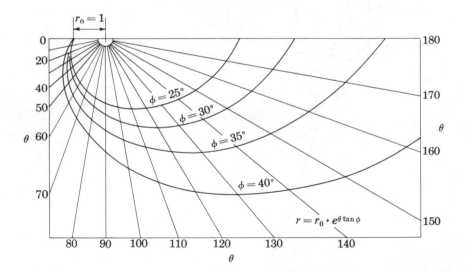

Figure 7.05h   Selected logarithmic spirals

7.06   *Earth Pressure of Cohesive Soils*

In general, it is probably wise to avoid the use of cohesive soil as back-fill material against retaining walls, primarily because of the difficulty of designing retaining walls that are both reliable and economical for this kind of soil. The strength properties of cohesive soils are subject to gross changes with time and climatic conditions. Clay backfills from which most of the water has dried may exert little or no pressure against even fairly high walls. If the same material begins to take on water, it swells. As it swells, the pressure against the wall may become very great, and considerable movement of the wall may be required before the pressure is reduced to the active pressure. Since such movement of the wall may not be entirely recoverable when the soil dries and shrinks, cracks may form between the soil and wall during dry periods, and fill with dust and soil. When the clay again becomes wet and swells, the wall is pushed another small increment of rotation. Thus, successive cycles of wetting and drying may in time topple the wall (as has frequently happened). When the use of cohesive backfill is unavoidable, detailed attention should be given to the provisions for drainage, the influence of seepage forces, method of placing the backfill, and measures for controlling variations in the water content of the backfill.

If it can be assumed that the soil has known properties that will not vary significantly during the life of the structure, procedures analagous to those used for cohesionless soils may be used to investigate the earth pressure against free standing walls. Additional forces due to the internal cohesion of the soil and its adhesion to the wall must be introduced into the analysis. Sometimes the adhesive force is (conservatively) omitted in the analysis on the assumption that it may be greatly reduced by the tendency of the soil to shrink away from the wall. If this should occur, there will be compensating changes in the soil properties. For this reason, it is believed that some adhesive force could be safely included in the analysis. Its limiting magnitude is governed by the unit cohesion c. This force, just as wall frictional resistance, can probably best be developed along a rough surface.

Most active failures in clay are characterized by a vertical (or nearly vertical) escarpment at the upper edge. Thus, it is prudent to assume that narrow shrinkage cracks may have opened to a depth of $\dfrac{2c}{\gamma_e} \tan\left(45 + \dfrac{\phi}{2}\right)$, or that tensile failure in this zone may precede the final slip. In Figure 7.06a, a general procedure based on successive trials is illustrated, the graphical methods used for cohesionless soils not being appropriate. Because of adhesion to the wall, the assumption that the slip surface is plane is farther from the truth than when a sand backfill is involved.

In Figure 7.06a, W_e is the weight of the soil mass $OABD$. The mass is held in equilibrium by the cohesion C, the adhesion C_a, the earth pressure E_a and the resultant F of the normal and frictional forces on the assumed slip surface. All of the forces act in a known direction and, except for E_a and F, are of known magnitude. Thus, the consruction of the force polygon to determine E_a is a simple matter. For low walls, it is quite possible that the analysis will indicate that the sense of E_a is opposite to that shown, signifying that the wall is not needed. However, the long term risk involved in omitting the wall has previously been discussed. One should not ignore in the analysis the possibility of water in the tension cracks producing hydrostatic pressure. In the chapter on stability of slopes, methods of investigating the stability of unbraced vertical cuts are discussed.

The passive earth pressure developed by cohesive soils may be investigated by the methods employing circular or spiral surfaces of potential

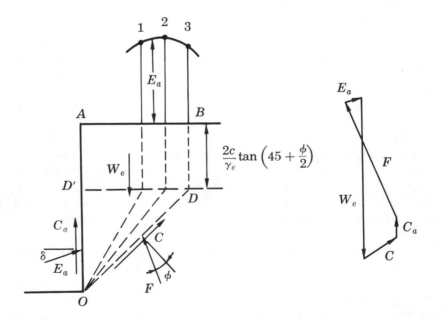

Figure 7.06a   Active earth pressure of cohesive soil

failure. It is usually convenient to consider the pressure E_p (resultant of normal and frictional forces on the wall) as being composed of two parallel parts: E_{p1}, due to the gravitational components of resistance; and E_{p2}, due to cohesive components. A procedure which may be followed when a circular failure arc is assumed is illustrated in Figure 7.06b. To avoid confusion, only one trial is shown.

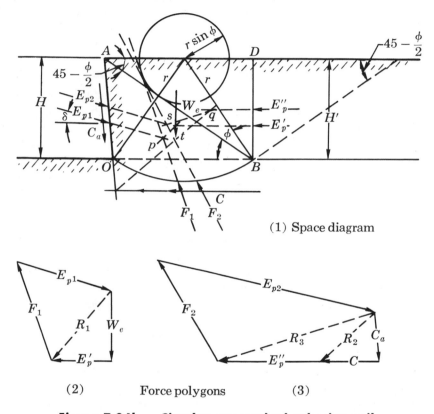

(1) Space diagram

(2)   Force polygons   (3)

Figure 7.06b   Circular arc method cohesive soil

The equilibrium of the soil mass $OADB$ under the action of the forces W_e, E'_p, E''_p, E_{p1}, E_{p2}, C, C_a, F_1, and F_2 is considered. Since the pairs (E_{p1}, E_{p2}) and (F_1, F_2) each represent one unknown force, the problem is statically determinate.

The solution is begun as if the soil were a cohesionless mass of weight W_e. The component E'_p of the passive Rankine pressure on BD due to the weight of the soil acts at the lower third point of BD, and the corresponding component of the passive pressure on the wall is E_{p1} acting at the lower third point of OA. As the force polygon, Figure 7.06b(2), is constructed to scale, the forces are laid out on the space diagram. Through t, the point of intersection of the lines of action of E_p' and W_e, a line is drawn parallel to R_1 to intersect the line of action of E_{p1} at point p. A line through p, tangent to the friction circle, determines the position and direction of F_1. The force polygon (2) may then be completed and E_{p1} found.

The soil is next treated as if it were a weightless mass having cohesive and adhesive properties. The component E_p'' of the passive Rankine pressure on BD due to cohesion $2cH' \tan \left(45 + \dfrac{\phi}{2} \right)$ acts at midheight of BD since the unit pressure, $2c \tan \left(45 + \dfrac{\phi}{2} \right)$, is independent of depth; i.e., uniformly distributed on BD. Similarly, the corresponding component E_{p2} of the passive pressure on the wall acts at mid-height of OA. The cohesive resistance C is equal to the unit cohesion c times the length of the chord OB, and is parallel to OB at a distance $r \cdot (\widehat{OB}/OB)$ from the center of the circle. The adhesive force C_a is equal to the unit adhesion c_a times the length OA, and is directed downward along the face of the soil mass. The force polygon (3) is begun by combining C_a and C into their resultant R_2. Through the point of intersection of C and C_a on the space diagram a line is drawn parallel to R_2 to intersect the line of action E_p'' at q. Through q a line is drawn parallel to R_3 (resultant of R_2 and E_p'') to intersect the line of action of E_{p2} at point s. A line through s tangent to the friction circle determines the position and direction of F_2 and permits completion of the force polygon (3).

The two force polygons of Figure 7.06b may be superimposed during construction in such a way that E_{p1} and E_{p2} are plotted head to tail along the same line, but there is no particular advantage in this. In any case, E_{p1} and E_{p2} are combined into a resultant E_p whose position between E_{p1} and E_{p2} is determined by the relative magnitudes of E_{p1} and E_{p2}. As in all preceding analyses, the results of at least three distinct trials must be studied to determine the minimum (critical) values of E_p.

If a logarithmic spiral is chosen to represent the slip surface, an analytical analysis in which moments are summed with respect to the center of the spiral is probably more convenient than a graphical solution. However, it is still simpler to accomplish the solution by parts, determining E_{p1} and E_{p2} separately as in the circular arc analysis. The principal difference in the two cases is in the determination of the cohesive resistance C.

In Figure 7.06c note that an infinitesimal length of arc is $ds = r(d\theta/\cos \phi)$. The cohesive resistance along ds is given by the product of the unit cohesion c and the arc length ds. Thus $dC = cr \, (d\theta/\cos \phi)$. The

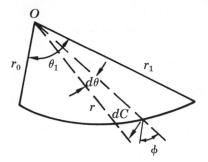

Figure 7.06c   Moment due to cohesion

moment of dC with respect to the center O of the spiral is found by re-
solving dC into two components, one directed along the radius toward O,
and the other perpendicular to the radius. The component perpendicular
to the radius is $dC \cos \phi = cr\, d\theta$. Thus,

$$dM_c = cr^2 d\theta$$

$$M_c = \int_0^{\theta_1} cr^2 d\theta = cr_0^2 \int_0^{\theta_1} e^{2\theta \tan \phi}\, d\theta$$

from which

$$M_c = \frac{c}{2 \tan \phi}(r_1^2 - r_0^2) \qquad \text{(Eq. 7.06}a\text{)}$$

Figure 7.06d shows two free body diagrams set up for the solution of
one trial. Part (1) of the figure treats gravitational components while
part (2) treats cohesive components. It is possible to treat all of these
forces at once, on a single free body diagram, but two independent equations of equilibrium would have to be solved simultaneously. By using
separate treatments, moments may be summed about O for each part,
yielding the two equations

$$E_{p1}d_1 = W_e d_2 + E_p' d_3$$
$$E_{p2}d_4 = M_c + E_p'' d_6 - C_a d_5 \qquad \text{(Eq. 7.06}b\text{)}$$

Equations 7.06b may be solved independently for E_{p1} and E_{p2} since all
other forces are known. These solutions are then added to obtain their resultant E_p. Other trials produce different values, generally, so that the
results of different trials must be studied to find the desired minimum
value for E_p.

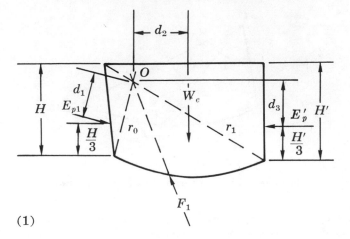

(1)

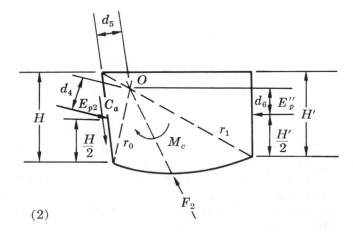

(2)

Figure 7.06d   Free body diagrams for spiral solution

7.07   Location of Critical Surface Analytically

Much of the time spent in making the solutions discussed in preceding sections is consumed in the repetitious work involved in making the successive trial solutions. Considerable advantage could be gained if, somehow, the critical slip surface could be defined in advance, so that a single

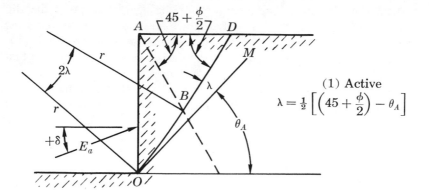

$$(1)\ \text{Active}$$
$$\lambda = \tfrac{1}{2}\left[\left(45 + \frac{\phi}{2}\right) - \theta_A\right]$$

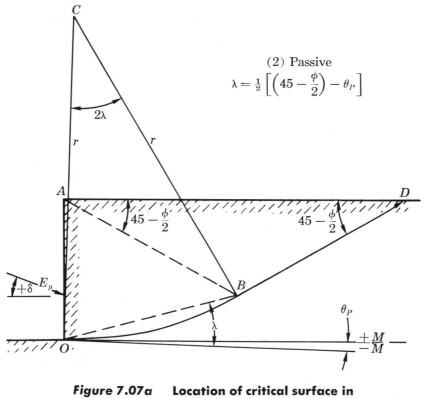

$$(2)\ \text{Passive}$$
$$\lambda = \tfrac{1}{2}\left[\left(45 - \frac{\phi}{2}\right) - \theta_P\right]$$

Figure 7.07a   Location of critical surface in cohesionless soil

analysis (graphical or otherwise) would yield the maximum E_a or the minimum E_p. Such a procedure is possible if consideration is limited to a particular mathematical representation of the general shape of the slip surface. For example, the slip surface trace might be assumed to consist of a circular arc smoothly joined to a straight line, as in Section 7.05b(1).

Based on the assumption just described, with the further limitation that the slopes of the tangents to the surface at the extremities of the circular arc are as indicated in Section 7.04. A. F. Abdul-Baki has made a general solution for the problem. His work covered both cohesionless and cohesive soils and included sloping, as well as horizontal, backfill surfaces. The solution consists of a number of graphs which provide data that permits the critical surface to be plotted at once. Figure 7.07a illustrates Abdul-Baki's procedure.

In the solution for the active case, Figure 7.07a(1), the slope angle θ_A of the tangent OM to the critical arc OB is obtained from Figure 7.07b. θ_A depends only on the angle of wall friction δ and the angle of internal friction ϕ of the backfill soil. With the value of θ_A obtained from Figure 7.07b, the angle λ is determined as shown in the figure. The chord OB of the arc OB is now obtained by constructing the angle $MOB = \lambda$ to

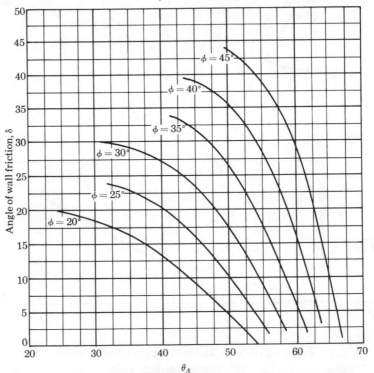

Figure 7.07b $\delta - \theta_A$ **relation for cohesionless backfill—**
After A. F. Abdul-Baki

define the point B where the chord intersects a line extending downward from A at an angle $45 + (\phi/2)$. Since the central angle of the arc is 2λ, the radius r may be easily computed when the length of chord is known. If desired, the center of the arc, C, can be found geometrically and the arc OB drawn. With the critical arc established, one trial as in Section $7.05b(1)$ suffices to determine E_a. The resultant F for the active pressure case is, of course, tangent to the opposite side of the friction circle than for the passive case illustrated in Section $7.05b(1)$. In the active case, the results differ only slightly from those obtained when a plane surface of failure is assumed.

A similar procedure for the passive case is illustrated in Figure $7.07a(2)$. In this case, AB and BD slope at $45 - (\phi/2)$, the angle θ_P is found from Figure $7.07c$, and λ is found as indicated in Figure $7.07a$. Note that θ_P may be either positive or negative; the expression for λ requires that the proper algebraic sign for θ_P be used. Note also that λ is plotted from the line OM so that, always, $\lambda = \angle MOB$. E_p is found from a single trial of the kind described in Section $7.05b(1)$.

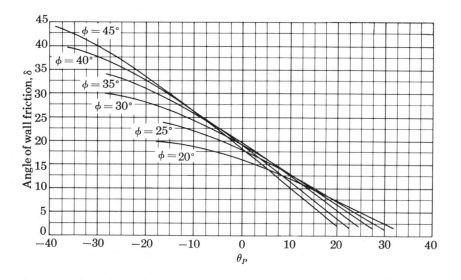

Figure 7.07c $\delta - \theta_p$ **relation for cohesionless soil—**
After A. F. Abdul-Baki

7.08　Uniform Surcharges

The effect of a uniform surcharge acting over the surface of a back-fill is to increase the resultant pressure against the retaining wall and to shift its line of action upward. The influence of the surcharge can be simply illustrated by writing the general expression for the pressure on a horizontal plane at depth z beneath the surface of a loaded area of infinite extent. Thus, $\sigma_z = q + \gamma_e z$, where q is load per unit area of surface. In general, the active pressure on a vertical plane is then

$$\sigma_a = -2c \tan\left(45 - \frac{\phi}{2}\right) + (q + \gamma_e z) \tan^2\left(45 - \frac{\phi}{2}\right)$$

It may be seen that the pressure is dependent upon two factors, c and q, that are independent of depth, and one factor, $\gamma_e z$, that varies in direct

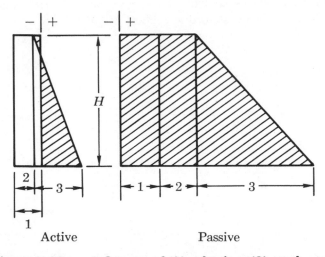

Figure 7.08a　**Influence of (1) cohesion, (2) surcharge, and (3) unit weight**

proportion to the depth. The nature of these influences is the same in the case of passive pressure, but the magnitude is greatly increased by the fact that the first term in the expression for σ becomes positive, and the angular function changes from $\left(45 - \frac{\phi}{2}\right)$ to $\left(45 + \frac{\phi}{2}\right)$. Figure 7.08a is a graphical illustration of the distribution of pressure against a free standing wall, the shaded areas representing an algebraic summation. Note that q and γ_e always exert a positive influence, whereas the influence of c is positive only for passive pressure.

Application of Culmann's graphical method for determining the active pressure of a surcharged, cohesionless backfill is illustrated in Figure 7.08b(1). Each increment of force plotted along the ϕ-line represents the weight of a soil wedge plus the total surcharge force acting on the surface of that wedge. The influence curve OCF represents the combined effects of soil weight and surcharge, whereas the curve $OC'F'$ represents the effect of soil weight alone. Thus the difference in EC and $E'C'$ represents the increase in E_a resulting from the presence of the surcharge. The failure surface is OCB.

It is apparent that the magnitude of the increase in E_a diminishes as the wall side boundary of the surcharged area moves toward the right from A. If the edge of the surcharge is at some point such as N in Figure 7.08b(2), the part OM of the influence curve depends only on the soil weight. At M (on the ray ON), a break in the curve appears, reflecting the influence of the surcharge.

If a tangent to the branch OM can be drawn parallel to the ϕ-line, the curve has passed one maximum point, and it is then necessary to note

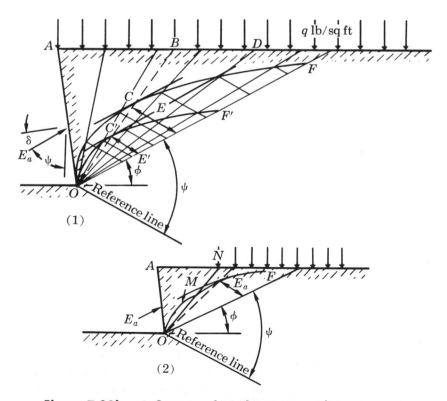

(1)

(2)

Figure 7.08b   Influence of surcharge on active pressure

whether any part of the branch MF lies above this tangent. If so, a greater (controlling) maximum point exists on MF; if not, the maximum on OM controls, and E_a is not influenced by the surcharge, nor is the position of the failure surface affected by it.

The method of solution illustrated is applicable to cases involving loaded areas of finite extent within the region AD when the influence curve OCF is drawn for the particular conditions of the problem. However, if the loaded area (or areas) becomes rather narrow in comparison with the height of the wall, it may be more appropriate to treat it as a line load.

The position of the line of action of E_a is influenced by the loading on the surface. If the entire surface of the fill is subjected to the surcharge, that part of E_a due to the surcharge acts at mid-height of the wall, while that part due to the soil weight acts at the lower third point. The resultant E_a of these two parts will then be some place between the mid-point and the lower third point, its exact location depending upon the relative magnitudes of the two component parts.

7.09   Line Loads Parallel to a Wall

It sometimes happens that there are loading conditions, such as continuous footing foundations parallel to a wall, or rows of parked vehicles, which may be reasonably approximated by a line load parallel to the wall. It is again convenient to employ the Culmann procedure to investigate the influence of the external loading.

In Figure 7.09a, let the curve $OC'F'$ represent the Culmann curve for the soil weight only, while $OC'CF$ is the Culmann curve including a line load of p lb ft^{-1} parallel to the wall at a distance AB from the wall. To some scale, OE' is the weight of the soil wedge $OAB + p$; i.e., $EE' = p$. For convenience, assume that C' is a point on the Culmann curve at which a line parallel to the ϕ-line is tangent. Then $EC' = E_a$ if no external loading exists. However, the addition of line load p results in an increase of pressure on the wall such that the Culmann curve rises from C' to C on the ray OB. If, for the moment, it is assumed that a tangent at C will either be parallel to the ϕ line or will intersect it to the right of E', then the active pressure including the effect of p is $E_a = E'C$. The effect of p on E_a is $\Delta E_a = E'C - EC'$.

The influence of p on E_a depends to some extent upon the position of p along the surface AD. If the point B (where p is applied) is assumed to occupy successively all possible positions between A and D, it will be found that there is one position B' for B for which the corresponding

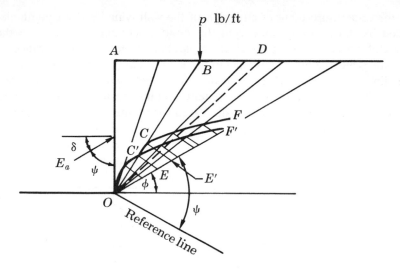

Figure 7.09a   Influence of line load on active pressure

tangent at C is parallel to the ϕ-line. Indeed, if p is anywhere to the left of B' the Culmann curve will have the same maximum point, so that $\Delta E_a = E'C - EC'$ for all positions of p between A and B'. However, as p moves from B' toward D, the corresponding $E'C$ will diminish. Let the ray OD be the one which cuts curve CF at the same point that CF is intersected by a tangent to $OC'F'$ parallel to the ϕ-line. Obviously, if p occupies any point to the right of D, the corresponding $E'C$ is less than EC', the maximum value of E_a due to soil weight alone. To the right of D, therefore, p has no influence on E_a nor on the position of the failure surface. CF and $C'F'$ are not quite parallel curves since the distance $C'C$ not only does not increase as the ray OB moves to the right, but in fact decreases to maintain a required constant projection on the ϕ-line.

To summarize the preceding, let it now be understood that at point C in Figure 7.09a a tangent to the curve CF is parallel to the ϕ-line. If p acts at any point to the left of B, $E_a = E'C$ and the failure plane is OB. If p acts at any point between B and D, E_a is given by the distance between the ϕ-line and the curve CF, in a direction parallel to the reference line; and the failure surface is a ray from O to the point of application of p. If p is to the right of D, it has no influence, and EC' (where C' is the maximum point on $OC'F'$) determines E_a.

While the magnitude of E_a is governed by the requirements stated above, its position along OA steadily rises as p approaches A. Its position may be approximated by assuming that the part EC' due to the soil weight acts at the lower third point of the wall, while the part ΔE_a due to p acts at the upper third point of a portion of the wall lying between points defined by drawing two lines from the point where the load acts on the backfill surface. One of the lines is parallel to the potential surface of failure, while the other is parallel to the ϕ-line. The procedure for locating the line of action of ΔE_a is illustrated in Figure 7.09b for the case when p acts between A and B and the potential failure surface is QB. If p acts between B and the point D (as discussed for Figure 7.09a), the location

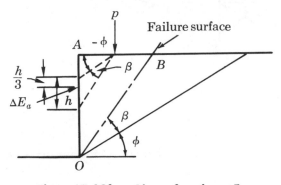

Figure 7.09b   Line of action ΔE_a

of the failure surface then depends on the position of p, extending from O to the point where p acts. Thus, the dimension h, in this case, has O as its constant lower limit, whereas its upper limit is found as in Figure 7.09b.

A more detailed study of the distribution of pressure on a wall, not only for the loading conditions just considered, but in general, may be made by assuming that every point along OA is at the foot of a potential surface of failure. Then, using procedures identical to those discussed for full height walls, the total earth pressure E_{a1}, E_{a2}, E_{a3}, etc., corresponding to wall faces AO_1, AO_2, AO_3, etc., may be found as point O is placed at successively greater distances from A. Generally, E_{a1} is assumed to vary uniformly over AO_1 with the pressure being zero at A, and the difference $E_{a(n+1)} - E_{an}$ is assumed to vary uniformly over the height of face $AO_{n+1} - AO_n$. If the distances $AO_{n+1} - AO_n = \Delta H$ are taken sufficiently small, the series of trapezoidal pressure diagrams produced will give a detailed picture of the distribution of pressure on the wall.

7.10   Backfill with Broken Surface

When the surface of the backfill cannot be defined by a single plane, the methods previously discussed for the sliding wedge can still be em-

ployed. For example, the Culmann curve is constructed following the
procedure of Section 7.05a(2). However, no special effort is made to
choose rays that subdivide the wedge into parts of equal weight. The
magnitude of E_a is affected by the surface configuration, but the effect
is accounted for by the method of solution and requires no special com-
ment. It is more important to recognize that the surface configuration influences the position of the resultant earth pressure E_a. The position of
E_a may be established by a detailed analysis of the kind described in
the last paragraph of Section 7.09. However, for practical purposes the
position of E_a may be found by simpler means.

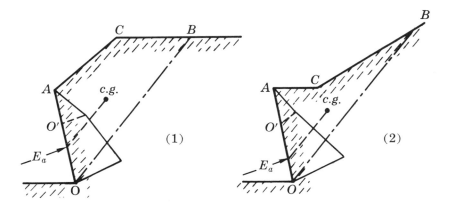

Figure 7.10a   Position of E_a when surface is broken

Figure 7.10a represents two possible ways in which the surface of a
backfill may be broken. If the surface were one of continuous curvature,
or even irregularly broken, the same method of solution for E_a could be
used. Suppose that OB in Figure 7.10a is the critical slip surface associated with the active pressure E_a on the wall OA. The line of action of E_a
may be found approximately by drawing a line through the center of
gravity of the soil mass parallel to OB. This line intersects the wall surface OA at about the same point as does the line of action of E_a. When
the surface is convex upward, as in (1), E_a acts above the lower third
point of the wall. When the surface is concave downward, as in (2), E_a
acts below the lower third point. The implied pressure distributions in the
two cases have been lightly shaded in the figure. That these are qualitatively reasonable follows from the fact that in (1) the increase in pressure
near the top of the wall is governed by the slope of AC, whereas below
some point O' the increase is less because it is governed by the horizontal

slope CB. Converse reasoning may be applied to the distribution shown in (2).

7.11   Wall with Broken Back

Gravity walls, and high retaining walls of most kinds, often contact the soil along a surface consisting of two or more intersecting planes. In gravity walls, the cross-section chosen in design is one in which such a broken surface is present on the backfill side of the wall. On the other hand, walls such as cantilever, buttressed, etc., that rest on broad base foundations often cannot conceivably rotate without incorporating a certain portion of the backfill as an integral part of the wall. For example, if the cantilever wall in Figure 7.11a should fail by rotation about its base, some part of the soil such as $OO'D$ must move with the wall. Slippage along contact surface $AO'O$, in this case, consists partly of a movement of the concrete wall relative to the backfill soil, and partly of a shearing failure through the backfill soil along OO'. In the analysis, it may be desirable to use different angles of wall friction δ along AO' and $O'O$, al-

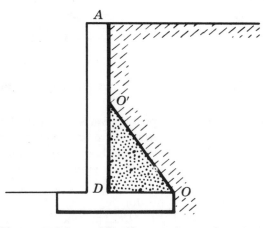

Figure 7.11a   Effective surface of contact

though this need not necessarily be done. In any case, the resultant earth pressures on AO' and $O'O$ will generally have different directions, which complicates the analysis.

In the analysis of this problem, a Culmann curve is used to find the pressure against the upper part of the wall, and an Engesser envelope [constructed somewhat differently than was done in Section $7.05a(3)$] is constructed for the lower part of the wall. Figure $7.11b$ illustrates the graphical solution of the problem. In the upper region of part (1) of the figure, a Culmann curve is drawn, following the usual procedure, to determine the active pressure E_{a1} on the upper part of the wall $O'A$. Next, an Engesser envelope is constructed for the entire wall $OO'A$, utilizing the entire mass of soil retained by the wall. In the space diagram, part (1), the rays Ob, Oc, . . ., Oi are drawn. Then the lines $P1$, $P2$, . . ., $P8$ are constructed so as to form an angle ϕ with the normals to the rays, Ob, Oc, . . ., Oi, respectively. The Engesser envelope (2) may now be constructed by laying off to scale along a vertical line the vectors $G\text{-}1$ = weight of OAb, $1\text{-}2$ = weight of Obc, etc., and drawing through the points 1, 2, . . .8 in (2) lines parallel, respectively, to lines $P1$, $P2$,. . .$P8$ in (1).

The active force E_a on the wall may be formed from its two components E_{a1} and E_{a2}, both acting in known directions. Since the magnitude of E_{a1} is known, its vector may be laid out to terminate at G. E_{a2} must extend from the Engesser envelope to the tail of vector E_{a1}, and E_a is shown as the resultant of these two. The failure surface does not necessarily coincide with one of the trial rays; but if it is assumed that the line $6\text{-}F$ is tangent to the Engesser envelope, the critical surface is Og, and the corresponding force polygon is $G\text{-}6\text{-}F\text{-}G$.

To determine the position of the line of action E_a, a line through the center of gravity of $OO'Ag$ may be drawn parallel to Og to intersect OO'. This point of intersection approximately establishes the position of E_a at the wall, and its direction is known from the Engesser construction. Alternatively, the method demonstrated in Figure $7.11a(3)$ can be used. With the magnitude of E_{a1} known, the pressure p_1 parallel to E_{a1} at O' may be determined on the basis of an assumed linear distribution of pressure on AO'. At the same point, it is reasonable to assume that the pressure p_2 parallel to E_{a2} is such as to make $p_2 = p_1/\cos \omega$. With p_2 thus established, and the magnitude of E_{a2} known from the Engesser construction, the pressure p_3 parallel to E_{a2} at O can be found. E_{a2} must act through the center of pressure of the trapezoid whose height is p_2 at O' and p_3 at O. The lines of action of E_{a1} and E_{a2} are extended to their intersection x, and the line of action of E_a passes through x in a direction parallel to FG.

It is deserving of mention that some recent wall designs have employed one or more horizontal shelves extending into the backfill. Often these are employed in connection with counterfort walls, as in Figure $7.11b$, although cantilever designs may also be made. Although no new principles are involved, the design has several advantages. It insures the incorporation of a substantial mass of earth as an effective part of the wall; earth pressures against lower vertical parts of the wall are greatly

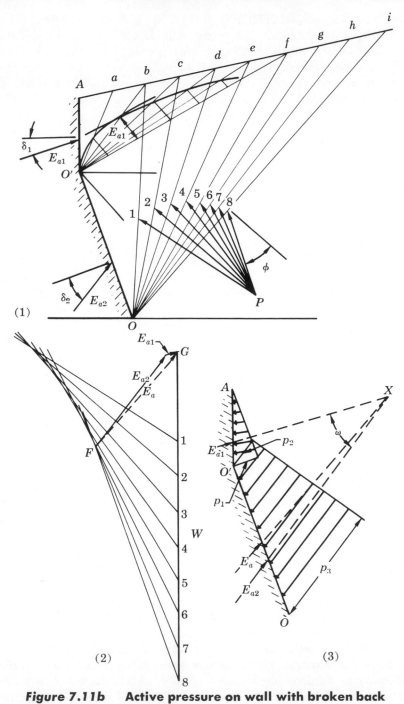

Figure 7.11b   Active pressure on wall with broken back

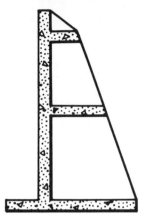

Figure 7.11c   Counterfort wall with shelves

reduced, making for economy in design; the shape of the potential slip surface between wall and soil is effectively controlled, simplifying analysis; and δ is effectively controlled almost exclusively by soil properties rather than by wall surface properties.

7.12   Influence of Water

For the sake of simplicity, the possible influence of water has been ignored in the preceding sections describing methods for determining earth pressures. It should not, however, be inferred that this influence is unimportant. It is probably accurate to say that a majority of retaining wall failures can be ascribed to the effects of static or flowing water acting in conjunction with those forces, or influencing those properties, upon which the design was based.

One of the most obvious causes of failure is the additional thrust arising from the permanent or temporary accumulation of static water behind a wall. In such cases, the unit weight of the soil below the water table is reduced by submergence so that the wall pressures due to the earth forces are smaller than those due to dry soil. But, when these forces are combined with the hydrostatic pressure of water acting perpendicular to the wall, the wall is subjected to a resultant force substantially greater than that of the active earth pressure alone. There may also occur a slight reduction in the angle of internal friction of cohesionless soil, but this reduction is smaller than the usual inaccuracies involved in the original

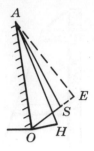

Figure 7.12a   Hydrostatic effects

selection of the value of ϕ to be used in the design. In Figure 7.12a, if *OAE* represents the pressure of a nearly dry cohesionless soil, the effect of raising the water table to the top of the wall is to reduce the earth pressure to *OAS* and to impose the additional pressure *OAH* due to water. Not only is *OAH* greater than *SAE* in magnitude, but also its direction imposes a greater overturning moment on the wall. It is usually not difficult to avoid imposing such additional force. Walls should be provided with adequate, dependable toe drainage systems consisting of weep holes and drainage collection systems, all incorporated with properly designed filters. If, for some reason, such provisions cannot be made, this fact should be recognized when the wall is designed. The possibility that drainage outlets may freeze shut should not be overlooked.

Another of the effects of static water is the appreciable increase in wall pressure resulting from an accumulation of water in the capillary zone (above the phreatic surface) in fine grained soils. When silty or clayey soils are used as a backfill, the wall design should be based on the assumption that the soil will at times be saturated, even though good wall drainage is provided. More serious, and more difficult to evaluate, is the effect of this water on the strength properties of cohesive soils. Generally, the strength parameters determined from laboratory tests of soaked samples should be used in the design. Even so, the cyclic effects of alternate wetting and drying of the soil may result in a gradual dislocation and eventual collapse of the wall.

Finally, the effects of flowing water need to be considered. Often in addition to the sum of the influences discussed above, water percolating through the backfill toward the drainage system exerts internal seepage forces that increase the pressure against the wall. One way of evaluating seepage effects is to construct a flow net in accordance with the principles explained in Chapter 3. On the basis of the flow net, the distribution of

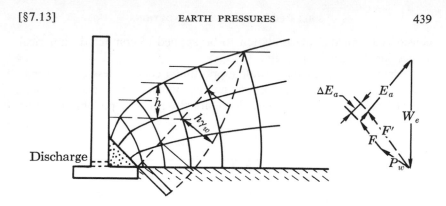

Figure 7.12b   Effect of seepage forces

hydrostatic pressure on any trial failure surface can be plotted. The hydrostatic head at any point along the trial surface is the vertical distance h between that point and the point where the corresponding equipotential line intersects the phreatic surface, as in Figure 7.12b. The hydrostatic pressure at the point is $h\gamma_w$. A resultant force P_w representing the distributed hydrostatic pressure may be incorporated in the equilibrium force polygon. The typical effect, as shown in Figure 7.12b, is to reduce the resultant normal and frictional force on the trial surface from F' to F and increase the active pressure by an amount ΔE_a. In this analysis, the saturated unit weight of the soil below the phreatic surface (and in fine grained soils above as well) should be used in computing W_e.

7.13   Wall Stability

The earth pressures not only govern the structural design of the wall itself, but also influence the dimensions and structural design of the wall foundation. Safety against sliding, overturning, and excessive settlement must be provided. All of these depend, at least partly, on the breadth of the foundation. It is customary to analyze for stability a wall having a foundation of reasonably assumed dimensions, and to adjust the dimensions, if necessary, in accordance with the results of the analysis. It is usually assumed that the upward pressure against the base varies linearly from heel to toe. Aside from those factors already mentioned in connection with the backfill material, the main elements of uncertainty in the analysis are the properties to be assigned to the foundation soil, the extent to which active and passive pressures of the foundation soil should be considered, and the interpretation to be applied to computed numerical values for the factor of safety.

Consider the stability of a wall supporting a cohesionless backfill material resting on a foundation soil having both cohesive and frictional properties; i.e., $s = c + \sigma \tan \phi$. There are often several possibilities to be

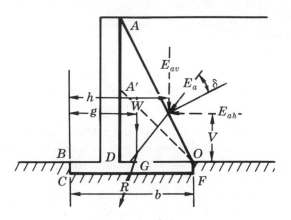

Figure 7.13a   Stability analysis

considered for the configuration of the failure surface between wall and soil in the case illustrated in Figure 7.13a. Separate analyses are required in investigating the stability when slippage along $OA'A$ is assumed in one trial and slippage along OA is assumed in another. In the illustration, the soil mass AOD is assumed to act as an effective part of the wall. The active pressure E_a per ft of wall length has been found using the methods of the preceding sections.

a.   Safety against Sliding

The horizontal force that tends to cause sliding along the base CF is the horizontal component E_{ah} of E_a. This is resisted by cohesion and friction on the base, and possibly by the passive earth resistance on CB (although it is probably best not to count on this unless it is certain that the soil there is intact and will always remain so). It is sufficient for the factor of safety against sliding to write

$$F.S._{\text{sliding}} = \frac{c_a b + (W + E_{av}) \tan \phi_a}{E_{ah}}$$

where

$\quad$ $F.S.$ = Factor of safety

$\quad$ W = Weight of wall, soil wedge AOD, and foundation

$\quad$ b = Breadth of base (CB)

$\quad$ c_a = Adhesion between base and soil

$\quad$ ϕ_a = Angle of frictional resistance between base and soil

If the factor of safety against sliding appears to be unreasonably low, it can be improved by extending a key downward below the base to call into play a reliable passive earth resistance.

b. Safety against Overturning

If the wall should more or less suddenly begin to tilt, the pressure on the base in the vicinity of F will be relieved, while the pressure near C will increase. In the extreme, it may be assumed crudely that the pressure along the base CF will have been reduced to zero, and that rotation occurs about C, where a very large concentrated force is presumed to act. Thus, the factor of safety against overturning is taken as the ratio of the moments, with respect to C, of the stabilizing forces W and E_{av} and the overturning force E_{ah}. Clearly, a factor of safety of unity is implied if the resultant R of W and E_a passes through C.

$$F.S._{\text{overturning}} = \frac{Wg + E_{av}h}{E_{ah}v}$$

where the quantities are as defined in Figure 7.13a. The presence of a key wall in the soil below the foundation slab introduces additional elements of uncertainty into the analysis, because the center of rotation to be used in the analysis must be chosen even more arbitrarily than before, and the nature of the pressures against the faces of the key is difficult to assess. At least, it may be safely assumed that the stability against overturning is not diminished by the presence of a key wall.

c. Bearing Capacity and Settlement

The ability of the foundation soil to carry safely the additional load imposed in a general way by the wall and backfill should be assessed (by the methods of Chapter 5) before any consideration is given to the detailed analysis and design of the wall. In the subsequent detailed design, the distribution of the pressure on the base of the foundation must be determined, and the implications in terms of bearing capacity and settlement have to be considered.

If the resultant force R in Figure 7.13a passes through the midpoint of CF, a uniform pressure equal to the vertical component of R divided by the breadth b is implied. As the position at which R cuts CF moves toward C, the pressure at C increases while that at F decreases. The distribution of pressure along CF is assumed to be linear. If R intersects CF within the middle third of its length, the resulting pressure prism is trapezoidal. The intensity of the pressure at C and F can be determined from the equations of static equilibrium, because the resultant pressure, $\frac{1}{2}(p_c + p_f)b$, must equal the vertical component of R, and its position coincides with the point where R intersects CF.

If R passes through the third point of CF nearest C, the pressure varies linearly from zero at F to a maximum of $2(R_v/b)$ at C. When R lies within the outer third of CF nearest C, a state of tension between soil and base adjacent to the opposite end is implied, as indicated in Figure 7.13b. However, such stresses will not develop; or, if developed, will not persist. Nevertheless, the maximum compressive stress CM will increase as the resultant moves toward C, and it is probably reasonable to assume that the volume of the stress prism CMN is equal to the vertical component of R.

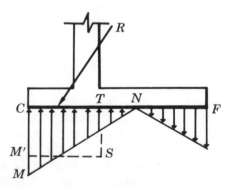

Figure 7.13b   Resultant outside of middle third

The theoretical distribution of pressure just discussed does not actually exist. The logarithmic relationship that exists between pressure and volume change of the soil results in a pressure redistribution as the soil yields by consolidation. The flexibility of the base also influences the pressure distribution. These effects tend to reduce the maximum pressure at C and to increase the pressures toward the middle of the base. An exact analysis of the conditions is impractical, if not impossible. In an analysis of the bearing capacity, it would be permissible to give qualitative recognition to these effects by analyzing a foundation of reduced width CT (Figure 7.13b) acted on by the stress prism $CM'ST$ (equal to CMN). No rules for formulating *CM'ST* are given here, as little factual data are available to serve as a guide.

In an analysis of the settlement, a principal concern is likely to be that of wall tilting. The overall effect of the wall and backfill is that of a terrace, with settlements at the boundary tending to be less than those in the interior, because the unloaded area outside the wall makes no contribution to the pressures causing settlement of the wall. Alone, this would tend to produce a rotation of the wall toward the backfill. This effect is slightly counteracted by the concentration of load at the terrace edge caused by the greater weight of the concrete. Most importantly, however, the usually greater pressures under the toe of the wall, due to the horizontal component of the pressure on the wall, tend to produce greater settlement at the toe. Provided that the terrace loading itself does not exceed the preconsolidation pressure of the foundation soil, the most significant effects are associated with the non-uniform distribution of pressure on the base of the foundation. Toe pressures in excess of the preconsolidation

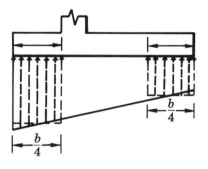

Figure 7.13c   Analysis of rotation

pressure of the soil may lead to appreciable outward rotation of the wall. The rotational tendency can be roughly determined by estimating the settlement of sections at the toe and heel, employing some method such as that illustrated in Figure 7.13c. If such an analysis indicates that the wall may tilt intolerably, the base dimensions may be altered to produce a more nearly uniform distribution of pressure. Methods for making settlement analyses were discussed in Chapter 4.

7.14   Braced Walls

A special problem in connection with earth pressure is associated with the use of braced walls to stabilize the vertical soil faces of trenches or other excavations. The classical earth pressure theories do not apply because the soil deformations permitted bear no resemblance to those assumed in the development of the theories. Hence, one must rely upon experience and the factual data obtained in a few controlled field tests.

Since the classical theories failed to provide the information needed to design the bracing for open cuts, there developed among practicing engineers, by the turn of the century, general, though possibly unjustified, dissatisfaction with the theories. The problem was thoroughly aired by Meem (1908) in a paper that attracted vigorous discussion. Almost without exception, the opinions expressed, based on solid evidence, indicated that the upper struts in braced cuts were much more heavily stressed, and the lower struts less severely stressed than would have been predicted on the basis of existing theories. Meem, and several of the discussers, presented theories that tended to provide results in conformity with the empirical knowledge at that time. The new theories, while enlightened and representing a substantial advance in the understanding of earth behavior, were conditioned by the individual experiences of those who proposed them and by the rather rudimentary concepts of soil properties that then existed. There was general agreement that cohesionless and cohesive soils required different treatment and that earth pressure and water pressure were dissimilarly distributed, requiring separate consideration. There was some disagreement concerning the angle of repose, which figured prominently in Meem's theory, and over the question of whether full or partial hydrostatic pressure would be exerted. This latter point, incidentally, was argued for many subsequent years in connection with the uplift pressures acting on the base of concrete and masonry dams.

a.   Cohesionless Soil

Terzaghi (1941) presented his General Wedge Theory which described the behavior of cohesionless soil behind a wall restrained at its top and yielding at the bottom. The theory takes arching into account, assumes that the center of pressure must lie near the midheight of the wall and that the angle of wall friction is known, and utilizes a spiral surface of sliding, intersecting the horizontal ground surface at 90°. The theory agrees well with observed phenomena. Terzaghi also discussed the results obtained in 1936 in measuring the lateral pressures against the bracing of an open cut in dense sand during construction of the Berlin subway. The measured pressure distributions were somewhat erratic, the discrepancies pointing to the fact that actual distributions are dependent not only upon the nature of the soil but also upon the sequence and care with which the braces are installed. These latter factors are not easily controlled in field situations, and pressure changes brought on by their variation cannot be reliably predicted. In spite of the erratic results mentioned above, the measurements showed that lateral pressure varied from zero at the surface to a maximum somewhere around mid-height, then to values that are substantially lower near the bottom, even when the sheathing penetrates several feet below the excavation. These results were in reasonable agreement with those that would be predicted by the general wedge theory.

Taking into consideration the results of the controlled field tests, as well as the results of large scale model tests conducted a few years previously, Terzaghi suggested the use of a trapezoidal distribution of lateral pressure for the design of bracing for open cuts in sand. Based on this earlier work, Terzaghi and Peck (1948) proposed that pressures of the magnitude and distribution shown in Figure 7.14a be used for the design of bracing for open cuts in dense sand. The diagram encompasses, for practical purposes, all of those pressure diagrams obtained in the Berlin tests.

In Figure 7.14a, the maximum pressure is taken as 0.8 times the horizontal component of the Coulomb active pressure intensity at depth H.

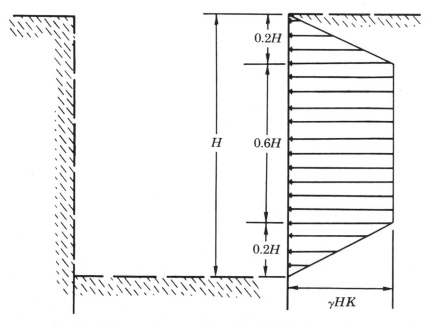

Figure 7.14a   **Assumed distribution of pressure on braced sheeting in dense sand —After Terzaghi and Peck**

For a vertical wall and horizontal backfill, the Coulomb total active pressure is

$$E_a = \frac{1}{2}\gamma_e H^2 \left[\frac{\cos\phi}{\sqrt{\cos\delta} + \sqrt{\sin(\phi+\delta)\sin\phi}}\right]^2 \qquad \text{(Eq. 7.14a)}$$

If $\delta = \phi$, this equation reduces to

$$E_a = \frac{1}{2}\gamma_e H^2 \frac{\cos\phi}{(1 + \sqrt{2\sin\phi})^2} \qquad \text{(Eq. 7.14b)}$$

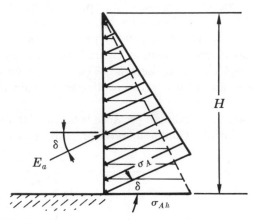

Figure 7.14b   Coulomb active forces

The Coulomb pressure E_a may be expressed as $E_a \cos\delta = \frac{1}{2}\sigma_{ah}H$, from which $\sigma_{ah} = (2/H) E_a \cos\delta$ (see Figure 7.14b). If the expression in Equation 7.14a is substituted in the preceding equation,

$$\sigma_{ah} = \gamma_e H \cos\delta \left[\frac{\cos\phi}{\sqrt{\cos\delta}\quad\sqrt{\sin(\phi+\delta)\sin\phi}}\right]^2 \qquad \text{(Eq. 7.14c)}$$

Since it is desired that $\gamma_e HK$ in Figure 7.14a be equal to $0.8\sigma_{ah}$, K is set equal to 0.8 times the coefficient of $\gamma_e H$ (note that $K = 0.8K_a$). K is a function only of ϕ and δ. The relationship among the three may be plotted in various ways, one of which is shown in Figure 7.14c. If K is found from this figure, the magnitude of the pressure $\gamma_e HK$ in Figure 7.14a may be easily determined. It is emphasized that the validity of this whole procedure has been firmly established only for dense sands.

Terzaghi and Peck (1948) have suggested that, for the purpose of estimating strut loads, the vertical wall be considered as hinged at the elevation of each strut, and treated as if it terminated at the bottom of

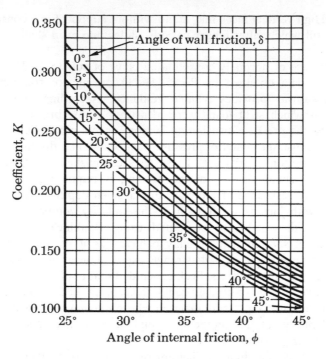

Figure 7.14c   Coefficient of lateral pressure for braced walls in dense sand

the excavation on a knife edge support. Since some margin of safety is already included in the pressure diagram, the factor of safety of the struts against buckling need not be set too high. The design of vertical members, for example sheet piling, supported by a system of wales and struts, may be based on the principle of continuity.

b.   Cohesive Soil

It is not possible to formulate general rules applicable to the pressures that will be exerted by cohesive soils. The behavior of overconsolidated clay, for example, is heavily influenced by the magnitude of the preconsolidation pressure and by the nature of the system of fissures or joints often found in this kind of clay. The pressures exerted against restraining walls are likely to vary considerably with time, to depend upon the kind of restraint initially imposed, and to alter radically with changing weather conditions. High vertical faces may stand without support for a considerable time in soil which, after longer periods, slides into even shallow excavations.

In the case of normally consolidated clays of soft to medium consistency, the data obtained by Peck (1943) during construction of the Chicago subway provides reliable guidance. According to the results of tests in which strut loads were measured in the bracing of several open cuts, the pressure distribution is more or less parabolic with depth. On the average, the center of pressure was located at a distance of 0.43H above the bottom of the cut. These tests established for the first time that only a small yielding of the bracing is required to develop the full shearing resistance of the clay. For a given depth of cut, pressures decrease with increasing strength of the soil. By comparing measured loads with the total load computed using Rankine's earth pressure theory, Peck showed that the clay behaved as if its angle of internal friction were zero and as if its strength were reduced about 25 per cent by progressive failure effects. Peck concluded that a safe (probably rather conservative) design of bracing could be accomplished on the basis of an assumed trapezoidal pressure diagram whose maximum ordinate depends on the depth of cut, and on the unit weight and average unconfined compression strength of the soil.

The pressure distribution diagram recommended by Peck (1943) is shown in Figure 7.14d. Peck suggested that the factor of 1.2 be used with

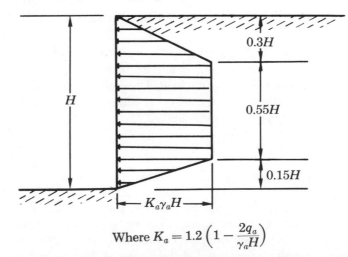

Where $K_a = 1.2 \left(1 - \dfrac{2q_a}{\gamma_a H}\right)$

Figure 7.14d   Assumed distribution of pressure on braced sheeting in normally consolidated clay

the Rankine value of K_a to compensate for scattering in the correlation of measured and computed values of total pressure. Terzaghi and Peck (1948) omit this factor. In the expression for K_a, q_a is the average value of the unconfined compression strength of good quality tube samples, and γ_a is the average unit weight of the soil. The depth of excavation should not exceed q/γ_e before the first row of bracing is installed, or the yield may become excessive.

For cohesive soils other than soft to medium normally consolidated clays, it is probably best to rely upon the empirical procedures for bracing developed from successful experience in the locality.

c. Water Pressure

Retaining walls used for temporarily stabilizing open cuts frequently contain openings in the form of cracks or joints so closely spaced that water pressure can never build up to appreciable magnitude behind the wall. However, this is not always the case. Therefore, the possibility that water may accumulate behind the wall must always be considered. If such a possibility exists, the bracing should be designed to withstand the full hydrostatic head of water in addition to the pressure that will be exerted by the soil. In this case, the soil will be buoyed by the presence of the water, so that the soil pressures may be computed on the basis of the submerged unit weight of the soil. The distribution of the soil pressure, however, will still not be hydrostatic, but in accordance with the principles previously discussed.

7.15 Anchored Bulkheads

In oceanside and riverside construction, it is frequently necessary to provide a reasonable depth of water immediately adjacent to a shore area where it is desired to unload or load ships or barges. At the same time, the land is generally built up to provide a level area for related activities and for storage. This dual aim is often satisfied by driving a row of sheet piling along the waterfront, and then dredging material from the water side and depositing (sometimes the same) material on the landward side. Such a row of sheet piling, driven some distance below the dredged depth and restrained near its top by tie rods anchored in the soil, is called an anchored bulkhead.

To a considerable extent, practices regarding the sizes of sheet piling and tie rods used and the depth to which the piling is driven have evolved on the basis of experience. Within the past twenty years, however, notable progress has been made in devising a theoretical approach to the solution of the problem. The theoretical advances have proceeded concurrently with experimental studies of model bulkheads and are related to the results of these studies. Because of the complexity of the problem, it is virtually impossible to devise a theoretical solution that correctly embraces all the factors involved. Probably the most difficult to evaluate with certainty is the true nature of the soil into which the piling will be driven and that which is to be used for the fill. Some of the other factors requiring evaluation are the kind of restraint imposed on the piling beneath the dredge line, the pressure exerted by the backfill, the influence of pile flexibility and tie rod yield, the angle of wall friction, and the effects of differences in the head of water on the two sides of the piling. Because of the uncertainties involved, a factor of safety of two or more is generally used in the design.

The purpose of this section is to provide a general knowledge of factors involved in the design of anchored bulkheads and to acquaint the reader with some of the design procedures. No one confronted with a major job involving bulkheads should proceed without studying the results of the excellent work of Tschebotarioff (1949), Rowe (1952), Hansen (1953), and Terzaghi (1954).

a.   Type of Earth Support

In the early development of methods for the design of bulkheads, use was made of the classical earth pressure theories in conjunction with some assumptions concerning the relative freedom of the embedded pile end to rotate. The two extreme concepts illustrated in Figure 7.15a and Figure 7.15b came to be recognized.

(1)   Free Earth Support

In the free earth support method it is assumed that no point of inflection, except just below the tie rod wale, occurs in the elastic curve of the pile. The resistance along the embedded portion consists entirely of the passive earth pressure acting on the water side of the pile. The simplicity of the computations associated with this assumption is attractive; but its reasonableness depends on the depth of embedment, the properties of the soil furnishing the resistance, and the stiffness of the pile.

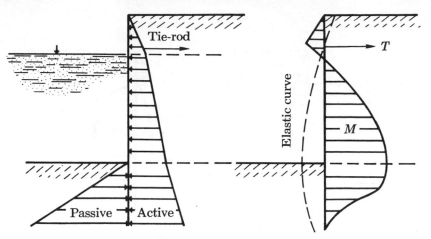

Figure 7.15a   Assumed earth pressure distribution free earth support

(2)   Fixed Earth Support

In the fixed earth support method, it is assumed that the depth of embedment is great enough to develop some degree of fixity at the lower end of the pile. There is some point along the embedded length about which the pile rotates, so that passive earth resistance acts on the water side of the pile above this point and on the landward side below the point. The elastic curve is forced to inflect somewhere between the point of rotation and the dredge line, resulting in a negative bending moment in the vicinity of the bottom and in a reduction of the positive bending moment as compared with a condition of free earth support. Obviously, this could result in some economy of design.

The experimental investigations of Tschebotarioff (1949) and Rowe (1952) disclosed that both the maximum bending moment and the anchor pull were usually smaller than would be predicted by the free earth support theory. Tschebotarioff proposed the use of a simple model that produces results in good agreement with much of the experimental work that has been done. His simplified "equivalent beam" procedure patterned after an earlier suggestion by Blum (1931), assumes a hinge at the dredge line. The required computations are quite easily made, for example see Tschebotarioff (1962).

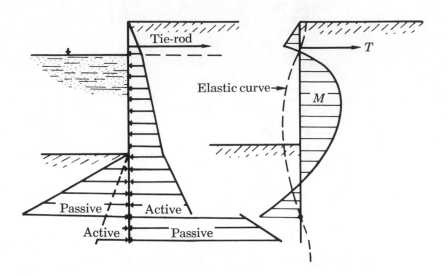

Figure 7.15b　**Assumed earth pressure distribution fixed earth support**

Rowe (1952) showed that the maximum bending moment and anchor pull depend upon the soil type, flexibility of the piling, and the ratios α and β that vary with depth of embedment and location of the tie rod wale. He suggested that these factors be introduced quantitatively into the computations by using sets of graphs relating these variables to the ratios M/M_{max} and T/T_{max}, where the max subscript refers to the maximum bending moment and anchor pull found by using the free earth support method. See Figure 7.15e for definition of α and β.

Terzaghi (1954), neglecting the small influence on M of changes in α and β for the usual ranges of these coefficients, presented simple graphs similar to those shown in Figures 7.15c and 7.15d which utilize the *flexibility number* $\rho = H^4/EI$ proposed by Rowe. Terzaghi also suggested the soil unit weights and earth pressure coefficients shown in Table 7.15a for use in making the free earth support computations. Rowe (1955) proposed a more reliable, but less readily applied, method of accounting for variations of the soil properties, utilizing a *soil stiffness modulus m.*

It should be noted that the earth pressure distribution assumed in either the free earth support or fixed earth support procedure is quite different from the actual distribution on real bulkheads. Nevertheless, satisfactory results may be obtained by using these assumed distributions in the man-

Table 7.15a
Unit Weights of Soils, and Coefficients of Earth Pressure
(After Terzaghi)

Type of soil	Unit weight[a] of moist soil		Unit weight[a] of submerged soil		Coefficient of active earth pressure, K_a			Friction angles[b]		Coefficient of passive earth pressure, K_p	Friction angles[b]	
	Minimum	Maximum	Minimum	Maximum	For back-fill	For soils in place		ϕ	δ	For soils in place	ϕ	δ
(1)	(2)	(3)	(4)	(5)	(6)	(7)		(8)	(9)	(10)	(11)	(12)
Clean sand:												
Dense.........	110	140	65	78		0.20		38	20	9.0	38	25
Medium........	110	130	60	68	0.35	0.25		34	17	7.0	34	23
Loose.........	90	125	56	63		0.30		30	15	5.0	30	20
Silty sand:												
Dense.........	110	150	70	88		0.25				7.0		
Medium........	95	130	60	68	0.50	0.30				5.0		
Loose.........	80	125	50	63		0.35				3.0		
Silt and clay[c]	$\dfrac{165(1+w)}{1+2.65w}$		$\dfrac{103}{1+2.65w}$		1.0	$1 - \dfrac{q_u}{\bar{p}+\gamma z}$				$1 + \dfrac{q_u}{\bar{p}+\gamma z}$		

a, In pounds per cu ft. *b*, These angles, expressed in degrees, are, ϕ the angle of internal friction, and δ the angle of wall friction, and are used in estimating the coefficients under which they are listed. *c*, The symbol γ represents γ or γ', whichever is applicable; p is the effective unit pressure on the top surface of the stratum; q_u is the unconfined compressive strength; w is the natural water content, in percentage of dry weight; and z is the depth below the top surface of the stratum.

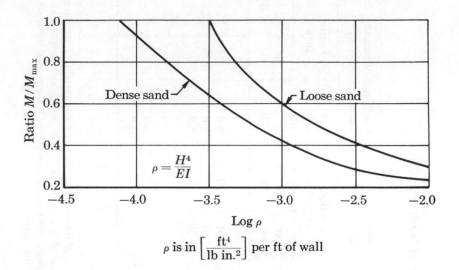

$$\rho = \frac{H^4}{EI}$$

ρ is in $\left[\dfrac{ft^4}{lb\ in.^2}\right]$ per ft of wall

Figure 7.15c **Relation between flexibility number ρ and anchor pull ratio—After Rowe**

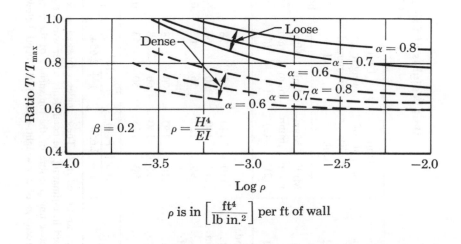

$$\rho = \frac{H^4}{EI}$$

ρ is in $\left[\dfrac{ft^4}{lb\ in.^2}\right]$ per ft of wall

Figure 7.15d **Relation between flexibility number and bending moment ratio— After Rowe**

ner outlined above. According to Hansen (1954) the results are usually more conservative than can be justified by experience. In the example which follows, the data and procedure proposed by Terzaghi are used. For procedures applicable to line loads or point loads acting on the fill, one may refer to Terzaghi (1954). When there is a differential head of water on the two sides of the bulkhead, the weight of soil on the active side can be increased and that on the passive side decreased in accordance with the seepage pressure accompanying the flow under the piling toward the water. According to Terzaghi, piling driven into silt or clay should be designed on the basis of free earth support without applying any moment reduction coefficient.

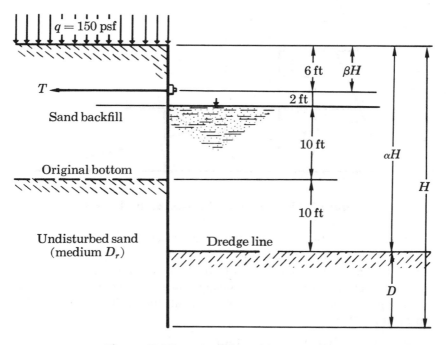

Figure 7.15e   Bulkhead installation

b.   *Example of Design*

Suppose that a 20 ft depth of water is to be provided by erecting an anchored bulkhead along a shore line where the water depth is presently 10 ft, and a clean sand of medium relative density exists to considerable depths beneath a nearly horizontal bottom. A storage area with a free-board of 8 ft is to provide a capacity for a uniform surcharge of 150 lb per sq ft adjacent to the bulkhead. Sand dredged from the bottom is to be used as a backfill. The position of the tie rod wale is set arbitrarily by overall anchorage considerations. Based on the conditions shown in Figure 7.15e, the length and section of the piling is to be determined, and the tie rod pull T found.

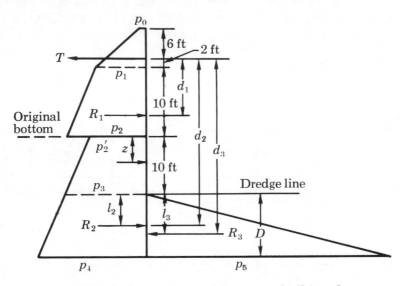

Figure 7.15f   Assumed forces on bulkhead

From Table 7.14a, choosing the most conservative values, $\gamma = 125$ lb ft^{-3}, $\gamma' = 63$ lb ft^{-3}, and $K_a = 0.35$ for the sand backfill; and $\gamma' = 68$ lb ft^{-3}, $K_a = 0.25$, and $K_p = 7.0$ for the undisturbed sand. A margin of safety will be introduced by applying a factor of safety F of 2 to the passive pressure (see p_5 below). First, evaluate the earth pressures: (refer to Figure 7.15f)

$$p_0 = qK_a = 150(0.35) = 52.5 \text{ psf}$$
$$p_1 = p_0 + \gamma h K_a = 52.5 + 125(8)0.35 = 402.5 \text{ psf}$$

Similarly,

$$p_2 = p_1 + 63(10)0.35 = 623 \text{ psf at bottom of fill}$$
$$p_2' = [150 + 125(8) + 63(10)]0.25 = 445 \text{ psf in undisturbed soil}$$
$$p_3 = p_2' + 63(10)0.25 = 615 \text{ psf}$$
$$p_4 = p_3 + 68(D)0.25 = 615 + 17D \text{ psf}$$
$$p_5 = \tfrac{1}{F}\gamma D K_p = \tfrac{1}{2}(68)D(7) = 238D \text{ psf passive pressure}$$

To determine the unknown depth of penetration D, moments are summed about T and equated to zero:

$$\Sigma M_T = 0 = R_1 d_1 + R_2 d_2 - R_3 d_3 \qquad \text{(Eq. 7.15a)}$$

where

$R_1 =$ resultant of all active pressures above dredge line

$R_2 =$ resultant of all active pressures below dredge line

$R_3 =$ resultant of all passive pressures below dredge line

$d_{1,2,3} =$ corresponding moment arms (see Figure 7.15f)

When the necessary computations are performed, it is found that

$$R_1 d_1 = 127,440 \text{ ft lb}$$
$$R_2 d_2 = 13,530D + 494.5D^2 + 5.67D^3 \text{ ft lb}$$
$$R_3 d_3 = 2618D^2 + 79.33D^3 \text{ ft lb}$$

Substituting these in Equation 7.15a, there results a cubic equation in D that can be conveniently solved by trial.

$$73.67D^3 + 2123.5D^2 - 13,530D = 127,440$$

Trial D	$f(D)$	Error
11	205,900	+78,460
10	150,720	+23,280
9	104,200	−23,240
9.5	126,800	− 640 Satisfactory root

A penetration of 9.5 ft would apparently provide a factor of safety of 2 against a passive earth failure. However, Terzaghi recommends that the depth of penetration be arbitrarily increased 20 per cent to safeguard against the effects of unintentional excess dredging, unanticipated local scour, and the presence of pockets of exceptionally weak material. Therefore, D will be set at 12 ft, necessitating a pile length of 40 ft. For this length, $\beta = 6/40 = 0.15$, and $\alpha = 28/40 = 0.7$.

The anchor pull T is obtained by summing forces in a horizontal direction for the equilibrium condition $(D = 9.5 \text{ ft})$.

$$T(\text{per ft of wall}) = R_1 + R_2 - R_3 \qquad \text{(Eq. 7.15a)}$$

Substituting the values $R_1 = 12,250$ lb, $R_2 = 6,600$ lb, and $R_3 = 10,750$ lb in Equation 7.15b, it is found that

$$T(\text{per ft}) = 12,250 + 6,600 - 10,750 = 8,100 \text{ lb}$$

From an examination of the pressure (force) diagram, Figure 7.15f, it is clear that the horizontal shear on the piling will be zero, and the bending moment a maximum, somewhere between the dredge line and the original ground surface. Let z represent the distance from the original surface to the point of zero shear in the piling. Then,

$$\frac{1}{2}(p_0 + p_1)8 + \frac{1}{2}(p_1 + p_2)10 + p_2'z + \frac{1}{2}(p_3 - p_2')\frac{z^2}{10} - T = 0$$

from which the following quadratic equation is obtained:

$$z^2 + 52.4z - 135.7 = 0$$

and $$z = 2.45 \text{ ft}$$

The maximum bending moment in the piling is now easily found by summing moments of all forces above a point 20.45 ft below the top of the piling. It is found that

$$M_{max} = 51,200 \text{ ft lb, or } 614,000 \text{ in. lb}$$

Terzaghi (1954) suggests that an allowable stress equal to $\frac{2}{3}$ of the yield point stress is reasonable in the case of steel sheet piles. If this is taken to be 27,000 psi, a section modulus of $614,000/27,000 = 22.8$ in.^{3} per lineal foot of wall is needed, if no permanent reduction is assumed. However, since there will probably be an allowable moment reduction due to flexibility, try a USS MP-110 arch web pile section. This section has the following properties: $S = 15.3$ in.^{3} ft^{-1} of wall, $I = 65$ in.^{4} ft^{-1} of wall, Wt. $= 32$ lb ft^{-2} of wall area (projected on a vertical plane).

For MP-110 pile, $\rho = \dfrac{H^4}{EI} = \dfrac{40^4}{30 \times 10^6 \times 65} = 0.00131$ ft^4 per lb in.^{2} per ft

$$\log \rho = \log (0.00131) = -2.882$$

From Figure 7.15b, M/M_{max} is approximately 0.5. Thus a section modulus of $0.5(22.8)$ is acceptable. Therefore, the MP-110 is satisfactory. However, it would be preferable to use a USS MZ-27 Z pile section having $S = 30.2$ in.^{3} per ft of wall, $I = 185$ in.^{4} per ft of wall, Wt. $= 27$ lb per sq ft of wall, even though the moment reduction factor is less favorable, because the MZ-27 is more than capable of taking the full free earth support moment. Moreover, it is more economical because it requires only 84 per cent as much steel as would be used in MP-110 piling.

According to Figure 7.15c, the anchor pull could be reduced to about $0.85(8,100)$ lb per ft of wall if the MZ-27 ($\log \rho = -3.336$) is used. However, the load on any given tie rod depends on a variety of factors besides the soil properties and flexibility number; e.g., inevitable disparities in the tie rod pulls due to unequal yielding of the supports. It is probably best, therefore, to design the tie rods and their anchors for the full free earth support pull of 8,100 lb, basing the size of bars on an allowable stress of 18,000 psi. Excessive yield of the tie rods or anchorages can be detrimental to the entire wall, and failure of one tie rod may lead to disaster. Spacing of the tie rods is determined by the size of bars finally selected.

c.   Precautionary Measures

The presence of large pockets of soil having less favorable properties than any discovered during the exploration is a possibility that diminishes with increased care and thoroughness of exploration. During exploration, the appearance of strata of different characteristics should be carefully noted, and their exact location and extent determined. In cohesionless strata, a reasonable number of standard penetration tests should be conducted, and cohesive strata should be sampled with thin wall sampling tubes so that their properties can be determined in the laboratory.

Contours of the bottom should be determined, with special attention given to contours that slope downward from the shore. Steep gradients in the slope produce marked differences in the passive resistance of the soil at the toe of the wall, and must be considered in the analysis.

Anchors for the tie rods may be provided in a variety of ways; by a second row of sheet piling, ordinary piles and batter piles, buried anchor blocks, or pile supported platforms. In any case, anchors should be set sufficiently far from the bulkhead so as not to be affected by the strains in the soil retained by the bulkhead. Tie rods, if buried, should pass through the backfill through openings or conduits that assure the absence of vertical forces on the rods in case the fill settles.

Problems connected with the desired life of the structure need also to be considered. The corrosivity of the environment may in some cases dictate the use of a special alloy steel. The installation should be subjected to periodic inspection throughout its life.

7.16   Anchor Blocks

Walls, plates, beams, and massive blocks buried in the soil are all occasionally used to provide anchorage for tie rods, guy wires, or, on a very large scale, suspension bridge cables. Their resistance to the imposed load is derived primarily from the passive resistance of the earth. Uncertainties exist as to how the anchor tends to move, the degree to which surface frictional forces may develop, the mass of earth that may be involved in any movement of the anchor, and the true pattern of potential rupture. These uncertainties, together with the doubt that always exists regarding soil properties and the magnitude of anchor movement that can be tolerated, lead to errors of unknown magnitude in any proposed theoretical design procedure.

Most of the applicable experimental and theoretical data have been derived from studies that dealt with retaining walls. There is, however, a great body of successful experience with the design and construction of anchors of all sizes. Apparently, the usual design methods, however crude and uneconomical, are generally safe, although excessive yield of anchorages has sometimes led to more serious difficulties.

In the case of tie rod anchors, the anchor wall should be set far enough from the bulkhead to ensure that the passive resistance wedge of the anchor does not encroach upon the active wedge of the soil supported by the wall. For full effectiveness, the anchor should lie entirely outside the wedge of soil bounded by the bulkhead and a plane rising from the toe of the bulkhead (in sand) at an angle of ϕ with the horizontal. In all anchor designs, a factor of safety of not less than 2 should be employed to guard against the possibility of excessive yield. Whenever possible, it is preferable to cast anchor blocks in contact with undisturbed soil, particularly if cohesive soil is involved.

a.   Anchors in Sand

In the case of tie rod anchors, which are generally subjected to a horizontal pull, the very simple analysis illustrated in Figure 7.16a may be used. It is assumed that the wall, or individual plate or block, extends downward from the surface to a depth H and that the tie rod is attached at the lower third point. The frictional forces which develop on the vertical faces as the passive wedge tends to be displaced upward and the active wedge downward are (conservatively) neglected. The frictional resistance along the base is also neglected unless the anchor wall or block is a rather massive concrete structure. Thus, the allowable pull on the tie rod is taken simply as the difference in the passive and active Rankine pressures, divided by an appropriate factor of safety F. For tie rod spacing L along an anchor wall, or breadth L of an anchor block, the allowable pull is

$$T = \frac{\gamma_e H^2 L}{2F}(K_p - K_a) \qquad \text{(Eq. 7.16a)}$$

where

$$K_p = \tan^2\left(45 + \frac{\phi}{2}\right) \text{ and } K_a = \tan^2\left(45 - \frac{\phi}{2}\right)$$

If the anchor is buried beneath the surface of the soil and the tie rod attached at mid-height, as in Figure 7.16b, the pattern of failure which develops is quite different from that which corresponds to the conditions shown in Figure 7.16a. Nevertheless, according to Terzaghi (1943), the

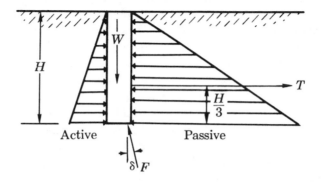

Figure 7.16a   Anchor wall in sand—horizontal pull

pull that can be developed is not significantly different from that of the wall in Figure 7.16a, provided that the height H' of the wall is not less than one-half the depth H to the base of the wall. Thus, Equation 7.16a may be used directly in such cases. On the other hand, if H' is small in comparison with H, failure of the anchor support more nearly resembles a bearing capacity failure with the anchor being dragged through the soil. In this case, the procedures used in the analysis of the bearing capacity of footings are more appropriate than the procedures described above. A procedure, based on the theory of elasticity, for estimating the movement

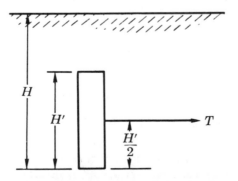

Figure 7.16b   Buried anchor

of buried rigid anchor plates subjected to horizontal pulls at their midpoints has been suggested by Douglas and Davis (1964).

The design of anchor blocks for guy cables must be attacked in a different manner. Usually, the weight of the block is such as to deserve consideration; and because of the vertical component of the guy tension the block tends to move upward relative to the soil, developing a negative angle of wall friction on the passive resistance face. The error associated with the assumption of a plane surface of failure on the passive side, in the event δ is not small, is on the unsafe side. Therefore, it is better to employ a procedure in which a curved failure surface is assumed. A simple graphical solution, using the ϕ-circle method, is illustrated in Figure 7.16c.

The block in Figure 7.16c has a breadth b and is buried in the soil to its full depth H. It is assumed that ϕ and δ are known. The active and passive pressures are both assumed to be distributed hydrostatically on the vertical faces so that E_a and E_p act at the lower third points. The guy wire acts at angle α to the horizontal and is attached to the block so as to pass through the plane of the passive face at a distance $d = (b/2)$ (tan α − tan δ) above the lower third point. The resultant of the normal and frictional forces on the base is F_1. According to the assumptions made, static equilibrium is assured by the system of concurrent forces acting on the block. The active pressure is computed by means of Coulomb's formula, Equation 7.14a. The forces T_1, E_p, and F_1 are known in direction, but not in magnitude.

Using the procedure shown in Figure 7.16c(3) and (4), the magnitude of E_p may be determined. E_p'' on the soil face H' is determined from the Rankine formula, $\frac{1}{2}\gamma_e(H')^2 \tan^2\left(45 + \frac{\phi}{2}\right)$. The force F_2 passes through the point of intersection of the lines of action of E_p and the resultant R_2 of the forces W_2 and E_p', and is tangent to the ϕ-circle. Thus, the magnitude of E_p may be found by constructing the force polygon (4). The procedure is repeated for at least three different assumed failure surfaces, E_p being plotted to scale above D, D' D'', etc., until the minimum value of E_p can be found from a curve 1-2-3 plotted through the resulting points. The force polygon (2) can be constructed and the magnitude of T_1 determined. Note that T_1, here, is the *ultimate* cable-stress per foot of length of the anchor block. The *allowable* cable stress T that may be applied to a block of length L, with a factor of safety F, is

$$T = \frac{L}{F} T_1 \qquad\qquad \text{(Eq. 7.16b)}$$

The possibility that the area surrounding the block may become submerged must be most carefully considered. If this should happen, the effective unit weights of the block and the soil would be reduced to their buoyant values, and T_1 may be reduced nearly 50 per cent from its value in dry and moist soil. Therefore, if the water table can rise to the surface, the work illustrated in Figure 7.16c should be accomplished using submerged unit weights, and the factor of safety applied to the results.

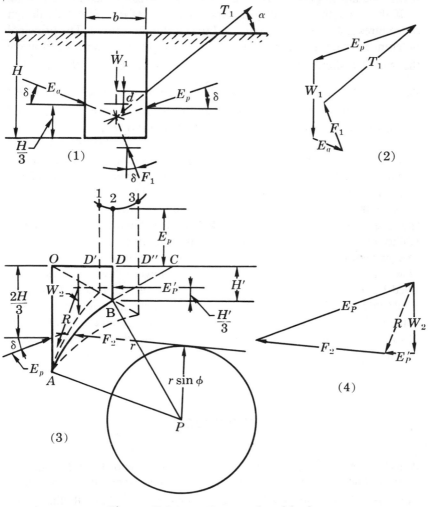

Figure 7.16c   Guy anchor block

b.   Anchors in Clay

The design of anchors supported in clay embraces greater uncertainties than those which exist for anchors in sand. Time effects, both dynamic and long term, are likely to be considerably more important than those for sands; the magnitude and influence of possible pore pressures is more difficult to predict; and the control of disturbance to the soil during construction takes on added meaning. Therefore, a factor of safety of not less than 3 should be used in routine work, depending upon the confidence which one has in the soil properties and cable stresses used in the design.

If the strength of the clay is expressed by $s = c + \overline{\sigma} \tan \phi$, design procedures similar to those described for sand may be used. The principal difference is that in Figure 7.16c an adhesive force C_a, downward along the wall OA, should be added; and a cohesive force $C = c\overline{AB}$, parallel to the chord $\overline{AB}$ and at a distance of $r\dfrac{\widehat{AB}}{\overline{AB}}$ from p, should be included. E'_d should, of course, include the additional resistance due to cohesion, and its line of action raised above the lower third point of H'.

Very often, the full load on the anchor is brought into play within a relatively short time interval. It may then be preferable to base the design on an assumed constant strength ($s = c$, $\phi = 0$), where c is found from unconfined compression tests or appropriate field tests.

Anchor yield is sometimes an important consideration, especially in the case of tie rod anchors for a bulkhead. The usually greater compressibility of clay (during consolidation) as compared with sand may lead to slow yielding, the effects of which may not be apparent for a considerable time. This is added reason for using the lower allowable stresses implied by a higher factor of safety. In any kind of soil, unless the anchor is already well below the surface, safety can be improved or disaster sometimes averted by applying surcharge on the passive resistance side of the anchor. Surcharge can also easily be included in the analysis without altering the basic procedures illustrated in Figure 7.16c.

REFERENCES

Abul-Baki, A. F., "A Direct Method for Determination of Earth Pressures on Retaining Walls," Ph.D. Thesis, Oklahoma State University (May, 1966).

Blum, H., "Einspannungsverhältnisse bei Bohlwerken," *Ernst*, Berlin, 1931.

Coulomb, C. A. "Essai sur une Application des Regles des Maximis et Minimis à quelques Problemes de Statique Relatifs à l'Architecture," *Mem. présentés à l'Academie Royale des Sciences par divers savants*, Vol. 7, Paris, 1776.

Douglas, D. J., and E. H. Davis, "The Movement of Buried Footings due to Moment and Horizontal Load and the Movement of Anchor Plates," *Geotechnique*, Vol. XIV, No. 2 (June, 1964).

Hansen, J. B. "Earth Pressure Calculation," *The Danish Technical Press*, The Institution of Danish Civil Engineers, Copenhagen, 1953.

Hansen, J. B., "Discussion of 'Anchored Bulkheads', Terzaghi (1954)," *Trans. Am. Soc. C.E.*, Vol. 119, 1954.

Hijab, W. A., "A Note on the Centroid of a Logarithmic Spiral Sector," *Geotechnique*, Vol. VI, No. 2 (June, 1956).

Meem, J. C., "The Bracing of Trenches and Tunnels, With Practical Formulas for Earth Pressure," *Trans. Am. Soc. C.E.*, Vol. LX (June, 1908).

Peck, R. B., "Earth Pressure Measurements in Open Cuts, Chicago (Ill.) Subway," *Trans. Am. Soc. C.E.*, Vol. 108, 1943.

Rankine, W. J. M., "On the Stability of Loose Earth," *Phil. Trans. Royal Soc.*, Vol. 147, London, 1857.

Rowe, P. W., "Anchored Sheet-Pile Walls," *Proc. I.C.E.*, Vol. 1, 1955.

Rowe, P. W., "A Theoretical and Experimental Analysis of Sheet Pile Walls," *Proc. I.C.E.*, Vol. 4, Part 1, 1955.

Terzaghi, K. "Anchored Bulkheads," *Trans. Am. Soc. C.E.*, Vol. 119, 1954.

Terzaghi, K. "General Wedge Theory of Earth Pressure," *Trans. Am. Soc. Am. Soc. C.E.*, Vol. 106, 1941.

Terzaghi, K., *Theoretical Soil Mechanics*, New York: John Wiley & Sons, Inc., 1943.

Terzaghi, K., and R. B. Peck, *Soil Mechanics in Engineering Practice*, New York: John Wiley & Sons, Inc., 1948.

Tschebotarioff, G. P., "Large Scale Model Earth Pressure Tests on Flexible Bulkheads," *Trans. Am. Soc. C.E.*, Vol. 114, 1949.

Tschebotarioff, G. P., "Retaining Structures," *Foundation Engineering,* ed. G. A. Leonards, New York: McGraw-Hill Book Company, Inc., 1962.

8   Slope Stability

8.01   General

While this chapter deals primarily with the mechanics of slope stability
analyses, it should not be inferred that this is the most difficult, or even
the most important, part of the total process employed in arriving at a
decision as to the safety of a given slope. To be sure, there are differences
in the results obtained from the various procedures that have been advo-
cated for accomplishing the mechanical analysis. Such differences often
arise from the way in which the initial assumptions fail to satisfy all of
the equations of equilibrium, or from fundamental differences in the definitions adopted for the factor of safety. It will be shown later that these
differences, while sometimes substantial, are not usually decisive. Indeed,
it turns out that most slope failures arise from causes that were unfore-
seen, or improperly evaluated, by the designer.

The difficulties of determining in advance the properties to be assigned
to the soil involved in the construction have been emphasized previously.
In slope stability problems, more than in any other class of earth construction problem, a reasonably correct prediction of the soil strength is
of the greatest importance. Because of the relatively low factors of safety

(often in the range of 1.2 to 1.8) traditionally used in embankment design, the assignment of unrealistically optimistic values to the soil strength parameters can be catastrophic. On the other hand, underestimation of the strength leads to unnecessary increases in the cost of construction.

A large percentage of the failures of natural and man-made slopes is associated with an unusual or unexpected influence of water. The presence of water may act both to decrease the strength of the soil and to increase the forces which must be resisted by it. Thus, many slope failures occur during or following periods of heavy rainfall, or when, for some other reason, abnormally high seepage pressures exist within the mass of soil. In the case of embankments which impound water or channelize its flow, failures may result from overtopping and consequent erosion, from piping of water through the embankment or its foundation, or from the undercutting of slopes. Other hazards are associated with cracking due to uneqal settlements; the use of improper compaction procedures, especially those that result in planes of separation between lifts; the improper installation of conduits through the embankment; and, in zoned dams, internal design that fails to provide adequate safeguards for the control of seepage and for counteracting the possible adverse effects of large settlements.

Much of the soil involved in earthworks owes its strength both to cohesion and to internal friction, that is, $s = c + \bar{\sigma} \tan \phi$, in which c and ϕ are *mathematical* parameters. However, useful insight into the behavior of slopes may be gained by considering briefly the purely cohesionless and the purely cohesive types.

a. Cohesionless Soil

A cohesionless soil depends for its strength only on the normal stresses acting between the grains and on its angle of internal friction. Such a soil, existing at a given void ratio, has properties that are relatively invariant—unaffected by the passage of time or the mere presence of water. An existing slope of this soil is made unstable only by an alteration of the intergranular stresses acting in the slope, or by an increase of the downslope component of the shearing stresses. In either case, if the action is due to the presence of water in the slope, the instability may be explained in terms of the stress in the pore water. Once movement is initiated in the slope it is impossible to imagine that it could continue in the form of a slippage of a relatively intact mass along a well defined slip surface. Failure of a slope of cohesionless material almost always occurs as a flow slide in which a churned-up mass of soil comes finally to rest on a very much flattened slope.

A flow slide results from the initial liquefaction of at least a portion of the soil mass. Once initiated, the action may involve progressively greater quantities of the mass. Since liquefaction can occur only in soils in which the void ratio is above a certain critical value, the stability of slopes can almost always be ensured by procedures that cause the soil to be placed at sufficiently great densities. Fortunately, this condition is not difficult to achieve using modern compaction equipment. Thus, as will be more precisely demonstrated in Section 8.05, there is practically no limitation (stemming from the properties of the embankment material) to the height to which dry cohesionless soil may be safely piled. As the soil is piled higher, inconsequential surface failures occur as grains tumble downslope to maintain the pile at its natural angle of repose. Because the strength is a function of the normal pressure, which increases in proportion to depth, deep rotational slides are not possible.

It is concluded that the most probable mode of failure is that of a flow slide initiated by sudden strain, such as might occur during an earthquake. In order to be susceptible to this kind of failure, the cohesionless soil must be in a relatively loose state and nearly saturated. Susceptibility is further increased as the average grain size decreases. The behavior of sand embankments subjected to earthquake shocks has been discussed in detail by Goodman and Seed (1966).

b.   Cohesive Soil

An ideally cohesive soil, however unlikely its occurrence in nature, is one whose entire strength along any surface is independent of the normal stresses on the surface. The true nature of cohesion—its causes, its permanency, and the ways in which it is influenced by mineralogical composition, grain size, ionic variables, etc.—is still not completely understood. Nevertheless, the behavior of a cohesive material under stress can be described satisfactorily for engineering purposes. Furthermore, it happens that natural clay soils always possess some frictional properties which behave, under some conditions, and temporarily, as if their strength were independent of the normal stresses. Under these conditions, the stability of slopes or embankments of clay can sometimes be simply analyzed as if the soil were purely cohesive.

The strength of an ideal homogeneous cohesive soil, being independent of the normal stress, would be the same at every point within an embankment or slope. The driving forces that tend to make the slope unstable generally increase, depending upon the geometry of the slope, as the mass of material treated in the analysis increases. Therefore, the most critical condition is likely to be discovered when the lower boundary (slip surface) is assumed to lie deep within the slope.

c. Natural Soils

There are natural cohesionless soils, such as dune sands, certain glacial deposits, etc., that frequently must be utilized or dealt with in earthworks. When present in a homogeneous embankment or slope, the question as to their stability or possible instability can usually be answered with confidence, even though the usual mechanics of stability analyses may not be at all applicable. Such soils are generally too permeable to be used in a homogeneous dam, but because of their stable characteristics are often used in the outer parts of zoned earth dams. When so used, their mode of failure will be influenced by the other parts of the structure, with the result that it then becomes reasonable to presume that slip surfaces may develop through zones of cohesionless soil.

Most soils used in earthworks are so-called c-ϕ soils, exhibiting both cohesive and frictional properties. If ϕ is high and c low, their behavior approaches that of sand; and if c is high and ϕ low, their behavior approaches that of the ideal cohesive soil. Slope failures tend to be shallow in the former, and to cut deeply in the latter. This knowledge is of some help in selecting trial surfaces for use in a stability study.

Slope stability investigations may be required in any of the following distinct cases: (a) compacted earthfill embankments, including rockfill and zoned dams; (b) cuts in natural ground, such as occur in many types of construction; and (c) natural slopes. Sometimes these cases may all be treated using identical analytical procedures, whereas at other times the kind of failure or shape of the slip surface may be clearly indicated by peculiarities of soil formation or by other circumstances. What is of prime importance is the recognition that the three cases are likely to be quite different when it comes to selecting the strength parameters for use in the study. Moreover, fundamental differences in the nature of the anisotropy of soft, normally consolidated clays and stiff, overconsolidated clays may be of greater importance than has been generally realized. See, for example, Kenney (1963). More skillful techniques of sampling, testing, and interpretation would be required if it should prove to be necessary to evaluate the anisotropic properties.

The preceding remarks help to underline the formidable complexities of problems dealing with *real* slopes. It is entirely fortuitous if an analysis is in perfect accord with all the facts. Yet, in spite of complexities and ignorance, engineers have to solve the problems. The best tools and most enlightened techniques available ought to be used. In subsequent sections, differences that arise from variations in the way the analytical procedures of engineering mechanics are applied should be viewed in the context of the whole problem. There are two basic questions to which reasonably correct answers must be supplied if the solution is to be reliable. The questions are:

(1) What are the soil properties?
(2) What is the most critical potential slip surface?

While this chapter is concerned with finding the answer to the second question, note well that the answer will be wrong unless the first question has already been answered correctly.

8.02   Historical Development

The construction of earthen embankments and of many kinds of engineering works, is as old as civilization itself. As a matter of fact, several members of the animal kingdom were constructing embankments on a small scale long before man appeared on earth. Much evidence remains that past efforts of "unenlightened" men in the field of earthworks were often successful, although it is impossible to say how frequently such efforts met with failure. Many ancient man-made embankments exist in China and the Middle East, and Rao (1961) describes 18 existing earth dams constructed in Southern India between 1000 and 1800 A.D. In this region, where gravelly soils were used, the embankments characteristically have steep slopes, 1.5:1 being not uncommon. In central India, there are some dams more than 800 years old. These dams, being made of clay soils, were generally built on much flatter slopes (4:1 and greater) than those of southern India. Apparently, embankment design can be reasonably successful when based on experience and intuition. These attributes are still of great importance in earthworks design. Yet, alone, they neither permit a quantitative assessment of the safety of the structure, nor furnish quantitative guides for effecting greater economy or for taking into account unusual conditions that may be encountered. Thus, it was inevitable that, when the proper tools of mathematics and mechanics became generally available, attempts would be made to analyze the problems quantitatively. Real progress had also to await the beginnings of an understanding of soil properties.

Much of the earlier work [for example, Culmann (1866)] was mathematical in nature and was based on an assumed plane surface of sliding. During this period it was generally assumed that only internal friction could be relied on, cohesion being only a transitory property, and that the angle of internal friction was the same as the angle of repose. This notion was practically worthless for dealing with cohesive soils, and could not be reconciled with practical observations. However, Collin (1846), in a richly documented study of slides in cohesive soils, showed that the slip surfaces were always curved (cycloidal, he believed) and proposed an analysis based on this observation. Collin also utilized laboratory direct shear tests to study clay properties, even noting a reduction of strength with time (creep effects). Apparently, Collin was too far ahead of his time. Although his work was occasionally referred to in the literature, its significance was not generally appreciated for a hundred years, when Skempton (1946) called attention to it. In the meantime, his precocious knowledge had been rediscovered and surpassed.

Modern developments leading to the present state of the art began during the second decade of this century. The revival of interest appears to have stemmed from several serious land slips that occurred in Sweden and from massive slides that took place during construction of the Panama Canal. There are probably two important causes for the rapid progress that followed this renewal of interest. Firstly, at about this time an improved and more widespread understanding of soil properties was developing, and interest in extending this knowledge was quickening. Secondly, there appeared on the scene the great, guiding genius of Terzaghi, who was to weld soil properties and mechanical principles into a coherent whole that laid the foundations for a new science.

The slip of the Stigberg Quay in the harbor of Gothenburg, Sweden, in 1916, touched off an investigation that was to have profound consequences. The character of the slide was thoroughly investigated, and some previous failures of a similar nature were restudied. From these investigations, it was concluded that the slip surfaces passed through the supporting clay along arcs that were nearly circular. Petterson (1916) and Hultin (1916) collaborated in analyzing the Stigberg Quay failure. For the first time, a method of analysis was used in which the failure surface was represented by a circular arc. According to the concepts of the time, the clay was treated as a purely frictional material. It is noteworthy that the concept of a "friction circle" and a subdivision of the mass into slices appeared in the analysis. Fellenius (1927) suggested the feasibility of treating clay as a purely cohesive soil ($\phi = 0$ analysis) and also considered that cohesion and friction may both be present. Based on a mathematical analysis, Fellenius prepared tables and charts for predicting the location of the critical surface of sliding. His work provided a powerful insight into the influence which the soil properties and the geometry of the slope have on the location of the critical surface, and drew wide attention to the use of the circular arc method of analysis. The use of circular arcs in analyzing stability became known, in time, as the "Swedish" method.

A detailed account of these developments has been given by Petterson (1955).

The methods developed in Europe during the first three decades of this century were apparently not widely known or practiced in connection with the design of earth dams in the United States as late as 1932. Justin (1932), in a comprehensive treatise on the design of earth dams, does not mention any method for analyzing the stability of slopes other than rule of thumb methods supposed to be helpful in establishing the permissible steepness of slopes. This negligence may have been justified by the low incidence of failures that could be attributed to slides. Out of 102 dam failures that had been reported between 1868 and 1930, Justin attributed not more than five to sliding. Most of them were caused by overtopping, piping along conduits, or piping through the dam or its foundation. Only crude theoretical procedures for analyzing seepage were generally available. In subsequent years, as the height of dams being built increased and the quality of available damsites became poorer, engineers became increasingly concerned about the possibility of failure by sliding, and recognized the necessity for improved methods for analyzing stability.

Krey (e.g., 1932) extended the applications of the friction circle with the result that such procedures are often referred to as the Krey "ϕ-circle" method. Taylor (1937), in a paper that helped to bring engineers of the United States up to date in matters of stability analysis, reviewed the various methods of analysis which had been proposed, compared results of different procedures of the Swedish method, and presented the results of theoretical analyses amplifying the work of Fellenius. Present practices largely make use of the Swedish method, and there have been numerous papers proposing refinement or modification of the procedures based on this method. Some of these will be mentioned in subsequent sections.

Other methods of analysis have been proposed from time to time. These have usually involved different assumptions concerning the shape of the failure surface. For example, various sliding wedge procedures are based on assumed planar slip surfaces. Collin and others have proposed using cycloidal slip surfaces, and Rendulic (1935) developed a method based on the use of a spiral slip surface. In certain situations, it is apparent that the critical slip surface, or a portion of it, will be planar. Consequently, methods are frequently used in which slip along planes or combinations of planes and arcs is supposed. Methods based on curved surfaces other than circular arcs are not often used because they are usually more complicated than the Swedish method and have no clear advantage over it.

Methods based on the theory of elasticity and plasticity attempt to analyze the state of stress and stress-deformation relationships within the mass of soil. So far, these have not been used much. They are generally quite complicated to apply, are inevitably based on erroneous assumptions concerning the soil properties, and there is uncertainty as to how the failure criteria should be established. In fairness, it must be pointed out that *every* method of analysis is based on some erroneous assumptions. These will be further discussed in the following section.

8.03   *Uncertainties in the Analysis*

At the very beginning, it is important to realize that a stable slope can be analyzed correctly only by taking into account the strains within the slope and the stress-deformation characteristics of the materials of the slope. Satisfactory techniques for doing this are not yet available, although it is possible that the advent of high speed computer technology may permit the development of approximate solutions of this kind. Such solutions would be of great academic interest, and could lead to a better understanding of slope behavior. From a practical standpoint, however, there is apparently no urgent need for these more sophisticated methods except, perhaps, for dealing with those soils such as highly sensitive clays and some heavily overconsolidated clays in which progressive failure may be an important consideration.

In view of the foregoing, the usual methods of analysis are based on assumptions that transform the problem into one which is statically determinate. It is usually assumed that the shearing resistance of the soil along the potential surface of failure is developed to the same extent at every point. This amounts to assuming that the shearing stresses develop in direct proportion to the strength, or that the factor of safety along the potential slip surface is the same everywhere. Note that, in general, this is *not* the same as saying that the shearing stresses are *uniformly* distributed along the surface. For example, the frictional resistance is proportional to the normal stresses on the surface of sliding. Since these normal stresses are not uniformly distributed but vary in an unknown manner along the arc, there must be some assumption, either tacit or expressed, about their distribution. These assumptions are discussed more fully in Section 8.09.

The actual shape of the failure surface which will develop (the critical surface) is not known unless failure actually occurs, a circumstance which no engineer desires except in deliberate field tests. Nevertheless, it is true that the greatest advances in the analysis of soil behavior result from careful studies of those failures that do occur. As a result, these events are viewed with mixed emotions by the profession—with despair by the engineer responsible for the design, and with somberly restrained glee by others. The usual assumptions regarding the shape of slip surfaces (circular arc, spiral, cycloid, or plane-surfaced wedges) are based on observation, intuition, or mathematical analysis; but the first of these has been by far the most influential in formulating present practices. To the extent that the assumed geometrical form only approximates the shape of the critical surface, error is introduced. This error is usually small, but it is always on the side of danger. Especially in natural slopes, the existence of thin seams of exceptional weakness or permeability may go unnoticed. Yet, they decisively influence the shape of the failure surface and the magnitude of the actual margin of safety.

The three-dimensional nature of the real problem is rarely considered in the analysis. Thus, in the usual procedures, the soil mass investigated is assumed to be defined by the external boundaries of the slope and by a plane or cylindrical surface (or some combination of these) on which sliding may occur. The influence of the resisting forces acting on the lateral boundaries of the mass is ignored. As a matter of fact, a clear distinction between lateral boundaries and the bottom boundary usually does not exist, because the trace of the slip surface is curved not only on cross-sectional planes, but also on planes perpendicular to both the slope and its cross-section. That is, the slip is often more nearly spherical than cylindrical. In any case, ignoring the finite lateral dimensions of the mass is conservative. The degree of conservativeness depends upon the actual dimensions of the slides that occur. If the width of the sliding mass is great compared to its length, the error in treating the problem as two-dimensional rather than three-dimensional is small. For embankments such as high dams built in narrow canyons a two-dimensional analysis may be overly conservative. A correct theoretical treatment of the problem is prohibitively difficult, but Sherard, *et al.* (1963) have proposed a solution which consists of combining the results of several two-dimensional analyses on different planes perpendicular to the axis of the dam.

The strength parameters to be used in the analysis are usually determined from triaxial tests in which either the effective stresses are known or the conditions are believed to be closely representative of those that will exist in the field. One of the most vexing problems is that of evaluating the nature and influence of the anisotropic state of stress that has existed in a stable embankment or slope. This question has been considered by Lowe and Karafiath (1960), who have suggested a laboratory test procedure that may approximate the field situation, and by Lo (1965). Lowe and Karafiath found that the effect of anisotropy was to produce a higher factor of safety for the dams so analyzed than would have been found by a conventional analysis. However, Lo, in a theoretical analysis more directly applicable to natural slopes and cuts, found that inclusion of the effects of anisotropic strength (greater vertically than horizontally) yielded factors of safety lower than would be found in a conventional analysis based on the major principal strength. Thus, while it is sometimes conservative to ignore anisotropy, it may sometimes be dangerous to do so.

In the case of cohesionless soils, there are some conditions for which the use of the angle of internal friction found from a triaxial test is conservative. For instance, Seed and Sultan (1966), in investigating the stability of embankments having a sloping cohesive core and a shell of cohesionless soil, found that the most reliable results were obtained when the shell material was assigned an angle of internal friction equal to that found from plane strain shear tests [e.g., see Leussink and Wittke (1964)]. Use of the angle of internal friction found from triaxial tests was conservative. However, in a full scale embankment, the conditions of restraint vary from point to point, depending upon the geometry of the embankment and the overall pattern of settlement. Thus, in practice, the use of conservative approaches is generally justified.

Both in natural slopes and in compacted embankments, the occurrence and location of cracks can hardly be predicted. In natural slopes, cracks usually result from shrinkage or from tensile stresses associated with the tendency toward downslope movement, whereas compacted embankments may crack from the same causes and also from the effects of differential settlements. Some cracking nearly always occurs, and its effect on stability is sometimes very important. The fact that slip surfaces often start at the bottom of existing cracks is evidence of the influence of cracking. Since there is no reliable way of predicting the extent and depth of possible cracks, assumptions regarding cracking should be conservative.

Finally, one of the greatest uncertainties is concerned with the magnitude of the pore pressures that will develop. There is no doubt that rises in pore pressure or increases in seepage forces have triggered the failure of many natural slopes and man-made cuts. In compacted embankments the pore pressure due to increasing load as the embankment is built up must be reckoned. Preliminary estimates are generally based on laboratory triaxial tests in which pore pressures are measured. Piezometers placed in the embankment and foundation permit the exercise of field control. On the basis of these observations the design may be altered or the rate of construction varied. Although really *sudden* drawdown of impounded water rarely occurs in large reservoirs, its effect on the stability of the upstream slope must be considered. Rapid drawdown seldom turns out to be a critical feature of the analysis because the possibility of its occurrence is remote and the consequences never catastrophic, since the water level is low. Therefore, a very small margin of safety for this condition can be tolerated.

Full discussion of the factors mentioned in this section is beyond the

scope of this work. While they may be of outstanding importance in arriving at a correct analysis of the stability, their influence does not invali-
date the principles of mechanics which underlie the analytical procedures.
However, evaluation of the reliability of the analysis must be based on a
consideration of the possible range of the uncertainties involved.

8.04   Factor of Safety

There is probably no facet of stability analysis that has evoked more
heated discussion in recent years than has the factor of safety. Discussion has centered on how it should be defined, how it should be determined, and what its proper magnitude should be. Unfortunately for
young engineers, none of these questions has really been settled. Moreover,
since such differences of opinion are bound to exist for a long time, the
engineer must develop a tolerant attitude toward the various viewpoints
while, at the same time, molding a philosophy which satisfies his own
needs. In arriving at his philosophy, the engineer must be pragmatic: an
acceptable philosophy is one that leads neither to catastrophic failures
nor to excessive waste of resources. In general, a reasonable margin of
safety should be provided against failure from any cause that can be
anticipated. The possibility of flaws in design or execution, errors in evaluating the properties of materials, errors in the analysis of hydrologic
or geologic data, and human errors, must all be considered. A quantitative
evaluation of their combined effects on the factor of safety is usually not
possible. A certain degree of risk must nearly always be assumed, but the
risk assumed should be inversely proportional to the potential loss of life
and property that would result from failure. This subject has been discussed with great insight by Casagrande (1965). Others have suggested
that a meaningful evaluation of the margin of safety, embracing all the
uncertainties, can only be gained through application of the theory of
probability.

It should by now be clear that the term "factor of safety," as it is
ordinarily used, has a severely restricted meaning. It is a number that
represents the results of computations made in accordance with some
adopted definition. It will be seen that the definition is always in the form
of a ratio. If the quantities comprising the ratio have been correctly determined or assumed, the results of the computations indicate the factor of
safety against a failure *of the type investigated*. Even this statement is not
so simple as it appears, for it will be shown that the same basic definition
for factor of safety may sometimes lead to different results.

a.　Definitions

It would be possible to devise a large number of definitions for the factor of safety, basing the definitions on various uncertain factors in the analysis. For example, definitions could be based on unit weight of material, height of slope, pore water pressure, elevation of water table, steepness of slope, surcharge loading, etc. It would be desirable for the factor of safety to reflect in some clear way the influence of the most uncertain factors in the analysis, so that the tolerance for error in these factors could be seen at a glance.

The most common basis for defining the factor of safety is the *strength* of the soil. This is a sensible basis for two reasons: (1) some uncertainty as to strength almost always exists, and (2) whatever the indirect causes leading to failure, the direct cause of a slide along the critical surface is that the shearing stresses along the surface have become equal to the available shearing strength. Thus

$$F_s = \frac{s}{\tau} \qquad \text{(Eq. 8.04}a\text{)}$$

where s = shearing strength and τ = shearing stress. In practice, these are generally expressed as average values along the potential slip surface. In general, $s = c + \sigma \tan \phi$, and $\tau = c' + \bar{\sigma} \tan \phi'$ (the primed quantities representing the *developed* cohesion and friction angle just required for equilibrium). Eq. 8.04a can then be transformed to

$$F_s = \frac{c + \bar{\sigma} \tan \phi}{c' + \bar{\sigma} \tan \phi'} \qquad \text{(Eq. 8.04}b\text{)}$$

In the case of an assumed cylindrical surface of sliding, Eq. 8.04a and 8.04b are also the same as

$$F_s = \frac{\text{Resisting moment}}{\text{Driving moment}} \qquad \text{(Eq. 8.04}c\text{)}$$

because the resisting moment *per unit length and width of arc* is $M_R = s \times R$, and the driving moment is $M_D = \tau \times R$, where R is the radius of curvature of the critical surface.

Other definitions have been used from time to time. For example, if it is assumed that all of the cohesive resistance is first mobilized, a factor of safety may be written in terms of the ratio of available frictional resistance to that which must be mobilized for equilibrium:

$$F_\phi = \frac{\tan \phi}{\tan \phi'} \qquad \text{(Eq. 8.04d)}$$

Conversely, if the full frictional resistance is assumed to be mobilized, a factor of safety may be similarly based on the cohesion:

$$F_c = \frac{c}{c'} \qquad \text{(Eq. 8.04e)}$$

In the case of a simple slope, bounded by two horizontal planes and an inclined plane, Eq. 8.04e is equivalent to

$$F_H = \frac{H(\text{crit})}{H} \qquad \text{(Eq. 8.04f)}$$

where H is the height of the slope (or depth of cut) and $H(\text{crit})$ is the maximum possible height of the slope, or that height corresponding to a factor of safety of unity.

Although all of these definitions produce the correct result ($F.S. = 1$) for slopes in critical equilibrium, the results are, in general, different when the slope is stable. Some of these differences may be illustrated by reference to Figure 8.04a. Suppose that at some point along the critical surface in a stable slope the normal stress, $\sigma = OA$, and the shearing stress, $\tau = AP$, correspond to the average normal and shearing stresses along the potential slip surface. According to the definitions above, factors of safety are:

$$F_s = \frac{AC}{AP}, \quad F_c = \frac{BC}{BP}, \quad \text{and } F_\phi = \frac{AB}{AP-BC}$$

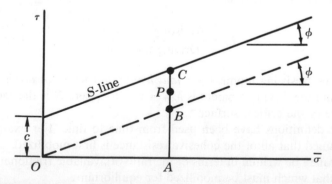

Figure 8.04a   Illustration of various factors of safety

It is apparent that these ratios are numerically different, and that F_s will always be the smallest. In fact, if $AP = AB$, F_c is infinitely great; and if $AP = BC$, F_ϕ is infinitely great. F_s is always finite, and is usually a more logical representation of the margin of strength beyond that required for equilibrium. Nevertheless, it may be questioned whether any of these accurately represents the factor of safety of the slope against an actual slip, for the true factor of safety depends on the *cause* of the eventual slip. In all of these definitions, it is assumed that the effective normal stress OA on the slip surface remains constant. This condition would be satisfied if the failure occurs as a gradual reduction of strength, with point C dropping until it coincides with P. For other causes of failure, such as an increase of load on the slope, there will almost certainly be changes in the effective stresses. In this case, the available strength at the time of failure is not represented by AC, but by some other ordinate to the S-Line. Because this is an important and controversial point, some further attention will now be given it.

In Figure 8.04b, the state of stress of certain elements along a slip surface is shown. According to the Mohr-Coulomb criterion, an element of soil fails along a slip plane oriented at an angle of $\left(45 + \dfrac{\phi}{2} \right)$ degrees

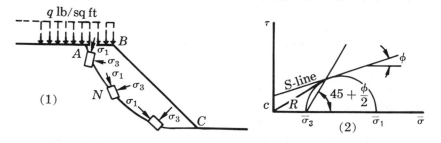

Figure 8.04b   Stresses along slip surface

with the major principal plane, when the resultant stress on that plane is represented by a vector R whose tip coincides with a point on the S-Line [See Figure 8.04b(2)]. If the arc ANC in Figure 8.04b(1) is the actual slip surface, the direction of the principal planes is fixed relative to the direction of a tangent to the arc. Therefore, the orientation of the principal planes changes along the arc. Suppose that the slip was caused by adding surcharge q to a saturated embankment ABC which had been stable for many years. The effective stresses at failure, on some element such as N, will depend on the rate at which q is applied and on the stress-dilatancy characteristics of the material, as represented, for example, by the Skempton pore pressure coefficient A. The various possible effects of adding the surcharge will now be traced.

In Figure 8.04c, let the stress circle C represent the *effective* state of stress on the element N of the stable embankment (before q is applied). If the additional load q is then applied so quickly that failure occurs before any drainage has taken place (zero volume change), the effective stress on the failure surface will depend on the pore pressure coefficient A. The vector curve V-2 would approximately correspond to $A = 1$, for which the effective major principal stress remains unchanged when the

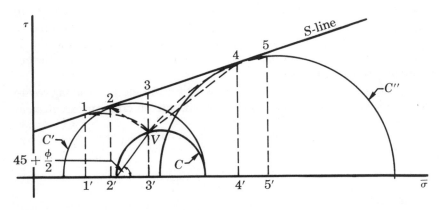

Figure 8.04c   Effective stress vector curves

load is applied. For this condition, the effective stresses are represented by the stress circle C'. However, depending upon the value of the pore pressure coefficient, the vector curve may vary from one similar to V-1 for highly sensitive clay, to one resembling V-5 for a dense, dilatant glacial till. Hence, in a total stress analysis making use of triaxial R Tests to duplicate field conditions, the computed factor of safety, $F_s = s/\tau$, could turn out to be anything between $\dfrac{1'-1}{3'-V}$ and $\dfrac{5'-5}{3'-V}$. On the other hand, if full drainage takes place as the surcharge is applied (pore pressures remaining constant), both the major and minor effective principal stresses will change. At failure, the state of stress is represented by some circle such as C'', and vector curve $V - 4$ traces the history of the effective stresses on the failure surface. In terms of the margin of safety against failure under a slowly applied surcharge, the actual factor of safety F_s is $\dfrac{4'-4}{3'-V}$.

If the analysis is now referred to a particular soil; e.g., one for which the pore pressure coefficient A is equal to unity, the varying results that may be obtained from a simple definition, $F_s = s/\tau$, for the factor of safety can be illustrated. In the ordinary total stress analysis $F_s = \dfrac{2'-2}{3'-V}$. In the widely used effective stress analysis, it is assumed that the normal effective stress on the critical surface is unchanged by the processes which cause a previously stable embankment to fail. According to this concept, $F_s = \dfrac{3'-3}{3'-V}$. For the cause of failure under consideration, this actually corresponds to failure in a partially drained condition, with the effective stress circle (not shown) tangent to the S-Line at point 3. In this example, the total stress analysis produces a smaller value for F_s than does the effective stress analysis; however, for dilatant soils the relationship would be reversed. In a general sense, neither of these procedures has a preferred status insofar as the truth is concerned. There *is* a "true" factor of safety F_s that depends on the degree of consolidation (or expansion) that occurs during the loading period. Its value lies somewhere between the ratios $\dfrac{2'-2}{3'-V}$ and $\dfrac{4'-4}{3'-V}$. There are several reasons why the true factor of safety cannot be determined in an analysis of the problem. The soil characteristics used in the analysis are found from laboratory tests of a small number of samples. Aside from the usual possibilities for error in analyzing the test results, it is improbable that the test specimens are truly representative of the field soils. Thus, neither the pore pressure coefficient A, nor the rate of consolidation, nor the position of the S-Line itself can be reliably stated for the field situation.

Now, all of this does not mean that engineers ought to stop trying to analyze the stability of slopes; it only means that they should recognize that, generally, the analysis does not yield the *actual* factor of safety of the slope. Experience has shown that embankments can be satisfactorily designed on the basis of nearly any properly defined factor of safety. However, when one has arrived at a numerical value for the factor, it is useful to be able to estimate about how far and in what direction from that value the truth probably lies. It is believed that the concepts just presented can be helpful in that respect.

A final illustration of how one definition can lead to different values of the factor of safety will be given because of its important bearing on some of the controversy that has developed. In Figure 8.04d a block is shown on an inclined plane. The resistance to sliding is purely frictional, and the block will be in static equilibrium provided that θ is less than the friction angle ϕ (i.e., $\mu = \tan \phi$). The shearing force F may be defined in two different ways: $F = N \tan \theta$ or $F = R \sin \theta$. Likewise, the available shearing resistance S is expressed either as $N \tan \phi$ or $R \sin \phi$. Apparently, the factor of safety, $F_s = S/F$, may be either $N \tan \phi / N \tan \theta = \tan \phi / \tan \theta$ or $R \sin \phi / R \sin \theta = \sin \phi / \sin \theta$. However, these ratios are not the same. The first definition is based on the tacit assumption that N

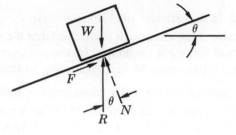

Figure 8.04d   Purely frictional resistance

remains constant while θ increases to its maximum value ϕ, while the second assumes that R remains constant. It is not possible for both conditions to be fulfilled simultaneously. In applications to slope stability problems, the cause for the increase of θ to ϕ has usually not been specified or it has been arbitrarily assumed; yet, this is really a crucial question, because the magnitude of the change in R or N depends on what causes the change in F. Odenstad (1955) has discussed these two alternatives for defining F_s for a frictional soil, and has shown that a mathematical relationship between the two can be easily derived.

b.   Application

In practice, the factor of safety F_s is by far the most commonly used. The basic definition for F_s, given by Eq. 8.04a, is quite uncomplicated, but it will be seen later that in some analyses it assumes, for convenience of computation, a form so intricate that its simple meaning is difficult to recognize. F_s is used in connection with both total stress analyses and effective stress analyses, although, for reasons already given, its value will generally be different in the two cases. The effective stress analysis is probably in greater favor at the present time, but there is no reason why the total stress ($\phi = 0$) analysis should not be used in the case of suddenly applied loads such as earthquake loadings, or even in connection with small cuts and embankments that are completed in a relatively short time. When the total stress analysis is used, the stress history of laboratory specimens prior to the undrained shear test should duplicate the field situation as nearly as possible.

The effective stress analysis is probably preferable for most large embankment sections because it permits a rapid re-evaluation of the factor of safety at any stage of the construction, based on field pore pressure measurements. If necessary, the design can be altered or the construction procedures varied to provide greater safety. However, various procedures utilizing effective stresses produce values of F_s that differ from each other. The reasons for the discrepancies are related to differences in the assumed distribution of stresses along the potential failure surface, and to differences in the way in which failure is supposed to be reached. The nature of these differences will be shown later, as the procedures are explained. The choice of which procedure is to be used is probably not of transcending importance, because the individual engineer tends to become accustomed to operating within a range of factors of safety that experience has shown to be satisfactory for the particular procedure he has adopted. Indeed, it appears that "higher" factors of safety in dams are sometimes sought by altering the analytical procedure, rather than by changing the design of the cross-section. It is, of course, quite obvious that changing the procedure of analysis cannot alter the *real* factor of safety; only the analyst's opinion is changed.

Lest the preceding remarks seem to have stripped all substance from the value of any analysis, the real worth of these procedures must be brought into focus. It is true that the factor of safety computed in the analysis is the factor of safety *only by definition*. However, to a greater or lesser extent this is true of *all* engineering analysis. Nevertheless, it is also true that design changes which affect the real factor of safety have corresponding effects on the defined factors of safety. Thus, the effect of changes in design can be evaluated with confidence. Moreover, formal analysis furnishes the only logical means for estimating the effect of unusual conditions, or for comparing the merits of alternate design proposals. The danger is that, in the routine drudgery of the computations, the object may evolve into that of filling in tables with rows of neat, mathematically correct figures. While this may be necessary, it is the least significant part of the work.

8.05   Infinite Slopes

An infinite slope consists of a body of material lying below an inclined plane of unlimited extent. The thickness, or depth of the mass, below the plane is unspecified. In nature, both the lateral extent and the depth of soil overlying rock are limited. Whereas the lateral boundaries of the mass that may slide are often indistinct, the lower boundary is usually sharply defined by an abrupt transition from one material to another. In spite of the dissimilarity between the infinite slope and real slopes, useful insight into the behavior of the latter can be gained from a study of the former. There are extensive natural slopes in which the soil conditions are more or less uniform. These slopes often bear the scars of failures that have involved the sliding of masses of soil having thicknesses which are small in comparison with their length and breadth. While the peripheral boundaries of the slip may be distinguished by curved slip surfaces, the major portion of the failure surface is often along a plane approximately parallel to the surface of the slope. The exact contours of the slip surface are greatly influenced by the inclination of bedding planes, the anisotropic strength characteristics, and the depth to rock or other strong substratum. The effects of water may influence both the time and mode of failure. Examples of these effects are increases of unit weight and seepage forces, reduction of strength by softening, and pore pressure rises in permeable thin layers or partings.

a. *Analysis*

In an infinite slope of homogeneous material the stress conditions on every vertical plane are presumed to be the same. Thus, on any element of the slope, such as is shown in Figure 8.05a, the forces on the two sides are equal and opposite, and may be ignored in the analysis. If the shearing force T on the base of the element becomes equal to the maximum shearing resistance of the material, the slope will be in critical equilibrium ($F.S. = 1$).

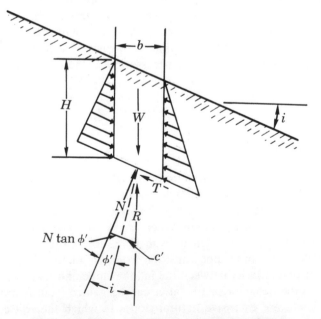

Figure 8.05a   Element of infinite slope

In Figure 8.05a, the slope element is assumed to have unit thickness perpendicular to the plane of the sketch. The weight of the element is $W = \gamma bH = R$, and the normal and tangential forces on the base are $N = \gamma bH \cos i$, and $T = \gamma bH \sin i$. From these and the dimensions of the base, the unit normal and tangential stresses may be found:

$$\bar{\sigma} = \frac{\gamma bH \cos i}{b/\cos i} = \gamma H \cos^2 i \qquad \text{(Eq. 8.05a)}$$

$$\tau = \frac{\gamma bH \sin i}{b/\cos i} = \gamma H \sin i \cos i \qquad \text{(Eq. 8.05b)}$$

The unit shearing stress may also be expressed in terms of the resistance that must be developed for equilibrium:

$$\tau = c' + \bar{\sigma} \tan \phi' = c' + \gamma H \cos^2 i \tan \phi' \qquad \text{(Eq. 8.05c)}$$

Setting the two expressions for τ equal to each other and rearranging the results, the following general relationship is found:

$$\frac{c'}{\gamma H} = \cos^2 i (\tan i - \tan \phi') \qquad \text{(Eq. 8.05d)}$$

The term on the left is a dimensionless ratio which Taylor (1937) called the *stability number*. For any assigned value for the developed friction angle ϕ', a relationship between the stability number and the slope angle i may be plotted. Such plots provide a convenient means for finding the required cohesion at any depth H, when i and ϕ' are given or assumed. (Graphs of this type were prepared by Taylor for use with finite, simple slopes, to be discussed later.) If the entire frictional resistance is assumed to be mobilized ($\phi' = \phi$) or if $\phi = 0$, Eq. 8.05d becomes, for a given slope angle, $c'/\gamma H = $ Constant. In this case, $F_c = c/c'$ by definition; and, for constant γ, c' depends only on H. Similarly, the depth H to the plane along which critical equilibrium exists is limited by the condition that $c' = c$. Thus, it is also seen that $F_c = H(\text{crit})/H$, as was mentioned in Section 8.04.

In connection with determining the factor of safety F_s, it is most commonly assumed that the cohesive and frictional resistances are developed in the same proportion, so that $F_s = s/\tau = \tan \phi/\tan \phi' = c/c'$. If this assumption is introduced into Eq. 8.05d, it is found that

$$F_s = \frac{c}{\gamma H \cos^2 i \tan i} + \frac{\tan \phi}{\tan i} \qquad \text{(Eq. 8.05e)}$$

Eq. 8.05e clearly indicates that the factor of safety of a slope in cohesionless soil ($c = 0$) is *independent of its height*, and that the slope is always stable when $i < \phi$. On the other hand, if $\phi = 0$ the factor of safety varies inversely as the height of the slope. These same principles also apply to finite slopes. [Note that for the infinite slope the height has been defined as the depth to a firm substratum.]

b.   Seepage Effects

As a simple demonstration of the effects of seepage, a slope in cohesionless soil of uniform depth overlying an impermeable base will be considered. Suppose that the surface of the ground water coincides with the surface of the slope, with the water flowing downslope above an impermeable base at depth H. The soil element shown in Figure 8.05b is saturated, and its total weight is $\gamma_{sat}Hb$. The forces on the vertical faces, including the hydrostatic forces, are balanced. Either the seepage forces

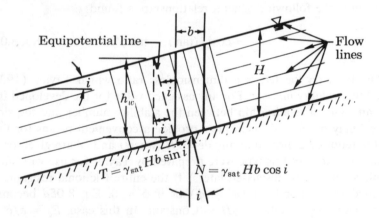

Figure 8.05b   Seepage in the slope

may be used in conjunction with the submerged unit weight, or, as will be done here, boundary static forces may be used with the total unit weight. The flow lines are parallel to the surface of the slope, and the equipotential lines are perpendicular to the flow lines. The effective normal stress on the base is

$$\bar{\sigma} = \gamma_{sat} H \cos^2 i - h_w \gamma_w = \gamma_{sat} H \cos^2 i - \gamma_w H \cos^2 i = H \cos^2 i (\gamma_{sat} - \gamma_w).$$

The term in parentheses is the buoyant unit weight γ'. Therefore, the unit stresses are $\bar{\sigma} = \gamma' H \cos^2 i$ and $\tau = \gamma_{sat} H \sin i \cos i$. As was done in arriving at Eq. 8.05d, two expressions for τ may be equated. Thus

$\gamma_{sat}H \sin i \cos i = \gamma'H \cos^2 i \tan \phi'$. Substituting $\tan \phi' = \tan \phi/F_s$, an expression for F_s (also F_ϕ, in this case) may be found:

$$F_s = \frac{H\gamma' \cos^2 i \tan \phi}{H\gamma_{sat} \sin i \cos i} = \frac{\gamma'}{\gamma_{sat}} \frac{\tan \phi}{\tan i} \qquad \text{(Eq. 8.05}f\text{)}$$

If Eq. 8.05f is compared with Eq. 8.05e, when $c = 0$ in the latter, it is seen that F_s in the submerged slope is smaller by a ratio of γ'/γ_{sat} than it would be for the same slope in a dry or moist condition. In cohesionless soils, the submerged unit weight is about one-half the saturated unit weight. Therefore, a slope that has a factor of safety of two when dry or moist will fail, or verge on the state of critical equilibrium, if the water table rises to the surface. Smaller reductions of the factor of safety will occur if the water table rises a shorter distance above the base.

A similar analysis could easily be made for cohesive soils to arrive at an expression analogous to Eq. 8.05e. This has not been done here for fear that it might lend itself to thoughtless use. For cohesionless soils the analysis is quite reliable, since ϕ is practically independent of moisture conditions. But in cohesive soils, the decrease of stability due to a reduction of c when the submerged slope softens may be of greater significance than the decrease due to seepage. This is a consideration which requires a detailed study of the soil properties.

8.06   Finite Slopes

With the exception of some extensive natural slopes having nearly uniform gradients, most stability analyses deal with slopes that can be conveniently treated as a whole. Such slopes are termed *finite*. A finite slope consists of a more or less steeply sloping grade that springs from a more nearly horizontal grade and terminates similarly. Figure 8.06a indicates that the contours may be quite irregular, and that parts of the slope may alone constitute lesser finite slopes. The distinguishing feature is that the dimensions of the slope are such that it is reasonable to analyze the stability of the whole mass with respect to sliding along various assumed surfaces of failure. It was previously explained that a two-dimensional analysis of the problem is usually made.

A great many of the slopes with which engineers deal have the simple form illustrated in Figure 8.06a(2), and many others can be satisfactorily approximated by this shape. These slopes, represented by two horizontal planes and a single inclined plane, are called *simple* slopes. Embankments such as dams, levees, and roadway fills, and many cuts for highways, rail-

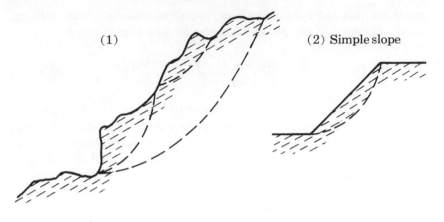

(1)

(2) Simple slope

Figure 8.06a   Finite slopes

roads, and canals may be analyzed as simple slopes. Even if this cannot be done (as, for example, when berms or other irregularities must be considered) the procedures are not much different than those for simple slopes.

Most of the theoretical work on which the present methods of analysis are based was concerned with simple slopes. Although several different methods of analysis have been proposed, the Swedish method has gained by far the widest popular acceptance. Except for certain "wedge" methods of analysis that are of historical interest or of practical value, the procedures to be described subsequently are all based on the Swedish method.

8.07   Wedge Method

Wedge methods of analysis have been in existence for a long time, the first ones probably being patterned on Coulomb's earlier work with earth pressures. The classical approach described below is usually attributed to Culmann (1866), although he unknowingly repeated what Français had done in about 1820. In all wedge methods, surfaces of sliding are assumed to be plane. Sometimes the slip surface is assumed to consist of two or more intersecting planes along which distinct blocks of soil may slide, subject to the interactive forces between the blocks as well as to the reactive forces along the slip surface. It should be noted that real slopes offer an internal resistance to a truly wedge-type failure, tending to fail along curved surfaces except where constrained to planes by the boundary conditions. Wedges have sharp corners and sudden directional changes which, at least in homogeneous materials, represent an unnatural configuration.

a. Classical Approach

The simple slope OA in Figure 8.07a(1) is composed of soil having a shearing strength $s = c + \overline{\sigma} \tan \phi$. OB is an arbitrary plane rising at an angle θ from the toe of the slope. The forces acting on the wedge OAB are its weight W, the resultant R of the normal and frictional forces (N

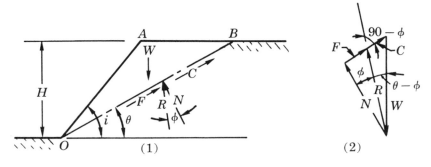

Figure 8.07a Classical wedge analysis

and F), and the cohesive resistance C. If it is assumed that the frictional resistance is fully developed, so that R is inclined at an angle ϕ to the normal, the critical height of the slope may be determined. Before this can be done, it is necessary to discover the critical value of θ; that is, the magnitude of θ corresponding to the particular orientation of OB for which the required *unit cohesion* is a maximum. In terms of the required unit cohesion c' and the dimensions of the wedge

$$C = c' \frac{H}{\sin \theta} \qquad \text{(Eq. 8.07a)}$$

The weight of the wedge is determined by its unit weight and dimensions:

$$W = \frac{1}{2} \gamma H \left(H \cot \theta - H \cot i \right) = \frac{1}{2} \gamma H^2 \left[\frac{\cos \theta}{\sin \theta} - \frac{\cos i}{\sin i} \right]$$

$$= \frac{1}{2} \gamma H^2 \left[\frac{\sin i \cos \theta - \cos i \sin \theta}{\sin i \sin \theta} \right] = \frac{1}{2} \gamma H^2 \left[\frac{\sin (i - \theta)}{\sin i \sin \theta} \right] \qquad \text{(Eq. 8.07b)}$$

Applying the law of sines to the equilibrium force polygon, Figure 8.07a(2),

$$\frac{C}{\sin(\theta - \phi)} = \frac{W}{\sin(90 - \phi)} \qquad \text{(Eq. 8.07}c)$$

Combining Eqs. 8.07a, b, and c, the required unit cohesion is found to be

$$c' = \frac{1}{2}\gamma H \frac{\sin(i - \theta)\sin(\theta - \phi)}{\sin i \sin(90 - \phi)} \qquad \text{(Eq. 8.07}d)$$

Differentiating c' with respect to θ, and setting the result equal to zero,

$$\frac{dc'}{d\theta} = \frac{\gamma H}{2\sin i \sin(90 - \phi)}[\sin(i - \theta)\cos(\theta - \phi) -$$

$$\sin(\theta - \phi)\cos(i - \theta)] = 0$$

from which

$$\tan(i - \theta) = \tan(\theta - \phi) \qquad \text{(Eq. 8.07}e)$$

Eq. 8.07e is satisfied, and the critical value of θ given, only when

$$\theta = \theta_c = \tfrac{1}{2}(i + \phi) \qquad \text{(Eq. 8.07}f)$$

Eq. 8.07f represents the magnitude, θ_c, of θ corresponding to the critical slip surface. Combining Eqs. 8.07f and 8.07d, the maximum value of the required cohesion is found to be

$$c' = \frac{1}{2}\gamma H\left[\frac{\sin^2 \tfrac{1}{2}(i - \phi)}{\sin i \sin(90 - \phi)}\right] = \frac{\gamma H}{4}\left[\frac{1 - \cos(i - \phi)}{\sin i \cos \phi}\right] \qquad \text{(Eq. 8.07}g)$$

The critical value for the height of the slope may be found from Eq. 8.07g. H(crit) corresponds to the development of the full cohesive resistance, $c' = c$, and is

$$H(\text{crit}) = \frac{4c}{\gamma}\left[\frac{\sin i \cos \phi}{1 - \cos(i - \phi)}\right] \qquad \text{(Eq. 8.07}h)$$

For the purely cohesive ($\phi = 0$) case, Eq. 8.07g reduces to $c' = (\gamma H/4)\tan \tfrac{1}{2}i$, and Eq. 8.07(h) becomes $H(\text{crit}) = (4c/\gamma)\cos \tfrac{1}{2}i$. For the special case of a vertical slope ($i = 90°$) in a purely cohesive soil, $H(\text{crit}) = 4c/\gamma$. This latter result is seen to agree with the value obtained by the Rankine earth pressure theory for the maximum possible unsupported height of a vertical face in cohesive soil. Moreover, in the case of a vertical slope, there is close agreement with the results obtained (e.g., by Fellenius) using a cylindrical sliding surface. However, as the slope becomes flatter, the error resulting from assuming a plane surface of sliding rapidly increases. For slopes as flat as those generally used in practice, the assumption of a plane slip surface in a homogeneous slope introduces an intolerably large error on the side of danger.

b.   Practical Applications

When the materials of the slope are non-homogeneous or anisotropic, the shape of the critical surface may be largely determined by the geometry of the cross-section of the slope and by the slope properties. Indeed, the location of the critical surface (or portions of it) may sometimes be better predicted by exercising good judgment than by blindly making a routine analysis. There are several kinds of problems in which a substantial part of the critical surface is likely to be planar, or nearly so. Some examples are: (1) spreading failures caused by the presence of thin, weak strata in the foundation soil, (2) stability of dams having sloping cores, (3) stability of hydraulic fill dams, (4) stability of natural slopes in which bedding planes or stratification is a feature, and (5) stability of natural slopes in jointed or fissured clays, or in overconsolidated clay-shales.

(1)   Spreading Failure

Various procedures involving the use of wedges could be devised for the analysis. Rendulic (1938) suggested a procedure based on the determination of the active earth pressure on several arbitrary vertical planes through the embankment. Some degree of internal consistency is maintained by a special adaptation of the Engesser graphical procedure for determining the active earth pressure. The embankment soil is assumed to be cohesionless in Rendulic's procedure, which is outlined in Figure 8.07b.

Several planes such as A-A', B-B', C-C', D-D' in Figure 8.07b(1) are chosen arbitrarily, and the active earth pressure on each determined according to the procedure illustrated in Figure 8.07b(2). Through D several rays are passed, both to the right and to the left. A normal is drawn to each ray, and a resultant force F on that surface is drawn at angle ϕ to each normal. The force polygons are constructed by drawing a vertical line WV and laying out the weights of the various trial wedges along this line. According to the Engesser procedure, a line is drawn from each point laid out on WV, the line being drawn parallel to the resultant F_n acting on the base of the wedge whose weight is represented by the distance of

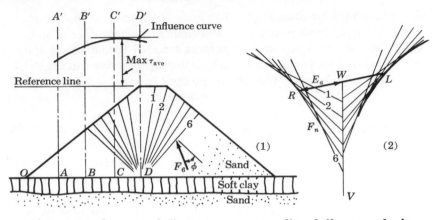

Figure 8.07b   Rendulic-Engesser spreading failure analysis

that point from W. An envelope is then drawn for these lines. The envelope to the left of WV corresponds to the trial wedges on the right side of D-D', while the envelope to the right of WV is for the trial wedges to the left of D-D'. The active pressure exerted by the soil on the right must be resisted by an equal and opposite force from the left of D-D'. Therefore, a line is drawn (by trial) through W so that the distances WR and WL are equal. The line RL is not generally horizontal, although it would be for a plane D-D' on the center line of a symmetrical embankment. The distance WR, to the scale used in laying out the diagram, is the active pressure E_a acting toward the left on D-D'. The average shearing stress on OD may now be found by dividing the horizontal component of E_a by the distance OD. This average stress is then plotted from the reference line, along the line D-D', to establish one point on the influence curve.

The described procedure is repeated for planes C-C', B-B', and A-A'. In each case, the horizontal component of E_a is divided by the appropriate length—OC, OB, or OA—to determine the average shearing stress on the base of the wedge under consideration. When the influence curve has been drawn, its maximum ordinate represents the maximum value which the average shearing stress on the base of any wedge may have.

If the strength of the soft clay is $s = c$, the factor of safety is $F_s = c/\max \tau_{ave}$. This procedure is not reliable if progressive failure of the clay is a possibility, as may be the case for highly sensitive clays. The procedure may, however, be slightly altered (see Terzaghi's *Theoretical Soil Mechanics*, p. 178) so that the shearing stress at specific points along the base may be determined, rather than average values along the base. If at any point $\tau = c$, progressive failure may emanate from that point if the soil is quite sensitive.

(2) *Sloping Core Dams*

The most recent study of this problem, by Seed and Sultan (1966), also included correlation with experimental results obtained from small scale models. Figure 8.07c illustrates the problem under consideration. An inclined core of cohesive soil is supported by a shell of cohesionless material, all resting on a hard foundation. The strength of the core is assumed constant, $s = c$, while the shell strength is given by $s = \bar{\sigma} \tan \phi$. The critical slip surface is assumed to consist of two planes: CO, along which the resistance to sliding depends on the strength of the core; and OA, along which the resistance is governed by the strength of the shell material. The interdependent equilibrium of the two wedges, AOB and OBC, is considered. In addition to their weights, OBC is acted on by the normal force N, the tangential force C, and the force P on plane OB, while AOB is acted on by P and the resultant force F on its base AO.

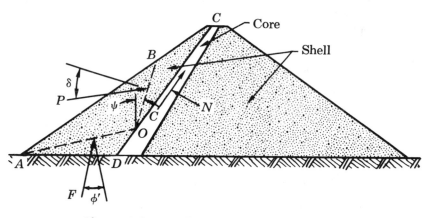

Figure 8.07c   Sloping core embankment

In a complete analysis, which is rather lengthy, the most critical position for point O has to be found by determining the factor of safety corresponding to different positions. The critical position for O depends on the assumptions made for the angles δ and ϕ. In addition, the most critical slope for OB must be found by varying the angle ψ for each position of O. In a stable embankment, $C = c' \cdot OC$ and F makes an angle of ϕ' with the normal, where $c' = c/F_s$ and $\tan \phi' = \tan \phi/F_s$. A trial and error procedure based on different assumed values for F_s is thus required.

Seed and Sultan found the best agreement with the experimental data when OB was inclined in its most critical position and $\delta = \phi'$, and when ϕ was taken as the value obtained from plane strain shear tests. The results were especially sensitive to changes in δ, but relatively insensitive to variations in ψ. The most conservative assessment of the factor of safety when OB was assumed to be vertical ($\psi = 0$) resulted from assuming $\delta = 0$ and using the ϕ value found from triaxial tests.

A fairly simple, and not unreasonably conservative, approach is to assume $\psi = 0$ and $\delta = \phi'$, making use of the value of ϕ found from triaxial tests. While Seed and Sultan used only one cross-section in their study, their conclusions would appear to apply qualitatively to other sections. However, plane strain conditions probably should not be assumed in a real embankment without careful consideration (see Section 8.03).

(3) Hydraulic Fill Dams

In a hydraulic fill dam, the soils are deposited in such a way that the coarser materials remain near the discharge pipes and form a strong shell, while the finer materials are carried to a central core pool where they eventually drop from suspension. During construction, and for some time afterward, the core may be of near-liquid consistency and the shell saturated with seeping water. There is a real danger that relatively sudden strains may take place which could cause liquefaction of parts of the shell. The resulting flow slide occurs suddenly, often with disastrous consequences. Flow slides cannot be rationally analyzed, but every precaution should be taken to ensure that conditions conducive to their development are not present.

There is also the possibility that failure may be caused by static forces. Several different procedures have been proposed for analyzing the stability under the action of static forces. One of the most recent is that of Fyedorov (1965). Most procedures are similar to that proposed by Gilboy (1934), which will now be described.

In Gilboy's procedure, it is assumed that the core exerts a hydrostatic (liquid) pressure against the shell, which is assumed to be granular. The ratio $R = \gamma(\text{core})/\gamma(\text{shell})$ is the basis for determining the factor of safety of the embankment. Gilboy analyzed the problem theoretically to determine the value of the ratio R required for equilibrium ($F.S. = 1$), and found the following relationship:

$$R = \frac{(C - A)\sqrt{1 + B^2} + \sqrt{C - A}\sqrt{C - B}\sqrt{1 + A^2}}{(1 + C^2) - (C - A)(C - B)} \qquad \text{(Eq. 8.07}i\text{)}$$

The dimensions A, B, and C in Eq. 8.07i are defined in Figure 8.07d. Since the height is unity, A, B, and C are actually ratios rather than dimensions. The ratio R found from Eq. 8.07i corresponds to a factor

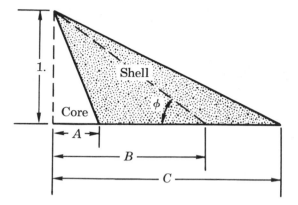

Figure 8.07d   Analysis of hydraulic fill

of safety of unity. The factor of safety in the actual embankment may be found if the unit weights of the materials of the core and shell are known. Thus

$$F. S. = \frac{R \text{ (available)}}{R \text{ (required)}}$$

The definition sketch, Figure 8.07d, simplifies the actual problem. In making a hydraulic fill, it is difficult to control the relative dimensions of the core and shell. Furthermore, the boundary between core and shell is likely to be a ragged and ill-defined transition zone. It is necessary to approximate this boundary by means of a line in order to use Gilboy's analysis.

(4)   *Natural Slopes*

Failures of natural slopes are phenomena that cannot be explained simply. Some causes of failure are well understood, while others have not yet been adequately explained. The failures always take place after a more or less lengthy period of stability, and are generally characterized as long-term failures. The extent to which creep phenomena, gradual reduction of strength, increase of unit weight, rise of pore pressure, or erosion have contributed to the failure is rarely known. Obviously, no analytical procedure is applicable to all cases; rather, the individual characteristics of each slope have to be studied to determine the kind of analysis that will be appropriate. In a good many cases, however, some type of wedge analysis turns out to be useful.

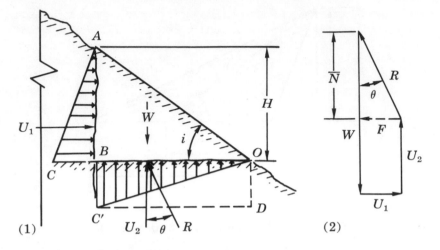

Figure 8.07e   Stratified, fissured slope

A slope in stratified, fissured soil is represented in Figure 8.07e. If it is supposed that a crack such as AC' may have opened deeply enough to intersect a horizontal parting of silt or sand (BO), it is possible that at some time the crack may fill with water. If this happens, a horizontal water pressure U_1, the resultant of pressure triangle ABC, pushes on the block ABO. Also, water seeping along the parting exerts an upward force U_2 as a result of the distributed pressure $BC'O$. This reduces the effective stress on the base BO to $N = W - U_2$. An analysis of the stability of the block ABO may be made as follows, if the parting consists of cohesionless soil:

$$W = \tfrac{1}{2}\gamma_m H^2 \cot i$$
$$U_1 = \tfrac{1}{2}\gamma_w H^2$$
$$U_2 = \tfrac{1}{2}\gamma_w H^2 \cot i$$
$$R = \bar{N} \sec \theta$$
$$R_H = R \sin \theta = \bar{N} \tan \theta$$

The quantities above are defined in Figure 8.07e. The frictional resistance, $F = R_H$, along BO must provide stability against horizontal movement of the block. This capability depends on the effective normal stress, $W - U_2$, and on the angle of internal friction of the soil in the parting. As long as $\theta < \phi$ the block is stable. To illustrate how precarious the situation is, assume $\gamma_m = 2\gamma_w$. Then $R_H = U_1$, or $\tfrac{1}{2}\gamma_w H^2 \cot i \tan \theta = \tfrac{1}{2}\gamma_w H^2$, from which $\tan \theta = \tan i$. Therefore, any slope steeper than the angle of internal friction of the material in the parting will fail, regardless of the magnitude of the average strength of the material comprising the slope. For the same ratio of unit weights, $\gamma_m/\gamma_w = 2$, the effective stress on BO will be reduced to zero ($U_2 = W$) if the outlet at O is frozen tight. Slippage will then proceed until the blockage at O is relieved, allowing drainage to reduce U_2. Stability will be regained if R_H becomes equal to U_1, which may itself be diminished by a reduction of the head of water as the crack widens. Repetitions of the process may eventually dislodge the block. If the parting BO is inclined downslope, the stability is further reduced.

The simple problem described above demonstrates the important effect of pore pressure changes in a confined permeable stratum or seam. The details are generally more complex than those of the illustration. For instance, the pore pressure changes may reflect the variation of artesian pressures over a broad area, and may be caused by climatological phenomena in some distant area at some former time. The exact relationships are determined by regional geological factors. Unlike the problem illustrated, slides sometimes result solely from a reduction of strength due to pore pressure rise, without any apparent change in the actuating forces. Many natural slopes have failed from causes similar to those described here. Stability often may be achieved by providing for the relief of pore pressures through a system of underdrains or bleeder wells.

Another factor that may lead to instability of slopes in cohesive soils is a gradual reduction of strength for reasons which are apparently unrelated to pore pressure changes. The reasons for such reductions in strength are not fully understood. However, two recent papers have thrown considerable light on the subject.

Skempton (1964) analyzed several slides that occurred in natural slopes that had been stable for a long time. Most of the slides were in stiff, fissured or jointed clays, but some were in intact clays. Skempton concluded that the initial (short-term) stability of the slopes probably depended upon the peak shearing strength of the clay. The long-term stability of slopes in intact clay also appeared to depend on the peak strength. However, in fissured or jointed clays there appears to be a gradual decrease from peak strength toward residual strength, and slopes in these materials fail if the average strength is reduced to the point where it no longer exceeds the average shearing stress along the critical surface. A typical relationship between peak and residual shear strength is shown in Figure 8.07f. The τ intercept for the envelope of residual strength circles is typically almost zero, so that residual strength may be expressed in terms of only a residual angle of internal friction ϕ_r. Reduction of strength to the residual value implies the imposition of relatively large strains. Skempton reckons that in slopes this reduction does not take place simultaneously along the entire critical surface.

In considering the failures of slopes in overconsolidated clays and

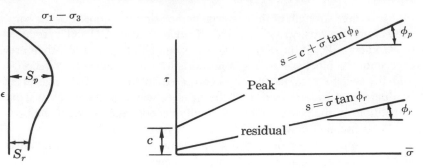

Figure 8.07f   Comparisons of peak and residual strengths

clay-shales, Bjerrum (1966) has suggested a mechanism whereby the strength may be reduced to the residual value progressively along the critical surface. According to his hypothesis, the reduction occurs due to large strains which begin at some point where a former constraint has been removed by natural or human causes. The movement occurs under the influence of the gravitational forces as a result of the relief of "locked-in" stresses, the magnitude of which are related to the geological history of the slope materials. The progress of the failure from its starting point is controlled by the geometry of the problem and the associated mechanics; and the rate at which the strains (and strength reductions) progress is regulated by the nature of the interparticle bonds. If strong diagenetic bonds are present, the progress will be very slow. A major portion of the eventual slip surface is usually plane, so that a sliding wedge analysis is appropriate. This is not the case for all of the slides investigated by Skempton, some of which were along nearly cylindrical surfaces and were best analyzed by the Swedish method.

8.08   Pore Pressures

The stability of a slope, and the computed factor of safety, may be highly dependent upon the magnitude and distribution of pore pressures within the slope. The prediction of pore pressures and the determination of their influence is usually more complicated than was indicated in the simple examples given in Sections 8.05 and 8.07. Since the reliability of an effective stress analysis depends on the accuracy with which the pore pressures are known, some methods for estimating pore pressures will be discussed before proceeding with the details of stability analysis.

There are three cases to be considered in connection with the prediction of pore pressures: (1) pressures due to hydrostatic head, (2) pressures exerted by water flowing through soil whose volume remains constant, and (3) pressures associated with stress changes, which initiate volume changes of the soil (consolidation or swelling).

Pressures due to hydrostatic head are easily determined if the position of the water table is known. Below the water table the soil is buoyed. The effective normal stress at a given point in the mass depends on the total unit weight of the soil above the water table, and on the submerged unit weight of soil below the water table. It is quite unlikely that the critical condition for slope stability will be associated with purely hydrostatic pore pressures. However, in some procedures the hydrostatic pressures are treated separately from pore pressures due to seepage or stress change.

a.   *Seepage Pressures*

When water flows through soil, the drag forces tend to displace the soil in the direction of flow. If flow is toward the surface (for example, toward the face of an embankment or cut), sufficiently large seepage forces will create an unstable condition in the soil. The effect of the seepage forces on a specified mass of soil can be most easily investigated by means of the "boundary neutral forces." In this procedure, the *total* unit weight of the soil, γ_{sat}, is used in the analysis; whereas, when the seepage forces are used directly, their effect on the submerged soil (γ') is analyzed. When the two procedures are correctly done they lead to the same result.

The boundary neutral forces can be evaluated from a flow net representing the pattern of seepage in the soil. Figure 8.08a shows two examples of the use of flow nets to determine boundary neutral forces. One

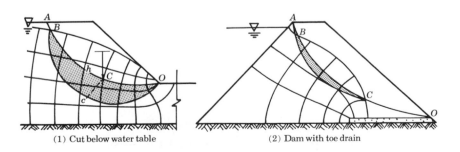

(1) Cut below water table   (2) Dam with toe drain

Figure 8.08a   Seepage forces

of these illustrates the flow pattern that would develop when a "dry" cut is made below the water table, while the other shows the pattern in a dam which is homogeneous except for a more permeable toe drain. The neutral pressures on a trial slip surface $ABCO$ are easily determined at points where the slip surface intersects an equipotential line. For example, at some point such as C the piezometric head is h, and the neutral pressure Cc on the slip surface is $h\gamma_w$. If this procedure is repeated at various points, the distribution of neutral pressure on the boundary may be plotted (to some scale) as the shaded area lying between BcO and BCO [Figure 8.08a(1)]. A similar procedure is used in the case of the dam (2). Note that the neutral pressure is zero at points where the slip surface intersects the seepage line, and that the generally sinusoidal distribution is typical.

When the level of a reservoir impounded by a symmetrical, homogeneous dam remains constant, the stability of the upstream face will not be critical because the water pressure acting on the face is greater than the neutral pressures along a potential slip surface. If the slope of the upstream face is steeper than that of the downstream face, or if non-homogeneity consists of having weaker soil near the upstream face, its stability should be investigated for the full reservoir condition. A more severe condition occurs if there is a sudden drawdown of the reservoir. In this case, the external water pressure is removed and flow toward the upstream toe begins. As will be shown in Section 8.11, the neutral stress on a potential failure surface may also be reduced by the drawdown; but the net effect of the drawdown is to increase the unstabilizing (driving) forces. A flow net which forms immediately after instantaneous drawdown in a simplified section is shown in Figure 8.08b(1), while that for a more realistic section is given in (2). The influence of rapid drawdown on a pervious embankment was investigated in great detail by Reinius (1948). The situation in an actual dam is changed considerably by the zoning of ma-

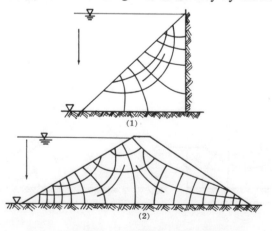

Figure 8.08b   **Sudden drawdown**

terials, by the presence of internal or toe drains, and by the permeability of the foundation. Nevertheless, it is possible to construct flow nets that take these into account, after which the neutral stresses may be determined.

In a total stress analysis, the effects of sudden drawdown are often approximated by assuming simply that the unit weight of the soil between the initial and final positions of the reservoir surface changes suddenly from γ' to γ_{sat}.

b.   Pore Pressures Due to Stress Changes

Stress changes may occur within an embankment or slope for a variety of reasons. For example, the loads will increase as the height of an embankment is raised. Thus, as construction progresses, pore pressure changes will be induced. The magnitude of the changes depends on the rate of construction, the properties of the embankment soil, and the embankment geometry. The latter two also govern the rate at which the excess pressures will be dissipated. While the design must be based on reasonable assumptions concerning the induced pore pressures, it is prudent to check these assumptions by means of field measurements so that timely changes of design or rate of construction may be instituted, if required. It is difficult to predict the induced pore pressures accurately because the compacted soils may vary in degree of saturation from place to place, and because there is not a reliable way of predicting the stress changes, which are generally anisotropic ($\Delta\sigma_1 \neq \Delta\sigma_3$). Consequently, it is usual to base the design on conservative assumptions, tempered by experience.

Other causes for stress increase in slopes are: earthquake or other dynamic forces, steepening of cuts, undercutting, rapid drawdown, and static surcharges of various kinds. Not only is the deviator stress (and, consequently, the shearing stress) changed by these forces, but, as was mentioned, the principal stresses generally change by different amounts.

Bishop (1954) has suggested that the pore pressure change be related to the change $\Delta\sigma_1$ in the major principal stress by means of a pore pressure coefficient $\bar{B}$, such that

$$\Delta u = \bar{B} \times \Delta\sigma_1 \qquad \text{(Eq. 8.08}a\text{)}$$

Skempton (1954) defined the coefficient $\bar{B}$ in terms of the pore pressure coefficients A and B and the changes in the principal stresses:

$$\frac{\Delta u}{\Delta\sigma_1} = \bar{B} = B\left[1 - (1 - A)\left(1 - \frac{\Delta\sigma_3}{\Delta\sigma_1}\right)\right] \qquad \text{(Eq. 8.08}b\text{)}$$

The theory of elasticity has sometimes been used to predict the stress changes arising from load increases; e.g., see Goodman and Brown (1963). However, in many practical problems, it is reasonable to simplify the procedure by assuming that the major principal stress is equal to the unit stress imposed on a horizontal plane by the weight of a column of soil above the point under consideration. In a built-up embankment, every point within the embankment was approximately at the surface during some stage of construction. The stress change $\Delta\sigma_1$ at any point along a potential slip surface in the completed embankment may then be expressed as $\Delta\sigma_1 = \gamma_m \cdot h$, where h is the vertical distance from the slip surface to the slope surface. If the pore pressures have not dissipated during construction, $\Delta u = \overline{B} \cdot \gamma_m h$, corresponding to a generally sinusoidal distribution along the slip surface. From a practical standpoint, the magnitude of B may be adjusted through experience or field observation to include the effects of partial pore pressure dissipation. The convenience of using this approach is apparent, and its reliability depends only on the accuracy with which $\overline{B}$ has been estimated. The selected value of B must really represent an average, because $\overline{B}$ is not constant along the slip surface. It is evaluated on the basis of laboratory tests and experience gained from field observations.

One of the pore pressure coefficients, B, varies between 0 and 1 as the degree of saturation varies between 0 per cent and 100 per cent, while the other coefficient, A, varies with the deviator stress, and has a different value in a stable embankment than it has in one on the verge of failure. Because $\overline{B}$ depends on A, which varies substantially according to soil type and pressure range, it is unwise to rely heavily on "typical" values for $\overline{B}$. However, in compacted embankments having a reasonable factor of safety, $\overline{B}$ is commonly between 0.2 and 0.8. Low plasticity soils compacted fairly dry would fall in the lower part of this range, while more plastic soils compacted on the wet side of optimum would tend toward the upper part of the range. Both Bishop (1954) and Morgenstern (1963) have shown that for the case of rapid drawdown in *saturated embankments of low permeability* it is reasonable to assume $\overline{B} = 1$ for preliminary analysis.

While the pore pressure change Δu due to stress increase may be expressed in terms of $\overline{B}$ and $\Delta\sigma_1$, it is the *total* pore pressure u that is required in a stability analysis using effective stresses. Bishop and Morgenstern (1960) have defined a pore pressure ratio in terms of an initial u_0, as

$$r_u = \frac{u}{\gamma h} = \frac{u_0}{\gamma h} + \frac{\overline{B}}{\gamma h} \times \Delta\sigma_1 \qquad \text{(Eq. 8.08c)}$$

If $\Delta\sigma_1$ is taken to be γh, then $r_u = u_0/\gamma h + \overline{B}$. If in addition $u_0 = 0$, as often may be nearly the case in compacted embankments at the time the soil is placed, the ratio $r_u = \bar{B}$. As in the case of $\bar{B}$, r_u is not constant through-out the cross-section. Therefore, an average value must be used if the analysis is to be kept fairly simple. Bishop and Morgenstern suggested an averaging technique that produces generally satisfactory results.

8.09   Swedish Method

The Swedish method includes all those procedures in which the slip surface is assumed to be circularly cylindrical. At the present time, there appears to be no practical necessity for considering curved slip surfaces of other shapes.

Procedures derived from the Swedish method may be divided into two general classes: (1) those that treat as a unit the entire mass of soil above the slip surface, and (2) those that divide the mass arbitrarily into vertical slices, the equilibrium of which may be separately considered. For con-venience, these will be termed the *mass* procedure and the *slices* procedure. The mass procedure is simpler in concept and in application than the slices procedure, but is not as versatile. The slices procedure is more appropriate when the critical surface passes through materials having different prop-erties, and is also readily applied to general cases involving composite slip surfaces. Thus, the slices procedure is generally used in analyzing the stability of major dams, which are almost always of zoned construction, while the mass procedure is more often used in connection with small dams, cuts, and natural slopes in relatively homogeneous and isotropic soils.

a.   Mass Procedure

Investigations to determine the most critical circle may be accom-plished in different ways, according to whether or not the soil is assumed to exhibit frictional properties. For fairly rapid load changes, it is often permissible to assume that $s = c$ (usually called a "$\phi = 0$" analysis). This does not necessarily mean that the strength is the same everywhere in the embankment, but only that it does not change under the specified loading conditions. However, it is sometimes found that the soil strength is about the same throughout the zone under consideration. In this case, the problem may be successfully solved on a purely theoretical basis since the manner of distribution of stress on the critical surface, although un-

known, is of less consequence that it is when the strength varies with
depth.

(1) $s = c$ *(independent of depth)*

Theoretically, the most critical circle in this case cuts to an infinite
depth and has an infinitely large radius. In nature, the depth of the slip
surface is always limited by the existence of a hard layer beneath the
slope. Both Fellenius and Taylor showed that for $i > 53°$ the most critical
circle passes through the toe of the slope. For $i < 53°$, the most critical
circle passes below the toe, and the factor of safety is dependent on the
depth to a hard stratum.

In Figure 8.09a, consider the possibility of a rotational slip along the
circular arc $ABCD$ against a resistance equal to the product of the unit
shearing resistance and the arc length. The center of the arc, O, is located
at an arbitrary distance above the slope on a horizontal line O'-O-O''.

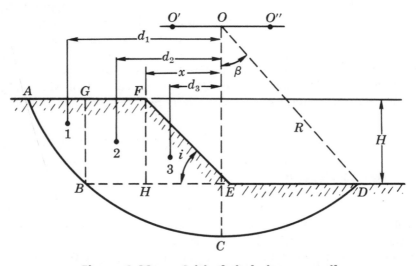

Figure 8.09a Critical circle in $s = c$ soil

Let the weight of ABG be W_1, the weight of $GBHF$ be W_2, and the weight
of FHE be W_3. The horizontal distance of O from the brow of the slope
is x. For a given radius R the moment arm d_1 is independent of x, while
d_2 and d_3 depend on x:

$$d_2 = \frac{1}{2}(R \sin \beta + x)$$

$$d_3 = x - \frac{H \cot i}{3}$$

The moment of segment BCD with respect to O is zero, while the moment $W_1 d_1$ of AGB is constant. The driving moment is

$$M_D = W_1 d_1 + W_2 d_2 + W_3 d_3$$
$$= W_1 d_1 + \frac{1}{2}\gamma H(R \sin \beta - x)(R \sin \beta + x) +$$

$$\frac{1}{2}\gamma H^2 \cot i \left(x - \frac{H \cot i}{3}\right) \qquad \text{(Eq. 8.09a)}$$

In order to see how the driving moment is influenced by the position of O on $O'-O-O''$, Eq. 8.09a may be differentiated with respect to x, holding R, H, β, and i constant, to evaluate x corresponding to a maximum M_D.

$$\frac{\partial M_D}{\partial x} = \frac{\gamma H}{2}[(R \sin \beta - x) - (R \sin \beta + x)] + \frac{1}{2}\gamma H^2 \cot i = 0$$

from which

$$x = \frac{1}{2} H \cot i \qquad \text{(Eq. 8.09b)}$$

Eq. 8.09b shows that for slip circles passing below the toe the driving moment is a maximum when the circle has its center directly above the mid-point of the slope. The length l of the arc $ABCD$, and therefore the magnitude of τl, is independent of x, as long as A is on the upper level of the slope and D is on the lower level. Thus, for circles of any radius R centered on any horizontal line above the slope, τ is a maximum when M_D is a maximum; and i.e., for a *midpoint circle*. As R increases, M_D must do likewise since every member of Eq. 8.09a increases. Because l, also, increases with R, it is not immediately apparent that τ will increase as R gets larger. However, Fellenius showed that the *most critical* midpoint circle cuts infinitely deeply beneath the slope. For this most critical circle, he proved that the corresponding stability number, $c'/\gamma H = 0.181$, is the maximum possible value for mid-point circles, and that this represents the critical condition for slope angles $i < 53°$.

For slopes steeper than 53°, Taylor showed that stability numbers greater than 0.181 exist for the critical circle through the toe, and concluded that deep-seated failures are possible in constant strength soils only when $i < 53°$. For steeper slopes toe failures will occur.

The depth to a hard surface is always limited. Since $c'/\gamma H$ has a maximum value of 0.181 when R is infinite, it follows that when the depth is limited the critical surface will be tangent to the hard layer, and that the corresponding stability number will be less than 0.181, provided that $i < 53°$. When the depth is limited, the stability number depends on the slope angle i. Taylor (1937) prepared a chart giving the relationship among i, D, and the stability number. See Figure 8.09b. Note that for shallow depths to rock, the likelihood that the most critical circle will be a toe circle (i.e., $n = 0$, in chart) increases as the slope becomes flatter.

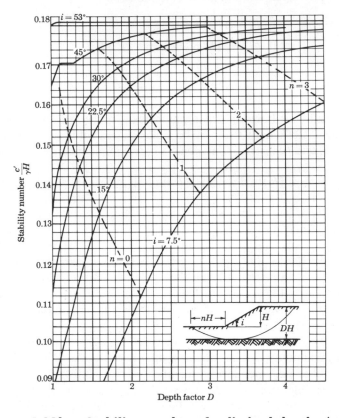

Figure 8.09b   Stability numbers for limited depth, $\phi = 0$, $s =$ constant—After Taylor, 1937

Fellenius also investigated circles passing through the toe of the slope, and found that the critical circle has its center situated approximately as shown in Figure 8.09c. The most critical toe circle is not necessarily the critical circle for the slope, as the latter may either emerge on the slope (called a slope circle) or be deep-seated, depending both on i and the depth to hard material. For slopes as flat as those generally analyzed, note that $\alpha = 35°$ and $\beta = 25°$ are satisfactory for preliminary trials for toe circles, and are numbers easily remembered.

$i°$	n	$α°$	$β°$
90	0	45	30
60	0.577	40	29
45	1.0	37	28
33.68	1.5	35	26
26.57	2.0	35	25
18.43	3.0	35	25
11.32	5.0	37	25

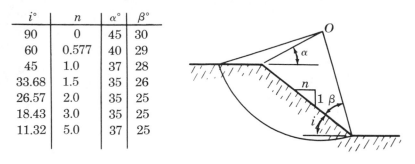

Figure 8.09c   Position of most critical circle through toe
$s = c$ (constant)

A general procedure for analysis, applicable to toe circles, slope circles, or mid-point circles, is illustrated in Figure 8.09d. The forces acting on the mass ACB are its weight W, through the centroid; the developed cohesive resistance C', parallel to chord $\overline{AC}$ and at a distance $a = R \cdot (\overparen{AC}/\overline{AC})$ from O; and the normal force N, acting through the intersection of the lines of action of W and C', and directed toward O. For any trial circle, C' may be quickly determined from an equilibrium force polygon. The corresponding τ is $C'/\overline{AC}$, since C' is the sum of the projections on $\overline{AC}$ of the incremental shear forces $\tau \cdot dl$ along the arc $\overparen{AC}$. Several trial circles are analyzed until the critical circle (maximum τ) may be identified. Then $F_s = c/\tau$.

If seepage toward the slope occurs, as in Figure 8.09e, the total weight W is equal to the sum of the weights of soil and water in the wedge. The

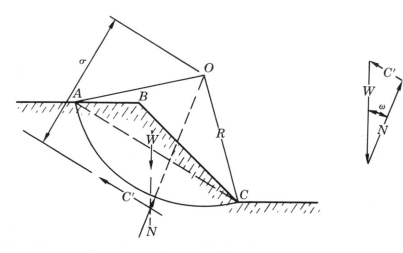

Figure 8.09d   Swedish circle analysis

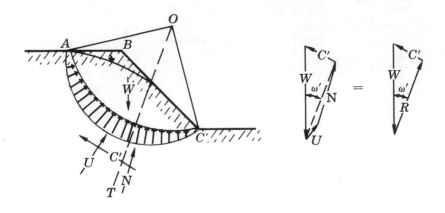

Figure 8.09e   Influence of seepage

pore pressure distribution along the arc may be found from the flow net (not shown), and its resultant U determined. The resultant of U and N must act along the line OT, through the intersection of W and C'. A comparison of Figure 8.09d and 8.09e shows that C' is increased by the seepage. Most of the increase is due to the increase in W; however, there will be some increase due to the fact that the line of action of W shifts slightly to the left for the seepage conditions shown, making $\omega' > \omega$. In effect, the solution may be made without specific knowledge of U and N, provided that the position of the seepage line is known, because the direction of R is defined by the line OT.

(2)   s = c (proportional to depth)

Although the actual distribution of shearing stress along a potential slip surface is not known, the stresses are assumed to be proportional to the strength. Above, this amounted to a uniform distribution of τ along the arc. In the present case, it means that the shearing stresses increase with depth along the arc. This means that the resultant shearing resistance, C', will not be parallel to the chord AC, but at some flatter slope, and that its moment arm will be somewhat smaller than in the case of a uniformly distributed stress, as shown in Figure 8.09f. Note that the position of N is only slightly affected.

A fairly common practice is to proceed as if the stresses were uniformly distributed, and determine τ just as in connection with Figure 8.09d. The factor of safety is then found from the ratio c_{ave}/τ, where c_{ave} is the average strength taken over the height of slope under consideration. For flat slopes this procedure may be considerably in error, because a disproportionate part of the slip surface will be in high strength materials (when a circular failure arc is assumed).

While the details will not be given here, Gibson and Morgenstern (1962) analyzed this problem mathematically, correctly accounting for an assumed linear increase of strength with depth. Their analysis showed that the factor of safety depends only on the slope angle i, being independent of the height of the slope. This is the same result that is found for cohesionless soil, although the critical surface is different, and quite unlike the result found for $s = c$ (constant) soils. Gibson and Morgenstern prepared a graph giving the relationship between the slope angle and the stability number for slopes between $0°$ and $90°$. The critical circles pass through or above the toe of the slope, so that the depth to rock has little, if any, influence on the stability of the slope.

It is appropriate at this time to mention the lack of uniformity among various authors in the definition of the *stability number*. Taylor first applied the name to the dimensionless ratio $c'/\gamma H$. Perhaps it would have been more logical to call this ratio an *in*stability number, since stability becomes more precarious as the ratio *increases*. Terzaghi and Peck employed the reciprocal, $\gamma H/c'$, and designated it as the *stability factor*. Others, for example, Janbu (1954) and Gibson and Morgenstern, used the same ratio as did Terzaghi and Peck, but called the ratio the stability number. To avoid confusion in making use of the various tables and graphs available, it is wise to check the definition used for stability number.

(3) $s = c + \sigma \tan \phi$ *(Friction Circle Analysis)*

When the resistance along a potential slip surface is due to two strength components, one independent of the normal pressure and one dependent on normal pressure, the soil is sometimes called a c-ϕ material. Similarly, an analysis which considers both kinds of resistance is termed a c-ϕ analysis. Graphical analyses of this type were developed by Fellenius and by Krey, making use of a friction circle, or ϕ-circle, for determining the direction of the resultant of the frictional and normal stresses on the slip surface. The procedure, in its simplest form, is illustrated in Figure 8.09g.

The resultant of the cohesive resistance, C', is assumed to be parallel to the chord AC and at a distance of $R(\widehat{AC}/\overline{AC})$ from O. F is the resultant of the frictional and normal stresses on the arc AC. The frictional resistance is assumed to be fully developed, so that F makes angle ϕ with

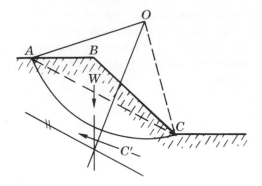

Figure 8.09f   Effect of non-uniform stress distribution

a normal to the arc and is thus tangent to a circle of radius $R \sin \phi$ centered at O. For equilibrium, F must pass through the intersection of the lines of action of C' and W. The unknown magnitudes of C' and F may be found by constructing the force polygon (2). Several trials are made, using different positions for O, until the minimum value, $F_c = C/C' = c/c'$ is found.

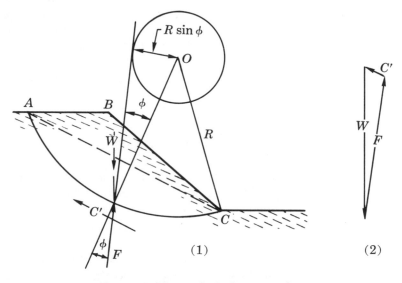

Figure 8.09g ϕ-circle procedure

While the above method is reasonably reliable, the method of handling the force F is not quite correct. On any element dl of the slip surface the resultant dF of the normal force dN and the frictional force dT is, indeed, tangent to the ϕ-circle. The manner in which the magnitude of dN changes along the arc is not really known, but both dT and dF must vary in magnitude in exactly the same way as does dN. Now, suppose that dN is assumed to be uniform along the arc. The resultant F of the elemental forces dF shown in Figure 8.09h(1) may be obtained from a string polygon (2).

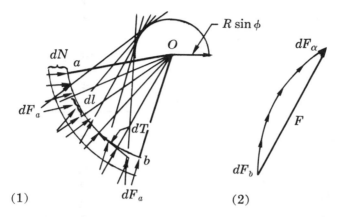

Figure 8.09h   Discussion of ϕ-circle correction

As $dl \rightarrow O$, the shape of the string polygon approaches the shape of the circular arc ab. In the limit $F/\Sigma dF = L_c/L_a$, where $L_c = $ chord length, and $L_a = $ arc length of ab. Now, since the moment of F about O must equal $\Sigma dF \cdot R \sin \phi$, then $F \cdot d = R \sin \phi \cdot \Sigma dF$, where d is the moment arm of F with respect to O. Thus

$$\frac{F}{\Sigma dF} \cdot d = R \sin \phi = \frac{L_c}{L_a} \cdot d$$

$$d = \frac{L_a}{L_c} \cdot R \sin \phi \qquad \text{(Eq. 8.09c)}$$

Therefore, F cannot be tangent to the ϕ-circle, but must be tangent to a larger circle, the diameter of which depends on the magnitude of the central angle of the failure arc. Use of the ϕ-circle rather than the "corrected" circle is equivalent to using a slightly conservative value of ϕ in the analysis.

The procedure used for investigating F can, of course, be applied directly to the tangential forces along the failure arc. Thus, if the dT are uniformly distributed along the arc, the resultant T of the tangential forces (whether frictional or cohesive) must be at a distance of $R(L_a/L_c)$ from O, and must be parallel to the chord. Applying the ϕ-circle correction to F is the same as correcting the moment arm of T. Thus, since the moment arm of N is zero, $T \cdot L_a/L_c \cdot R = F \cdot L_a/L_c \cdot R \sin \phi$. Substitution of $T = N \tan \phi = F \cos \phi \cdot \tan \phi = F \sin \phi$ makes the two sides identical.

However, the assumption that the dT are uniformly distributed is generally inconsistent with the requirements for equilibrium, because this implies that the dN are also uniformly distributed. Thus T must be parallel to the chord AC, and N perpendicular to it, as shown in Figure 8.09*i*.

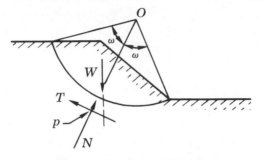

Figure 8.09i   Symmetrical distribution

Since the point p, where T and N intersect, does not generally lie directly below the center of gravity of the mass, moment equilibrium is not satisfied. The same limitation exists for any other distribution in which the dN are symmetrically disposed about the bisector of the central angle, although the moment arm of T will be affected.

The effects of different assumptions regarding the distribution of the normal stresses are summarized in Figure 8.09*j*. The occurrence of cases

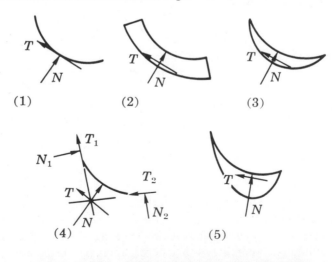

**Figure 8.09j   Effect of various distributions
of normal stress**

(1) and (4) in real slopes is inconceivable, but these cases represent the extremes possible in the position of T. If the normal stress is concentrated at any one point, T will be tangent to the arc at that point, giving it the *minimum* possible moment arm. If the normal stresses are concentrated equally $(N_1 = N_2)$ at the two ends of the arc, T will be parallel to the chord and positioned at the intersection of the end tangents, giving it the *maximum* possible moment arm. If $N_1 \neq N_2$, T will still act through the intersection of the end tangents, but will not be parallel to the chord; therefore, its moment arm will be smaller than when $N_1 = N_2$. Case (2) has already been discussed: the moment arm of T is $R(L_a/L_c)$. Such a distribution is unlikely. Cases (3) and (5) represent distributions for which the normal stress is more nearly concentrated than it is in case (2). Therefore, the moment arm of T in these two cases will be smaller than it is for case (2). For practical purposes, T, in cases (3) and (5), may be assumed to be about half-way between the arc and the position corresponding to case (2). Taylor (1937) has given the required corrections to be applied to the radius of the ϕ-circle for distributions (2) and (3). Case (5) probably represents the most likely distribution in a real slope, and the required ϕ-circle correction would be only slightly less than that for case (3).

It is concluded that a reasonable procedure in making the ϕ-circle analysis is to increase the radius r of the ϕ-circle to some value r' in accordance with the correction given by Taylor for sinusoidal distribution:

$$r' = \frac{1 - (2\omega/\pi)^2}{\cos \omega} \cdot r$$

where ω is one-half the central angle of the arc. Alternatively, two concentric circles may be drawn at O; one having a radius $r = R \sin \phi$, and the other having a radius $r'' = r(L_a/L_c)$. The resultant F may then be directed so as to pass approximately midway between two points defined by the intersections of the two circumferences with a radius perpendicular to F.

A final important point is concerned with the assumption that full frictional resistance develops, and with the use of F_c rather than F_s for the factor of safety. It might be argued that some assumed factor of safety F_ϕ could be applied to obtain a starting value for ϕ'; i.e., $\phi' = \tan^{-1} (\tan \phi / F_\phi)$. The corresponding F_c could then be found by the ϕ-circle procedure. After one or two adjustments in the F_ϕ estimate for a given trial circle, F_c can be made to equal F_ϕ. When this is true,

$$F_c = F_\phi = F_s = \frac{s}{\tau} = \frac{c + \overline{\sigma} \tan \phi}{c' + \overline{\sigma} \tan \phi'}$$

Proceeding in this way to other trial circles, the slip circle for which F_s is a minimum can be found. However, this slip circle *will not be the same* as the critical circle found by the first procedure, in which a minimum F_c is found while holding $F_\phi = 1$. Therefore, it is necessary to inquire as to which is really the critical surface.

The critical surface is properly described as that surface along which slip will occur *if a slide develops*. Except by accident, this surface will not have a circular trace; however, in the absence of constraining boundary conditions, there is no more reasonable recourse than to investigate the possibility of failure along a circularly cylindrical surface. It has already been shown that the critical surface in cohesionless soil coincides with the surface of the slope, and that the critical circle in purely cohesive soil cuts as deeply as possible. In a c-ϕ (c = constant) soil, the depth to which a *failure* arc will cut depends only on the frictional properties of the soil. At failure, both the cohesive and frictional resistance will be fully developed. Therefore, the critical circle must be found by some procedure in which the *full frictional resistance* is assumed to be developed. The procedure in which a minimum F_c is found when $F_\phi = 1$ satisfies this requirement. However, since F_c often gives a misleading impression as to the safety of the slope, it is desirable to determine F_s for the critical circle corresponding to a minimum F_c. In fact, once the critical circle has been discovered, there is no reason that a factor of safety, according to any definition whatsoever, cannot be found.

As an aid in selecting the location of trial circles for use in the analysis, certain facts are now summarized: (1) for cohesionless soil, the critical circle has an infinite radius and coincides with the slope surface, (2) for purely cohesive soil, slope angle less than 53°, the critical circle cuts to an infinite depth (infinite radius) and is centered above the mid-point of the slope, and (3) for purely cohesive soil, $i > 53°$, the critical circle is a toe circle having its center approximately above the midpoint (see Figure 8.09c) unless the slope becomes very steep. Therefore, the center of the critical circle in all cases should be found to lie within the shaded area shown in Figure 8.09k. Contours representing equal factors of safety generally plot as oblong curves within the shaded area. By judicious selection of trial centers, the number of trials necessary may be kept within reasonable limits.

Charts such as those produced by Fellenius, Taylor (e.g., see Figure 8.09l, which is based on Taylor's work), and others may in rare cases provide the factor of safety without any need for trial solutions. However, most practical problems involve boundary constraints, seepage, pore pressures, or other complicating factors not included in the charts. Meyer (1958) has suggested a simple means for including seepage effects in a stability chart analysis.

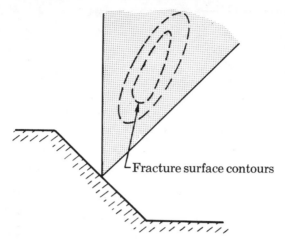

Fracture surface contours

Figure 8.09k **Probable zone of centers for critical circles**

b. *Slices Procedure*

In this procedure, the soil mass is divided into a number of slices, as shown in Figure 8.09m. The slices need not be the same width. Breaks in the surface or sudden transitions from one material to another along the trial surface are generally made to coincide with boundaries between slices. Otherwise, slice widths are often made about equal.

Let it be assumed for generality that pore pressures due to one of the causes discussed in Section 8.08 exist within the slope depicted in Figure 8.09m. If the slope is stable, every slice of any trial mass must be in equilibrium under its own weight and the action of the forces on its boundaries. The forces acting on an internal slice, number 4, are shown in (2). In addition to its weight, the slice is subjected to normal and shearing forces on its sides and base. The total normal forces, H and N, represent the resultants of intergranular and pore water stresses. None of the H or V forces is known with any degree of certainty; but they influence the magnitudes of N and S, which are of primary interest. In order to solve the problem, it is necessary to make some assumptions regarding the H and V forces. Let $\Delta H = H_L - H_R$ and $\Delta V = V_L - V_R$. The equilibrium force polygon is shown in (3), where S is represented as the sum of the developed cohesive resistance, C', and the frictional resistance $\overline{N} \tan \phi'$. N is on the perpendicular bisector of the base chord, while S is parallel to the chord.

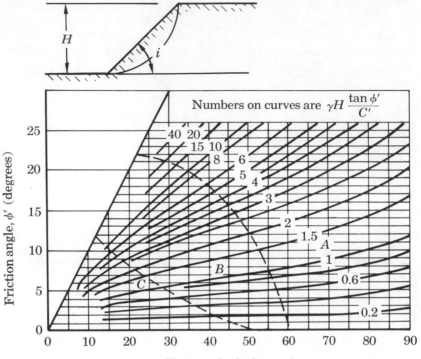

Figure 8.09l   Stability chart—C-ϕ soil—After Taylor

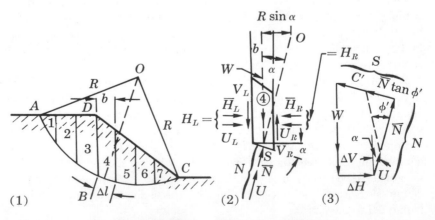

Figure 8.09m   Slices procedure

When the equilibrium of the whole mass is considered, the internal forces on the slice boundaries have no direct influence because they occur in equal and opposite pairs. The driving moment is equal to the sum of the moments of the weights of the slices. If α is the angle between the base chord and the horizontal [Figure 8.09m(2)]

$$M_D = \Sigma W \cdot R \sin \alpha$$

The resisting moment is

$$M_R = \Sigma S \cdot R = \Sigma \tau \cdot \Delta l \cdot R$$

where

$$\tau = c' + \overline{\sigma} \tan \phi'$$
$$\Delta l = \text{length of base arc of a slice (a variable)}$$

The shearing stress τ may also be expressed in terms of the strength parameters and the factor of safety F_s, which will henceforth be designated simply as F. Thus,

$$\tau = \frac{1}{F} (c + \overline{\sigma} \tan \phi)$$

and

$$M_R = \Sigma \frac{1}{F} (c + \overline{\sigma} \tan \phi) \Delta l \cdot R \qquad \text{(Eq. 8.09d)}$$

Since, for equilibrium, $M_D = M_R$

$$\Sigma W \cdot R \sin \alpha = \Sigma \frac{1}{F} (c + \overline{\sigma} \tan \phi) \Delta l \cdot R$$

Because R is constant, and F is assumed to be constant along the critical circle, these terms may be factored out of the summations. Then,

$$F = \frac{\Sigma (c + \overline{\sigma} \tan \phi) \Delta l}{\Sigma W \sin \alpha} \qquad \text{(Eq. 8.09e)}$$

The effective normal stress $\overline{\sigma}$ may be expressed in terms of the forces on the slice:

$$\overline{\sigma} = \overline{N}/\Delta l = (N-U)/\Delta l = (N/\Delta l) - u \qquad \text{(Eq. 8.09f)}$$

If, in the force polygon (3), forces are summed in the direction of N, it is found that

$$N = (W + \Delta V) \cos \alpha - \Delta H \cdot \sin \alpha \qquad \text{(Eq. 8.09g)}$$

If Eqs. 8.09e, f, and g are now combined, it is found that

$$F = \frac{\Sigma [c \cdot \Delta l + (W \cos \alpha - u \cdot \Delta l) \tan \phi + (\Delta V \cos \alpha - \Delta H \sin \alpha) \tan \phi]}{\Sigma W \sin \alpha}$$

$$\text{(Eq. 8.09h)}$$

The resultant forces, ΔH and ΔV, on the sides of any slice are not known. They depend on the strains within the slope and on the stress-deformation behavior of the soil, and cannot be determined by statics. The easiest way to dispose of the problem is simply to ignore the side forces; i.e. assume that the resultants on the two sides are equal and opposite. This assumption forms the basis of a procedure that is quite commonly used. The assumption results in the disappearance of the last term inside the brackets in Eq. 8.09h, and leads to the simplified expression

$$F = \frac{\Sigma[c{\cdot}\Delta l + (W\cos\alpha - u{\cdot}\Delta l)\tan\phi]}{\Sigma W\sin\alpha} \qquad \text{(Eq. 8.09i)}$$

For some applications, such as in the analysis of compacted embankments (see Section 8.08), the expression may be further simplified by introducing $u{\cdot}\Delta l = \overline{B}\cdot\left[\dfrac{W}{b}\right]{\cdot}\Delta l = W{\cdot}\overline{B}{\cdot}\sec\alpha$, assuming Δl to be about equal to the length of the base chord. Then

$$F = \frac{\Sigma[c{\cdot}\Delta l + W(\cos\alpha - \overline{B}\sec\alpha)\tan\phi]}{\Sigma W\sin\alpha} \qquad \text{(Eq. 8.09j)}$$

The effect of ignoring the side forces now needs to be determined. The fact that these are internal forces means that $\Sigma\Delta H = 0$ and $\Sigma\Delta V = 0$, if there are no external loads on the slope. However, it does not follow that the terms, $\Sigma\Delta V \cdot \cos\alpha\tan\phi$ and $\Sigma\Delta H \cdot \sin\alpha\tan\phi$, which were dropped in arriving at Eq. 8.09i are also zero. In fact, these terms are zero only when α and ϕ are constant along the slip surface, and can be factored from the summations. This condition would correspond to slip along a planar surface in homogeneous soil. Another effect of ignoring the side forces is shown by working backwards from Eq. 8.09g to Eq. 8.09e. Clearly, the effective stress on the base of a specified slice will, in general, be different when the side forces are considered. Thus, there is an effect on the distribution of the normal stresses, and frictional stresses, along the slip surface. In addition, when combined with the notion that τ is proportional to s all along the slip surface, the assumption fails rather seriously to satisfy the requirements for static equilibrium of the various slices. Finally, unless a failed slope is being analyzed, the weight W entering into the computations is that which is present in a stable slope. Unless the prospective failure is presumed to result from a reduction of strength, the actual factor of safety will depend on those (different) loads existing at the time of failure (see Section 8.04).

Bishop (1955) proposed a procedural modification that has been well received. In his modification, the factor of safety, while still defined as M_R/M_D, is the factor by which the shear strength must be reduced to attain limiting (plastic) equilibrium all along the slip surface. The substitutions, $(c \cdot \Delta l)/F$ for C' and $N \tan \phi/F$ for $N \tan \phi'$, are introduced directly into the equilibrium force polygon, Figure 8.09m(3), to reflect this fact. (The revised polygons is shown in Figure 8.09p.) Now, regardless of how the side forces are treated, some degree of interdependency is implied by the fact that the unit shearing stress is the same along the base of every slice. To illustrate this important point, consider what happens if a deliberate attempt is made to ignore the side forces.

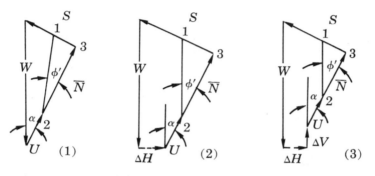

Figure 8.09n   Effect of specifying plastic equilibrium

Figure 8.09n shows the force polygons for a particular slice constructed in the usual way (1), and using Bishop's modification (2) or (3). In (1), the shearing stress S depends on W and α. F is not specified for this slice. Therefore, the angle 1-2-3, representing the developed angle of friction, may have any value. It is subject only to the restriction that point 1 must divide S into parts such that $C/C' = \overline{N} \tan \phi/ \overline{N} \tan \phi'$, and point 2 must lie on the head of the known U vector. $\overline{N}$ is entirely fixed by the known magnitudes of W, U, and α.

Using Bishop's modification, point 1 is fixed by the requirement that $C' = C/F$, where F is the same all along the slip surface. The direction of 1-2 is fixed by the requirement that angle 1-2-3 $= \phi' \tan^{-1} (\tan \phi/F)$. Point 2 must lie at the head of the U vector, but the positions of the vectors U and $\overline{N}$ are determined only by specifying something about the relative magnitudes of the ΔH and ΔV vectors needed to close the polygon. If, arbitrarily, ΔV is taken to be zero, the polygon is as in (2). In general, the tail of the U vector will not coincide with the head of vector W. Therefore, N and $\overline{N}$ will generally differ from those obtained by the first procedure, and it is implied that there is some vector ΔH—or a pair of vectors, ΔH and ΔV as in (3)—required to close the polygon. Thus, even though the side forces were ignored, their presence is shown to be necessary. N and $\overline{N}$ turn out differently when sets of ΔH and ΔV are chosen so as to satisfy the equilibrium of all slices than they do when ΔV is arbitrarily set to zero for all slices. However, the latter greatly simplifies the procedure, and Bishop has shown that the resulting factor of safety does not usually differ significantly from that found using compatible sets of ΔH and ΔV.

Figure 8.09p shows the force polygon with the shearing stress expressed in terms of the components $c \cdot \Delta l/F$ and $\overline{N} \tan \phi/F$. If forces are summed vertically, as Bishop has done, instead of in the direction of N, a different expression for N will be found than that given in Eq. 8.09g. The effective normal force may also be found, and is

$$\overline{N} = \frac{W + \Delta V - \Delta l \left(u \cos \alpha + \dfrac{c}{F} \sin \alpha \right)}{\cos \alpha + \dfrac{\tan \phi \cdot \sin \alpha}{F}} \qquad \text{(Eq. 8.09}k\text{)}$$

If Eq. 8.09k is divided by Δl to obtain $\overline{\sigma}$, and the result is then substituted into Eq. 8.09e, it is found that

$$F = \frac{\sum \left[c \cdot b + \Delta V \tan \phi + (W - ub) \tan \phi \right] \dfrac{\sec \alpha}{1 + \dfrac{\tan \phi \tan \alpha}{F}}}{\Sigma W \sin \alpha} \qquad \text{(Eq. 8.09}l\text{)}$$

The preceding equation may be considerably simplified by assuming $\Delta V = 0$ (as discussed above), and $u = r_u \left[\dfrac{W}{b} \right]$ or $u = \overline{B} \left[\dfrac{W}{b} \right]$, when the latter assumption is appropriate (see Section 8.08). Then

$$F = \frac{\sum \left[cb + W(1 - \overline{B}) \tan \phi \right] \dfrac{\sec \alpha}{1 + \dfrac{\tan \phi \tan \alpha}{F}}}{\Sigma W \sin \alpha} \qquad \text{(Eq. 8.09}m\text{)}$$

Janbu, Bjerrum, and Kjaernsli (1956) introduced a computational convenience by defining a factor $\dfrac{1}{m_\alpha} = \dfrac{\sec \alpha}{1 + \dfrac{\tan \phi \tan \alpha}{F}}$, and plotting m_α as

a function of α and $\tan \phi/F$, as shown in Figure 8.09q. This may be used with either Eq. 8.09l or Eq. 8.09m. Either may also be simplified by factoring b from the summation if the slices are all of the same width. Probably, the best general form for the factor of safety equation, when assuming $\Delta V = 0$, is

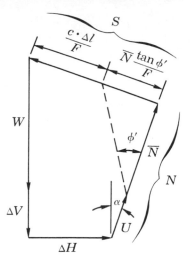

**Figure 8.09o   Force polygon for plastic equilibrium
all along slip surface**

$$F = \frac{\Sigma\left[cb + (W - ub)\tan\phi\right]\cdot\dfrac{1}{m_\alpha}}{\Sigma W \sin\alpha} \qquad\text{(Eq. 8.09}n\text{)}$$

It will be noticed that F appears on both sides of Eqs. 8.09l, m, and n, so that several trial values of F may be required for each trial circle in order to satisfy the relationship. A starting value for F may be guessed, or estimated using some simpler procedure.

The simplified form, Eq. 8.09i, generally leads to a lower computed value of F than that found using Eq. 8.09n. Neither form represents a condition for which the statical equilibrium of the slices is satisfied. However, this defect appears to be less severe in the case of Eq. 8.09n, as has been frequently demonstrated by comparing the results to those obtained when a statically acceptable set of side forces is introduced. The difference in the results of the two equations is accentuated as the central angle of the arc increases; and, as shown by Bishop (1955), the difference also increases with increasing pore pressure.

It should be noted that when the same statically acceptable set of side forces (from the infinity of such sets) is used in conjunction with either Eq. 8.09h or Eq. 8.09l the results will be identical. Moreover, it makes little difference which set of acceptable side forces is used, since, among these sets, the result appears to vary not more than about 1%

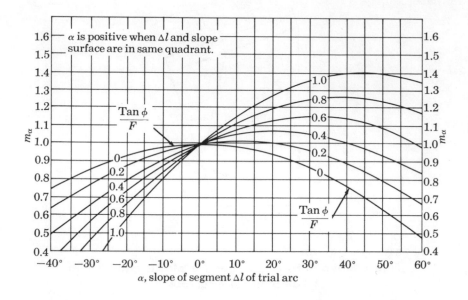

Figure 8.09p   Chart for determining m_α—After Janbu, et al

(Bishop, 1955). An acceptable set of side forces may be obtained by trial, using either the equations of equilibrium for the slices, or employing a graphical procedure such as, for example, that demonstrated most recently by Seed (1966).

It was mentioned that not only does F differ between the simplified procedure and Bishop's modified procedure, but the critical circle is also different. The second result actually follows from the first. In both cases, the location found for the critical circle depends on the developed friction angle, $\tan \phi/F$, and this differs in the two cases. Neither procedure discovers the actual critical circle unless the slope is indeed on the verge of failure, because the *full* friction angle, ϕ, determines the position of the critical circle. However, the critical circle found from the modified procedure is consistent with the associated assumption that failure occurs when the strength is reduced by a ratio of $1/F$ from its initial value. If ϕ is known with considerable confidence, the critical circle in many cases could best be found using the ϕ-circle procedure with full friction and a reasonable (say, sinusoidal) distribution of the normal stresses. Additional refinement sometimes could be gained by using that critical circle along with the "correct" slices procedure. Obviously, the factor of safety would be greater than that associated with the critical circle found from the slices procedure alone. Thus, even a "correct" slices procedure may yield a somewhat conservative value for F, the degree of conservatism rising as the computed value for F increases. The preceding remarks do not apply when the critical surface is delineated by boundary conditions, discontinuities, etc.

It should be mentioned that no attempt is made here to cover all of the variations in the slices procedure which can be found in the literature. Many useful suggestions have been made which should be studied by those who are frequently required to analyze embankment or slope stability. Most of the variations are concerned with facilitating the computations, and involve no fundamental differences other than those illustrated by the two procedures already discussed.

A final note of caution is required in conformity with experience: it would seem wise to *require* higher values for the computed factors of safety when a refinement of procedure results in consistently higher values. The number of failures has been sufficient to show that the design of embankments in the past has not been overly conservative. A true factor of safety as low as 1.5 is already rather bold. Much higher values are used with even such relatively uniform and well-controlled materials as steel and concrete. The principal worth of refined analytical procedures in connection with slope stability is in the additional understanding which can be brought to bear on the problem.

8.10   Examples of Analyses

A simple numerical example is now given to illustrate the procedures described in Section 8.09. While most practical problems are more complex than this example, the procedures for solving complex problems (at least, insofar as a single trial circle is concerned) are not fundamentally different from those used with simple problems. The example consists of a problem in which the soil of a homogeneous slope, or embankment, is the same as that which lies under the slope. Thus, an opportunity is afforded for comparing the ϕ-circle and slices procedures.

The slope in Figure 8.10a is 85 feet high, and rises at an angle of 30° with the horizontal. The properties of the soil are as follows:

$$s = 850(\text{psf}) + \overline{\sigma} \tan 15°$$

$$\gamma_m = 115 \text{ lb/cu ft}$$

a. ϕ-Circle Procedure

Although the critical circle (or minimum F) often must be found by making several trials such as that in Figure 8.10a, in this simple case Taylor's data were used to locate the critical circle directly. For $i = 30°$ and $\phi = 15°$, Taylor (1937) gives the angles $\alpha = 27°$ and $\beta = 39°$ for the critical circle. The corresponding radius of curvature turns out to be 148 feet, by graphical construction. The critical circle is a toe circle that begins about 19 feet from the brow of the slope, and dips slightly below a horizontal plane through the toe before emerging at the toe.

Two ϕ-circles are shown in the figure: one is uncorrected, while the other has been corrected for the case of a frictional resistance uniformly distributed along the arc. Since the actual frictional resistance will be somewhat concentrated beneath the lower central part of the arc, the resultant F of the normal and frictional forces will be directed so as to be tangent to a circle (not drawn) having a radius intermediate to the two described above. The cohesive resistance is assumed to be distributed uniformly along the arc, so that C' is parallel to the chord AC and at a distance of $148(L_a/L_c) = 148(201.5/186.2)$ feet from O.

The gravitational force W acts through the centroid of the mass. The centroid may be located experimentally or analytically. It is easy to find

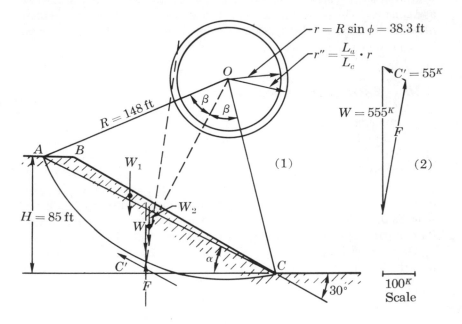

Figure 8.10a   **Friction circle solution**

the centroid of the triangle ACB by geometry. The weight of the triangular mass (of unit thickness) is

$$W_1 = \tfrac{1}{2}(19)(85)(0.115) = 92.8 \text{ kips}$$

The centroid of the circular segment below AC lies on the bisector of the central angle of the arc at a distance from O of

$$d = \frac{4R}{3} \cdot \frac{\sin^3 \beta}{2\beta - \sin 2\beta} = \frac{4(148)}{3} \cdot \frac{\sin^3 39°}{\frac{2\pi}{180}(39) - \sin 78°} = 127.8 \text{ ft}$$

and its weight is

$$W_2 = A \cdot \gamma_m = R^2 \left(\beta - \frac{\sin 2\beta}{2} \right) (0.115) = 4020\,(0.115) = 462.3 \text{ kips}$$

The total weight of the mass is $W = 555.1$ kips, and the position of the line of action may be found by summing moments of W_1 and W_2 with respect to any convenient point; e.g., the toe of the slope.

Now, the point of intersection of the lines of action of W and C' is found; and F is drawn through this point, tangent to the corrected ϕ-circle, as described above. The force polygon is then drawn as shown in Figure 8.10a(2), and the force C' scaled from it. Then, $c' = C'/L_c = 85/186.2 = 0.457$ kips/sq ft. Thus

$$F_c = F_H = \frac{850}{457} = 1.86$$

It should be noted, also, that the solution can be obtained with very little effort by making use of the chart in Figure 8.09l. Note that for $i = 30°$ and $\phi = 15°$, $H \tan \phi'/c' = H \tan \phi/c = 5.7$ (from the chart). Thus, the critical height of the slope, with friction and cohesion fully developed, is $H(\text{crit}) = 5.7(850)/115 \tan 15° = 157.2$ ft, and

$$F_H = F_c = \frac{157.2}{85} = 1.85$$

The chart may also be used to find F_s for the slope height of 85 feet, since $\tan \phi'/c' = \tan \phi/c$. Thus,

$$\frac{\gamma H \tan \phi'}{c'} = \frac{\gamma H \tan \phi}{c} = \frac{115(85) \tan 15°}{850} = 3.08$$

From the chart, for $i = 30°$, the corresponding ϕ' is 11.5°, and

$$F_s = \frac{\tan 15°}{\tan 11.5°} = 1.32$$

This, of course, corresponds to $c' = 850/1.32 = 645$ psf.

F_s could also be found by making additional trials, using the *same* center of curvature O, in which ϕ-circles are drawn (and corrected) for different assumed values of ϕ'. When a ϕ-circle is found satisfying the relationship $\tan \phi / \tan \phi' = c/c'$, F_s is determined.

Some additional remarks may be helpful in connection with the use of the Stability Chart, Figure 8.09*l*. Regions A and B represent slopes for which the critical circle is a toe circle. In region B, the critical circle dips below a horizontal plane through the toe before emerging at the toe, while in region A the low point of the critical circle is at the toe. In region C, the critical circle is not a toe circle, but emerges on the plane beyond the toe.

In accordance with the initial assumptions, the ϕ-circle procedure satisfies all the requirements for static equilibrium of the mass.

b. Slices Procedure (Common)

Using the critical circle found from the ϕ-circle procedure the mass is divided into a number of slices, as in Figure 8.10*b*. It is usual to divide the mass into 5 to 10 slices. In the example, 9 slices are used. Slice di-

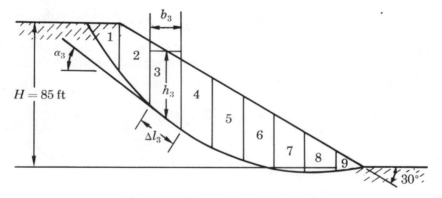

Figure 8.10b   Slices procedure

mensions and other pertinent data are given in Table 8.10*a*. Also, in Col. (7) of this table, $\Sigma W \sin \alpha$ is obtained for use as the tangential stress in finding F. Computations are facilitated by a tabulation such as is shown in Table 8.10*b*, from which the shearing resistance is found by summing the items in Col. (11). The factor of safety is determined from Eq. 8.09*i* or *j*, in which u or $\overline{B}$ is zero in this case. Thus,

$$F = \frac{\Sigma[c{\cdot}\Delta l + W \cos \alpha \tan \phi]}{\Sigma W \sin \alpha}$$

$$F = \frac{306.7}{246.1} = 1.25$$

Table 8.10a
Properties of Slices

(1)	(2)	(3)	(4)	(5)	(6)	(7)
Slice No.	b (ft)	h (ft)	W (kips)	α (degrees)	Δl (ft)	$W \sin \alpha$ (kips)
1	19	19	41.5	59	37	35.6
2	19	37.5	81.9	46.5	27	59.4
3	19	43	93.9	37.3	24	56.9
4	19	44	96.0	28.5	21	45.7
5	19	41.5	90.6	20	20	31.0
6	19	36	78.6	12	19.5	16.3
7	19	27	58.9	5	19	5.1
8	19	17	37.1	-2.8	19	-1.8
9	14	6	13.1	-9.2	14.5	-2.1
						$\Sigma = 246.1$

Table 8.10b
Common Procedure

(1)	(8)	(9)	(10)	(11)
Slice No.	$c \cdot \Delta$ (kips)	$W \cos \alpha$ (kips)	$W \cos \alpha \tan \phi$ (kips)	(8) + (10) (kips)
1	31.4	21.4	5.7	37.1
2	23.0	56.4	15.1	38.1
3	20.4	74.6	20.0	40.4
4	17.8	84.3	22.6	40.4
5	17.0	85.1	22.8	39.8
6	16.6	76.9	20.6	37.2
7	16.1	58.7	15.7	31.8
8	16.2	37.0	9.9	26.1
9	12.3	12.9	3.5	15.8
				$\Sigma = 306.7$

c.   *Slices Procedure (Modified, $\Delta V = 0$)*

Using the data compiled in Table 8.10a, the computations are carried out as shown in Table 8.10c. In this case, the factor of safety must be determined by trial. As a starting value for F, the above result ($F = 1.25$) is used. For this assumed value of F, it is found from Eq. 8.09n, setting $u = 0$, that $F = 1.30$. This does not check closely with the assumed value, $F = 1.25$, so a new trial is made, this time assuming a value of 1.31 for F. This is found to check satisfactorily:

$$F = \frac{\Sigma\left[c{\cdot}b + W \tan \phi\right] \cdot \dfrac{1}{m_a}}{\Sigma W \sin \alpha}$$

$$F = \frac{322.2}{246.1} = 1.31$$

The values for m_α are obtained from Figure 8.09g. As many new trials as are necessary may be made, but rarely are more than two or three needed. Each trial requires an additional sub-column in Cols. (11) and (12) of Table 8.10c.

d.   *Commentary*

It is seen that the modified slices procedure checks well with the ϕ-circle procedure, and that these two procedures indicate a higher factor of safety than is found by the common slices procedure. The difference increases as the central angle of the arc gets larger, and, generally, when pore pressures are present. When applicable, the ϕ-circle procedure is probably the simplest and most reliable. The common slices procedure is always conservative, and, for this reason, a smaller factor of safety may be acceptable when using this procedure. Unfortunately, the degree of conservatism varies with the specific conditions of the problem. When the friction angle is rather low and/or the slope fairly flat, the common procedure is likely to be overly conservative. It seems preferable, generally, to use the modified procedure as a basis for judging the safety of a slope, when the ϕ-circle procedure is not appropriate. As was mentioned in Section 8.09, even the modified procedure is somewhat conservative because it neglects the ΔV side forces, and also gives an erroneous indication of the critical circle.

An indication of the difference in the common and modified procedures with regard to the distribution of the stresses along the slip surface is

Table 8.10c
Modified Procedure

(1)	(8)	(9)	(10)	(11)		(12)	
				m_α		$(10) \div (11)$	
Slice No.	$c \cdot b$ (kips)	$W \tan \phi$ (kips)	$(8) + (9)$ (kips)	$F_1 = 1.25$	$F_2 = 1.31$	$F_1 = 1.25$	$F_2 = 1.31$
1	16.1	11.1	27.2	0.70	0.69	38.8	39.4
2	16.1	21.9	38.0	0.85	0.84	44.7	45.2
3	16.1	25.2	41.3	0.94	0.93	43.9	44.4
4	16.1	25.7	41.8	0.99	0.98	42.2	41.6
5	16.1	25.3	41.4	1.02	1.01	40.6	41.0
6	16.1	21.1	37.2	1.02	1.02	36.5	36.5
7	16.1	15.8	31.9	1.01	1.01	31.6	31.6
8	16.1	9.9	26.0	0.99	0.99	26.3	26.3
9	11.9	3.5	15.4	0.95	0.95	16.2	16.2
						$\Sigma = 320.8$	$\Sigma = 322.2$
						$F = 1.30$	$F = 1.31$

given in Figure 8.10c. Part (1) of the figure shows the equilibrium force polygon for slice No. 1 of the example in Figure 8.10b. A shearing force of 35.6 kip is required for equilibrium. Figures 8.10c(2) and (3) show

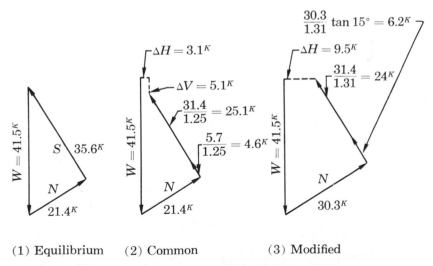

(1) Equilibrium   (2) Common   (3) Modified

Figure 8.10c   Comparison of force polygons

the shearing resistance provided by the assumptions of the common and modified procedures, respectively. In neither case does the force polygon close, the deficiencies being indicated by the dashed vectors. In (3), the normal force was computed using Eq. $8.09k$. Note especially the difference in N in (2) and (3). Note also that although (3) appears to have a greater closure deficiency than (2), this kind of deficiency, when averaged over the slope, causes only an insignificant disagreement with the factor of safety found when the side forces are correctly treated.

If pore pressures are present in the slope, these may easily be included in the computations by adding the columns ($u \cdot \Delta l$) and ($W \cos \alpha - u \cdot \Delta l$) to Table 8.10$b$, and columns ($u \cdot b$) and ($W - u \cdot b$) to Table 8.10$c$.

8.11   Sudden Drawdown

Without attempting to outline detailed procedures, the effects of sudden drawdown of an open water surface adjacent to a slope will be considered from a qualitative viewpoint. The effect of sudden drawdown on the stability of the slope may be wholly understood in terms of the pore pressure changes that occur. Only relatively impermeable embankments are considered, because there are only minor effects in materials which drain freely enough to allow water to escape as rapidly as the water surface is lowered. The hazard of failure, but not of catastrophe, is greater when the quantity of water impounded is small.

Pore pressures are affected in two ways by a sudden drawdown. One of these is associated directly with the change in elevation of the water adjacent to the slope; and the other is related to the deformations that occur in the slope, and to the stress-dilatancy characteristics of the soil. Neither of these effects can be precisely predicted, but their general influence may be indicated.

Figure 8.11a(1) represents the pore pressures and other forces acting on a mass of soil in an embankment adjacent to an open water surface after a long period of equilibrium. Consider, at first, the purely cohesive ($\phi = 0$) case. The shearing resistance C' opposes only the moment due to the buoyed weight of the soil mass. It will be assumed, probably incorrectly, that C' is parallel to the chord AC, representing a uniform distribution of shearing resistance (or shearing stress) along the arc. The water forces, U_1 and U_2, as is shown in (2), must exactly balance the $V\gamma_w$ (volume × unit weight of water) component of the total weight W. Therefore, in the space diagram (1), U_1 and U_2 intersect on the line of action of W. Also, $\bar{N}$ and C' intersect on the line of action of W, and exactly balance

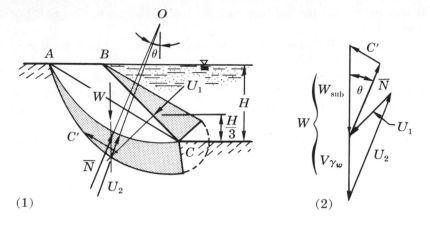

(1)

(2)

Figure 8.11a   Submerged slope in equilibrium

the buoyed weight, W_{sub}, of the soil mass. The complete equilibrium force polygon is in Figure 8.11a(2).

Suppose that the water surface is now quickly lowered to the toe of the slope. Neglecting for the moment the effects of deformation on the pore pressure, the force U_1 disappears, and U_2 shifts position to coincide with $\overline{N}$. W and $\overline{N}$ are unchanged from Figure 8.11a(2) if no drainage has occurred. Therefore, U_2 must be immediately reduced as indicated in Figure 8.11b(2). The distribution of u is not known, but it would resemble that shown in Figure 8.11b(1). If additional cohesive resistance is available, it will be mobilized to produce the substantially larger C' which

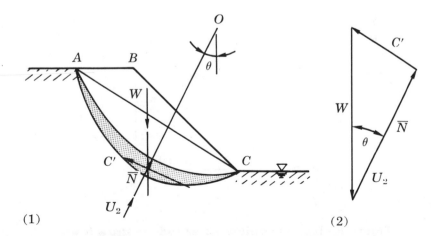

(1)

(2)

Figure 8.11b   Conditions after sudden drawdown

is required for equilibrium (compare the force polygons in Figures 8.11*a* and 8.11*b*).

For the $\phi = 0$ analysis, pore pressure changes due to deformations in the slope during rapid drawdown alter only the relative magnitudes of U_2 and $\overline{N}$. A positive change in U_2 gives rise to an equal reduction in N, with the total $\overline{N}$ and C' being unaffected. Similarly, a negative change in U_2 has no effect on C'. Thus, stress-dilatency characteristics need not be considered.

On the other hand, if the soil possesses frictional properties (c-ϕ material), $\overline{N}$ changes if there is an increase or decrease of pore pressure as the slope deforms under the added stress. The change in $\overline{N}$ influences the frictional resistance that is available to maintain equilibrium. If the soil is dilatant the negative change in u increases $\overline{N}$ and contributes to stability. A slope in contractive soil has its stability further endangered by the positive pore pressure changes accompanying deformation. Since the stress changes and deformations are not uniform along the potential slip surface, the distribution of the resulting pore pressure changes is not known. However, the qualitative result of the stress-deformation effects in a c-ϕ soil is illustrated in Figure 8.11*c*, for both dilatant and contractive characteristics. In the figure, U represents the resultant pore pressure when only the direct effects of lowering the water surface are considered. The corresponding C' is shown. The stress-dilatancy effects on U are represented by $+\Delta U$ for a contractive soil and by $-\Delta U$ for a dilatant soil. The corresponding changes, $\Delta C'_{(+)}$ or $\Delta C'_{(-)}$, in the required cohesion illustrate how the factor of safety is affected by the volume change char-

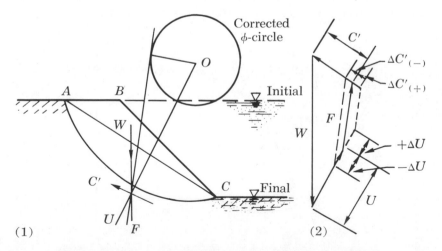

Figure 8.11c   Conditions after sudden drawdown in c-ϕ soil

acteristics of the soil, F increasing in a dilatant soil and decreasing in one which tends to contract.

8.12   Summary and Special Topics

In the preceding sections, the general characteristics of slides and of factors which affect the stability of slopes were discussed. In addition, the historical development of procedures for analyzing stability was briefly traced, and some of the common procedures were described in considerable detail. It was also mentioned that excessive preoccupation with procedural details may stifle the thought processes and thwart the application of mature judgment. On the other hand, there is an equal danger that judgment may be too hastily formed, without due consideration of the timeless principles of mechanics. One cannot always believe what he *thinks* he sees. Often, he sees too little, and on the basis of inadequate evidence may be led to wrong conclusions. Thus, while theory must not be divorced from reality, the reality itself is frequently obscure or only dimly comprehended.

There are many kinds of stability problems that, presently, are not well understood. Yet, attempts to reconcile theory and reality in some of these difficult problems has been enlightening. While the scope of this chapter does not permit full consideration of these "problem" areas, some of them will be briefly discussed. These comments are intended more as a stimulant to further study than as a complete analysis of the present state of the art.

a.   Natural Slopes and Cuts in Natural Slopes

This classification embraces such a large range of problems that it is foolish to comtemplate any kind of general solution for the stability of natural slopes. The variety of materials occurring in natural slopes is great; and the processes which, with time, lead to failure are uncertain.

Skempton (1964) has shown that the notion of a residual shear strength expressed solely in terms of an angle of internal friction can be useful in analyzing failures in stiff, fissured clays. On the other hand, failures in stiff, intact clays appear to be governed by a peak strength expressed in terms of both friction and cohesion. Bjerrum (1966) combined the concept of residual strength with a suggested mechanism for progressive failure in analyzing slopes in heavily overconsolidated clay-shales. Bjerrum and Kjaernsli (1957) analyzed a number of slides and also some stable slopes in normally consolidated and overconsolidated intact clays. The most satisfactory results for predicting the long-term stability were obtained from an effective stress $(c\text{-}\phi)$ analysis using Bishop's procedure. A $\phi = 0$ analysis was found to be far too conservative, predicting factors of safety well below unity, even for most of the stable slopes. The same kind of results were found by Kjaernsli and Simons (1962) in connection with the analysis of soft, silty clay banks along the Drammen River. The soil strength there is proportional to the depth, and the analyses were made by arbitrarily considering the strength to be constant within each of several horizontal layers 5 feet thick. A slices procedure was advantageous in this situation. In contrast with the conclusions of Bjerrum and Kjaernsli, Hansen (1962) maintains that an undrained analysis *is* acceptable in such cases, provided that the *in situ* strength of the soil has been correctly evaluated. He has shown that the factor of safety found in the usual $\phi = 0$ analysis may be rather reliably corrected using an expression which introduces factors that depend on the stress history of the embankment soil.

Kenney (1963) analyzed the stability of cuts in soft soils for which the strength is proportional to the depth. Circular failure arcs were assumed, and both short-term and long-term stability were analyzed. Critical arcs always emerged at or above the toe. Short-term analyses were based on the ratio of undrained strength to effective overburden pressure, $s_u/\overline{p}$, while residual strength in terms only of a residual angle of internal friction was used in analyzing the long-term stability. Either short-term or long-term conditions could be critical, with short-term failures being most probable when the ratio $s_u/\overline{p}$ is less than about 0.2.

In investigating a short-term slip of stiff, fissured clay into a deep excavation, Skempton and La Rochelle (1965) presented an interesting strength hypothesis. It was noted that the shear strength at the time of the slip appeared to be only about 55 per cent of the normal undrained strength of the clay. This was attributed to the existence of the fissures and to the probable migration of pore water under the changed stress conditions. The probable proportion of the slip surface passing along fissures was estimated, and it was shown that the strength reduction could be related to the softening of the soil adjacent to fissures. Here, softening reduced the strength to approximately the same value as the residual strength of the soil, and the slope failure could thus be explained without resorting to any progressive failure mechanism. That is, movement could have occurred (as apparently it did) along the entire slip surface simultaneously, governed by the average strength.

For dealing with cuts in soft shales and clay-shales, Lane (1961) has suggested the feasibility of an empirical approach based on an analysis of the performance of existing slopes. From observations of both stable slopes and slopes which had failed, Lane plotted the slope height as a function of the slope angle, and constructed a curve that divides the graph into stable and unstable regions. In making use of such a chart, the similarity in geology and in the effects of seepage of the slope under consideration and of the slopes on which the chart is based must be carefully evaluated.

b.   Quick Clays

These unusual soils, distinguished by sensitivities in excess of 16, are common in Scandinavian countries, particularly Norway, and occur at other scattered locations in North America and elsewhere. In Norway, slides in this material have caused extensive damage. The slides are characterized by their flask-like shape (in plan), corresponding to the sometimes enormous volumes of soil that flow out in near liquid form through a constricted opening. Bjerrum (1955) has described the retrograde (backward) development of these slides, in which a continuing series of slides spreads from an initial slip. The reason for the initial slip, and the causes of the termination of the spreading, are often not clear. According to Bjerrum, the stability cannot be predicted by a conventional analysis of the "overall" stability of the material involved in the movement. He also considers that progressive failure is not responsible for the character of the slide.

Eide and Bjerrum (1955) analyzed a slide in clay having sensitivities ranging between 80 and 150. Apparently, the initial slip was along a circular arc, and, unlike the retrogressive action described above, the secondary slip was along a nearly planar surface *ahead* of the primary slip. A $\phi = 0$ analysis on the composite slip surface produced an indicated factor of safety of approximately unity, so that the full strength appears to have been mobilized along the whole slip surface. These analyses are made more difficult by the presence of a hard crust having a higher shear strength.

Contrary to the concepts expressed above, Kjellman (1955) used the idea of progressive failure to explain some large slides in Sweden in clay of somewhat lower sensitivity (about 10) than those above, pointing out that quick clays must behave similarly.

c.   Embankments on Soft Soils

When relatively low embankments are placed on soft, cohesive soils, the safety of the embankment is likely to depend on the properties of the foundation soils. Sometimes it is practicable to attempt to increase the strength of the foundation by installing sand drains and/or using preconsolidation techniques. At other times, it is simpler to reduce the shearing stresses by constructing one or more berms next to the principal embankment to afford a more gradual transition from loaded to unloaded area. Usually, complications arise due to variations in soil properties, depth to firm substratum, and embankment geometry.

Jakobson (1948) has suggested using a $\phi = 0$ Swedish circle analysis, in which berms are furnished as required. The principal difficulty is in determining the width of berm necessary. The method has been used successfully in Scandinavia, generally as a basis for preliminary design. Golder and Palmer (1955) analyzed the failure of a low seashore embankment on a soft clay foundation, and found that a $\phi = 0$ analysis based on undrained triaxial tests gave excellent results ($F = 1$). However, a $\phi = 0$ analysis based on vane shear test results, and a $c - \phi$ analysis based on the results of drained triaxial tests both erred on the side of danger.

The failure of an embankment on a thin layer of peat was studied by Ward, Penman, and Gibson (1955). The slip occurred some time after construction, and was attributed to a reduction of average shear strength due to redistribution of pore pressures produced in the peat by the added load. In this case, an effective stress ($c - \phi$) analysis using wedges produced good results.

Varved clays sometimes present difficult problems when used as a foundation for embankments. Milligan, Soderman, and Rutka (1962) analyzed a failure that occurred under these circumstances. In this case, good results were obtained from a $\phi = 0$ analysis based on field vane shear strengths. The embankment was successfully redesigned using a system of berms to spread the load.

For control of the rate of construction of embankments on soft soils, Lobdell (1959) advocates a $c - \phi$ analysis using the procedure of slices, so that the pore pressure variation with depth and position under slope can be introduced. The stability at various stages of construction is then analyzed on the basis of field pore pressure measurements.

d. Earthquake Effects

The question of stability under earthquake loading has become increasingly important as the height of embankments constructed or contemplated has risen. The use of the older methods, in which an equivalent, horizontal static force is substituted for the actual dynamic forces, raises some serious theoretical objections on the basis of the magnitude, position, direction, and duration of the equivalent force in comparison with the actual loading. There has recently been a great deal of activity in the investigation of earthquake effects, particularly by Seed and his co-workers at the University of California, Berkeley.

Newmark (1965) advanced the important idea that earthquake effects on embankments should be judged on the basis of the deformations they produce, rather than on any direct concern with a factor of safety. If, in a normally stable embankment, the factor of safety should drop below unity during an earthquake, the condition can exist for only a very short interval of time. The deformations produced as a consequence do not proceed to failure before they are arrested by a reversal or cessation of the forces which have caused them. However, because of the rapidly recurring nature of the loading, there may be significant cumulative subsidence of the slope. Newmark defines a *dynamic* factor of safety for assessing the probable effects of the earthquake motions.

For embankments of cohesionless soil, Seed and Goodman (1964) used a similar approach involving the determination of a "yield" acceleration which is a property only of the material and the slope geometry. The displacements depend on the direction and duration of the imposed acceleration, provided that it exceeds the yield acceleration. In predicting the yield acceleration, it is suggested that the plane strain angle of internal friction be used, and that the existence of a small shear strength intercept (which is not, however, cohesion) be recognized. Goodman and Seed (1966) showed that the earthquake induced displacements in embankments of dense sand are concentrated in thin shear zones near the surface of the slope. A method is suggested for estimating the slump, or settlement of the crest. In loose sands, the greatest danger is from liquefaction, a phenomenon not readily amenable to analysis.

Seed and Martin (1966) give the range of seismic coefficients employed in the usual pseudo-static analysis, and discuss the deficiencies of this kind of analysis. Advancing the suggestions of Newmark, they propose a method of evaluating static seismic forces that would cause the same deformations as do the actual dynamic forces. Since seismic effects are more severe in the upper parts of high embankments, the feasibility of using a seismic force *series* is explained. In such a series, the seismic force coefficient diminishes as greater proportions of the height (measured down from the crest) are successively analyzed. Seed (1966) further implements the analysis by introducing consideration of the time history of the forces caused by an earthquake, and by evaluating the soil behavior under simulated earthquake loading conditions.

For cohesive soils, Seed and Chan (1966) show that the strength of clay under pulsating loads (as in earthquakes) differs from that found either in static or transient load tests. The strength under pulsating load was found to be smaller than the transient load strength, often being near the normal undrained strength of the clay. In sensitive clays, the pulsations may produce stresses which, while not causing failure directly, create pore pressures such that creep movement is initiated which leads to failure some time after the vibrations have stopped.

In a theoretical study of infinite clay slopes underlain by a hard layer, Finn (1966), assuming the clay to have the properties of a rigid visco-plastic solid, analyzed the behavior of slopes subjected to a uniform horizontal acceleration. He derived equations for the acceleration coefficient k_y necessary to cause yield of the slope, the acceleration $k_y \cdot g$ being required to just cause yield at the interface with the underlying hard material.

Seed and Clough (1963) utilized models to study the earthquake resistance of sloping core dams. The results indicated that even very strong earth motion will not produce catastrophic failures, but only a slight settlement of the crest and bulging of the lower side slopes. It appeared that deformations could be essentially eliminated by using a seismic coefficient corresponding to the maximum ground acceleration, and using an appropriate strength increase for the rapid loading condition. Clough and Pirtz (1956) had previously shown that rock-fill dams with impervious cores are highly resistant to strong earth motions, sloping core dams being a little better than those with central cores.

e.   Zoned Dams

Factors apart from considerations of stability—e.g., control of seepage, economic utilization of materials, etc.—often require that embankments be built using dissimilar materials in various parts of the dam. When so constructed, thought must also be given to the stability existing for various possible arrangements of the materials. The complexity of the zoning sometimes makes a normal stability analysis difficult or impossible, so that the good sense and judgment of the designers must be relied on. An illustration of the intricate zoning patterns which are fairly typical are those of the Tuttle Creek Dam in central Kansas [see Lane and Fehrman (1960)].

Bird (1961) discloses some of the uncertainties in earth dam design in his description of the development from preliminary to final form of the designs of the Terminus and New Hogan Dams. The design changes were dictated by the discovery of unexpected properties of the soils during laboratory studies, and by the discovery during detailed field investigations that the availability of various materials differed from that which had been assumed.

It often happens with zoned dams that the critical surface of potential failure can be predicted by inspection. Usually, this surface consists, at least in part, of planes. A wedge analysis is frequently appropriate, but sometimes the analysis is facilitated (with sufficient reliability being maintained) by approximating a series of adjoining planes by means of a single circular arc.

f. Computer Analysis

The labor of stability computations can often be lessened by using a high speed computer. For organizations whose work frequently entails stability studies, great economy may be effected by writing a computer program, or by obtaining an existing one, that is appropriate for whatever computer facility is available. Little and Price (1958) describe a computer program that uses Bishop's procedure for the Swedish method to compute the factor of safety. Horn (1960) prepared a similar program for the Illiac computer at the University of Illinois. This program can accommodate a variety of conditions with regard to zoning, water table position, and surface loading.

Morgenstern and Price (1965) utilized a computer for analyzing the stability for any assumed shape of slip surface. Their expression for the factor of safety for this general case is based on the principle of limiting equilibrium, after the manner of Bishop. In making the solution it is necessary to assume a slip surface configuration and some reasonable distribution of the (internal) forces acting on the sides of the slices. Variations in soil strength and in pore pressure can be accommodated in the solution.

REFERENCES

Bird, J. M., "Uncertainties in Earth Dam Design," *Journal Soil Mechanics and Foundations Division*, Proc. Am. Soc. C.E., Vol. 87, No. SM3 (June, 1961).

Bishop, A. W., "The Use of Pore Pressure Coefficients in Practice," *Geotechnique*, Vol. IV, No. 4 (December, 1954).

Bishop, A. W., "The Use of the Slip Circle in the Stability Analysis of Slopes," *Geotechnique*, Vol. V, No. 1 (March, 1955).

Bishop, A. W., and N. Morgenstern, "Stability Coefficients for Earth Slopes," *Geotechnique*, Vol. X, No. 4 (December, 1960).

Bjerrum, L., "Mechanism of Progressive Failure in Slopes of Overconsolidated Plastic Clays and Clay Shales," Third Terzaghi Lecture, Presented at ASCE Structural Engineering Conference, Miami, Florida (February 1, 1966).

Bjerrum, L., "Stability of Natural Slopes in Quick Clay," *Geotechnique*, Vol. V, 1955.

Bjerrum, L., and B. Kjaernsli, "Analysis of the Stability of Some Norwegian Natural Clay Slopes," *Geotechnique*, Vol. VII, No. 1 (March, 1957).

Casagrande, A., "Role of the 'Calculated Risk' in Earthwork and Foundation Engineering," *Journal Soil Mechanics and Foundations Division*, Proc. Am. Soc. C.E., Vol. 91, No. SM4 (July, 1965).

Clough, R. W., and D. Pirtz, "Earthquake Resistance of Rock-Fill Dams," *Journal Soil Mechanics and Foundations Division*, Proc. Am. Soc. C.E., Vol. 82, No. SM2 (April, 1956).

Collin, A., *Landslides in Clays*, Translation by W. R. Schriever, University of Toronto Press, 1956.

Culmann, C., "Die Graphische Statik," Zurich, 1866.

Eide, O., and L. Bjerrum, "The Slide at Bekkelaget," *Geotechnique*, Vol. V, 1955.

Fellenius, W., "Erdstatische Berechnung mit Reibung und Kohäsion und unter Annahme Kreiszylindrischer Gleitflächen," W. Ernst & Sohn, Berlin, 1927. (See also Transactions 2nd Congress on Large Dams, Vol. IV, Washington, D.C., 1936.)

Finn, W. D. L., "Earthquake Stability of Cohesive Slopes," *Journal Soil Mechanics and Foundations Division*, Proc. Am. Soc. C. E., Vol. 92, No. SM1 (January, 1966).

Fyedorov, I. V., "Slope Stability in Hydraulic Fill Structures," Sixth International Conference on Soil Mechanics and Foundation Engineering, Vol. II, 1965.

Gibson, R. E., and N. Morgenstern, "A Note on the Stability of Cuttings in Normally Consolidated Clays," *Geotechnique*, Vol. VII, No. 3 (September, 1962).

Gilboy, G., "Mechanics of Hydraulic Fill Dams," *Journal Boston Soc. C.E.*, Vol. XXI, No. 3 (July, 1934).

Golder, H. Q., and D. J. Palmer, "Investigation of a Bank Failure at Scrapsgate, Isle of Sheppy, Kent," *Geotechnique*, Vol. V, 1955.

Goodman, L. E., and C. E. Brown, "Dead Load Stresses and the Instability of Slopes," *Journal Soil Mechanics and Foundations Division*, Proc. Am. Soc. C.E., Vol. 89, No. SM3 (May, 1963).

Goodman, R. E., and H. B. Seed, "Earthquake Induced Displacements in Sand Embankments," *Journal Soil Mechanics and Foundations Division*, Proc. Am. Soc. C.E., Vol. 92, No. SM2 (March, 1966).

Hansen, J. B., "Relationships Between Stability Analysis with Total and with Effective Stress," *Bulletin No. 15*, The Danish Geot. Inst., Copenhagen, 1962.

Horn, J. A., "Computer Analysis of Slope Stability," *Journal Soil Mechanics and Foundations Division*, Proc. Am. Soc. C.E., Vol. 86, No. SM3 (June, 1960).

Hultin, S., "Grusfyllningar för Kajbyggnader," Teknisk Tidskrift 46:292, 1916.

Janbu, N., "Stability Analysis of Slopes with Dimensionless Parameters," *Harvard University Soil Mech. Series*, No. 46, January, 1954.

Janbu, N., L. Bjerrum, and B. Kjaernsli, "Veiledning ved løsning av Fundamenteringsoppgaver," Pub. No. 16, Norwegian Geot. Inst., Oslo, 1956.

Jakobson, B., "The Design of Embankments on Soft Clays," *Geotechnique*, Vol. I, No. 2 (December, 1948).

Justin, J. D., *Earth Dam Projects*, New York: John Wiley & Sons, Inc., 1932.

Kenney, T. C., "Stability of Cuts in Soft Soils," *Journal Soil Mechanics and Foundations Division*, Proc. Am. Soc. C. E.,Vol. 89, No. SM5 (September, 1963).

Kjaernsli, B., and N. Simons, "Stability Investigations of the North Bank of the Drammen River," *Geotechnique*, Vol. XII, No. 2 (June, 1962).

Kjellman, W., "Mechanics of Large Swedish Landslips," *Geotechnique*, Vol. V, 1955.

Krey, H., *Erddruck, Erdwiderstand, und Tragfähigkeit des Baugrundes*, 4th Ed. (Ehrenberg Revision) Berlin: Ernst & Sohn, 1932.

Lane, K. S., "Field Slope Charts for Stability Studies," Proceedings Fifth International Conference on Soil Mechanics and Foundations, Vol. II, 1961.

Lane, K. S., and R. G. Fehrman, "Tuttle Creek Dam of Rolled Shale and Dredged Sand," *ournal Soil Mechanics and Foundations Division*, Proc. Am. Soc. C.E., Vol. 86, No. SM6 (December, 1960).

Leussink, H., and W. Wittke, "Difference in Triaxial and Plain Strain Shear Strength," Symposium of Shear Testing of Soils, ASTM Special Pub. No. 361, 1964.

Little, A. L., and V. E. Price, "The Use of Electronic Computer for Slope Stability Analysis," *Geotechnique*, Vol. VIII, No. 3 (September, 1958).

Lobdell, H. L., "Rate of Constructing Embankments on Soft Foundation Soils," *Journal Soil Mechanics and Foundation Division*. Proc. Am. Soc. C.E., Vol. 85, No. SM5 (October, 1959).

Lo, K. Y., "Stability of Slopes in Anisotropic Soils," *Journal Soil Mechanics and Foundations Division*, Proc. Am. Soc. C.E., Vol. 91, No. SM4 (July, 1965).

Lowe III, J., and L. Karafiath, "Effect of Anistropic Consolidation on the Undrained Shear Strength of Compacted Clays," Conference on Shear Strength of Cohesive Soils, Soil Mechanics and Foundations Division, *Proc. Am. Soc. C.E.*, University of Colorado, Boulder, Colorado, 1960.

Meyer, O. H., "Computation of the Stability of Slopes," *Journal Soil Mechanics and Foundations Division*, Proc. Am. Soc. C.E., Vol. 84, No. SM4 (October, 1958).

Milligan, V., L. G. Soderman, and A. Rutka, "Experience with Canadian Varved Clays," *Journal Soil Mechanics and Foundations Division*, Proc. Am. Soc. C.E.,Vol. 88, No. SM4 (August, 1962).

Morgenstern, N. R., "Stability Charts for Earth Slopes During Rapid Drawdown," *Geotechnique*, Vol. XIII, No. 2 (June, 1963).

Morgenstern, N. R., and V. E. Price, "The Analysis of the Stability of General Slip Surfaces," *Geotechnique*, Vol. XV, No. 1 (March, 1965).

Newmark, N. M., "Fifth Rankine Lecture: Effects of Earthquakes on Dams and Embankments," *Geotechnique*, Vol. XV, No. 2 (June, 1965).

Odenstad, S., "Correspondence to Secretary of ICE," *Geotechnique*, Vol. V, 1955.

Petterson, K. E., "Kajaset i Goteborg des 5te mars 1916," Teknisk Tidskrift, 46:289, Vol. V, 1916.

Petterson, K. E., "The Early History of Circular Sliding Surfaces," *Geotechnique*, Vol. V, 1955.

Rao, K. L., "Stability of Slopes in Earth Dams and Foundation Excavations," *Proceedings Fifth International Conference on Soil Mechanics and Foundations*, 1961.

Reinius, E., "The Stability of the Upstream Slope of Earth Dams," *Swedish State Commission for Building Research*, Bulletin No. 12, 1949.

Rendulic, L., "Der Erddruck im Strassenbau und Brückenbau," Forschungsarb. Strassenwesen, Band 10, Volk und Reich Verlag, Berlin, 1938.

Rendulic, L., "Ein Beitrag zur Bestimmung der Gleitsicherheit," *Der Bauingenieur*, Vol. 16, 1935.

Seed, H. B., "A Method for Earthquake Resistance Design of Earth Dams," *Journal Soil Mechanics and Foundations Division, Proc. Am. Soc. C.E.*, Vol. 92, No. SM1 (January, 1966).

Seed, H. B., and C. K. Chan, "Clay Strength Under Earthquake Loading Conditions," *Journal Soil Mechanics and Foundations Division, Proc. Am. Soc. C.E.*, Vol. 92, No. SM2 (March, 1966).

Seed, H. B., and R. W. Clough, "Earthquake Resistance of Sloping Core Dams," *Journal Soil Mechanics and Foundations Division, Proc. Am. Soc. C.E.*, Vol. 89, No. SM1 (February, 1963).

Seed, H. B., and R. E. Goodman, "Earthquake Stability of Slopes of Cohesionless Soil," *Journal Soil Mechanics and Foundations Division, Proc. Am. Soc. C.E.*, Vol. 90, No. SM6 (November, 1964).

Seed, H. B., and G. R. Martin, "The Seismic Coefficient in Earth Dam Design," *Journal Soil Mechanics and Foundations Division, Proc. Am. Soc. C.E.*, Vol. 92, No. SM3 (May, 1966).

Seed, H. B., and H. A. Sultan, "Stability Analysis for Sloping Core Embankments," *Publication of the Soil Mechanics and Bituminous Materials Laboratory*, University of California, Berkeley (March, 1966).

Sherard, J. L., R. J. Woodward, S. F. Giezinski, and W. A. Clevenger, *Earth and Earth Rock Dams* (Chapter 7, Stability Analyses), New York: John Wiley & Sons, Inc., 1963.

Skempton, A. W., "Fourth Rankine Lecture: Long Term Stability of Clay Slopes," *Geotechnique*, Vol. XIV, No. 2 (June, 1964).

Skempton, A. W., "Alexandre Collin, 1808-1890, Pioneer in Soil Mechanics," Transactions Newcomen Soc., Vol. 25, 1946. Also in *Geotechnique*, Vol. I, No. 4.

Skempton, A. W., "The Pore Pressure Coefficients A and B," *Geotechnique*, Vol. IV, No. 4 (December, 1954).

Skempton, A. W., and P. La Rochelle, "The Bradwell Slip: A Short Term Failure in London Clay," *Geotechnique*, Vol. XV, No. 3 (September, 1965).

Taylor, D. W., "Stability of Earth Slopes," *Journal Boston Soc. C.E.* (July, 1937).

Ward, W. H., A. Penman, and R. E. Gibson, "Stability of a Bank on a Thin Peat Layer," *Geotechnique*, Vol. V, 1955.

PROBLEMS AND QUESTIONS

Problems and Questions

Chapter 1

1. Describe the differences in an acceptable plan for exploration and sampling for both a light warehouse structure and a heavy, important office building when preliminary inquiries have been able to elicit only the following information about the general soil conditions of the area. [Note that each of the parts, (a) through (f) below, constitutes a separate and distinct problem.]

   (a) Stiff, overconsolidated clays of undetermined depth.
   (b) Soft clay overlying rock at shallow depth.
   (c) Slightly overconsolidated clays overlying rock at a depth of 290 ft.
   (d) Alluvial sand deposits of undetermined depth.
   (e) Flood plain deposits in a river valley.
   (f) 20 ft of sand underlain by normally consolidated clay of unknown thickness.

2. A field vane test using a vane apparatus 3 in. in diameter and 6 in. in length required a maximum torsional moment of 552 in-lb applied to the shaft. The test was made in saturated clay 1 ft below the bottom of a drilled hole. What is the apparent shearing strength of the clay? About what unconfined compression strength should be expected from a sample taken in a 2-in. diameter Shelby tube?

   Ans. (a) 6 psi (0.43 tons/ft^2).

   (b) Probably about 0.75 tons/ft^2.

3. During a field density test, 3.82 lb of sandy clay were removed from a hole having a volume of 0.31 ft³. The oven dried weight of the soil was 3.31 lb. Determine the moisture content and dry density of the soil.

4. In what ways may inspection of existing structures prove beneficial to the foundations engineer and his client, who proposes to erect a new structure in a built-up area?

5. Of what value are field density tests to the soils engineer in helping him to apply his knowledge of the compaction characteristics of the soil to the benefit of his client or employer?

6. The difference in elevation of two leveling stations is to be determined by means of a water level. One pair of readings is: Station 1—6.245 cm, Station 2—11.361 cm. After exchanging the instruments on the two stations, the readings are: Station 1—6.120 cm, Station 2—11.486 cm. Is Station 2 lower than Station 1? What is the difference in the elevation of the two stations? Are the two instruments constructed identically insofar as the instrument constants d are concerned?
   Ans. (b) Difference in elevation is 5.241 cm.

7. How would a temperature differential between stations affect the readings of the water levels? What changes, if any, would be required in the procedures employed in determining station elevations?

8. Discuss the differences, if any, in the shear strengths indicated by field vane shear tests and laboratory unconfined compression tests. (It is suggested that pertinent references at the end of Chapter 1 be studied, particularly those of the Royal Swedish Geotechnic Institute. In addition, strength comparisons have been made in a large number of papers other than those listed.)

9. Discuss the use of field measurements of settlements and pore pressures as a means for ensuring the safety of an embankment during and following its construction.

Chapter 2

1. A four-story apartment house, with basement, is to be built. For the various soil profiles listed below, determine those types of foundation systems that could almost surely be eliminated from consideration, those that would, at least, be feasible for the given conditions, and the one that would probably be most satisfactory from the standpoint of performance. (Cost is not to be considered at this time.)

   Profile I   0–30 ft: Heavily overconsolidated clays and clay-shales.
            Below 30 ft: Stratified sandstone and shales.
            Water table at −40 ft, climate semi-arid.

Profile II   0–50 ft: Alluvial sand deposits that vary erratically in gradation and relative density.

50–60 ft: Stiff clay.

Below 60 ft: Shale bed rock formation.

Water table at −30 ft, climate normal continental U. S.

Profile III   0–10 ft: Artificial fill, mostly sand and gravel, with considerable rubble.

10–15 ft: Silty fine sand.

15–22 ft: Peat, normally consolidated.

22–60 ft: Clay stratum, overconsolidated in upper ten ft (drying crust) and normally consolidated below.

Below 60 ft: Igneous bed rock.

Water table at −12 ft, humid climate.

Profile IV   0–20 ft: Slightly overconsolidated clay.

20–25 ft: Fairly loose, fine sand.

25–30 ft: Normally consolidated clay.

30–70 ft: Sand deposits, mostly fairly dense, but with some loose pockets or lenses.

70–80 ft: Dense gravel overlying bed rock.

Water table at −15 ft, humid climate.

Chapter 3

1. A continuous sheet-pile wall penetrates to mid-depth of a stratum of isotropic, pervious soil having a thickness of $2H$ above an impervious base. The water surface on one side of the wall is at a height of H above the surface of the pervious layer, while on the other side the water surface is at a height of $H/2$. Draw the flow net for the conditions described. (It is suggested that three flow channels be used.) Based on the flow net, compute the quantity of flow beneath a 100-ft length of the wall if the pervious soil has a coefficient of permeability of 20×10^{-4} cm/sec. *Ans.* $q = 0.74\,H$ gpm.

2. The base of a concrete dam has a thickness of $3D$ from face to face, and rests at a depth of D in an isotropic sand stratum which has a total thickness of $2D$ above an impervious base. The reservoir level is at a depth D above the surface of the sand, and the tail water elevation is $3D/4$ below the reservoir surface. Assuming the dam to have vertical faces, construct the flow net for flow beneath the dam. Also, compute the quantity of flow for a 500-ft length of dam if the coefficient of permeability is 10×10^{-4} cm/sec. *Ans.* $q = 1.11\,D$ gpm.

3. For the conditions described in Problem 2, derive mathematically, by progressive subdivision of the flow net, the entrance velocity or discharge velocity at an infinite distance from the sheet-pile wall.

4. Under a differential head, water seeps through pervious, isotropic soil beneath an impervious obstruction. The impervious mass rests on the surface of the soil stratum, which is 100 ft thick. The distance across the mass is also 100 ft, and a sheet-pile wall extends from the downstream toe of the mass to a depth of 50 ft. Draw the flow net for these conditions and determine the shape factor.

5. Determine the seepage pressure per unit volume of soil, acting in the direction of the flow lines. Also, determine a numerical value for the critical hydraulic gradient for the upward flow of water through an average sand.

6. The downstream face of a homogeneous, isotropic earth dam is inclined at 45° to the horizontal. Starting at any arbitrary point on the face, plot the line of seepage. Use at least five equipotential drops along the line of seepage.

7. From consideration of an enlarged flow net in the vicinity of the discharge point, prove that the discharge point can not, in general, coincide with the elevation of the tail water.

8. An ogee overflow type of concrete dam, 100 ft from face to face, rests at a depth of 5 ft in isotropic sand having a coefficient of permeability of 20×10^{-4} cm/sec. Sheet-pile walls at the toe and heel of the dam extend to a depth of 25 ft into the sand stratum, which has a thickness of 75 ft above an impermeable base. The difference in elevation of the headwater and tailwater is 30 ft.
   (a) Draw the flow net.
   (b) By means of the piezometric surface, plot the distribution of the hydrostatic uplift pressure on the base of the dam.
   (c) Compute the seepage loss beneath a 350-ft length of the dam.
   Ans. (c) $q = 0.217$ ft^3/sec.

9. A homogeneous earth dam 100 ft high has a crest width of 35 ft. The embankment is made of isotropic soil, $k = 1 \times 10^{-4}$ cm/sec, over an impervious foundation, and both the upstream and downstream faces have a 2:1 slope. Assuming the reservoir level to be at the crest of the dam, and the tail water elevation to be zero,
   (a) determine the position of the discharge point of the line of seepage using the Schaffernach construction.
   (b) plot the entire line of seepage.
   (c) compute the quantity of flow, using
       (1) the results of part (a) above.
       (2) the simple Dupuit equation, $q = kh^2/2d$.
   Ans. (c), (1) $q = 0.0038$ ft^3/min/ft.
            (2) $q = 0.0033$ ft^3/min/ft.

10. State all conditions which the line of seepage must fulfill, and explain why the hydraulic gradient at any point on the line of seepage is equal to the sine of the angle of slope of the seepage line.

11. Prove that the velocity of flow is zero at any point in a flow net where a flow line intersects an equipotential line at an angle less than 90°.

12. Show that the maximum possible velocity of flow along the line of seepage is equal to the coefficient of permeability of the material.

13. Suppose that the dam described in Problem 9 is to be constructed of soil having a $k = 0.1 \times 10^{-4}$ cm/sec, but that a highly pervious downstream toe section is to be incorporated into the design. The upstream toe of the highly pervious section lies directly under the downstream edge of the crest of the dam, sloping upward on a 2:1 slope to intersect the downstream face of the dam. Construct the entire flow net for this dam. Compute the seepage loss through the dam
    (a) directly from the flow net.
    (b) by means of the basic parabola, using the corrected entrance point illustrated in Fig. 3.06e.
    Ans. (a) $q = 10.7 \times 10^{-4}$ cfm/ft.
          (b) $q = 8.5 \times 10^{-4}$ cfm/ft.

14. State briefly why the line of seepage should be kept a safe distance from the downstream face of an earth dam. What means could be used to accomplish this if the dam rests on an impervious foundation, and only a relatively small quantity of highly pervious material is available? If the coefficient of permeability of the highly pervious material is many times greater than that of the soil used in the remainder of the dam, will the position of the line of seepage depend significantly on the ratio of the coefficients of permeability?

15. List the control measures that may be used in dams and dam foundations to combat the undesirable effects of seepage, and explain the function of each.

16. An impervious embankment 500 ft from upstream to downstream toe rests on a pervious foundation 100 ft thick. A sheet pile cut-off extends to a depth D beneath the center of the embankment. Construct separate flow nets for the conditions $D = 0$, $D = 50$ ft, and $D = 90$ ft, and plot a curve showing the relationship between per cent of cut-off and seepage loss expressed as per cent of seepage loss for the $D = 0$ condition.
    Ans. (partial) 90 per cent cut-off produces about a 25 per cent reduction of flow.

17. Using the flow net drawn in Problem 4, plot the lines of equal pressure corresponding to 20, 40, 60, 80, 100, 120, and 140 ft heads of water. Assume that the water level is 60 ft above the ground surface at the upstream side and that the tail water elevation is 10 ft above the ground surface.

18. An impervious dam having a dimension D from toe to toe rests on an upper layer of pervious soil having a coefficient of permeability of k_1. Beneath this is another pervious stratum of permeability k_2. Both strata

are $D/4$ in thickness, and the lower boundary is impervious. Draw flow nets for seepage through the pervious foundation when

(a) $k_1 = 3k_2$.

(b) $k_2 = 3k_1$.

19. In a varved clay, the average thickness of the silt layers is 0.5 in. and the average thickness of the clay layers is 0.3 in. Assuming that the silt layers have a coefficient of permeability of 0.05×10^{-4} cm/sec and the clay layers 75×10^{-9} cm/sec, compute k_{max} and k_{min} for the soil.
   Ans. $k_{max} = 0.034 \times 10^{-4}$ cm/sec, $k_{min} = 195 \times 10^{-9}$ cm/sec.

20. Explain briefly the two principal conditions which a protective filter must fulfill. By means of an appropriate sketch show the numerical criteria recommended by K. Terzaghi.

21. A well used for a pumping test penetrates to an impervious stratum at a depth of 54.7 ft below the permanent water table. The well is pumped at a rate of 281 gpm until a steady condition is reached. In one observation well at a distance of 25 ft from the pumping well, the depth of water above the impervious base is 45 ft. In another observation well on the same radial line at a distance of 100 ft, the water elevation is 48 ft above the base.

(a) Compute the coefficient of permeability of the soil in units of 10^{-4} cm/sec, assuming the soil to be homogeneous and isotropic.

(b) Compute the radius of influence, R.

22. A horizontal stratum of sand has a coefficient of permeability of 200×10^{-4} cm/sec, and an effective porosity of 0.15. The water table in the sand was originally at a height of 60 ft above the underlying impervious boundary. The ground water table is to be lowered by means of well points for an excavation 30 ft $\times$ 50 ft. At what steady rate q must water be pumped from the system in order to lower the water table 15 ft in the middle of the area in a period of 10 days?
   Ans. $q = 410$ gpm.

23. The ground water table is at a height of 80 ft above an impermeable base underlying a sand stratum which has a $k = 400 \times 10^{-4}$ cm/sec and an effective porosity $n' = 0.2$. A full depth well is installed and pumped at a constant rate of 400 gpm for 3 days. Assuming that $\alpha = 1$ and $\sqrt{4(\alpha + 2)/\alpha 3}$, compute the distance from the well to which the drawdown extends and the drawdown at a distance of 100 ft from the well.
   Ans. $R_t = 1100$ ft, $s_{100} = 2$ ft.

24. Ground water flows toward a water front in a sand stratum which is underlain by a horizontal impervious base. The depth of water in the open body of water is 20 ft, and the bottom coincides with the surface of the impervious base. A fully penetrating 1-ft diameter test well is installed at a distance of 250 ft from the water front. Before pumping, the water level in this well was 30 ft above the impervious base. The well

is pumped at a rate of 75 gpm until a steady state is reached, when the water level in the well is at a height of 17 ft above the base. Compute the coefficient of permeability of the sand, assuming it to be homogeneous and isotropic.

25. Two wells are sunk 150 ft apart in a sand stratum of $k = 500 \times 10^{-4}$ cm/sec overlying a horizontal impervious base. The ground water table was originally 40 ft above the base. Each well is pumped at a rate of 300 gpm until a steady state is reached. The corresponding radius of influence is estimated to be 2000 ft. The wells are 2 ft in diameter.

(a) Derive the drawdown curve along a vertical plane through the two wells by graphical superposition.

(b) Compute the drawdown at a point midway between the two wells.

(c) Compute the height at which the water surfaces in the wells stand above the impervious base.

Ans. (b) 12.7 ft, (c) 16.7 ft.

Chapter 4

1. In what respects are foundation settlements on sand similar to those on loess? In what respects do they differ, particularly with regard to large settlements?

2. List the factors that tend to introduce imprecision into settlement computations. How should this imprecision be reflected in the statement of the results of the computations?

3. Explain why settlement of an overconsolidated clay under a given load is less than that of a normally consolidated clay. Discuss the possible magnitude of the difference in settlement of the two. Under what circumstances may swelling occur?

4. A uniform load increase of 3000 lb/sq ft is to be applied over a very large area where the subsurface soil profile consists of 12 ft of coarse sand overlying a 32-ft thick stratum of normally consolidated clay which, in turn, rests on bed rock. At a distance of 10 ft above the bed rock, the clay stratum contains a thin, but apparently continuous, layer of sand. Assume that the sand layer provides free drainage for the clay above and below. The water table is at a depth of 10 ft below the ground surface. The coarse sand has a $G_s = 2.68$ and $n = 0.4$. A laboratory consolidation test on an undisturbed sample of the normally consolidated clay provided the following information:

Thickness of test specimen = 2.54 cm.

Points on the virgin branch of the $e - \log p$ curve:

$e_1 = 0.564$ $p_1 = 1.72$ kg/sq cm

$e_2 = 0.462$ $p_2 = 3.02$ kg/sq cm

Time for 50 per cent consolidation $= 4.6$ min.

G_s for clay $= 2.74$

For the proposed load increase, estimate

(a) the total settlement of the 32-ft clay layer.

(b) the time for 50 per cent settlement.

(c) the time for 20 per cent settlement.

(d) the time for 95 per cent settlement.

(e) the settlement 2 years after application of the load.

(f) the time required for 95 per cent settlement if the thin sand layer not been present in the clay stratum.

(g) the average coefficient of permeability of the clay over the pressure range 1.62 to 2.84 kg/cm^2.

Ans. (approximately) (a) 35 in.

                               (b)   6 months.

                               (c) 31 in.

                               (f) 29 years.

                               (g) 64×10^{-9} cm/sec.

5. The footing plan for a certain structure supported on spread footings consists of variously sized footings whose centers may be laid out to form a pattern of 3 rows and 5 columns. The rows are numbered 1, 2, and 3, and the columns are lettered A, B, C, D, and E. The distance between rows 1 and 2 is 20 ft, and between rows 2 and 3 the distance is 25 ft. Distances between the columns are as follows: A to B—25 ft, B to C—12 ft, C to D—30 ft, and D to E—15 ft. Footings are proportioned to produce contact pressures of 8000 lb/ft^2, and vary in size as follows:

        Footings 1E and 3E—5 ft $\times$ 5 ft.

        Footing 1A—6 ft $\times$ 6 ft.

        Footings 1B and 2E—7 ft $\times$ 7 ft.

        Footings 1C, 1D, 2A, 3A, 3B, and 3C—8 ft $\times$ 8 ft.

        Footing 3D—9 ft $\times$ 9 ft.

        Footing 2B—10 ft $\times$ 10 ft.

        Footing 2C—11 ft $\times$ 11 ft.

        Footing 2D—12 ft $\times$ 12 ft.

The footings are to be at a depth of 8 ft below the surface of a normally consolidated clay stratum 52 ft thick, overlying rock. The water table is at a depth of 9 ft below the surface, i.e., 1 ft below the bottom of the footings. An undisturbed sample taken from a depth of 14 ft had a natural void ratio of 0.564. A consolidation test specimen 2.54 cm thick required 12 minutes to achieve 50 per cent consolidation. [*Note:* G_s must be estimated, and C_c approximated by the method described in Section 4.03.]

(a) Determine the total settlements of all footings, and draw the settlement profiles for all rows and columns of footings.

(b) Construct settlement profiles which represent the conditions after an elapsed time of one year. (Assume that the bed rock is impervious, and that drainage occurs freely along a plane coinciding with the base of the footings.)

Ans. (partial) Total settlement of footing 2C is about 14 in.

6. Why are sand piles sometimes ineffective in producing the anticipated magnitude of settlement, and in accelerating the rate of settlement? [*Note:* For those interested in further pursuing this topic, it is suggested that the literature pertaining to more recent developments, in which cardboard wicks are used, be studied. The student should note whether the uncertainties of this method are the same as those for sand piles.]

7. Making use of the charts given in this chapter, compare the magnitudes of the vertical pressures under the following conditions according to the Boussinesq and Westergaard solutions for a pressure of 1 kip/sq ft acting on the surface
   (a) at a depth of 5 ft beneath the center of a 5 ft × 5 ft square.
   (b) at a depth of 5 ft beneath one corner of a 5 ft × 5 ft square.
   (c) at a depth of 10 ft beneath the center of a 6 ft × 10 ft rectangle.
   (d) at a depth of 10 ft beneath the midpoint of a long side of a 6 ft × 10 ft rectangle.
   (e) at a depth of 20 ft beneath a point outside a 60 ft × 80 ft rectangle, the point being located 15 ft from one corner on the extension of a diagonal.

8. For a total load of 100 kips, compare the vertical pressure at a depth of 10 ft beneath the point of application of a concentrated load with that beneath the center of a square 5 ft × 5 ft, and with that beneath the center of a circle 5 ft in diameter. Use the Boussinesq charts.

9. What effect does the stiffness of a structural frame have on the pattern of settlements produced by the loads on individual footings? What is the effect on the stresses present in the structural frame?

Chapter 5

1. At a certain point within a stressed mass, compressive stresses of 9000 psi and 1000 psi act on the horizontal and vertical planes, respectively. The shearing stress on these same planes is 1000 psi, the shear having a clockwise sense on the vertical sides of an element at the point.
   (a) Determine the magnitude of the principal stresses and the orientations of their planes.
   (b) Determine the magnitude of the maximum shearing stress, and illustrate the results on a sketch of a properly oriented element.
   Ans. (partial) (a) $\sigma_1 = 9270$ psi compression, major principal plane is at angle of 10.3° (clockwise) from the horizontal,
   (b) $\tau_{max} = 4270$ psi.

2. A cylindrical specimen of material having a linear relationship between shearing strength and normal stress failed in unconfined compression under an axial stress of 5000 psi. Failure planes developed at angles of 30° with the axis of the specimen.
   (a) Determine the shearing strength of the material on a plane of zero normal stress.

(b) Determine the angle of internal friction of the material.

(c) Determine the magnitudes of the normal and shearing stresses on the failure planes in the unconfined compression test.

(d) At what tensile stress would failure occur in a uniaxial tensile test?

(e) At what shearing stress would a cylindrical specimen fail in pure torsion?

Ans. (a) 1440 psi. (b) 30°. (c) $\sigma_{ff} = 1250$ psi. $\tau_{ff} = 2160$ psi. (d) 1660 psi. (e) 1250 psi.

3. Using the indicated procedures, compute the ultimate bearing capacity per unit of area of a footing 4 ft wide placed 3 ft below the surface of a soil having a shearing strength of $s = 0.1$ kg/cm^2 $+ \sigma$ tan 18°.

(a) Principal stress method.

(b) Sliding wedge method.

(c) Krey ϕ-circle method.

Ans. (partial) (a) 5470 psf.

4. Compute the unit ultimate bearing capacity, using the principal stress method, for the following conditions.

(a) On clay, for which it is assumed that $s = c = 500$ psf.

    (1) Width $= 2$ ft, depth $= 0$ ft.

    (2) Width $= 6$ ft, depth $= 0$ ft.

    (3) Width $= 2$ ft, depth $= 6$ ft.

    (4) Width $= 6$ ft, depth $= 6$ ft.

(b) On sand, for which $s = $ tan 40°, using the same footing widths and depths as in part (a) above.

Ans. (partial) (a) (1)   2250 psf.

               (4)   3440 psf.

         (b) (2) 14150 psf.

5. When tested using customary procedures, a certain clay is found to have a shear strength of 800 psf. On the basis of crude tests, the creep strength is estimated to be 300 psf. A large area of the surface of the clay stratum is to be loaded to an intensity of 1800 psf. Estimate the unit pressures which must be supplied by adjoining berms in order to provide a factor of safety of 2 against long-term failure.

6. What is the basic reason for the much greater influence of footing width and depth for footings on sand compared to those on clay?

7. For surface footings on sand and on clay, discuss the probable influence on bearing capacity of a rise of the water table from some depth below the footing to the surface of the ground.

8. Describe the approximate distribution of pressure beneath footings on sand and on clay, and discuss the feasibility of designing footings on the basis of bending moments corresponding to an assumed uniform distribution of contact pressure.

9. What theoretical and practical objections may be raised to the use of dynamic pile-driving formulas for estimating the bearing capacity of floating piles in clay? What other procedures are available for estimating the bearing capacity of such piles?

10. Discuss the practical significance of the fact that piles pulled from clay are frequently encased by a considerable thickness of soil; i.e., they do not pull cleanly from the ground. What is the probable theoretical explanation of this?

11. What unsatisfactory performance may result if the load applied to a group of floating piles is made equal to the allowable bearing capacity of a single pile (based on a load test) multiplied by the number of piles in the group? Explain.

12. Floating piles are to be used to support a mat foundation, 160 ft × 64 ft, on clay ($s = c$). The maximum diameter of the piles is to be 14 in., and no pile is to be placed closer than 2.5 ft from the edge of the mat. Determine the critical spacing of the piles, i.e., the spacing for which the bearing capacity of the pile group is equal to the sum of the bearing capacities of the individual piles. For purposes of this problem, neglect the bearing capacity of the soil below the tips of the piles.
Ans. Distance from center to center is approximately 9.75 ft.

Chapter 6

1. Formulate a precise description (and explanation) of the process of shrinkage in clay. Why does the clay again increase in volume when water is made available?

2. In reptitious shrinking and swelling, the difference between minimum and maximum volume of the soil generally decreases with each repetition of the process for the first few times. How would you explain this fact? Would you expect cyclic, seasonal volumetric changes in natural clay deposits to vary in the same manner? If not, describe the nature of the variations that might occur.

3. Describe the difficulties that may develop when light buildings are supported on shallow, continuous footings on clay soils in a semi-arid region.

4. Explain why excessive differential movement may occur when there is a considerable difference in the total loads carried by adjacent footings, even though all footings exert the same unit contact pressure on the soil.

5. What troubles may develop in paved streets because of the construction of utilities lines in ditches crossing beneath the pavement? Try to compose a satisfactory set of specifications for the construction of such facilities.

6. Describe the conditions under which swelling of clay soil may lead to the collapse of the roof of a building while the walls are still reasonably intact.

7. What type of foundation construction for light structures may be used to overcome, at least in part, the adverse effects of swelling soils?

8. What essential detail in the construction of grade beams must be employed to insure the satisfactory performance of a pier and grade beam foundation system in a region of desiccated clay soils?

9. Why are heavy structures founded on desiccated clay less prone to severe damage than are light structures on the same soil? Describe the damage that may occur even to heavy structures, and how it may be prevented.

10. Under what conditions may the presence of trees cause damage to buildings founded on clay?

11. Describe some satisfactory methods for casting ground floor slabs in such a way as to avoid damage to the slab in the event that the underlying soils swell.

12. List the factors that must be evaluated before the design of a stiffened slab-on-grade is undertaken.

Chapter 7

1. Describe the active and passive states of plastic equilibrium. How is the "at rest" state of elastic equilibrium related to these?

2. Solve Problem 1 of Chapter 5, graphically, making use of the pole of the Mohr circle.

3. Suppose that a vertical bank of cohesive soil, $s = c + \sigma \tan \phi$, exists in a state of active plastic equilibrium.
   (a) Develop an expression for the intensity of the horizontal stress that must be maintained at the top of the bank.
   (b) Develop an expression for the depth to which a state of tension exists in the bank.
   (c) Are these stress conditions possible on an exposed face of an actual vertical bank? Explain.

4. Prove that a positive angle of wall friction is a beneficial influence; i.e., that it reduces the active earth pressure on a wall and increases the passive earth resistance. [*Hint:* a convenient proof may be obtained from an analysis of the basic force polygon.]

5. State the assumptions upon which the Rankine method and the Coulomb sliding wedge method of earth pressure determination are based. Under what conditions will the two methods yield identical results?

6. With the aid of a Mohr-Coulomb diagram determine the shape of the potential surface of sliding in cohesionless backfill ($\phi = 38°$) retained by a vertical wall ($\delta = 24°$). The backfill surface is horizontal. For both the active and passive cases, and for both positive and negative angles of wall friction, determine the slope of the failure surface at the toe of the wall and at the surface of the backfill. Careful graphical solutions are acceptable.

Ans. (partial) Active case ($-\delta$), at toe: 73° slope, at surface: 64° slope.

7. A sand backfill with a horizontal surface is in contact with a wall along a vertical face 14 ft high. Pertinent properties of the sand are: $e = 0.58$, $S = 18$ per cent, $\phi = 38°$, and the angle of wall friction is zero. Using graphical procedures, determine the resultant active and passive earth pressures using
(a) Culmann's procedure.
(b) Engesser's procedure.
(c) Poncelet's procedure.
Ans. $E_a = 2540$ lb, $E_p = 45,500$ lb.

8. Using the same data as in Problem 7, with the exception that a positive wall friction angle, $\delta = 30°$, is to be used, determine the resultant passive earth pressure using the circular arc procedure. Note that, in this case, a positive wall friction angle means that the wall exerts a downward drag on the vertical face of the soil.

9. Repeat Problem 8 using the logarithmic spiral procedure.

10. A cohesive backfill, $\phi = 26°$, $c = 800$ psf, $\nu_e = 110$ lb/ft³, carries a uniform surcharge of 250 psf on its horizontal surface. The face of the wall in contact with the soil has a slope of 1 horizontally to 5 vertically along a vertical height of 15 ft. Assume that $\delta = 18°$ and assume an adhesive resistance equal to 500 psf. Determine the passive earth resistance using
(a) the circular arc procedure.
(b) the logarithmic spiral procedure.

11. For the same wall and soil conditions given in Problem 7, except that a wall friction angle of 30° is to be used, determine the location of the critical surfaces for both the active and passive pressure conditions using the procedure given by Abdul-Baki.

12. A sand backfill, $e = 0.62$, $\phi = 40°$, slopes upward on a 15° slope from the top of a vertical wall 15 ft high. The angle of wall friction is 15°. At a horizontal distance of 6 ft from the wall, the mat foundation of a building exerts a uniform pressure of 4000 lb/ft², and the mat extends for a considerable distance both parallel and perpendicular to the wall. The elevation of the mat is such that its bottom is 3 ft below the ground surface along its edge nearest the wall. Assuming that the sand is dry, determine the active earth pressure on the wall using the Culmann graphical procedure.
Ans. $E_a = 5700$ lb/lin ft of wall.

13. For the same wall and backfill soil as were given in Problem 12, but with a horizontal backfill surface, determine the resultant active earth pressure on the wall if there is a line load of 4000 lb/ft parallel to the wall, acting on the surface at a distance of 4 ft from the wall. Determine also the position of the line of action of E_a.

14. A gravity wall 14 ft high retains a sand backfill which slopes upward from the top of the wall on a 20° slope. The upper 4 ft of the face of the wall in contact with the soil is vertical, while the lower part of the wall slopes downward beneath the backfill on a slope of 1 horizontally to 2 vertically. The properties of the sand are: $n = 0.40$, $S = 14$ per cent, and $\phi = 40°$. The angle of wall friction is 20°. Determine the magnitude and position of the resultant active earth pressure on the wall.
Ans. $E_a = 5600$ lb.

15. A concrete cantilever retaining wall is used to retain sand, $e = 0.6$, $\phi = 38°$, which slopes upward on a 15° angle from the top of the wall. The wall, 8 ft high and 1 ft thick, is supported on a foundation $6\frac{1}{2}$ ft wide and 1 ft thick. There is a clear distance of $1\frac{1}{2}$ ft from the toe of the foundation to the exposed face of the wall. The foundation is cast in undisturbed clay, $\nu_e = 115$ lb/ft³, $c = 0.2$ kg/cm², and $\phi = 18°$, with the top surface of the foundation flush with the surface of the clay. A key 1 ft thick extends below the bottom of the foundation, directly beneath the wall. Estimate the factor of safety of the wall with respect to both sliding and overturning. Also, determine the pressure distribution on the bottom of the foundation.
Ans. FS(sliding) is about 3.2, FS(overturning) is about 1.7.

16. Determine the distribution of pressure against braced sheeting used to retain dry sand $\nu_e = 100$ lb/ft³, $\phi = 36°$, along the vertical sides of an excavation 20 ft deep. Assume a wall friction angle of 15°.

17. A concrete anchor block 2 ft thick and 10 ft deep (length unspecified) is placed with its upper surface flush with the surface of the ground. The soil, to a depth of 30 ft, consists of clay having the properties $e = 0.6$, $G_s = 2.7$, $c = 0.2$ kg/cm², and $\phi = 22°$. The block is to resist a cable pull acting upward at an angle of 36° with the horizontal. Determine the maximum cable pull that the anchor can resist per foot of its length.
Ans. $T =$ approximately 30 tons.

18. A footing 4 ft square is concentrically loaded by a shore which slopes 30° from the vertical. By cutting away the soil to form a bench whose face slopes at an angle of 30° with the horizontal, the footing is placed so that it lies in a plane perpendicular to the axis of the shore. The width of the face of the bench is 4 ft, the same as the width of the footing, and the ground surfaces above and below the bench are horizontal. The soil consists of clay, $\nu_e = 110$ lb/ft³, $c = 0.3$ kg/cm², $\phi = 14°$. Neglecting the resistance on lateral surfaces of shear, determine the ultimate load which may be applied to the footing. Use the ϕ-circle procedure.

Ans. P_{ult} = approximately 40 tons.

Chapter 8

1. Define the factors of safety F_s, F_c, and F_ϕ, and illustrate why their numerical values differ.

2. At a point along the critical surface (a plane) in an infinite slope, the normal stress is 863 psf, and the shearing stress is 321 psf. The strength of the soil along this surface is $s = 300$ psf $+ \bar{\sigma} \tan 16°$. Determine F_s, F_c, and F_ϕ.

Ans. 1.7, 4.05, and 11.75.

3. Explain why the factor of safety F_s appears to offer the most logical definition for general use.

4. Derive expressions for the normal and shearing stresses in an infinite slope in terms of the unit weight of the soil, height of the slope, and the slope angle.

5. What is the effect on the factor of safety of an infinite slope of cohesionless soil if the ground water table rises to the surface from great depths?

6. A sand embankment 30 ft high, with a crest width of 10 ft and side slopes of 1½:1, is placed over a thin stratum of soft clay whose strength may be taken as $s = c = 500$ psf. The sand has a unit weight of 116 lb/ft³ and an angle of internal friction of 36°. Using Rendulic's procedure, determine the maximum value of the average shearing stress along the clay surface, and compute the factor of safety against a spreading failure.

7. A hydraulic fill dam 25 ft high is constructed with soil that provides a fine-grained core with a unit weight (saturated) of 120 lb/ft³, and a coarse-grained shell having a unit weight of 105 lb/ft³. The core is 6 ft wide at the top and 16 ft wide at the bottom. The total crest width of the dam is 12 ft, and the outer faces of the shell are on 1.6:1 slopes. Determine the factor of safety of the dam using Gilboy's method.

8. Determine F_s and F_H for a slope cut in homogeneous, saturated clay, $s = c = 0.46$ tons/ft². The cut is made on a 2½:1 slope, and the height of the slope is 32 ft. Assume that the critical surface corresponds to a toe failure. Figure 8.09 *b* may used in the analysis.

9. A homogeneous embankment is built of clay soil of unit weight 120 lb/ft³, whose strength is $s = 800$ psf $+ \bar{\sigma} \tan 14°$. The embankment is 45 ft high, with a crest width of 15 ft and side slopes of 3:1. It rests on a foundation of stiff clay. Using a ϕ-circle, trial and error procedure, determine

F_c. For the same critical circle, determine F_s. Would the critical circles actually be the same for the two conditions?

10. For the same embankment as in Problem 9, assume that a very thin layer of weak soil ($s = c = 400$ psf) exists at the base of the embankment. Devise a combination circular arc-planar slip method of analysis, and determine the factor of safety F_s. For convenience, assume that the full strength of the weak layer will be developed, and that the margin of safety resides solely in the embankment soil.

11. Discuss the various ways (at least four) in which the effects of water may cause an embankment to fail.

12. A homogeneous dam 60 ft high built of clay having a unit weight of 125 lb/ft^3 and a strength of $s = 400$ psf $+ \bar{\sigma} \tan 20°$. The dam is constructed over bed rock, and has side slopes of 2:1 upstream and 3:1 downstream. Neglecting pore pressures, determine F_s using the common slices procedure, and compare it with the value found using Bishop's modification.

13. Repeat Problem 12 assuming that construction pore pressures must be considered. The estimated value of $\bar{B}$ is 0.3.

14. Analyze the upstream face of the dam in Problem 12 for the condition of rapid drawdown following a long period during which the reservoir surface has been stable at an elevation 6 ft below the crest of the dam.

AUTHOR INDEX

Author Index

SUBJECT INDEX

Subject Index